MATHEMATICS
for SEG GCSE
Intermediate Tier

Tony Banks ● Tony Fisher ● Paul Newton
Peter Balaam ● Bruce Balden ● David Alcorn

Causeway Press Limited

Published by Causeway Press Ltd
P.O. B0x 13, Ormskirk, Lancashire L39 5HP

First published 1999
Reprinted 1999

British Library Cataloguing-in-Publication Data.
A catalogue record for this book is available from the British Library.

ISBN 1-873929-87-0

Acknowledgements
Exam questions
Past exam questions, provided by Southern Examining Group, are denoted by the letters SEG and the
year of the exam. Where specimen questions are used the letter S appears after the applicable year.
The answers to all questions are entirely the responsibility of the authors/publisher and have neither
been provided nor approved by SEG.

Page design
Alan Fraser
Billy Johnson

Reader
David Hodgson

Artwork
Alan Fraser
David Alcorn

Cover design
Waring-Collins Partnership

Typesetting by Bibliocraft, Dundee
Printed and bound by Scotprint, Musselburgh, Scotland

preface

Mathematics for SEG GCSE - Intermediate Tier has been written to meet the requirements of the revised National Curriculum in Mathematics and provides full coverage of all GCSE examination syllabuses for first examination in 2000 at the Intermediate Tier of entry.

The book is suitable for students preparing for assessment at the Intermediate Tier of entry on either a 1-year or 2-year course or as a revision text.

In preparing the text, full account has been made of the new requirements for students to be able to solve problems in mathematics both with and without a calculator. Whilst there has been no artificial division of subject content into calculator and non-calculator work, non-calculator questions and exercises have been incorporated throughout the book where appropriate.

The planning of topics within chapters and sections has been designed to provide efficient coverage of the syllabus. Depending on how the book is to be used you can best decide on the order in which chapters are studied.

Chapters   1 - 12   Number
Chapters 13 - 19   Algebra
Chapters 20 - 32   Shape, Space and Measures
Chapters 33 - 38   Handling Data

Each chapter consists of fully worked examples with explanatory notes and commentary; carefully graded questions, a summary of key facts and skills and a review exercise. The review exercises provide the opportunity to consolidate topics introduced within the chapter and consist of exam-style questions, which reflect how SEG intend to assess the work, plus lots of past examination questions (marked SEG).

Further opportunities to consolidate skills acquired over a number of chapters are provided with section reviews. There is a final exam questions section with a further compilation of exam and exam-style questions, organised for non-calculator and calculator practice, in preparation for the exams.

Some chapters include ideas for investigational, practical and statistical tasks and give the student the opportunity to improve and practice their skills of using and applying mathematics. The section on GCSE Mathematics Coursework, on page 482, is a useful reference when trying any of the ideas for investigation.

contents

CHAPTER 8 Fractions

CHAPTER 9 Percentages

CHAPTER 10 Ratio

CHAPTER 19   Quadratic and Other Equations

CHAPTER 20   Angles

CHAPTER 21   Triangles

CHAPTER 27 · Enlargements and Similar Figures

CHAPTER 28 · Volumes and Surface Areas

CHAPTER 29 · Pythagoras' Theorem

CHAPTER 30 · Trigonometry

Whole Numbers

The numbers 0, 1, 2, 3, 4, 5, . . . can be used to count objects.
Such numbers are called **whole numbers**.
There are other types of numbers, including fractions, decimals and negative numbers which you will
meet in later chapters.

Place value

Our number system is made up of the digits 0, 1, 2, 3, 4, 5, 6, 7, 8 and 9.
The position a digit has in a number is called its **place value**.
In the number 5384 the digit 8 is worth 80, but in the number 4853 the digit 8 is worth 800.

Reading and writing numbers

$8543 = 8 \times 1000 + 5 \times 100 + 4 \times 10 + 3 \times 1$
The number 8543 is written or read as, "eight thousand five hundred and forty-three."
For numbers bigger than one thousand split the number into groups of three digits, starting from the
units column.

EXAMPLES

1 Write the number 56843 in words.

56 843 Fifty-six *thousand* eight hundred and forty-three.

2 Write the number 4567205 in words.

4 567 205 Four *million* five hundred and sixty-seven *thousand* two hundred and five.

1. Split the numbers into groups of 3 digits.
2. Combine the numbers of millions and thousands with the number less than 1000.

Exercise 1.1

1 Write the following numbers in figures.
(a) three hundred and ninety-six
(b) five thousand and ten
(c) seventy thousand two hundred
(d) nine million two thousand and fifty-one
(e) seven hundred and sixty-two million five hundred and four thousand and nineteen
(f) twenty million two hundred and two thousand and twenty

2 Write the following numbers in words.
(a) 84
(b) 23590
(c) 93145670
(d) 764809
(e) 6049
(f) 9080004

3 In the number 3<u>8</u>4 the value of the underlined figure is 80.
Give the value of the underlined figure in the following.
(a) 62<u>3</u>4
(b) 12<u>3</u> 456 789
(c) 95 <u>6</u>70
(d) <u>2</u>003
(e) 9<u>4</u> 705
(f) 423<u>6</u>

Numbers in ascending and descending order

| Smallest number | ascending order | Largest number |

| Largest number | descending order | Smallest number |

④ 2564 = 2000 + 500 + 60 + 4
Write these numbers out in the same way.
(a) 6374   (c) 2 003 708
(b) 999   (d) 987 123

⑤ Write the following numbers in ascending order.
(a) 74, 168, 39, 421
(b) 3842, 5814, 3874, 3801, 4765

⑥ Write the following numbers in descending order.
(a) 399, 425, 103, 84, 429
(b) 279 434, 209 646, 1 070 483, 209 951

⑦ Using the digits 4, 6, 7, 1 and 5 (do not use the same digit more than once)
(a) make the biggest five-digit number,
(b) make the smallest five-digit number.
In each case explain your method.

⑧ Using the digits 8, 5, 4 and 3 make as many four-digit numbers as you can. Use each digit just once in each four-digit number, e.g. 8543.
Put your numbers in ascending order.
How many beginning with the number eight do you have?

Non-calculator methods for addition

Writing numbers in columns

Write the numbers in tidy columns according to place value.
Add together the numbers of units, tens, hundreds, etc.
If any of these answers comes to more than 10 then something is carried to the next column.

EXAMPLE

Work out 4567 + 835.

```
  4 5 6 7      7 + 5 = 12                  which is 2 carry 1.
+   8 3 5      6 + 3 + carried 1 = 10,  which is 0 carry 1.
  5 4 0 2      5 + 8 + carried 1 = 14,  which is 4 carry 1.
  ¹ ¹ ¹        4 + carried 1 = 5.
```

Using a number line

A number line shows a different method for adding numbers.
With practice you should not need to draw a number line.

EXAMPLE

Work out 26 + 37.

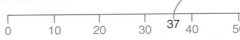

26 + 37 is the same as 37 + 26.
37 + 20 = 57   (adding 20)
57 + 6 = 63   (adding 6)
So 26 + 37 = 63.

  Exercise 1.2

Do not use a calculator for this exercise.

① Work out these by writing the numbers in columns.
(a) 765 + 23   (f) 3495 + 8708
(b) 27 + 56   (g) 67 + 89 + 45
(c) 76 + 98   (h) 431 + 865 + 245
(d) 324 + 628   (i) 9 + 187 + 54 + 3210
(e) 1273 + 729   (j) 123 456 + 876 544

② The last four attendances at a football stadium were:
21 004
19 750
18 009
22 267
What is the combined total?

3 Here is a number line for $18 + 15$.

(a) What is $18 + 10$?

(b) What is $18 + 15$?

4 Draw a number line for each of the following sums and work out the answers.

(a) $34 + 15$ (c) $17 + 56$

(b) $23 + 48$ (d) $28 + 27$

5 Work these out in your head.

(a) $24 + 32$ (c) $65 + 27$

(b) $19 + 16$ (d) $38 + 84$

Non-calculator methods for subtraction

Writing numbers in columns

Write the numbers in columns according to place value. The order in which the numbers is written down is important.

Then, in turn, subtract the numbers of units, tens, hundreds, etc.

If the subtraction in a column cannot be done, because the number being subtracted is greater, borrow 10 from the next column.

Work out $7238 - 642$.

$$\begin{array}{r} 7238 \\ -\ 642 \\ \hline 6596 \end{array}$$

Units: $8 - 2 = 6$

Tens: $3 - 4$ cannot be done, so borrow 10 from the 2 in the next column. Now $10 + 3 - 4 = 9$.

Hundreds: $1 - 6$ cannot be done, so borrow 10 from the 7 in the next column. Now $10 + 1 - 6 = 5$.

Thousands: $6 - 0 = 6$.

You can use addition to check your subtraction. Does $6596 + 642 = 7238$?

$$\begin{array}{r} 6596 \\ +\ 642 \\ \hline 7238 \end{array}$$

EXAMPLES

1
$$\begin{array}{r} 1762 \\ -\ 873 \\ \hline 889 \end{array}$$

2
$$\begin{array}{r} 3006 \\ -\ 1847 \\ \hline 1159 \end{array}$$

3
$$\begin{array}{r} 9012 \\ -\ 5678 \\ \hline 3334 \end{array}$$

Addition is the opposite (inverse) operation to subtraction.

If $a - b = c$,

then $c + b = a$.

Check the answers by addition.

Exercise 1.3

Do not use a calculator for this exercise.

 Work these out by writing the numbers in columns. Use addition to check your answers.

(a) $978 - 624$ (c) $1754 - 470$ (e) $5070 - 2846$ (g) $8045 - 1777$

(b) $843 - 415$ (d) $407 - 249$ (f) $2345 - 1876$ (h) $10\,000 - 6723$

2 Here is a number line for $43 - 16$.

-6   -10

0   10   20   27 30 33   40 43   50

(a) What is $43 - 10$?
(b) What is $43 - 16$?

3 Draw a number line for each of the following questions and work out the answers.
(a) $56 - 28$ (c) $44 - 19$
(b) $64 - 18$ (d) $73 - 38$

4 Work these out in your head.
(a) $26 - 9$ (c) $204 - 99$
(b) $87 - 37$ (d) $1003 - 999$

Multiplication of whole numbers

It is very useful to know your Multiplication Tables up to 10×10.

×	1	2	3	4	5	6	7	8	9	10
1	1	2	3	4	5	6	7	8	9	10
2	2	4	6	8	10	12	14	16	18	20
3	3	6	9	12	15	18	21	24	27	30
4	4	8	12	16	20	24	28	32	36	40
5	5	10	15	20	25	30	35	40	45	50
6	6	12	18	24	30	36	42	48	54	60
7	7	14	21	28	35	42	49	56	63	70
8	8	16	24	32	40	48	56	64	72	80
9	9	18	27	36	45	54	63	72	81	90
10	10	20	30	40	50	60	70	80	90	100

Activity

How quickly can you answer the following questions?
  9×5 6×6 7×4 9×6 8×7 9×7 8×8
Working with a partner ask each other questions from the table.

Non-calculator method for short multiplication

Short multiplication is when the multiplying number is less than 10, e.g. 165×7.
One method multiplies the units, tens, hundreds etc. in turn.

```
  1 6 5
×     7
-------
1 1 5 5
  1 4 3
```

Units: $7 \times 5 = 35$, which is 5 carry 3.
Tens: $7 \times 6 = 42 +$ carried $3 = 45$, which is 5 carry 4.
Hundreds: $7 \times 1 = 7 +$ carried $4 = 11$, which is 1 carry 1.
There are no more digits to be multiplied by 7, the carried 1 becomes 1 thousand.

EXAMPLES

1
```
  1 6 2
×     4
-------
  6 4 8
    2
```

2
```
  9 0 7 1
×       7
---------
6 3 4 9 7
      4
```

3
```
  4 8 3 5
×       8
---------
3 8 6 8 0
  6 2 4
```

Multiplying a whole number by 10, 100, 1000, . . .

When you multiply a whole number by:

10   The units become 10s, the 10s become 100s, the 100s become 1000s, and so on.

100   The units become 100s, the 10s become 1000s, the 100s become 10 000s, and so on.

1000   The units become 1000s, the 10s become 10 000s, the 100s become 100 000s, and so on.

EXAMPLES

$753 \times 10 = 7530$
$753 \times 100 = 75\ 300$
$753 \times 1000 = 753\ 000$

We can show these multiplications in a table.

100 000s	10 000s	1000s	100s	10s	Units	
			7	5	3	
		7	5	3	0	←753×10
	7	5	3	0	0	←753×100
7	5	3	0	0	0	←753×1000

$100 = 10 \times 10$
Multiplying a number by 100 is the same as multiplying the number by 10 and then by 10 again.

Explain any patterns you can see.

Multiplying a whole number by multiples of 10 (20, 30, 40, . . .)

Work out 753×20.

This can be written as:

$$753 \times 20 = 753 \times 10 \times 2$$
$$= 7530 \times 2$$
$$= 15\ 060$$

$20 = 10 \times 2$

Exercise 1.4

Do not use a calculator for this exercise.

1 Work these out using a method you find easiest.
- (a) 21×4
- (b) 17×5
- (c) 36×7
- (d) 183×3
- (e) 264×8
- (f) 3179×5
- (g) 4012×6
- (h) 6012×7

2 Write down the answers to the following questions. You do not have to show any working.
- (a) 132×10
- (b) 123×100
- (c) 47×1000
- (d) 384×100

3 What number should be put in the box to make each of these statements correct?
- (a) $231 \times 10 = \Box$
- (b) $\Box \times 1000 = 514\ 000$
- (c) $172 \times \Box = 17\ 200$

4 Use a non-calculator method to calculate these products
- (a) 253×30
- (b) 357×20
- (c) 537×40
- (d) 615×20
- (e) 186×70
- (f) 239×90
- (g) 412×80
- (h) 142×70
- (i) 632×30
- (j) 260×50

5
- (a) Describe a method of multiplying by 200, 300, 400, and so on.
- (b) Describe a method of multiplying by 2000, 3000, 4000, and so on.

Non-calculator method for short division

The process of dividing a number by a number less than 10 is called **short division**.
Short division relies on knowledge of the Multiplication Tables.
What is $32 \div 8$, $42 \div 7$, $72 \div 9$, $54 \div 6$?

Work out $882 \div 7$.

$$7\overline{)8\,^18\,^42}$$
$$1\,2\,6$$

Starting from the left:
$8 \div 7 = 1$ remainder 1, which is 1 carry 1.
$18 \div 7 = 2$ remainder 4, which is 2 carry 4.
$42 \div 7 = 6$, with no remainder.
So $882 \div 7 = 126$.

You may set your working out like this:
$$\frac{1\,2\,6}{7\overline{)8\,^18\,^42}}$$

You can check your division by multiplying.
Does $126 \times 7 = 882$?

Multiplication is the opposite (inverse) operation to division.
If $a \div b = c$,
then $c \times b = a$.

EXAMPLES

1 $$6\overline{)1\,4\,^27\,^30}$$
$$2\,4\,5$$

2 $$9\overline{)2\,7\,6\,^63}$$
$$3\,0\,7$$

Dividing a whole number by 10, 100, 1000, . . .

When you divide a whole number by:
10   The 10s become units, the 100s become 10s, the 1000s become 100s, and so on.
100   The 100s become units, the 1000s become 10s, the 10 000s become 100s, and so on.
1000   The 1000s become units, the 10 000s become 10s, the 100 000s become 100s. and so on.

Examples
$7530 \div 10 = 753$
$12\,400 \div 100 = 124$
$631\,000 \div 1000 = 631$

10 000s	1000s	100s	10s	Units
	7	5	3	0
		7	5	3	←753 ÷ 10

Draw tables to show the other division sums. Explain any patterns you can see.

Dividing a whole number by multiples of 10 (20, 30, 40, . . .)

Work out $7530 \div 30$.

$7530 \div 30$
$= (7530 \div 10) \div 3$
$= 753 \div 3$ (dividing by 10)
$= 251$ (dividing by 3)

$30 = 10 \times 3$
Dividing by 30 is the same as dividing by 10 and then dividing by 3.

Exercise 1.5

Do not use a calculator for this exercise.

1 Calculate these divisions. Show your working clearly. State the remainder if there is one.
Use multiplication to check your answers.
(a) $85 \div 5$ (c) $816 \div 6$ (e) $3146 \div 8$ (g) $9882 \div 9$
(b) $471 \div 3$ (d) $455 \div 6$ (f) $824 \div 4$ (h) $80\,560 \div 4$

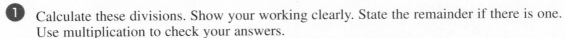

2 Write down the answers to the following questions. You do not have to show your working.
(a) $4560 \div 10$
(b) $465\,000 \div 1000$
(c) $64\,000 \div 1000$
(d) $65\,400 \div 100$

3 What number should be put in the box to make each of these statements correct?
(a) $56\,400 \div \boxed{} = 564$
(b) $\boxed{} \div 1000 = 702$
(c) $35\,000 \div \boxed{} = 3500$

4 Use a non-calculator method to work these out.
(a) $7590 \div 30$
(b) $71\,100 \div 900$
(c) $21\,480 \div 40$
(d) $13\,000 \div 500$
(e) $263\,700 \div 900$
(f) $329\,600 \div 800$
(g) $130\,000 \div 500$

Long multiplication

Long multiplication is used when the multiplying number is greater than 10, e.g. 24×17.

Work out 24×17.

```
      2 4
    × 1 7
    ─────
    1 6 8   ←24 ×  7 = 168
  + 2 4 0   ←24 × 10 = 240
    ─────
    4 0 8
```

A standard non-calculator method for doing long multiplication multiplies the number by:

● the units figure, then

● the tens figure, then

● the hundreds figure, and so on.

All these answers are added together.

EXAMPLES

1
```
      1 4 5
    ×   6 2
    ───────
    2 9 0     ←145 ×  2
  + 8 7 0 0   ←145 × 60
    ───────
    8 9 9 0
```

2
```
        2 7 3
    ×   2 3 4
    ─────────
    1 0 9 2     ←273 ×   4
    8 1 9 0     ←273 ×  30
  + 5 4 6 0 0   ←273 × 200
    ─────────
    6 3 8 8 2
```

Long division

Long division is used when the dividing number is bigger than 10. It works in exactly the same way as short division, except that all the working out is written down.

Consider $952 \div 7$.

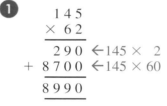

$9 \div 7 = 1$ and a remainder.
What is the remainder?
$1 \times 7 = 7$ (write below the 9).
$9 - 7 = 2$ (which is the remainder).
Bring down the next figure (5) to make 25.
Repeat the above process.
$25 \div 7 = 3$ and a remainder.
$3 \times 7 = 21$, $25 - 21 = 4$ (remainder).
Bring down the next figure (2) to make 42 and repeat the process.
$42 \div 7 = 6$, but there is no remainder.
$6 \times 7 = 42$, $42 - 42 = 0$ (remainder).
There are no more figures to be brought down and there is no remainder.
So $952 \div 7 = 136$.

Using short division:

```
  7)9²5⁴2
    1 3 6
```

Long division process
→ ÷ (obtain biggest answer possible)
× } calculates
− } the remainder
└─ Bring down the next figure
Repeat process until there are no more figures to be brought down.

EXAMPLE

Work out $24\,087 \div 37$.

$$\begin{array}{r} 6\ 5\ 1 \\ 3\ 7\overline{)2\ 4\ 0\ 8\ 7} \\ 2\ 2\ 2 \\ \hline 1\ 8\ 8 \\ 1\ 8\ 5 \\ \hline 3\ 7 \\ 3\ 7 \\ \hline 0 \\ \hline \end{array}$$

Both 2 and 24 are smaller than 37 so $240 \div 37$ is the first division to be made.
$240 \div 37 = 6$ and a remainder.
$6 \times 37 = 222, \quad 240 - 222 = 18$ (remainder).
Bring down next figure (8) to make 188 and repeat the process.
$188 \div 37 = 5$ and a remainder.
$5 \times 37 = 185, \quad 188 - 185 = 3$ (remainder).
Bring down next figure (7) to make 37 and repeat the process.
$37 \div 37 = 1$.
$1 \times 37 = 37, 37 - 37 = 0$ (no remainder).

There are no more figures to be brought down and there is no remainder.
So $24\,087 \div 37 = 651$.

(Check: Using multiplication $651 \times 37 = 24\,087$.)

Exercise 1.6

In this exercise use non-calculator methods. Show your working clearly.

Multiplication

1 42×32

2 76×32

3 143×34

4 265×42

5 718×54

6 1038×74

7 765×451

8 9852×672

Division

9 $7871 \div 17$

10 $4582 \div 29$

11 $9471 \div 77$

12 $4864 \div 19$

13 $7560 \div 15$

14 $20\,928 \div 32$

15 $11\,368 \div 28$

16 $11\,232 \div 54$

Order of operations in a calculation

What is $4 + 3 \times 5$? It is not sensible to have two possible answers.
It has been agreed that calculations are done obeying certain rules:

First	Brackets and Division line
Second	Divide and Multiply
Third	Addition and Subtraction

EXAMPLES

1 $4 + 3 \times 5 \quad = \quad 4 + 15 \quad = \quad 19$

2 $10 \div 2 + 3 \quad = \quad 5 + 3 \quad = \quad 8$

3 $(5 + 6) \times 3 + 4 \quad = \quad 11 \times 3 + 4 \quad = \quad 33 + 4 \quad = \quad 37$

4 $\frac{12}{11 - 8} - 3 \quad = \quad \frac{12}{3} - 3 \quad = \quad 4 - 3 \quad = \quad 1$

This is the same as $12 \div (11 - 8) - 3$. So the division line is the same as brackets.

Exercise 1.7

1 Work these out without a calculator.

(a) $7 + 6 \times 5$

(b) $7 - (6 - 2)$

(c) $24 \div 6 + 5$

(d) $7 \times 6 + 8 \times 2$

(e) $10 \div 5 + 8 \div 2$

(f) $(5 - 2) \times 7 + 9$

(g) $4 \times 12 \div 8 - 6$

(h) $9 \times 9 - 5 \times 5$

(i) $(9 + 5) \times (9 - 5)$

(j) $\frac{22 - 4}{17 - 8} + 12 \div 3$

(k) $\frac{6 \times 3 - 2}{2 \times 2} + 3 \times 8$

(l) $\frac{(3 + 7) \times 10 - 19}{(2 + 1) \times (8 - 5)} - 3 \times 3$

2 Choose from the four signs $+$, $-$, $\times$ and $\div$ to make these sums correct.

(a) 5   6   7 = 37

(b) 5   6   7 = 47

(c) 15   8   9 = 87

(d) 15   8   9 = 129

(e) 15   8   9 = 111

(f) 15   5   3 = 6

(g) 5   24   6 = 1

(h) 19   19   7   0 = 1

(i) 4   4   7   2 = 30

3 Using all the numbers 6, 3, 2 and 1 in this order, brackets and the signs $+$, $-$, $\times$ and $\div$ make all the numbers from 1 to 10.

$6 - 3 \times 2 + 1 = 1$, $6 - 3 - 2 + 1 = 2$,   and so on.

Problems involving number

The number skills you have met in this chapter can be applied to practical situations.

EXAMPLES

○ ○ ○ ○ ○ ○ ○ ○ ○ ○ ○

Set your working out clearly so that someone can follow what you are doing.

Harold loads 5 parcels each weighing 3 kg and 4 parcels each weighing 7 kg onto a trolley. the unloaded trolley weighs 18 kg. What is the total weight of the trolley and the parcels?

Total weight $= (5 \times 3) + (4 \times 7) + 18 \, \text{kg}$

$= 15 + 28 + 18 \, \text{kg}$

$= 61 \, \text{kg}$

The total weight of the trolley and parcels is 61 kg.

How could a calculator be used to answer this problem?

Exercise 1.8

You should be able to do this exercise without using your calculator. Having completed the exercise use a calculator to check your working.

1 Claire is 16 cm taller than Rachel. Their heights add up to 312 cm. How tall is Rachel?

2 Look at this price list.

(a) What is the total cost of a can of drink and a packet of crisps?

(b) What change does Alec get from £2, if he buys 2 bars of chocolate, a doughnut and 3 packets of biscuits?

(c) How much does Lisa save if she buys 2 packets of crisps and a can of drink instead of a pack of biscuits and 2 bars of chocolate?

School Tuck Shop
Price List

Can of drink	36p
Packet of crisps	22p
Bar of chocolate	28p
Doughnut	25p
Pack of biscuits	39p

3   The caretaker set out 17 rows of chairs. There are 15 chairs in each row. How many more chairs are needed to provide seats for 280 people?

4   The total weight of a carton which contains 6 eggs is 520 g. If the carton weighs 70 g, what is the weight of each egg?

5   A cupboard is 90 cm wide. It is placed between two walls which are 160 cm apart. The gap between the cupboard and each wall is the same. What is the size of the gap?

6   A roll of wire is 550 cm long. From the roll, Hilary cuts 3 pieces which each measure 85 cm and 4 pieces which each measure 35 cm. How much wire is left on the roll?

7   A box, which contains 48 matches, has a total weight of 207 g. If each match weighs 4 g, what is the weight of the empty box?

8   The admission charges to a zoo are £4 for a child and £7 for an adult. Zoe is organising a trip to the zoo for a group of people and worked out that the total cost would be £336. She collected £84 from the adults in the group.
(a)   How many children are in the group?
(b)   What is the total number of people in the group?

What you need to know

You should be able to:
- Read and write whole numbers expressed in figures and words.
- Order whole numbers.
- Recognise the place value of each digit in a number.
- Use mental methods to carry out addition and subtraction.
- Carry out accurately non-calculator methods for addition and subtraction.
- Know the Multiplication Tables up to 10×10.
- Carry out multiplication by a number less than 10 (short multiplication).
- Multiply whole numbers by 10, 100, 1000, . . .
- Multiply whole numbers by 20, 30, 40, . . .
- Carry out division by a number less than 10 (short division).
- Divide whole numbers by 10, 100, 1000, . . .
- Divide whole numbers by 20, 30, 40, . . .
- Carry out long multiplication.
- Carry out long division.
- Know the order of operations in a calculation.

IDEAS FOR INVESTIGATION

Write down a three digit number	e.g.	569
Write in words		five hundred and sixty-nine
Count the letters		23
Write this number in words		twenty-three
Count the letters		11
Write this number in words		eleven
and so on . . .		6

(i)   What number do you end up with?
(ii)   Repeat the process starting with a different number.
(iii)   Do you always end up with the same number?

1 (a) Write 870302 in words.
(b) Write three million twenty-seven thousand four hundred and nine in figures.

2 Using all the digits 4, 8, 7, 2, 9 and 5, once only
(a) write the biggest six digit number you can,
(b) write the lowest six digit number you can.

3 In the game of darts the scores of the three darts are added together. These are then taken away from the current total to calculate the new total. In each case work out the score of the three darts and the new total.

	Current Total	1st dart	2nd dart	3rd dart	Score	New Total
(a)	501	60	18	19	[ ]	[ ]
(b)	420	19	57	38	[ ]	[ ]
(c)	301	50	25	17	[ ]	[ ]

4 Work out the following. Show your working.
(a) 465 + 12 + 1582 (b) 2465 − 1878

5 Look at this list of numbers.
24, 7542, 9, 394, 4376, 384
(a) Write the numbers in ascending order.
(b) Write down the value of the digit 5 in the number 7542.
(c) Subtract the lowest number from the highest number.

6 Work out the following. Show your working clearly.
(a) 718 × 9 (b) 1446 ÷ 6

7 Write down the answers to these questions.
(a) 735 × 100 (c) 3 020 000 ÷ 1000
(b) 214 × 30 (d) 18 480 ÷ 40

8 Angelique is taking 149 pupils to the theatre to see the Royal Ballet. The cost of the theatre tickets is £23 per person.
Without using a calculator, work out the total cost of the tickets.
You **must** show all your working.

SEG 1996

9 Sue has collected £544 from her friends at work for theatre tickets.
The tickets cost £17 each.
Without using a calculator, work out the number of theatre tickets she can buy.
You **must** show all your working.

SEG 1996

10 Calculate these. Remember to do the operations in the right order.
(a) $2 + 6 \times 8$ (b) $(9 - 4) \times (3 + 7)$

(c) $7 \div 8 + 1$ (d) $\dfrac{(5 \times 6 - 3) - 21 \div 3}{2 \times 3 + 4}$

11 The price of an airline ticket to New York is £199 plus £14 for tax and £6 for airport security checks.
Douglas buys two tickets. What should the total cost be?

SEG 1995

Numbers and quantities are not always whole numbers.

The number system you met in Chapter 1 can be extended to include **decimal numbers**, such as tenths, hundredths, thousandths, and smaller numbers.

A **decimal point** is used to separate the whole number part from the decimal part of the number.

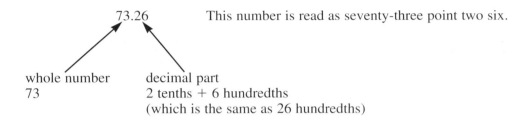

73.26   This number is read as seventy-three point two six.

whole number   decimal part
73   2 tenths + 6 hundredths
                (which is the same as 26 hundredths)

Place value

In the number 1.53 the digit 1 is worth 1 unit = 1
                    the digit 5 is worth 5 tenths = 0.5
                    the digit 3 is worth 3 hundredths = 0.03

$1.53 = 1 + 0.5 + 0.03$

○ ○ ○ ○ ○ ○ ○ ○ ○ ○
1 unit = 10 tenths
1 tenth = 10 hundredths
1 hundredth = 10 thousandths
… and so on.

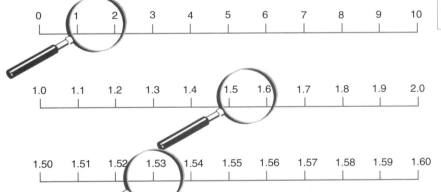

The first digit after the decimal point represents **tenths**.

The second digit after the decimal point represents **hundredths**.

The number 1.53 can be represented by a diagram.

1 unit

5 tenths

3 hundredths

11

Ordering decimals

Compare the numbers 52.359 and 52.36. Which number is the biggest?

You can use a grid to compare the numbers.

tens	units		tenths	hundredths	thousandths
5	2	•	3	5	9
5	2	•	3	6	

Start by comparing the digits with the greatest place value, the tens.
Both numbers have 5 tens, so move down to compare the units.
Both numbers have 2 units, so move down to the tenths.
Both numbers have 3 tenths, so move down to the hundredths.
52.359 has 5 hundredths but 52.36 has 6 hundredths.
So 52.36 is bigger than 52.359.

A similar method can be used to place a list of decimal numbers in order.

Exercise 2.1

1 List the following decimals in ascending order.

(a) 3.1, 3.01, 3.001, 3.15, 3.2, 2.99.

(b) 3.567, 3.657, 3.576, 3.765, 3.675, 3.756.

(c) 0.1, 0.55, 0.45, 0.5, 0.4, 0.15, 0.2, 0.35, 0.3, 0.25.

2 List the following decimals in descending order.

(a) 9.87, 8.79, 9.78, 7.89, 8.97, 7.98.

(b) 0.00015, 0.15, 1.5, 0.015, 0.0015, 15.

(c) 2.67, 2.7, 2.599, 2.701, 3.1, 2.6, 1.9, 3.05, 2.81.

3 In the number 17.4<u>6</u>2 the value of the underlined figure is 0.06. Give the value of the underlined figures in the following.

(a) 27.<u>4</u>3

(b) 36.42<u>9</u>

(c) 2<u>8</u>5.03

(d) 0.7<u>5</u>3

4 Write down the numbers shown by these diagrams.

(a)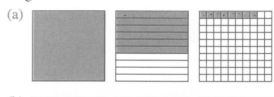

(b)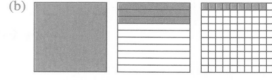

(c)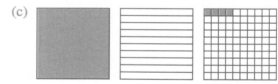

5 Compare the numbers 47.5074 and 47.506. Which is the bigger number?

6 Compare the numbers 93.07 and 93.072. Which is the smaller number?

7 2.564 = 2 + 0.5 + 0.06 + 0.004
Write these numbers in the same way.

(a) 7.62 (c) 7.541

(b) 37.928 (d) 20.503

Non-calculator methods for addition and subtraction of decimals

Write the numbers in tidy columns according to place value.
This is easily done by keeping the decimal points in a vertical column.
Start the addition or subtraction from the right, just as you did for whole numbers.
Use the same methods for carrying and borrowing as well.

EXAMPLES

1 Work out 42.6 + 0.75 + 9

```
  4 2.6
    0.7 5
+   9.0
  ─────
  5 2.3 5
    ₁ ₁
```

2 Work out 17.1 − 8.72

```
    ⁶ ¹⁰ ¹
  1 7.1 0
−   8.7 2
  ─────
    8.3 8
```

You can write 9 as 9.0 or 9.00 to keep your figures tidy.
This does not change the value of the number.
42.6 can be written as 42.60
17.1 can be written as 17.10

Money

1360p can be written as £13.60

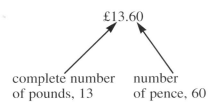

£13.60

complete number of pounds, 13   number of pence, 60

£6 can be written as £6.00
There must be exactly **two** figures after the decimal point when a decimal point is used to record amounts of money.

EXAMPLE

I buy a newspaper for 45p, a set of batteries for £2.50 and a book of stamps for £2.
What is the total cost?
How much change should I get from £5?

Working in pounds.

```
    0.4 5          5.0 0
    2.5 0        − 4.9 5
+   2.0 0        ─────
  ─────          0.0 5
    4.9 5
```

The total cost is £4.95. The change is £0.05 or 5p.

Other uses of decimal notation

Many measurements are recorded using decimals, including time, distance, weight, volume, etc. The same rules for addition and subtraction can be applied if all the measurements involved are recorded using the same units.

Exercise 2.2

Do this exercise without using your calculator, showing your working clearly.
Having completed the exercise you can use a calculator to check your answers.

1 Work out
   (a) 5.14 + 3.72   (b) 7.065 + 5.384   (c) 11.8 + 5.69

2 (a) Work out
       (i)   9.47 − 3.24   (ii) 37.6 − 13.28   (iii) 45.04 − 20.36
   (b) Show how addition can be used to check each of the answers in part (a).

3 Work out
   (a) 6.54 + 0.27 + 0.03   (b) 79.1 + 7 + 0.23
   (c) 10 − 4.78   (d) 9.57 − 4.567
   (e) 2.22 + 0.78   (f) 9.13 − 7.89
   (g) 5.564 + 0.017 + 10.2   (h) 17.1 − 8.82
   (i) 9.123 + 0.71 + 6.2   (j) 9.123 − 2.85

4   Add these amounts of money. Calculate the change from the given amount.

     (a)   (i)   45p, 63p, 79p, £1.43   (ii)   What is the change from £5?
     (b)   (i)   £2.47, £6, £1.50, £1.27   (ii)   What is the change from £15?
     (c)   (i)   31p, £0.25, 27p   (ii)   What is the change from £10?
     (d)   (i)   £12, £3.57, 67p   (ii)   What is the change from £50?

5   Fred cuts three pieces of wood of length 0.95 m, 1.67 m and 2.5 m from a plank 10 m long. How much wood is left?

6   In bobsleigh the times of four runs are added together.

Team A records	37.03 sec	37.76 sec	36.89 sec	37.25 sec
Team B records	37.27 sec	37.45 sec	37.64 sec	36.72 sec
Team C records	36.87 sec	37.51 sec	37.03 sec	38.12 sec

     (a)   Work out the total time for each team.
     (b)   The team with the lowest time wins. Put the teams in order 1st, 2nd and 3rd.

7   Swimmer A finishes the 100 m freestyle in 51.371 seconds. Swimmer B finishes in 52.090 seconds. How long after Swimmer A does Swimmer B finish?

8   In skiing the times of two runs are added together.
     (a)   Skier A has times of 47.12 seconds and 48.09 seconds. What is her total time?
     (b)   Skier B completes her first run in 47.49 seconds. What time does she have to better to have an overall time faster than Skier A?

Multiplying and dividing decimals by powers of 10 (10, 100, 1000, . . .)

When you multiply a decimal by:

10   Each figure moves 1 place to the left.
100   Each figure moves 2 places to the left.
1000   Each figure moves 3 places to the left.
       … and so on.

When you divide a decimal by:

10   Each figure moves 1 place to the right.
100   Each figure moves 2 places to the right.
1000   Each figure moves 3 places to the right.
       … and so on.

EXAMPLES

276 has the same value as 276.0

Noughts can be used as place fillers to locate the decimal point, as in $2.76 \times 1000 = 2760$. If the nought was omitted the value of all other figures would change.

Multiplication

			2 • 7	6	
		2	7 • 6			$\leftarrow 2.76 \times 10 = 27.6$
	2	7	6 •			$\leftarrow 2.76 \times 100 = 276$
2	7	6	0 •			$\leftarrow 2.76 \times 1000 = 2760$

Division

3 • 4	5				
0 • 3	4	5			$\leftarrow 3.45 \div 10 = 0.345$
0 • 0	3	4	5		$\leftarrow 3.45 \div 100 = 0.0345$
0 • 0	0	3	4	5	$\leftarrow 3.45 \div 1000 = 0.00345$

Exercise 2.3

Do this exercise without using a calculator.

1 Work out the following.
- (a) 25.06 × 10
- (b) 25.06 × 100
- (c) 25.06 × 1000
- (d) 0.93 × 10
- (e) 0.93 × 100
- (f) 0.93 × 1000
- (g) 0.0623 × 10
- (h) 7.238 × 100
- (i) 0.0623 × 1000
- (j) 9.451 × 10
- (k) 9.451 × 100
- (l) 9.451 × 1000

2 Work out the following.
- (a) 37.7 ÷ 10
- (b) 37.7 ÷ 100
- (c) 37.7 ÷ 1000
- (d) 0.27 ÷ 10
- (e) 0.27 ÷ 100
- (f) 0.27 ÷ 1000
- (g) 189.02 ÷ 10
- (h) 189.02 ÷ 100
- (i) 189.02 ÷ 1000
- (j) 9 ÷ 10
- (k) 9 ÷ 100
- (l) 9 ÷ 1000

3
- (a) Multiply 0.064 by
  - (i) 10 (ii) 100 (iii) 1000
- (b) Divide 0.064 by
  - (i) 10 (ii) 100 (iii) 1000

4
- (a) A fountain pen costs £2.05
  - (i) How much do 10 cost?
  - (ii) How much do 100 cost?
  - (iii) How much do 1000 cost?
- (b) One lap of a cycling track is 0.504 km.
  - (i) How far is 10 laps?
  - (ii) How far is 100 laps?
  - (iii) How far is 1000 laps?
- (c) 100 calculators cost £795. How much does one cost?
- (d) 1000 pencils cost £120. How much does one cost?
- (e) 10 litres of petrol cost £6.69. How would the cost of 1 litre be advertised?

5 Write down pairs of calculations which give the same answer.

12.3 × 1000   12.3 ÷ 100   12.3 × 0.1   12.3 ÷ 0.01   12.3 × 10   12.3 ÷ 0.1
12.3 × 100   12.3 × 0.001   12.3 ÷ 0.001   12.3 ÷ 10   12.3 ÷ 1000   12.3 × 0.01

Multiplying decimals

The result of multiplying two numbers is called the **product**.

Activity

Use a calculator to multiply these decimals.

5.924 × 2.34   5.2 × 6.4   6 × 3.7   5.1 × 6.02   2.16 × 5.79

Count the total number of decimal places in the numbers to be multiplied together.
For example, 5.924 has three decimal places (there are three figures to the right of the decimal point) and 2.34 has two decimal places. The product of 5.924 and 2.34 has five decimal places. Can you find a rule?

How many decimal places does your rule predict 0.5 × 0.5 should have?

Non-calculator method for multiplying decimals

To multiply decimals without using a calculator:

1 Ignore the decimal points and multiply the numbers using long multiplication

2 Count the total number of decimal places in the numbers being multiplied together.

3 Place the decimal point so that the answer has the same total number of decimal places.

EXAMPLES

1 Work out 1.752×0.23.

```
      1.7 5 2
    × 0.2 3
  ─────────
    5 2 5 6   ←1752 × 3
  3 5 0 4 0   ←1752 × 20
  ─────────
  0.4 0 2 9 6    The answer must have 5 decimal places because 1.752 has 3 and 0.23 has 2.
```

$1.752 \times 0.23 = 0.40296$

2 Work out 4.25×0.18.

```
      4.2 5
    × 0.1 8
  ─────────
    3 4 0 0   ←425 × 8
    4 2 5 0   ←425 × 10
  ─────────
  0.7 6 5 0    The answer must have 4 decimal places because 4.25 has 2 and 0.18 has 2.
```

$4.25 \times 0.18 = 0.7650$ This can be written as 0.765 which has the same value as 0.7650.

3 Work out 0.038×0.024.

```
      0.0 3 8
    × 0.0 2 4
  ───────────
      1 5 2   ←38 × 4
      7 6 0   ←38 × 20
  ───────────
  0.0 0 0 9 1 2    The answer must have 6 decimal places because 0.038 has 3 and 0.024 has 3.
```

$0.038 \times 0.024 = 0.000912$ (In this case 3 extra 0s are put in front of 912 in order to give the answer the required number of decimal places.)

Exercise 2.4

Do this exercise without using a calculator, showing your working clearly.
Having completed the exercise you can use a calculator to check your answers.

1 Calculate these products.

(a) 2.5×3.5	(b) 28.7×1.9	(c) 4.12×0.25	(d) 6.9×4.32
(e) 0.01×0.07	(f) 0.1×0.1	(g) 0.01×0.01	(h) 134×0.73
(i) 10.7×5.4	(j) 0.074×0.0024		

2 What is the cost of each of these lengths of material?
    (a)   7 metres of sheeting at £1.99 a metre.
    (b)   4.5 metres of linen at £2.24 a metre.
    (c)   7.8 metres of satin at £6.95 a metre.
    (d)   3.25 metres of silk at £8.24 a metre.

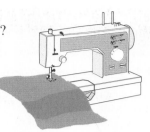

3 (a)   £1 can be exchanged for 9.75 French francs.
       What is the value in French francs of
         (i)   £3.60,   (ii) 60p,   (iii) £54.20?

    (b)   £1 can be exchanged for $1.64 US dollars.
       What is the value in US dollars of
         (i)   £7.50,   (ii) 75p,   (iii) £36.50?

Select
CHEESES
Price per kilogram

Cheddar	£3.20
Cotherstone	£5.20
Sage Derby	£3.25
Stilton	£6.20

4 Work out the cost for each of these portions of cheese.
    (a)   0.7 kg of Stilton.
    (b)   1.65 kg of Cheddar.
    (c)   0.8 kg of Sage Derby.
    (d)   0.45 kg of Cotherstone.

Dividing decimals

Non-calculator method for dividing decimals

Work out $11.06 \div 0.7$.
It is easier to divide by a whole number than by a decimal.
Multiply the dividing number by a power of 10
(10, 100, 1000, . . .) so that it becomes a whole number.
$0.7 \times 10 = 7$.
Multiply the number to be divided by the same power of 10.
$11.06 \times 10 = 110.6$.
If necessary the answer will have a decimal point in the same place.

$110.6 \div 7$ has the same value as $11.06 \div 0.7$.

$$7 \overline{)\ 1\ 1\ ^40.^56}$$
$$\ 1\ 5.8$$

So $11.06 \div 0.7 = 15.8$

> Use the same method of working as you used for dividing whole numbers. The decimal point moves vertically to the same position in the answer.

EXAMPLE

1 8 video tapes cost £14.
How much does each tape cost?

You must work out $14 \div 8$

$$8 \overline{)\ 1\ 4.^60^40}$$
$$\ 1.7\ 5$$

One video tape costs £1.75

> Noughts can be added to the end of a decimal. Adding noughts does not change the value of the number. 14 has the same value as 14.00. Continue dividing until either there is no remainder or the required accuracy is obtained (see Chapter 3).

2 Work out 2.898 ÷ 0.23.

0.23 × **100** = 23 (whole number)
2.898 × **100** = 289.8

289.8 ÷ 23 has the same value as 2.898 ÷ 0.23 and can
be worked out using long division.

2.898 ÷ 0.23 = 12.6

```
            1 2.6
   2 3 ) 2 8 9.8
        - 2 3
            5 9
          - 4 6
          1 3 8
        - 1 3 8
                0
```

Exercise 2.5

Do this exercise without using a calculator, showing your working clearly.
Having completed the exercise you can use a calculator to check your answers.

1 Work out
   (a)   2.46 ÷ 0.2
   (b)   0.146 ÷ 0.05
   (c)   2.42 ÷ 0.4
   (d)   100.1 ÷ 0.07
   (e)   0.0025 ÷ 0.05
   (f)   0.05 ÷ 0.004
   (g)   4.578 ÷ 0.7
   (h)   0.3 ÷ 0.008

2 Use long division to work out the following.
   (a)   81.4 ÷ 2.2
   (b)   15.12 ÷ 2.7
   (c)   7 ÷ 0.16
   (d)   11.256 ÷ 0.24
   (e)   0.1593 ÷ 0.015
   (f)   16.074 ÷ 0.47

3 A steel bar is 12.73 metres long. How many
pieces 0.19 metres long can be cut from it?

4 A jug holds 1.035 litres. A small glass
holds 0.023 litres. How many of the small
glasses would be required to fill the jug?

5 (a)   A pack of 7 tape cassettes costs
         £9.45. How much does each tape
         cassette cost?
   (b)   13 oranges cost £1.43. How much
         does each orange cost?
   (c)   12 rolls cost £1.08. How much does
         each roll cost?
   (d)   25 litres of petrol cost £16.70.
         What is the cost of 1 litre of petrol?
   (e)   A 3-litre bottle of lemonade costs
         £1.41. A half-litre bottle costs 25p.
         Which is the better buy?

What you need to know

Without using a calculator you should be able to:

● Add and subtract decimals.

● Use decimal notation for money and other measures.

● Multiply and divide decimals by powers of 10 (10, 100, 1000, . . .)

● Multiply decimals by other decimals.

● Divide decimals by other decimals.

● Carry out a variety of calculations involving decimals.

● Realise the effect that multiplying by a number between 0 and 1 has.

● Realise the effect that dividing by a number between 0 and 1 has.

Choose any positive whole number   e.g. 20
On a calculator multiply 20 by several positive decimal numbers
e.g. 3.7, 0.24, 23.1, 0.98
20 × 3.7 = 74 (bigger than 20)
20 × 0.24 = 4.8 (smaller than 20)

Find a condition for a number to multiply 20 and make the answer **smaller** than 20.

Is the same condition true for any number other than 20?
*i.e. for a number to multiply 15 and make the answer **smaller** than 15.*

Now divide 20 by several positive decimal numbers e.g. 3.7, 0.24, 23.1, 0.98
20 ÷ 3. = 5.405405 . . . (smaller than 20)
20 ÷ 0.24 = 83.33333 . . . (bigger than 20)

Find a condition for a number to divide into 20 and make the answer **bigger** than 20.

Is the same condition true for any number other than 20?
*i.e. for a number to divide 15 and make the answer **bigger** than 15.*

Review Exercise

Questions 1 to 9.
Do not use a calculator.
You must show all your working.

1 (a) (i)   1.045 + 9.7 + 10
      (ii)   9.89 + 0.017 + 4.5
      (iii) 72.4 + 100.4 + 0.92 + 5.5
   (b) (i)   9.75 − 8.88
      (ii)   10 − 5.67
      (iii) 4.1 − 2.57
   (c) Check the subtractions in part (b)
        with an addition.

2 A 4 × 100 m relay team runs the four
   stages in 10.01 s, 9.93 s, 10.15 s and 9.91 s.
   What is the overall time for the team?

3 Two pieces of wood of length 97 cm and
   1.78 m are sawn from a plank 5.12 m
   long.
   How much wood is left?

4 (a) Multiply 7.62 by
        (i) 10   (ii) 100   (iii) 1000

   (b) Divide 7.62 by
        (i) 10   (ii) 100   (iii) 1000

5 (a) Multiply 87.3 by
        (i) 20   (ii) 30   (iii) 40

   (b) Divide 87.3 by
        (i) 20   (ii) 30   (iii) 40

6 (a) A calculator costs £4.95. How much
        do 50 cost?
   (b) 20 textbooks cost £159.80.
        How much does one cost?

7 Calculate these products.
   (a) 7.4 × 6.3
   (b) 3.76 × 2.7
   (c) 176.5 × 0.6

8 Calculate these divisions.
   (a) 16.56 ÷ 2.3
   (b) 98.8 ÷ 0.08
   (c) 5480 ÷ 0.4

9 (a) 12 × y gives an answer less than 12.
        Give three possible positive values
        for y.
   (b) 12 ÷ z gives an answer greater than
        12. Give three possible values for z.

Questions 10 and 11.
You may use a calculator.

10 (a) Work out $\dfrac{24.076}{1.5 + 3.7}$

SEG 1994

11 Tony uses his calculator to work out
   $$\frac{4.2 \times 86}{3.2 \times 0.47}$$
   What answer should he get?

SEG 1994

CHAPTER 3

Approximation and Estimation

Approximation

In real-life it is not always necessary to use exact numbers. A number can be **rounded** to an **approximate** number. Numbers are rounded according to how accurately we wish to give details. For example, the distance to the Sun can be given as 93 million miles.

Can you think of other situations where approximations might be used?

Rounding to the nearest 10, 100, 1000

If there were 21 152 people at a football match the newspaper report could say, "21 000 at the football match".

Consider the number 7487.
The same number can be rounded to different degrees of accuracy depending on the situation.

Rounding to the nearest 10

7487 is between 7480 and 7490, but it is closer to 7490.
7487 rounded to the nearest 10 is 7490.

7480   7487   7490

Rounding to the nearest 100

7487 is between 7400 and 7500, but it is closer to 7500.
7487 rounded to the nearest 100 is 7500.

7400   7487   7500

Rounding to the nearest 1000

7487 is between 7000 and 8000, but it is closer to 7000.
7487 rounded to the nearest 1000 is 7000.

7000   7487   8000

The number 7487 can be approximated as 7490, 7500 or 7000 depending on the degree of accuracy required.

It is a convention to round a number which is in the middle to the higher number.
75 to the nearest 10 is 80.
450 to the nearest 100 is 500.
8500 to the nearest 1000 is 9000.

EXAMPLES	Rounded to the nearest 10	Rounded to the nearest 100	Rounded to the nearest 1000
7547	7550	7500	8000
973	970	1000	1000
62 783	62 780	62 800	63 000
9125	9130	9100	9000

EXAMPLE

The number of visitors to the local museum was reported as 2600, to the nearest hundred.
What is the smallest possible number of visitors?
What is the greatest possible number of visitors?

The smallest possible number of visitors is 2550.
The greatest possible number of visitors is 2649.

Exercise 3.1

1 Copy and complete this table.

Number	Round to the nearest 10	Round to the nearest 100	Round to the nearest 1000
7613	7610	7600	8000
977			
61 115			
9714			
623			
9949			
5762			
7501			
7500			
7499			

2 Write down these figures to appropriate degrees of accuracy.
(a) There were 19 141 people at the football match.
(b) There were 259 people on the plane.
(c) Tom had 141 marbles.
(d) The class raised £49.67 for charity.
(e) There are 129 students in Year 7.
(f) The population of the town is 24 055.
(g) The land area of the country is 309123 km².
(h) The distance to London is 189 km.
(i) Sarah spent £50.99 on CDs.
(j) There were 693 students in the school.

3 Write down a number each time which fits these roundings.
(a) It is 750 to the nearest 10 but 700 to the nearest 100.
(b) It is 750 to the nearest 10 but 800 to the nearest 100.
(c) It is 8500 to the nearest 100 but 8000 to the nearest 1000.
(d) It is 8500 to the nearest 100 but 9000 to the nearest 1000.

4 "43 000 spectators watch thrilling Test Match".
The number reported in the newspaper was correct to the nearest thousand.
What is the smallest possible number of spectators?

5 Carl has 140 postcards in his collection.
The number is given to the nearest ten.
What is the smallest and greatest number of postcards Carl could have in his collection?

6 "You require 2700 tiles to tile your swimming pool."
This figure is correct to the nearest 100.
What is the greatest number of tiles needed?

Rounding in real-life problems

In a real-life problem a rounding must be used which gives a commonsense answer.

EXAMPLES

1 A Year group in a school are going to Alton Towers. There are 242 students and teachers going.
Each coach can carry 55 passengers.
How many coaches should be ordered?

$242 \div 55 = 4.4$
This should be rounded up to 5.

4 coaches can only carry 220 passengers
$(4 \times 55 = 220)$.

2 Filing cabinets are to be placed along a wall.
The available space is 460 cm.
Each cabinet is 80 cm wide.
How many can be fitted in?

$460 \div 80 = 5.75$
This should be rounded down to 5.

Although the answer is nearly 6 the 6th cabinet would not go in.

Exercise 3.2

1 49 students are waiting to go to the Sports Stadium. A minibus can take 15 passengers at a time. How many trips are required?

2 A classroom wall is 7 m long. How many tables 120 cm long could be fitted along the wall?

3 How many desks or tables in your classroom could be fitted along a suitable wall?

4 76 people are waiting to go to the top of Canary Wharf. The lift can only take 8 at a time. How many times must the lift go up?

5 A group of 175 people are going to Margate. Coaches can take 39 passengers. How many coaches should be ordered?

6 There are 210 students in a year group. They each need an exercise book. The exercise books are sold in packs of 25. How many packs should be ordered?

7 Car parking spaces should be 2.5 m wide. How many can be fitted into a car park which is 61 m wide?

8 A sweet manufacturer puts 17 sweets in a bag. How many bags can be made up if there are 500 sweets?

9 How many 26p stamps can be bought for £5?

10 How many grapefruits, each costing 29p can be bought for £1.50?

Rounding using decimal places

What is the cost of 1.75 metres of material costing £1.99 a metre?
    $1.75 \times 1.99 = 3.4825$
The cost of the material is £3.4825 or 348.25p.
This is a silly answer. After all you can only pay in pence.
A sensible answer is £3.48 correct to two decimal places (nearest penny).
This means that there are only two decimal places after the decimal point.

Often it is not necessary to use an exact answer.
Sometimes it is impossible, or impractical, to use the exact answer.

To round a number to a given number of decimal places

When rounding a number to 1, 2, 3 or more decimal places:
- (i) Write the number using one more decimal place than asked for.
- (ii) Look at the last decimal place and
    - if the figure is 5 or more round up,
    - if the figure is less than 5 round down.
- (iii) When answering a problem remember to include any units and state the degree of approximation used.

EXAMPLES

1 Write 2.76435 to 2 decimal places.
Write the number down using one more decimal place. 2.76**4**
Look at the last decimal place. **4**
This is less than 5, so round down.
Answer 2.76

2 Write 2.76285 to 3 decimal places.
Write the number using 4 decimal places.
2.762**8**
The last decimal place is 5 or more, so round up.
Answer 2.763

3 Write 7.104 to 2 decimal places.
7.104 = 7.10 to 2 d.p.
The zero is written down because it shows the accuracy used, 2 decimal places.

4 5.98 = 6.0 to 1 d.p.
Notice that the next tenth after 5.9 is 6.0.

Notation
Often decimal place is shortened to d.p.

Exercise 3.3

1 Copy and complete this table.

Number	d.p.	Answer
2.367	1	2.4
0.964	2	
0.965	2	
3.9617	3	
3.9617	2	
3.9617	1	
0.056	2	
567.654	2	
567.654	1	
4.991	2	
4.996	2	

2 Carry out these calculations giving the answers correct to
(a) 1 d.p. (b) 2 d.p. (c) 3 d.p.

6.12 × 7.54   89.1 × 0.67
90.53 × 6.29   98.6 ÷ 5.78
67.2 ÷ 101.45

3 In each of these short problems decide upon the most suitable accuracy for the answer.
Then work out the answer. Give a reason for your degree of accuracy.

(a) 1.74 metres of cloth at £6.99 a metre.
(b) 1.74 metres of cloth at £2.05 a metre.
(c) 0.454 kg of cheese at £5.21 a kg.
(d) 7 equal sticks measure 250 cm in total when lying end to end. How long is each stick?
(e) A packet of 6 blank videotapes costs £7.99. How much does one cost?

Approximation and Estimation

Rounding using significant figures

Consider the calculation $600.02 \times 7500.97 = 4500732.0194$
To 1 d.p. it is 4500732.0, to 2 d.p. it is 4500732.02.
The answers to either 1 or 2 d.p. are very close to the actual answer and are almost as long.
There is little advantage in using either of these two roundings.
The point of a rounding is that it is a more convenient number to use.

Here is another calculation $12.34 \div 74380 = 0.000164907\ldots$
To 1 d.p. it is 0.0, to 2 d.p. it is 0.00, to 3 d.p. it is 0.000
None of these answers is helpful.

Another kind of rounding uses **significant figures**.
The **most** significant figure in a number is the non-zero figure which has the greatest place value.
Noughts which are used to locate the decimal point and preserve the place value of other figures are not significant. For example, in the number 0.00328 the most significant figure is the 3 which represents 3 thousandths.

To round a number to a given number of significant figures

When rounding a number to 1, 2, 3 or more significant figures:

(i)   Start from the most significant figure and count the required number of figures.

(ii)   Look at the next figure to the right of this and

- if the figure is 5 or more round up,

- if the figure is less than 5 round down.

(iii)   Add noughts, as necessary, to locate the decimal point and preserve the place value.

(iv)   When answering a problem remember to include any units and state the degree of approximation used.

EXAMPLES

1   Write 4 500 732.0194 to 2 significant figures.

The figure after the first 2 significant figures **45** is 0.
This is less than 5, so round down, leaving 45 unchanged.
Add noughts to 45 to locate the decimal point and
preserve place value.
So 4 500 732.0194 = 4 500 000 to 2 sig. fig.

Notation
Often significant
figure is shortened
to sig. fig.

2   Write 0.000364907 to 1 significant figure.

The figure after the first significant figure 3 is 6.
This is 5 or more, so round up, 3 becomes 4.
So 0.000364907 = 0.0004 to 1 sig. fig.

Notice that the noughts before the 4 locate the decimal point and preserve place value.

Choosing a suitable degree of accuracy

In some calculations it would be wrong to use the complete answer from the calculator.
The result of a calculation involving measurement should not be given to a greater degree of accuracy than the measurements used in the calculation.

What is the area of a rectangle measuring 4.6 cm by 7.2 cm?

$4.6 \times 7.2 = 33.12$
Since the measurements used in the calculation (4.6 cm and 7.2 cm) are given to 2 sig. fig. the answer should be as well.
33 cm^2 is a more suitable answer.

Exercise 3.4

1 Copy and complete this table.

Number	sig. fig.	Answer
456 000	2	460 000
454 000	2	
7 981 234	3	
7 981 234	2	
1290	2	
0.000567	2	
0.0937481	2	
0.0937481	3	
0.0937481	4	
0.010245	2	
0.02994	2	

2 Carry out these calculations giving the answers correct to
(a) 2 sig. fig.   (b) 3 sig. fig.   (c) 4 sig. fig.

672×123 6.72×12.3
78.2×12.8 $7.19 \div 987.5$
$124 \div 65300$

3 In each of these short problems decide upon the most suitable accuracy for the answer.
Then work out the answer, remembering to state the units.
Give a reason for your degree of accuracy.

(a) The area of a rectangle measuring 7.9 cm by 6.4 cm.
(b) The area of a rectangle measuring 13.2 cm by 11.9 cm.
(c) The area of a football pitch measuring 99 m by 62 m.
(d) The length of 13 tables was measured at 16 m. How long was each table?
(e) The area of a farmer's field measuring 320 m by 480 m.

Estimation

It is always a good idea to find an **estimate** for any calculation.
An estimate is used to check that the answer to the actual calculation is of the right magnitude (size).
If the answer is very different to the estimate then a mistake has possibly been made.

Estimation is done by approximating every number in the calculation to 1 significant figure.
The calculation is then done using the approximated values.

3

Approximation and Estimation

EXAMPLES

1 Without using a calculator find an estimate for the calculation 31.1×1.9.
Then, using long multiplication, find the actual value of the product. Compare your answers.

31.1×1.9
Approximating: $31.1 = 30$ to 1 sig. fig.
$\qquad\qquad\quad 1.9 = 2$ to 1 sig. fig.
$30 \times 2 = 60$ (estimate)
Now work out 31.1×1.9

$$
\begin{array}{r}
3\,1.1 \\
\times \quad 1.9 \\
\hline
2\,7\,9\,9 \\
+ \quad 3\,1\,1\,0 \\
\hline
5\,9.0\,9
\end{array}
$$
$\leftarrow 311 \times 9$
$\leftarrow 311 \times 10$
(actual value)

It is easy to make a mistake. If you thought the actual answer was 590.9 (because the decimal point was placed wrongly) then comparing 590.9 to 60 should point out the mistake.

Is 59.09 reasonably close to 60?   Yes.

2 Estimate $\dfrac{78.5 \times 0.51}{18.7}$

Approximating: $78.5 = 80$ to 1 sig. fig.
$\qquad\qquad\quad 0.51 = 0.5$ to 1 sig. fig.
$\qquad\qquad\quad 18.7 = 20$ to 1 sig. fig.

$\dfrac{80 \times 0.5}{20} = \dfrac{40}{20} = 2$ (estimate)

Using a calculator $\quad \dfrac{78.5 \times 0.51}{18.7} = \dfrac{40.035}{18.7} = 2.140909\ldots$

Is 2.140909 reasonably close to 2?   Yes.

Exercise 3.5

Questions 1 and 2.
Do not use a calculator. Show any working clearly.

1 By using approximations to 1 significant figure find estimates to these products.
Then carry out the calculations with the original figures.
Compare your estimate to the actual answer.
    (a) 4.2×1.8 (b) 8.9×3.1 (c) 48.1×4.2 (d) 103.4×2.9

2 Find estimates to these divisions by using approximations to 1 significant figure.
Then carry out the calculations with the original figures.
Compare your estimate to the actual answer.
    (a) $10.78 \div 4.9$ (b) $19.68 \div 4.1$ (c) $30.4 \div 3.2$ (d) $203.49 \div 5.1$.

Questions 3 and 4.
You may use a calculator to answer these questions.

3 Find estimates to these calculations by using approximations to 1 significant figure.
Then carry out the calculations with the original figures.
Compare your estimate to the actual answer.
    (a) $\dfrac{7.9 \times 3.9}{4.8}$ (b) $\dfrac{400 \times 0.29}{6.2}$ (c) $\dfrac{81.7 \times 4.9}{1.9 \times 10.3}$

4 Estate Agents sometimes quote the floor area of a flat in square metres.
They quote an estimate so that buyers can easily compare one flat with another.
Write down the lengths and widths of each room to 1 significant figure.

(a) Obtain an estimate of the total floor area of the two flats.

Meadow View Flat		**Park View Flat**	
Reception 1	4.1 m × 6.9 m	Reception 1	3.9 m × 5.1 m
Reception 2	3.9 m × 5 m	Reception 2	4 m × 3.8 m
Bedroom 1	3.2 m × 3.7 m	Bedroom 1	4.1 m × 3.9 m
Bedroom 2	2.9 m × 2.1 m	Bedroom 2	3.1 m × 2.9 m

(b) Work out the actual floor area of each flat. Compare the estimates.

What you need to know

- A number can be rounded to an **approximate** number.
- How to approximate using **decimal places**.
  When rounding a number to 1, 2, 3 or more decimal places:
  - (i) Write the number using one more decimal place than asked for.
  - (ii) Look at the last decimal place and
    - if the figure is 5 or more round up,
    - if the figure is less than 5 round down.
- How to approximate using **significant figures**.
  When rounding a number to 1, 2, 3 or more significant figures:
  - (i) Start from the most significant figure and count the required number of figures.
  - (ii) Look at the next figure to the right of this and
    - if the figure is 5 or more round up,
    - if the figure is less than 5 round down.
  - (iii) Add noughts, as necessary, to locate the decimal point and preserve the place value.
- When answering a problem remember to include any units and state the degree of approximation used.
- Choose a suitable degree of accuracy.
- Use approximation to **estimate** that the actual answer to a calculation is of the right magnitude (size).

Review Exercise

Questions 1 to 7.
You may use a calculator.

1 Round 8475
  (a) to the nearest 10   (b) to the nearest 100   (c) to the nearest 1000

2 The exact number of people who watched the cup final on TV was 6 732 125.
  (a) (i) Copy and complete this newspaper headline with a sensible rounded number.

  "...................... WATCH CUP FINAL ON TV"

  (ii) Copy and complete this sentence.
  My number is rounded to the nearest .... people.

  (b) The number given in the newspaper was given to the nearest thousand.

  "110 000 LISTEN TO NEW RADIO STATION"

  What is the **smallest** possible number of listeners?

SEG 1996

3 Calculate $72.5 \div 7.9$
  - (a) to 1 decimal place,
  - (b) to 2 decimal places,
  - (c) to 3 decimal places.

4 Calculate $107.9 \div 72.5$
  - (a) to 1 significant figure,
  - (b) to 2 significant figures,
  - (c) to 3 significant figures.

5 Use your calculator to evaluate the following.
Give your answer correct to one decimal place.

$$\frac{13.2 + 24.7}{21.3 - 17.2}$$

SEG 1996

6 Jane's classroom is rectangular. She measures the length and width of the floor. The length is 6.73 m. The width is 5.62 m.
  - (a) Calculate the area of the classroom floor. Write down all the figures in the answer shown on your calculator.
  - (b) (i) The classroom is to be carpeted.
    Give your answer to an appropriate degree of accuracy.
    - (ii) Explain why you chose this degree of accuracy.

SEG 1994

7 Find estimates to these calculations by using approximations to 1 significant figure.
Then carry out these calculations with the original figures. Use a calculator.
Compare your estimate to the actual answer.

  - (a) $\dfrac{42.1 \times 2.97}{2.017 \times 31}$

  - (b) $\dfrac{38.2 + 60.17}{1.95 \times 5.12}$

  - (c) $\dfrac{61.4 \times 1.87}{49.2 - 28.8}$

8 (a) **Without using a calculator** explain why 20 is a good estimate for $414 \div 23$.
  - (b) **Without using a calculator** find the exact value of $414 \div 23$.
    You **must** show all your working.

SEG 1995

9 John uses his calculator to work out

$$\frac{0.39 \times 85.2}{5.8}$$

He gets an answer of 57.3.
Without using a calculator, use approximation to find whether John's answer is of the correct order of magnitude.
You **must** show all your working.

SEG 1996

10 Flour costs 48p per kilogram. Brett bought 205 kg and shared it equally among 14 people. He calculated that each person should pay £0.72.

Without using a calculator, use a rough estimate to check whether this answer is about the right size. **You must show all your working**.

SEG 1994

CHAPTER 4 Negative Numbers ● ● ● ● ● ● ● ●

In Chapter 1 we used a number line
to show whole numbers.
This number line can be extended to
include **negative whole numbers**.

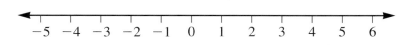

−5 −4 −3 −2 −1 0 1 2 3 4 5 6

Negative whole numbers, zero and positive whole numbers are called **integers**.
−5 can be read as "minus five" or "negative five".
A number written without a sign before it is assumed to be positive. +5 has the same value as 5.
Real-life situations which use negative numbers include temperature, bank accounts and depths below
sea-level.
Can you think of any other situations where negative numbers are used?

Ordering numbers

As you move from left to right along a number line the
numbers become bigger.
−1 is bigger than −100, because −1 is to the right of
−100.
Sometimes other words are used:
        smallest and lowest mean the same,
        biggest, largest and highest mean the same.
This method can be used to place numbers and
measurements in order of size.

EXAMPLE

List these temperatures
from coldest to hottest:
21°C, −4°C, −25°C,
−25°C, −6°C, 5°C.

−25°C, −19°C, −6°C,
−4°C, 5°C, 21°C.

Exercise 4.1

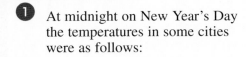

1 At midnight on New Year's Day
the temperatures in some cities
were as follows:

Edinburgh	−7°C
London	0°C
Moscow	−22°C
New York	−17°C
Rome	3°C
Colombo	21°C
Cairo	15°C

(a) Which city recorded the
highest temperature?
(b) Which city recorded the
lowest temperature?
(c) List the temperatures from
coldest to hottest.

2 List these temperatures from coldest to
hottest.

(a) 23°C, −28°C, −3°C, −7°C, 19°C,
−13°C.
(b) −9°C, −11°C, 12°C, 10°C, −7°C, 0°C.
(c) 27°C, 18°C, −29°C, −15°C, −27°C,
2°C.
(d) 20°C, −15°C, 15°C, −20°C, 5°C, 0°C,
−5°C, 10°C, −10°C.

3 List these numbers from lowest to highest.

(a) 31, 52, −78, 51, −39, −16, −9, 30, 11.
(b) 5, 3, 1, −1, −3, −5, −4, −2, 0, 2, 4.
(c) 99, −103, 104, 5, −3, 1, 52, −63, −19,
10.
(d) 50, 30, 10, −10, −30, −50, −40, −20,
0, 20, 40.
(e) 27, 30, −30, 17, 16, 0, −15, −10, 8.

Subtracting a larger number from a smaller number

Work out $3 - 5$.
To work out smaller number − larger number
   (i)   Do the calculation the other way round. $3 - 5$ becomes $5 - 3$.
   (ii) Put a minus sign in front of the answer. So $3 - 5 = -2$.

This is the same as starting at 3 on a number line and going 5 places to the left, to get to -2.

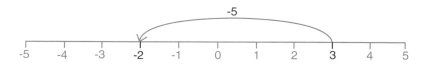

EXAMPLES

1 Work out $7 - 13$.
Do $13 - 7 = 6$.
Then $7 - 13 = -6$.

2 Calculate $21 - 34$.
Do $34 - 21 = 13$.
Then $21 - 34 = -13$.

3 Alec has £50 in his bank account. He writes a cheque for £80. What is his new balance?

His new balance is given by the calculation £50 − £80.
$80 - 50 = 30$.
So $50 - 80 = -30$.
The new balance is −£30.
This means that Alec's account is overdrawn by £30.

Exercise 4.2

Do not use a calculator for this exercise.

1 Work out the following.
   (a) $4 - 7$ (b) $8 - 12$ (c) $13 - 20$ (d) $24 - 56$
   (e) $20 - 20$ (f) $23 - 50$ (g) $29 - 90$ (h) $20 - 21$

2 (a) Draw a number line to show each of these statements.
   (i) $7 - 10 = -3$ (ii) $3 - 6 = -3$ (iii) $-1 - 3 = -4$

   (b) Explain how a number line can be used to work out the following.
   (i) $5 - 6$ (ii) $4 - 8$ (iii) $-2 - 2$

3 What number should be put in the box to make each of these statements correct.
   (a) $7 - \boxed{} = -2$ (b) $\boxed{} - 6 = -5$ (c) $9 - \boxed{} = -3$
   (d) $-3 - 7 = \boxed{}$ (e) $\boxed{} - 50 = -20$ (f) $10 - \boxed{} = -5$

4 (a) Mr Armstrong has £25 in the bank. He writes a cheque for £100. What is his new balance?

   (b) After paying a bill of £60 by cheque, Claire's bank balance is £20 overdrawn. What was Claire's bank balance before paying the bill?

Addition and subtraction involving negative numbers

Imagine two points on a ladder, A and B, 5 rungs apart.
We can use $+$ and $-$ signs to describe movement between these points.

$+$ means first part of a movement $-$ means opposite (return) movement	$+$ means climb upwards $-$ means climb downwards

Start at A
To get from A to B: $\quad + (+5)$

first movement $\qquad$ climb up 5 rungs

Then to get from B back to A, do the opposite: $\quad - (+5)$

opposite

Start at B
To get from B to A: $\quad + (-5)$

first movement $\qquad$ climb down 5 rungs

Then to get from A back to B, do the opposite: $\quad - (-5)$

opposite

In number work the minus sign has two uses.

1. To locate numbers on a number line.
   -3 is three places below/to the left of 0.

2. To show the operation of subtraction.
   $9 - 5$ means
   "9 take away 5".

To get from A to B we can use either $+ (+5)$ or $- (-5)$.
Both of these can be replaced by $+5$ (climb up 5 rungs).

To get from B to A we can use either $- (+5)$ or $+ (-5)$.
Both of these can be replaced by -5 (climb down 5 rungs).

Notice that the signs $+$ and $-$ each had two meanings.
$+$ = first part of the movement **and** climb up.
$-$ = second part of the movement **and** climb down.

$+ +$ can be replaced by $+$
$- -$ can be replaced by $+$
$+ -$ can be replaced by $-$
$- +$ can be replaced by $-$

EXAMPLES

1 Work out
$-4 + (-5)$.

$-4 + (-5)$
Replace $+ -$ by $-$
$= -4 - 5$
$= -9$

2 Work out
$7 - (-6)$.

$7 - (-6)$
Replace $- -$ by $+$
$= 7 + 6$
$= 13$

3 Work out
$-4 + -3 + 6 - -5 - +3$.

$-4 + -3 + 6 - -5 - +3$
Replace signs
$= -4 - 3 + 6 + 5 - 3$
$= 1$

Exercise **4.3**

Do not use a calculator for this exercise.

1 Work out.

(a) $\quad -3 + (+5)$
(b) $\quad 5 + (-4)$
(c) $\quad -2 + (-7)$
(d) $\quad -1 + (+9)$

(e) $7 + (-3)$
(f) $15 + (-20)$
(g) $-11 + (+4)$

(h) $-8 + (-7)$
(i) $3 + (+3) + (-9)$
(j) $-7 + (-5) + 6$

2 Work out.
(a) $8 - (-5)$
(b) $-4 - (-10)$
(c) $10 - (+3)$
(d) $6 - (-1)$
(e) $-5 - (-10)$
(f) $-4 - (+8)$
(g) $-7 - (-6)$
(h) $2 - (-9)$
(i) $5 - (+5) + 9$
(j) $-10 - (-6) + 4$

3 Work out.
(a) $-3 - (-8)$
(b) $5 + (-2)$
(c) $7 - (+4)$
(d) $-9 - (-5) + (-3)$
(e) $7 + (-8) - (+5)$
(f) $-2 - (-7) - 6$

4 Work out.
(a) $10 + 5 - 8 + 6 - 7$
(b) $12 + 8 - 15 + 7 - 20$
(c) $30 - 20 + 12 - 50$
(d) $6 + 12 - 14 - 4$
(e) $37 - 23 - 24 - 25$
(f) $12 + 13 + 14 - 20$

5 Work out.
(a) $5 + (-4) - (-3) + 2 - (-1)$
(b) $5 - 4 + (-3) - (-2) + (-1)$
(c) $10 - (-11) + (-12) + 13 - (-14)$
(d) $-7 - (-7) + 6 + (-3) + (-9)$
(e) $12 + 8 - (-8) + 9 - (-1)$
(f) $15 - (-5) + 5 - (-10) + (-20)$
(g) $-5 + (-5) + (-5) + (-5) - (-5)$
(h) $5 - (-5) - (-5) - (-5) - (-5)$
(i) $1 - (-2) - (-3) - (-4) - (-5)$
(j) $-6 + 7 - 8 + (-9) - (-10)$

6 What is the difference in temperature between
(a) London and Rome,
(b) Edinburgh and Rome,
(c) Moscow and New York,
(d) Cairo and Colombo,
(e) Moscow and Cairo?

Edinburgh	$-7°C$
London	$0°C$
Moscow	$-22°C$
New York	$-17°C$
Rome	$3°C$
Colombo	$21°C$
Cairo	$15°C$

7 The temperature inside a freezer was $-23°C$.
After two hours the temperature had risen by $8°C$.
What is the temperature in the freezer then?

Multiplication involving negative numbers

The multiplication table can be extended to include negative numbers.

Remember:
$+ \times + = +$
$- \times - = +$
$+ \times - = -$
$- \times + = -$

Describe any patterns you can see in the table.

Second number

F	×	−5	−4	−3	−2	−1	0	1	2	3	4	5
i	−5	25	20	15	10	5	0	−5	−10	−15	−20	−25
r	−4	20	16	12	8	4	0	−4	−8	−12	−16	−20
s	−3	15	12	9	6	3	0	−3	−6	−9	−12	−15
t	−2	10	8	6	4	2	0	−2	−4	−6	−8	−10
	−1	5	4	3	2	1	0	−1	−2	−3	−4	−5
n	0	0	0	0	0	0	0	0	0	0	0	0
u	1	−5	−4	−3	−2	−1	0	1	2	3	4	5
m	2	−10	−8	−6	−4	−2	0	2	4	6	8	10
b	3	−15	−12	−9	−6	−3	0	3	6	9	12	15
e	4	−20	−16	−12	−8	−4	0	4	8	12	16	20
r	5	−25	−20	−15	−10	−5	0	5	10	15	20	25

EXAMPLES

1 Work out $(+7) \times (-5)$.

Signs: $+ \times - = -$
Numbers: $7 \times 5 = 35$
So $(+7) \times (-5) = -35$

2 Work out $(-4) \times (-8)$.

Signs: $- \times - = +$
Numbers: $4 \times 8 = 32$
So $(-4) \times (-8) = 32$

○○○○○○○○
Work logically
Work out the sign first.
Then work out the
numbers.

Exercise 4.4

Do not use a calculator for this exercise.

1 $(+7) \times (+5)$

2 $(-7) \times (+5)$

3 $(-7) \times (-5)$

4 $5 \times (+2)$

5 $(+5) \times (-2)$

6 $(-1) \times (-1)$

7 $8 \times (-3)$

8 $(-5) \times 9$

9 $(-8) \times (-8)$

10 $(-7) \times 6$

11 $8 \times (-10)$

12 $(+5) \times (-2) \times (+2)$

13 $(+4) \times (-3) \times (-5)$

14 $(-3) \times (-2) \times (-5)$

15 $(-5) \times (+3) \times (-4)$

Division involving negative numbers

Division is the opposite (inverse) operation to multiplication.
If $a \times b = c$,
then $c \div b = a$ and $c \div a = b$.

If $(+5) \times (-2) = -10$,
then $(-10) \div (-2) = +5$ and $(-10) \div (+5) = -2$.

$+ \div + = +$
$- \div - = +$
$+ \div - = -$
$- \div + = -$

The rules for multiplying negative numbers are also used when dividing negative numbers.

EXAMPLES

1 Work out $(+8) \div (-2)$.

Signs: $+ \div - = -$
Numbers: $8 \div 2 = 4$
So $(+8) \div (-2) = -4$.

2 Work out $(-6) \div (-0.3)$.

Signs: $- \div - = +$
Numbers: $6 \div 0.3$ is the same as $60 \div 3 = 20$
So $(-6) \div (-0.3) = 20$.

Exercise 4.5

Do not use a calculator for this exercise.

1 $(-8) \div (+2)$

2 $(-8) \div (-2)$

3 $(+20) \div (+4)$

4 $(+20) \div (-4)$

5 $(-20) \div (+4)$

6 $(-20) \div (-4)$

7 $(+18) \div (+3)$

8 $(-18) \div (+3)$

9 $(-24) \div (-6)$

10 $(+24) \div (-3)$

11 $(+24) \div (+3)$

12 $(+4) \div (+0.5)$

13 $(+4) \div (-0.5)$

14 $(-4) \div (+0.5)$

15 $(-4) \div (-0.5)$

16 $(+15) \div (+2)$

17 $(-15) \div (+2)$

18 $(-7.5) \div (-5)$

19 $(-6) \div (-1.5)$

20 $(+6) \div (-1.5)$

Using a calculator

Calculations involving negative numbers can be carried out using an ordinary scientific calculator.
Work out $5 + (-7)$.
Enter the calculations into the calculator using the key sequence:

$\boxed{5}$ $\boxed{+}$ $\boxed{7}$ $\boxed{+/-}$ $\boxed{=}$

You should get the answer -2.
If your calculator works in a different way refer to the instruction booklet supplied with the calculator or ask someone for help.

Use your calculator to check your answers to questions in Exercise 4.4 and 4.5.

What you need to know

You should be able to:
- Use **negative numbers** in context such as temperatures, bank accounts.
- Realise where negative numbers come on a **number line**.
- Put numbers in order (including negative numbers).
- Add ($+$), subtract ($-$), multiply ($\times$) and divide ($\div$) with negative numbers.

You will also meet Negative Numbers further on:
   They may be solutions to equations.
   Negative co-ordinates on graphs.
   They may be substituted into algebraic formulae.

Review Exercise

Do not use a calculator for this exercise.

1 Calculate

(a) $7 - 11$

(b) $12 - 19$

(c) $20 - 50$

(d) $23 - 55$

(e) $30 - 30$

(f) $73 - 40$

(g) $73 - 74$

(h) $73 - 73$

(i) $60 - 100$

(j) $19 - 9$

2 Calculate

(a) $9 - (-4)$

(b) $10 - (-2)$

(c) $-5 - (-6)$

(d) $-6 - (-5)$

(e) $-12 - (-13)$

(f) $12 + 7 + (-23) + 6 + (-17)$

(g) $-13 + 4 + (-9) + 10 + 11 + 12$

3 Carry out these multiplications.
(a) $(+6) \times (+4)$
(b) $(+6) \times (-4)$
(c) $(-6) \times (+4)$
(d) $(-6) \times (-4)$
(e) 8×5
(f) $(-8) \times 5$
(g) $8 \times (-5)$
(h) $(-8) \times (-5)$

4 Carry out these divisions.
(a) $(+50) \div (-10)$
(b) $(-12) \div (-6)$
(c) $(-18) \div 3$
(d) $24 \div 6$

5 In Gdansk, Poland, the temperature on one day in January rose from $-7°F$ to $+22°F$.
By how many degrees did the temperature rise?

SEG 1995

6

The butter is stored in a cold room at $-20°C$.
How many degrees is this below the required storage temperature?

SEG 1995

7 Simon took some chicken pieces out of the freezer. The temperature of the chicken pieces was $-20°C$.
Two minutes later he measured the temperature of the chicken pieces to be $-7°C$.

(a) By how many degrees had the temperature risen?

(b) After another two minutes the temperature had risen again by the same amount.
What is the new temperature?

SEG 1995

8 Poppy's bank account is overdrawn by £79. She pays in a cheque and then has a balance of £112.
How much has she paid into her bank account?

SEG 1996

9 Find out the missing numbers. Use the code to replace each number with a letter.
What does the message say?

-7	-6	-5	-4	-3	-2	-1
A	B	C	E	G	I	M

0	1	2	3	4	5	6	7
N	O	R	S	T	U	V	W

First word $-1 + -1 = [?]$

Second word $-25 \div +5 = [?]$
$3 - 10 = [?]$
$7 + -7 = [?]$

Third word $-20 \times [?] = 0$
$8 - 7 = [?]$
$-35 \div [?] = -5$

Fourth word $[?] \times -8 = -40$
$-5 - [?] = -8$
$-6 \times [?] = 24$

Fifth word $-1 + [?] = -1$
$-1 + -3 = [?]$
$-1 \times 3 = [?]$
$-42 \div 6 = [?]$
$[?] \times -3 = -12$
$[?] \times -4 = 8$
$-30 \div -5 = [?]$
$-12 - -8 = [?]$

Sixth word $-5 - [?] = -5$
$-5 \times -1 = [?]$
$-5 \div [?] = 5$
$-2 \times 3 = [?]$
$3 - 7 = [?]$
$-5 - -7 = [?]$
$5 - -[?] = 8$

10 The temperature inside a fridge is $3°C$.
The temperature inside a freezer is $-18°C$.

(a) How much colder is it inside the freezer than inside the fridge?

(b) Calculate $\dfrac{9 \times (-18)}{5} + 32$

to find the temperature of the freezer in degrees Fahrenheit.

SEG 1996

CHAPTER 5

Indices

Activity

Cut a piece of paper into **2 pieces**.

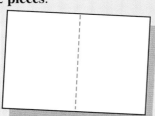

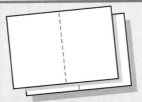

Put the pieces on top of each other.
Cut the pile in half.
How many pieces have you got?

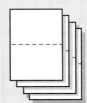

Put **all** the pieces on top of each other.
Cut the pile in half again.
How many pieces?

Continue putting the pieces on top of each other and cutting the pile in half.

Copy and complete this table to show your results.

0 cuts gives 1 piece 1 cut gives 2 pieces 2 cuts gives 4 pieces 3 cuts gives 8 pieces 4 cuts gives . . . 5 cuts gives . . . 6 cuts gives . . .	$4 = 2 \times 2$ $8 = 2 \times 2 \times 2$	In shorthand 2×2 can be written as 2^2. In shorthand $2 \times 2 \times 2$ can be written as 2^3.

Write down the shorthand form of $2 \times 2 \times 2 \times 2 \times 2 \times 2 \times 2 \times 2 \times 2 \times 2$.
Write down the number of pieces for 20 cuts in shorthand form.
Write down the number of pieces for n cuts in shorthand form.
What are the values of 2^1 and 2^0?

Index form

Numbers written in shorthand form like 2^5 are said to be **index** form.
This is sometimes called **power** form.

An expression of the form $a \times a \times a \times a \times a$ can be written in index form as a^5.

a^5 is read as 'a to the **power** 5'.
a is the **base** of the expression.
5 is the **index** or **power**.
(The plural of index is **indices**).

There are two special results that you might have noticed when doing the activity.

$2^0 = 1$ and $3^0 = 1$	In general: $a^0 = 1$

$2^1 = 2$ and $3^1 = 3$	In general: $a^1 = a$

Remember
Any number raised to the power 1 is the number itself.
Any number raised to the power zero is 1.

EXAMPLES

Expression	Index form	Read as	Value
$4 \times 4 \times 4 \times 4 \times 4$	4^5	'4 to the power 5'	1024
$6 \times 6 \times 6$	6^3	'6 to the power 3'	216
$2.1 \times 2.1 \times 2.1 \times 2.1$	2.1^4	'2.1 to the power 4'	19.4481

Exercise **5.1**

Do questions 1 and 2 without using a calculator.

1 (a) Cut a piece of paper into three pieces.
   Put the pieces on top of each other and cut the pile into three pieces.

   How many pieces have you got?

Piece of paper

(b) Put all the pieces on top of each other and cut the pile into three pieces again.

   How many pieces have you got?

First cut

(c) Continue putting the pieces on top of each other and cutting the pile into three.

   (i) Copy and complete this table to show your results.

Second cut

0 cuts gives 1 piece 1 cut gives 3 pieces 2 cuts gives 9 pieces 3 cuts gives 27 pieces 4 cuts gives . . . 5 cuts gives . . .	$9 = 3 \times 3$ $27 = 3 \times 3 \times 3$	In shorthand 3×3 can be written as 3^2. In shorthand $3 \times 3 \times 3$ can be written as 3^3.

   (ii) Work out the value of 3^6.
   (iii) Write down the shorthand form of $3 \times 3 \times 3 \times 3 \times 3 \times 3 \times 3 \times 3 \times 3 \times 3$.
   (iv) Write down the number of pieces for 20 cuts in shorthand form.
   (v) Write down the number of pieces for n cuts in shorthand form.
   (vi) What are the values of 3^1 and 3^0?

2 Write down the value of:
   (a) 2^7 (b) 3^3 (c) 6^2 (d) 8^4 (e) 10^{10} (f) 4^7 (g) 0.2^0
   (h) 12^3 (i) 11^1 (j) 7^3 (k) 3^5 (l) 18^0 (m) 27^1 (n) 0.2^2

3 (a) Copy and complete this table of the powers of 10.

Expression	Index form	Value
$10 \times 10 \times 10 \times 10 \times 10 \times 10$ $10 \times 10 \times 10 \times 10 \times 10$	10^6 10^5 10^4	1 000 000
$10 \times 10 \times 10$		
10		100
		1

(b) Complete a similar table for: (i) the powers of 5,   (ii) the powers of 4.
(c) What do you notice about numbers raised to the power zero?

4 Write each of the following in index form.
   (a) $4 \times 4 \times 4 \times 4$
   (b) $3 \times 3 \times 3 \times 3 \times 3 \times 3 \times 3 \times 3$
   (c) $8 \times 8 \times 8 \times 8 \times 8 \times 8 \times 8 \times 8 \times 8$
   (d) $0.3 \times 0.3 \times 0.3$
   (e) $1.6 \times 1.6 \times 1.6 \times 1.6 \times 1.6$
   (f) $12 \times 12 \times 12 \times 12 \times 12 \times 12 \times 12$

Square numbers and cube numbers

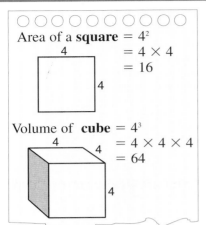

Area of a **square** = 4^2
= 4×4
= 16

Volume of **cube** = 4^3
= $4 \times 4 \times 4$
= 64

There is a special term for numbers raised to the **power 2**.
For example:

4×4 is written as 4^2 and is read as '4 squared'.
2.3×2.3 is written as 2.3^2 and is read as '2.3 squared'.

A whole number **squared** is called a **square number**.
For example: $4^2 = 16$, so 16 is a **square number**.

There is also a special term for numbers raised to the **power 3**.
For example:

$4 \times 4 \times 4$ is written as 4^3 and is read as '4 cubed'.
$2.3 \times 2.3 \times 2.3$ is written as 2.3^3 and is read as '2.3 cubed'.

A whole number **cubed** is called a **cube number**.
For example: $4^3 = 64$, so 64 is a **cube number**.

Powers on the calculator

Calculations with numbers written in index
notation can be done on a scientific calculator using the $\boxed{x^y}$ button.

EXAMPLES

1 Calculate the value of 2.6^4

To do the calculation enter the following sequence into your calculator.

$\boxed{2}$ $\boxed{.}$ $\boxed{6}$ $\boxed{x^y}$ $\boxed{4}$ $\boxed{=}$

This gives $2.6^4 = 45.6976$

2 Calculate the value of $5^3 \times (2^4 + 2^3)$.

To do the calculation enter the following sequence into your calculator.

$\boxed{5}$ $\boxed{x^y}$ $\boxed{3}$ $\boxed{\times}$ $\boxed{(}$ $\boxed{2}$ $\boxed{x^y}$ $\boxed{4}$ $\boxed{+}$ $\boxed{2}$ $\boxed{x^y}$ $\boxed{3}$ $\boxed{)}$ $\boxed{=}$

This gives $5^3 \times (2^4 + 2^3) = 3\,000$

3 Samantha pressed the following sequence of keys on her calculator.

$\boxed{1}$ $\boxed{.}$ $\boxed{5}$ $\boxed{x^2}$ $\boxed{\times}$ $\boxed{3}$ $\boxed{.}$ $\boxed{5}$ $\boxed{x^y}$ $\boxed{3}$ $\boxed{=}$

(a) What was the calculation that Samantha had to work out?
(b) What answer did she get?

(a) Samantha was asked to work out $1.5^2 \times 3.5^3.$
(b) The answer she got was 96.46875

To square a
number use the $\boxed{x^2}$
button.
Some calculators
also have a cube
button.

4 Find the value of x in: (a) $2^x \times 5 = 160$ (b) $5^x \times 4 = 2500$

(a) $2^x \times 5 = 160$
Dividing through by 5 gives:
$2^x = 32$
$2^5 = 32$ so $x = 5$.

(b) $5^x \times 4 = 2500$
Dividing through by 4 gives:
$5^x = 625$
$5^4 = 625$ so $x = 4$.

5 Find the value of x in $3^6 = 27^x$

To calculate 3^6 enter this sequence in your calculator:

$\boxed{3}$ $\boxed{x^y}$ $\boxed{6}$ $\boxed{=}$

This gives $3^6 = 729$.
Now use your calculator to find the values of the powers of 27.
This gives: $27^0 = 1$ $27^1 = 27$ $27^2 = 729$
$3^6 = 27^2$ and $x = 2$.

Exercise 5.2

Use your calculator for all the questions in this exercise.

1 Calculate the value of each of these expressions.
(a) 2.4^5 (b) 1.2^3 (c) 0.7^2 (d) $3^4 + 3^2$ (e) $2^6 - 2^2$
(f) $2^5 \times 3^3$ (g) $3^5 \times 2^3$ (h) $4^5 \times 0.5^3$ (i) $4^5 \div 0.5^3$ (j) $1.4^5 \div 2.5^2$

2 Calculate the value of each of these expressions.
(a) $2 + 2^2 + 2^3 + 2^4$ (b) $3 + 3^2 - 3^3 + 3^4$ (c) $3^3 \times (2^7 - 2^5)$
(d) $4^2 \times (3^4 + 3^2)$ (e) $3^3 \times 2^4 + 3^4 \times 2^3$ (f) $(5^4 + 5^2) \div (2^7 - 2^5)$
(g) $5^3 \times (4^5 - 4^2) + 6^3$ (h) $3^3 \div (2^7 - 2^5)$ (i) $(5^3 - 5^2) \times (6^3 - 2^4)$

3 Calculate the value of:
(a) 3.4^0 (b) 0.014^0 (c) 8400^0 (d) 72.9^0 (e) -7^0
What can you say about numbers raised to the power zero?

4 Calculate the value of:
(a) 6.7 squared   (b) 3.4 cubed   (c) 0.7 squared   (d) 0.04 cubed

5 Complete the list of square numbers from 1^2 to 20^2.
Explore the difference patterns in your list.
Can you find 21^2 from 20^2, 51^2 from 50^2, . . .?

6 Complete the list of cube numbers from 1^3 to 10^3.
Explore the difference patterns in your list.

1	4	9	16	25	...
	3	5	7	...	
		2	2	...	

1	8	27	64	125	...
	7	19	37	...	
		12	18	...	
			6	...	

7 Find the value of x in:
(a) $3^x \times 2 = 54$ (b) $2^x \times 7 = 7$ (c) $3^x \times 11 = 33$ (d) $5^x \times 4 = 100$
(e) $2^x \times 3 = 192$ (f) $5^x \times 7 = 875$ (g) $3^x \times 5 = 405$ (h) $7^x \times 2 = 686$

8 Find the value of x in:
(a) $3^4 = 9^x$ (b) $25^2 = 5^x$ (c) $2^9 = 8^x$ (d) $4^6 = 64^x$ (e) $10^6 = 1000^x$

Square roots and cube roots

The inverse (opposite) of raising to a power is called taking a **root**.

Two special roots are:
the inverse of squaring called the **square root** and
the inverse of cubing called the **cube root**.

For example:

The square root of 9 is 3 because $3^2 = 9$

The cube root of 64 is 4 because $4^3 = 64$

$\sqrt{6.25} = 2.5$ because $2.5^2 = 6.25$

$\sqrt[3]{1.728} = 1.2$ because $1.2^3 = 1.728$

Most calculators have a square root button and some scientific calculators also have a cube root button.

However, square roots and cube roots can be worked out on a calculator without using these buttons. A method called **trial and improvement** can be used.

EXAMPLE

You are asked to find the cube root of 18.6 but your calculator does not have a cube root button.
You know that $2^3 = 8$ and $3^3 = 27$.
Use trial and improvement and a calculator to find the cube root of 18.6 to an accuracy of one decimal place.
Show your method clearly.

2^3	$= 2 \times 2 \times 2$	$= 8$	so the cube root of 8 is 2	
3^3	$= 3 \times 3 \times 3$	$= 27$	so the cube root of 27 is 3	So try 2.5 *Why?*
2.5^3	$= 2.5 \times 2.5 \times 2.5$	$= 15.625$	so the cube root of 15.625 is 2.5	So try 2.6 *Why?*
2.6^3	$= 2.6 \times 2.6 \times 2.6$	$= 17.576$	so the cube root of 17.576 is 2.6	So try 2.7 *Why?*
2.7^3	$= 2.7 \times 2.7 \times 2.7$	$= 19.683$	so the cube root of 19.683 is 2.7	So try 2.65 *Why?*
2.65^3	$= 2.65 \times 2.65 \times 2.65$	$= 18.609625$	so the cube root of 18.609625 is 2.65	

This shows that the cube root of 18.6 lies between 2.6 and 2.65.
So correct to one decimal place the cube root of 18.6 is 2.6.

Remember

When using trial and improvement:

(a) Work methodically using trials first to the nearest whole number, then to one decimal place etc . . .

(b) Do at least one trial to one more decimal place than the required accuracy to be sure of your answer.

Exercise 5.3

Use your calculator for the questions in this exercise.

1
(a) Use the method of trial and improvement to find the square roots of:
   (i) 20   (ii) 108   (iii) 7.6
   Give your answers to an accuracy of one decimal place.

(b) Check each of your answers using the square root button.

2 Use the method of trial and improvement to find the cube roots of:
(a) 45   (b) 200   (c) 4.6
Give your answers to an accuracy of one decimal place.

3 Use the method of trial and improvement to find the length of the side of a square carpet of area 55 m².
Give your answer to an accuracy of two decimal places.

4 Use the method of trial and improvement to find the length of the side of an ice cube of volume 4500 mm³.
Give your answer to an accuracy of two decimal places.

Negative powers

The $\boxed{x^y}$ button can be used to explore negative powers.

To calculate 10^{-1} enter the sequence:

$\boxed{1}$ $\boxed{0}$ $\boxed{x^y}$ $\boxed{1}$ $\boxed{+/-}$ $\boxed{=}$

This gives $10^{-1} = 0.1$

To calculate 10^{-2} enter the sequence:

$\boxed{1}$ $\boxed{0}$ $\boxed{x^y}$ $\boxed{2}$ $\boxed{+/-}$ $\boxed{=}$

This gives $10^{-2} = 0.01$

Changing 0.1 and 0.01 to fractions shows that $10^{-1} = \frac{1}{10}$ and $10^{-2} = \frac{1}{100} = \frac{1}{10^2}$

> 10^{-1} is called the **reciprocal** of 10.
> Reciprocals are numbers raised to
> the **power −1**.
> *What button on a scientific
> calculator calculates reciprocals?*

Activity

Use your calculator to show that $10^{-3} = \frac{1}{10^3}$.
Copy and complete these tables of powers.

Powers of 10

10^3	=	1 000
10^2	=	100
10^1	=	10
10^0	=	1.
10^{-1} =	0.1	$= \frac{1}{10}$
10^{-2} =	0.01	$= \frac{1}{10^2}$
10^{-3} =	0.001	$= \frac{1}{10^3}$
10^{-4} =		=
10^{-5} =		=

Powers of 2

2^3	=	8
2^2	=	4
2^1	=	
2^0	=	
2^{-1} =	0.5	$= \frac{1}{2}$
2^{-2} =	0.25	$= \frac{1}{2^2}$
2^{-3} =		=
2^{-4} =		=
2^{-5} =		=

Remember

To change a fraction to a
decimal.

$\frac{1}{8} = 1 \div 8 = 0.125$

To change a decimal to a
fraction.

$0.25 = \frac{25}{100}$

which simplifies to $\frac{1}{4}$

$0.0625 = \frac{625}{10\ 000}$

which simplifies to $\frac{1}{16}$

*Complete a similar table for the
powers of 5.
Write down expressions for
10^{-n}, 2^{-n} and 5^{-n}.*

The rule for negative powers

A negative power can be written as a positive power using the rule $a^{-n} = \frac{1}{a^n}$

EXAMPLES

1 Write using positive powers:
(a) 3^{-2}　　　　(b) 5^{-4}

(a) $3^{-2} = \frac{1}{3^2}$　　　(b) $5^{-4} = \frac{1}{5^4}$

2 Write as a fraction:
(a) 2^{-3}　　　　(b) 5^{-2}

(a) $2^{-3} = \frac{1}{2^3}$　　　(b) $5^{-2} = \frac{1}{5^2}$

　　　$2^{-3} = \frac{1}{8}$　　　　　　$5^{-2} = \frac{1}{25}$

Use your calculator for question 1 only.

 (a) Calculate the value of each of these expressions.
  (i) 2.5^{-2} (ii) 1.25^{-4} (iii) 20^{-1} (iv) 0.625^{-4} (v) 0.1^{-5}
  (b) Write down some numbers which give a number greater than 1 when raised to a negative power.
  (c) Write down some numbers which give a number between 0 and 1 when raised to a negative power.
  (d) Explain your answers to (b) and (c).

 Write each of the following as a fraction:
  (a) 2^{-1} (b) 3^{-3} (c) 5^{-3} (d) 2^{-4} (e) 4^{-3} (f) 10^{-5}

Multiplying and dividing numbers with powers

EXAMPLES

This example introduces a method for multiplying powers of the same number.

 (a) Calculate the value of $6^5 \times 6^4$ in power form.

$6^5 = 6 \times 6 \times 6 \times 6 \times 6$

$6^4 = 6 \times 6 \times 6 \times 6$

$6^5 \times 6^4 = (6 \times 6 \times 6 \times 6 \times 6) \times (6 \times 6 \times 6 \times 6)$

$\quad\quad = 6 \times 6 \times 6 \times 6 \times 6 \times 6 \times 6 \times 6 \times 6$

This gives: $6^5 \times 6^4 = 6^9$

(b) Calculate the value of $3^2 \times 3^6$ in power form.

$3^2 = 3 \times 3$

$3^6 = 3 \times 3 \times 3 \times 3 \times 3 \times 3$

$3^2 \times 3^6 = (3 \times 3) \times (3 \times 3 \times 3 \times 3 \times 3 \times 3)$

$\quad\quad = 3 \times 3 \times 3 \times 3 \times 3 \times 3 \times 3 \times 3$

This gives: $3^2 \times 3^6 = 3^8$

Check each of these results with your calculator.
Can you see a quick way of working out the power of the answer?

This example introduces a method for dividing powers of the same number.

2 (a) Calculate the value of $6^7 \div 6^4$ in power form.

$$6^7 \div 6^4 = \frac{6 \times 6 \times 6 \times \cancel{6} \times \cancel{6} \times \cancel{6} \times \cancel{6}}{\cancel{6} \times \cancel{6} \times \cancel{6} \times \cancel{6}}$$

$$= 6 \times 6 \times 6$$

$$= 6^3$$

This gives: $6^7 \div 6^4 = 6^{7-4} = 6^3$

(b) Calculate the value of $4^5 \div 4^3$ in power form.

$$4^5 \div 4^3 = \frac{4 \times 4 \times \cancel{4} \times \cancel{4} \times \cancel{4}}{\cancel{4} \times \cancel{4} \times \cancel{4}}$$

$$= 4 \times 4$$

$$= 4^2$$

This gives: $4^5 \div 4^3 = 4^{5-3} = 4^2$

Check each of these results with your calculator.
Can you see a quick way of working out the power of the answer?

Rules for multiplying and dividing powers of the same number

Multiplying

When multiplying:
powers of the same base are **added**.

In general: $a^m \times a^n = a^{m+n}$

Dividing

When dividing:
powers of the same base are **subtracted**.

In general: $a^m \div a^n = a^{m-n}$

EXAMPLES

1 Simplify $2^6 \times 2^{-3}$.
Leave your answer in power form.

$$2^6 \times 2^{-3} = 2^{6+\,-3}$$
$$= 2^{6-3}$$
$$= 2^3$$

$2^6 = 2 \times 2 \times 2 \times 2 \times 2 \times 2$

$2^{-3} = \frac{1}{2^3} = \frac{1}{2 \times 2 \times 2}$

$2^6 \times 2^{-3} = 2 \times 2 \times 2 \times 2 \times 2 \times 2 \times \frac{1}{2 \times 2 \times 2}$

$= \frac{2 \times 2 \times 2 \times 2 \times 2 \times 2}{2 \times 2 \times 2}$

$= 2 \times 2 \times 2 = 2^3$

Remember
When multiplying and dividing powers with different bases each base must be dealt with separately. *Why?*

2 Simplify:
(a) $3^4 \times 2^3 \times 3^{-5} \times 2^5$ (b) $\dfrac{5^2 \times 6^8 \times 7^2}{5^3 \times 6^5 \times 7^{-1}}$
Leave your answers in power form.

(a) $3^4 \times 2^3 \times 3^{-5} \times 2^5 = 3^4 \times 3^{-5} \times 2^3 \times 2^5$
$= 3^{4+\,-5} \times 2^{3+5}$
$= 3^{-1} \times 2^8$

(b) $\dfrac{5^2 \times 6^8 \times 7^2}{5^3 \times 6^5 \times 7^{-1}}$
$= 5^{2-3} \times 6^{8-5} \times 7^{2-\,-1}$
$= 5^{2-3} \times 6^{8-5} \times 7^{2+1}$
$= 5^{-1} \times 6^3 \times 7^3$

3 Simplify:
(a) $10^{-4} \div 10^{-2}$ (b) $3^4 \times 5^{-2} \times 3^{-5} \times 5^7$
Leave your answers in power form using **positive** powers only.

(a) $10^{-4} \div 10^{-2} = 10^{-4-\,-2}$
$= 10^{-4+2}$
$= 10^{-2} = \frac{1}{10^2}$

(b) $3^4 \times 5^{-2} \times 3^{-5} \times 5^7 = 3^4 \times 3^{-5} \times 5^{-2} \times 5^7$
$= 3^{4+\,-5} \times 5^{-2+7}$
$= 3^{-1} \times 5^5 = \frac{5^5}{3}$

Exercise 5.5

Do not use a calculator in this exercise.

1 Simplify each of these expressions. Leave your answers in power form.
(a) $2^5 \times 2^2$ (b) $4^3 \times 4^6$ (c) $6^2 \times 6$ (d) $8^4 \times 8^3$ (e) $7^4 \times 2^3 \times 7^3 \times 2^5$

2 Simplify each of these expressions. Leave your answers in power form using positive powers only.
(a) $2^{-3} \times 2$ (b) $5^5 \times 5^{-7}$ (c) $3^{-2} \times 3$ (d) $8^{-2} \times 8^{-3}$ (e) $9^2 \times 9^{-2}$

3 Simplify each of these expressions. Leave your answers in power form.
(a) $2^5 \div 2^2$ (b) $4^7 \div 4^5$ (c) $6^2 \div 6$ (d) $8^4 \div 8^3$ (e) $3^{11} \div 3^5$

4 Simplify each of these expressions. Leave your answers in power form using positive powers only.
(a) $2^{-3} \div 2$ (b) $5^5 \div 5^{-7}$ (c) $3^{-2} \div 3$ (d) $7^{-4} \div 7^{-3}$ (e) $11^{-2} \div 11^3$

5 Simplify each of these expressions. Leave your answers in power form.
(a) $8^{-3} \times 8^5$
(b) $7^2 \div 7^7$
(c) $2.5^{-2} \div 2.5^{-1}$
(d) $4^3 \times 4^2 \times 4^{-5}$
(e) $10^{-3} \div 10^{-2}$
(f) $6^{-3} \times 6^4 \div 6^5$
(g) $0.1^{-7} \div 0.1^5$
(h) $5^{-7} \div 5^2 \times 5^6$

6 Simplify each of these expressions. Leave your answers in power form.
(a) $4^{-3} \times 4^5 \times 8^5 \times 8^2$
(b) $4^{-1} \times 5^5 \times 5^{-7} \times 4^2$
(c) $\dfrac{6^7 \times 9^2}{6^2 \times 9}$
(d) $\dfrac{3^5 \times 4^5 \times 7}{3^2 \times 4 \times 7^3}$

7 Simplify each of these expressions. Leave your answers in power form using positive powers only.
(a) $2^{-5} \times 5^3 \times 2^3 \times 5^2$
(b) $3^{-1} \times 8^5 \times 3^{-2} \times 8^{-1}$
(c) $\dfrac{2^5 \times 5^2}{2^2 \times 5^{-3}}$
(d) $\dfrac{4^{-1} \times 7^2 \times 9^{-1}}{4^{-3} \times 7^5 \times 9^3}$

Multiplying and dividing algebraic expressions with powers

The rules for multiplying and dividing powers can be used to simplify algebraic expressions involving powers.

Remember
When multiplying or dividing expressions that include both numbers and powers:
multiply or **divide** the **numbers**,
add or **subtract** the **powers**.
Deal with the powers of different bases **separately**.

EXAMPLES

1 Simplify each of these expressions.
(a) $x^3 \times x^8 = x^{3+8} = x^{11}$
(b) $2x^2 \times 5x^7 = (2 \times 5) \times (x^2 \times x^7) = 10 \times x^{2+7} = 10x^9$
(c) $x^3 y^2 \times xy^4 = (x^3 \times x) \times (y^2 \times y^4) = x^{3+1} \times y^{2+4} = x^4 y^6$
(d) $(x^3 y^2)^2 = (x^3 y^2) \times (x^3 y^2) = (x^3 \times x^3) \times (y^2 \times y^2) = x^6 y^4$
(e) $(3x^4)^2 = (3x^4) \times (3x^4) = (3 \times 3) \times (x^4 \times x^4) = 9x^8$

2 Simplify each of these expressions.
(a) $x^8 \div x^5 = x^{8-5} = x^3$
(b) $6y^6 \div 2y^4 = (6 \div 2) \times (y^6 \div y^4) = 3 \times y^{6-4} = 3y^2$

3 Simplify each of these expressions.
(a) $\dfrac{xy^3 \times x^4 y^5}{x^2 y^4}$

$= xy^3 \times x^4 y^5 \div x^2 y^4 = (x \times x^4 \div x^2) \times (y^3 \times y^5 \div y^4) = (x^{1+4-2}) \times (y^{3+5-4}) = x^3 y^4$

(b) $\dfrac{(4ab)^2 \times 3ab^3}{6ab^{-4}}$

$= (4ab)^2 \times 3ab^3 \div 6ab^4 = (4^2 \times 3 \div 6) \times (a^2 \times a \div a) \times (b^2 \times b^3 \div b^4) = 8a^2 b$

Exercise 5.6
Do the questions in this exercise without using a calculator.

1 Simplify each of these expressions.
(a) $a^4 \times a^3$
(b) $x^{11} \times x^5$
(c) $b^4 \times b$
(d) $t^5 \times t^2$
(e) $x^5 \times x^2 \times x$
(f) $4b^4 \times 2b^3$
(g) $3t^5 \times 2t$
(h) $4x^2 \times 2x^4$
(i) $5y^5 \times 5y^3$
(j) $2x^3 \times 3x^5 \times 2x$
(k) $x^5 y \times xy^4$
(l) $yz^3 \times y^3 z$
(m) $x^2 y^4 \times x^3 y^3$
(n) $3r^5 s \times 2r^4 s^3$
(o) $3p^5 q^4 \times p^2 q^3 \times 4pq$

2 Simplify each of these expressions.
(a) $(b^4)^2$
(b) $(x^2)^3$
(c) $2(x^4)^3$
(d) $(2y^3)^2$
(e) $(3a^2)^4$
(f) $(x^2 y^3)^2$
(g) $(3ab^2)^3$
(h) $(5p^3 q^4)^2$
(i) $(2x^5 y)^4$
(j) $(5rs^2 t^3)^3$

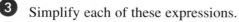

3 Simplify each of these expressions.

(a) $a^4 \div a^3$ (b) $x^{11} \div x^5$ (c) $x^2 \div x$ (d) $x^{11} \div x^{11}$

(e) $a^3 \div a$ (f) $8b^5 \div 2b^2$ (g) $6y^3 \div 3y$ (h) $15z^3 \div 3z$

(i) $6x^6 \div 2x^2$ (j) $16t^3 \div 4t^2$ (k) $x^5y \div xy$ (l) $p^3q^6 \div pq$

(m) $8r^5s^3 \div 2r^4s^3$ (n) $6x^5y \div 2x^4y$ (o) $qr^3s^3t^3 \div rs^3t^2$

4 Simplify each of these expressions.

(a) $(x^5y^4 \times x^2y^3) \div xy$ (b) $12n^5 \div (3n^3 \times 2n)$ (c) $40r^5 \div (5r \times 2r^3)$

(d) $(4pq^3 \times p^2q^2) \div 2p^2$ (e) $a^2b^2c^4 \div abc$ (f) $18x^2y^2z \div 6x^2yz$

(g) $\dfrac{rs^2t \times r^2s^5t^4}{r^2s^4t^3}$ (h) $\dfrac{a^3b^3c^4 \times a^2b^2c^3}{ab^4c^6}$ (i) $\dfrac{6x^2y^3z^2 \times 3xy^2z^4}{2x^3y^4z^3}$

(j) $\dfrac{(5ab^2)^2 \times 3ab^5}{15a^2b^4}$ (k) $\dfrac{4xy^2z^5 \times 3x^2y^3z^4}{6xy^4z^2}$ (l) $\dfrac{(8lm)^2 \times (2l^2m)^3}{(2lm)^5}$

What you need to know

- An expression such as $a \times a \times a \times a \times a$ can be written in a shorthand way as a^5.
  This is read as 'a to the power 5'.
  The number a is the **base** of the expression. 5 is the **power** or **index**.
  Powers can be calculated using the $\boxed{x^y}$ button on a scientific calculator.

- Numbers raised to the power 2 are **squared**.
  Whole numbers squared are called **square numbers**.
  Squares can be calculated using the $\boxed{x^2}$ button on a scientific calculator.
  The inverse (opposite) of squaring a number is called finding the **square root**.

- Numbers raised to the power 3 are **cubed**.
  Whole numbers cubed are called cube **numbers**.
  The inverse (opposite) of cubing a number is called finding the **cube root**.

- **Reciprocals** can be calculated using the $\boxed{\frac{1}{x}}$ button on a scientific calculator.

- Powers of the same base are **added** when **multiplied**.
  Powers of the same base are **subtracted** when **divided**.
  Any number raised to the power zero equals 1.
  A negative power can be written as a positive power.

$$a^2 = a \times a$$
$$a^1 = a$$
$$a^0 = 1$$
$$a^{-1} = \frac{1}{a}$$
$$a^{-2} = \frac{1}{a^2}$$

$$a^m \times a^n = a^{m+n}$$
$$a^m \div a^n = a^{m-n}$$
$$a^0 = 1$$
$$a^{-n} = \frac{1}{a^n}$$

IDEAS FOR INVESTIGATION

The squares of whole numbers can be written as the sum of consecutive odd numbers.

$$1^2 = 1 \qquad 2^2 = 1 + 3 \qquad 3^2 = 1 + 3 + 5$$

Continue this pattern. Can you find a general rule for n^2.

The cubes of whole numbers can also be written as the sum of consecutive odd numbers.

$$1^3 = 1 \qquad 2^3 = 3 + 5 \qquad 3^3 = 7 + 9 + 11$$

Continue this pattern. Can you find a general rule for n^3.

Other powers of whole numbers can also be written as the sum of consecutive odd numbers. This is how the pattern starts for the powers of 4 and 5.

$$1^4 = 1 \qquad 1^5 = 1 \qquad 2^4 = 7 + 9 \qquad 2^5 = 15 + 17$$

Investigate the connection between other powers and the sum of consecutive odd numbers.

Review Exercise

Questions 1 to 9.
Do not use a calculator.

1 Write each of the following as a power of 10.
  (a) 100 (b) 1 000 000 (c) 1 (d) 0.1 (e) 0.001
  (f) 0.000 001 (g) 0.000 000 001 (h) 10 (i) 0.01 (j) 0.000 01

2 Write down the value of:
  (a) 2^5 (b) 1^{10} (c) 5^4 (d) $4^4 + 4^2$ (e) $3^4 + 3^2$
  (f) $5^4 - 5^3$ (g) $2^3 + 2^5$ (h) $7^0 + 7^2$ (i) $2^1 + 2^4 + 2^5$ (j) $3^0 + 3^1 + 3^2 + 3^3$

3 Write each of the following as a fraction.
  (a) 2^{-2} (b) 2^{-3} (c) 3^{-1} (d) 5^{-3} (e) 8^{-2} (f) 2^{-5}

4 Simplify fully each of these expressions.
Leave your answers in power form.
  (a) $3^6 \times 3^2$ (b) $5^4 \times 5^7$ (c) $9^5 \times 9$ (d) $4^8 \times 4^5$ (e) $2^5 \times 3^3 \times 2^3 \times 3^7$
  (f) $4^8 \div 4^3$ (g) $7^6 \div 7$ (h) $8^3 \div 8^0$ (i) $6^7 \div 6^3$ (j) $3^8 \times 3^3 \div 3^2$
  (k) $2^{-5} \times 2^2$ (l) $5^{-3} \times 5^{-4}$ (m) $4^{-2} \div 4$ (n) $3^8 \div 3^{-5}$ (o) $2^{-4} \times 7^3 \times 2^{-3} \times 7^{-1}$

5 Simplify fully each of these expressions.
Leave your answers in power form using positive powers only.
  (a) $2^{-4} \times 5^6 \times 2^3 \times 5^{-2}$ (b) $2^{-3} \times 7^5 \times 2 \times 7^{-5}$ (c) $\frac{3^{-3} \times 5}{3^2 \times 5^{-3}}$ (d) $\frac{2^{-1} \times 3 \times 5^{-1}}{2 \times 3^{-1} \times 5^{-1}}$

6 Simplify fully each of these expressions.
  (a) $a^2 \times a^5$ (b) $y^2 \times y^5 \times y$ (c) $x^2 \times x^3 \times x^4$ (d) $4x^2 \times 2x^3$
  (e) $4x^5 \times 4x$ (f) $x^3y \times xy^3$ (g) $a^2b^3 \times a^5b^2$ (h) $p^3q^4 \times p^5q^2$
  (i) $4x^2y \times 3x^3y^5$ (j) $x^3y \times 3x^5y^3 \times 2xy^2$

7 Simplify fully each of these expressions.
  (a) $a^5 \div a^3$ (b) $p^2 \div p$ (c) $y^5 \div y^5$ (d) $6x^2 \div 2x$
  (e) $9x^7 \div 3x^2$ (f) $7x^7 \div x^2$ (g) $x^2y^2 \div xy$ (h) $x^5y^2 \div xy^2$
  (i) $5x^6y^2 \div x^3y$ (j) $8x^4y^2z^3 \div 2x^2yz^2$

8 Simplify fully each of these expressions.
  (a) $(x^3)^3$ (b) $(a^3)^2$ (c) $(3x^2)^2$ (d) $(2p^5)^3$
  (e) $(2t \times 4t^2)^2$ (f) $(3x^3)^3$ (g) $(a^3b)^2$ (h) $(5x^2y)^2$
  (i) $(5p^5)^2$ (j) $(2t^5)^3$ (k) $(4x^3)^2$ (l) $(2s^2t \times 4st)^3$

9 Simplify fully each of these expressions.
Leave your answers in power form.
  (a) $(x^3y^2 \times x^4y^2) \div xy$ (b) $20t^7 \div (2t^2 \times 5t^4)$ (c) $(15x^2 \times 2x^3) \div 10x$
  (d) $(4xy^5 \times 3x^2y^3) \div 6y^2$ (e) $(a^2b^2)^2 \div ab^4$ (f) $\frac{xy \times x^2y^5}{x^2y^3}$
  (g) $\frac{8a^2b \times 5ab^2}{10a^3b^3}$ (h) $\frac{(5xy^2)^3 \times 2xy^3}{25x^2y^5}$ (i) $\frac{8ab^2c^3 \times 6a^2b^3c^5}{12a^2b^4c}$

Questions 10 to 15.
You may use a calculator to answer these questions.

10 Copy and complete these tables for:
(a) the powers of 4,   (b) the powers of 8.

Power form	Expression	Value
4^3		
4^2	4×4	
4^1		
4^0		
4^{-1}		0.25
4^{-2}		
4^{-3}		

Power form	Expression	Value
8^3		
8^2		
8^1		
8^0		
8^{-1}		
8^{-2}		
8^{-3}		

11 I am trying to find the square root of 12. The table shows my first three tries.
(a) Copy and complete the table.

1st try	3	$3 \times 3 = 9$	too low
2nd try	4	$4 \times 4 = 16$	too high
3rd try	3.5	$3.5 \times 3.5 = 12.25$	too high
Give a sensible 4th try		....	....
Give a better 5th try		....	....

(b) (i) Use your calculator to find the square root of 12.
Write down all the numbers on your calculator display.
(ii) Write your answer correct to three decimal places.

SEG 1994

12 Julio is trying to find the cube root of 17. His calculator does not have a cube root button so he has to work out his answer by trial and improvement.
He calculates $2.5 \times 2.5 \times 2.5 = 15.625$
$2.6 \times 2.6 \times 2.6 = 17.576$
Continue this method to find the cube root of 17 correct to two decimal places.
You **must** show all your working.

SEG 1995

13 Calculate the value of:
(a) $12^5 \div 2^3$ (b) $0.3^3 + 0.3^5$ (c) $0.3^3 \times 0.3^5$
(d) $3^4 + 2^5 \times (3^2 + 3^5)$ (e) $2^5 \times (8^3 - 4^5)$ (f) $8^5 \times (2^3 + 4^2)$
(g) $(2.8^3 + 2.8^5) \div 2^3$ (h) $(1.2^4 + 2^3) \times (1.2^4 - 2^3)$ (i) 6.5^{-3}
(j) $1.5^3 + 1.5^{-2}$ (k) $2.5^{-3} \times 2.5^3$ (l) $5^5 \times (5^3 - 5^{-2})$

14 Calculate the value of each of these expressions.
(a) $2^{-1} + 2^2 + 2^{-3}$ (b) $2^6 \times (2^3 + 2^{-3})$ (c) $(1.5^4 + 2.5^{-3}) \div 2^{-4}$
(d) $(5^3 + 5^{-3}) \times (2^5 + 2^{-5})$ (e) $(4^{-1} + 4^2) \div 4^{-2}$ (f) $(2.5^{-1} + 2.5^2) \div 10^{-2}$

15 Find the value of x in:
(a) $2 = 1 + 9^x$ (b) $25^2 = 5^x$ (c) $2^6 = 4^x$
(d) $2^x \times 3 = 192$ (e) $5^x \times 3 = 375$ (f) $2^x + 4^x = 72$
(g) $2 + 10^x = 2.001$ (h) $1 + 2^x = 1.25$ (i) $2^3 \times 2^x = 2$

CHAPTER 6

Multiples, Factors and Primes

Multiples

5, 10, 15, 20, . . . are **multiples** of 5.
6, 12, 18, 24, . . . are **multiples** of 6.
The 8th **multiple** of 7 is $8 \times 7 = 56$

Factors

Pairs of **whole numbers** which have a product of
6 are 1×6 and 2×3.
1, 2, 3, and 6 are called **factors** of 6.

Prime numbers

3 appears twice only in the table of multiples.
It has just two factors, 1 and 3.
Numbers like this are called **prime numbers**.

A prime number has exactly **two** factors,
1 and the number itself.

The number 1 is not a prime number because
it has only one distinct factor.
The first few prime numbers are:
2, 3, 5, 7, 11, 13, 17, 19, . . .

A table of multiples

	1	2	3	4	5	6	7	8	9	10
1	1	2	3	4	5	6	7	8	9	10
2	2	4	6	8	10	12	14	16	18	20
3	3	6	9	12	15	18	21	24	27	30
4	4	8	12	16	20	24	28	32	36	40
5	5	10	15	20	25	30	35	40	45	50
6	6	12	18	24	30	36	42	48	54	60
7	7	14	21	28	35	42	49	56	63	70
8	8	16	24	32	40	48	56	64	72	80
9	9	18	27	36	45	54	63	72	81	90
10	10	20	30	40	50	60	70	80	90	100

What name is given to the numbers in the shaded boxes?

EXAMPLE

Find **all** the factors of 25.

Method 1
Find **all** the pairs of whole numbers
that have a product of 25.
$25 \times 1 = 25$
$5 \times 5 = 25$

Method 2
Find **all** the whole numbers that
divide exactly into 25.
$25 \div 1 = 25$ Factors 1 and 25
$25 \div 2 = 12.5$ No factors
$25 \div 3 = 8.333 \ldots$ No factors
$24 \div 4 = 6.25$ No factors
$25 \div 5 = 5$ Factor 5
Why stop here?

1, 5 and 25 are all the factors of 25.

Exercise 6.1

Do not use a calculator.

1 Write down the first five multiples of:
  (a) 12   (b) 19   (c) 20   (d) 45   (e) 85

2 Find all the factors of:
  (a) 12   (b) 36   (c) 60   (d) 80   (e) 45

3 3, 4, 5, 9, 14, 20, 27, and 35.
  Which of the above numbers are
  (a) multiples of 9,   (d) factors of 54,
  (b) multiples of 7,   (e) prime numbers?
  (c) factors of 20,

4 (a) How many multiples of 6 are factors of 36?
  (b) How many multiples of 5 are factors of 120?
  (c) How many factors of 300 are multiples of 15?
  (d) How many factors of 2310 are prime numbers?

Prime factors

The factors of 18 are 1, 2, 3, 6, 9 and 18.
Two of these factors, 2 and 3, are prime numbers.
The **prime factors** of 18 are 2 and 3.

Those factors of a number which are prime numbers are called **prime factors**.

Products of prime factors

All numbers can be written as the product of their prime factors.
For example:

$$6 = 2 \times 3$$
$$20 = 2 \times 2 \times 5$$
$$70 = 2 \times 5 \times 7$$
$$168 = 2 \times 2 \times 2 \times 3 \times 7$$

Powers can be used to write numbers as the product of their prime factors in a shorter form.
For example:

$$20 = 2^2 \times 5$$
$$168 = 2^3 \times 3 \times 7$$
$$200 = 2^3 \times 5^2$$
$$108 = 2^2 \times 3^3$$
$$360 = 2^3 \times 3^2 \times 5$$
$$2160 = 2^4 \times 3^3 \times 5$$
$$12\,600 = 2^3 \times 3^2 \times 5^2 \times 7$$
$$1\,000\,000 = 2^6 \times 5^6$$

Use the $\boxed{x^y}$ *button on your calculator to check that these statements are true.*

A **factor tree** can be used to help write numbers as the product of their prime factors.
For example, this factor tree shows that:

$$40 = 2 \times 20$$
$$40 = 2 \times 2 \times 10$$
$$40 = 2 \times 2 \times 2 \times 5$$
$$40 = 2^3 \times 5$$

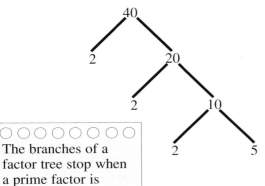

The branches of a factor tree stop when a prime factor is obtained.

So 40 written as the product of its prime factors is $2^3 \times 5$.

EXAMPLES

1 Find the prime factors of 42.

First find the factors of 42.

Method 1
$$42 \times 1 = 42$$
$$21 \times 2 = 42$$
$$14 \times 3 = 42$$
$$7 \times 6 = 42$$

Method 2

$42 \div 1 = 42$	Factors 1 and 42
$42 \div 2 = 21$	Factors 2 and 21
$42 \div 3 = 14$	Factors 3 and 14
$42 \div 4 = 10.5$	No factors
$42 \div 5 = 8.4$	No factors
$42 \div 6 = 7$	Factors 6 and 7

Why stop here?

Factors of 42 are 1, 2, 3, 6, 7, 14, 21 and 42.
2, 3 and 7 are prime numbers.
The prime factors of 42 are 2, 3, 7.

2 Write 50 as the product of its prime factors.

The factor tree shows that:
$$50 = 2 \times 25$$
$$50 = 2 \times 5 \times 5$$

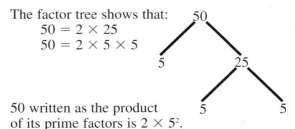

50 written as the product of its prime factors is 2×5^2.

3 Write the factors of $2^4 \times 3^2$ as the products of their prime factors.

Pairs of numbers with the product $2^4 \times 3^2$ are:
1 and $2^4 \times 3^2$
2 and $2^3 \times 3^2$
3 and $2^4 \times 3$
2^2 and $2^2 \times 3^2$
2×3 and $2^3 \times 3$
3^2 and 2^4
$2^2 \times 3$ and $2^2 \times 3$

Remember:
When **multiplying** the powers are **added**.

The factors of $2^4 \times 3^2$ written as the products of their prime factors are:
1, 2, 3, 2^2, (2×3), 3^2, $(2^2 \times 3)$, 2^4, $(2^3 \times 3^2)$, $(2^2 \times 3^2)$, $(2^4 \times 3)$, $(2^3 \times 3^2)$, $(2^4 \times 3^2)$.

*$2^4 \times 3^2$ is a **square number**. Why?*
*$2^4 \times 3^2$ is not a **cube number**. Why?*

Do not use a calculator for questions 1 to 3.

1 Find the prime factors of:
(a) 12 (b) 20 (c) 28 (d) 45 (e) 66

2 Write the following numbers as products of their prime factors.
(a) 12 (b) 20 (c) 28 (d) 45 (e) 66

3 (a) A number written as the product of its prime factors is $2^5 \times 3^3$.
Find all the factors of this number. Write them as products of their prime factors.

(b) A number written as the product of its prime factors is $5^3 \times 7^4$.
Find all the factors of this number. Write them as products of their prime factors.

4 Each of the following numbers are written as products of their prime factors:
$2^3 \times 5^3$, $2^6 \times 5^6$, $2^2 \times 3^3 \times 5^2$, $2^4 \times 3^2 \times 5^8$, $3^2 \times 5^2 \times 11^4$, $3^3 \times 5^6 \times 13^3$.

(a) Calculate each of the numbers.

(b) Which of the numbers are square numbers? Which are cube numbers?
How can you tell just by looking at the powers?

5 Numbers are made using the rule $a^3 \times b^2 \times c^2$ where a, b and c are different prime numbers.
The smallest number is 1800, which is given by $2^3 \times 3^2 \times 5^2$.
Find the next three numbers.

6 Write each of the numbers 24, 40, 54 as the product of their prime factors.
What do you notice?
Find the next three numbers.

7 Write each of the numbers 60, 84, 90 as the product of their prime factors.
What do you notice?
Find the next three numbers.

Lowest common multiples

The first few multiples of three are: 3, 6, 9, 12, **15**, 18, 21, 24, 27, **30**, 33, 36, 39, 42, **45**, . . .
The first few multiples of five are: 5, 10, **15**, 20, 25, **30**, 35, 40, **45**, 50, . . .

15, 30, 45, . . . are multiples of both 3 **and** 5.
They are called **common multiples** of 3 and 5.

The smallest number that is a multiple of both 3 and 5 is 15.
The **lowest common multiple** of 3 and 5 is 15.

The lowest common multiple (**LCM**) of two numbers is the smallest number that is a multiple of them both.

EXAMPLE

Find the lowest common multiple of 20 and 45.
Start with the multiples of 45:
                45, 90, 135, 180, 225, 270, . . .
Which is the lowest multiple of 45 which is also
a multiple of 20?
Multiples of 20:   20, 40, 60, 80, 100, 120,
                    140, 160, **180**, . . .

So the lowest common multiple of 20 and 45 is 180.

Alternative method
$1 \times 45 = 45$
Does 45 divide by 20? No.
$2 \times 45 = 90$
Does 90 divide by 20? No.
. . . and so on.
$4 \times 45 = 180$
Does 180 divide by 20? Yes.
LCM of 20 and 45 is 180.

Highest common factors

The factors of 20 are: **1, 2,** 4, **5, 10,** 20.
The factors of 50 are: **1, 2, 5, 10,** 25, 50.

1, 2, 5 and 10 are factors of both 20 **and** 50.
They are called the **common factors** of 20 and 50.

The largest number that is a factor of both 20 and 50 is 10.
The **highest common factor** of 20 and 50 is 10.

$$20 \times 1 = 20 \qquad 50 \times 1 = 50$$
$$10 \times 2 = 20 \qquad 25 \times 2 = 50$$
$$5 \times 4 = 20 \qquad 10 \times 5 = 50$$

The highest common factor **(HCF)** of two numbers is the largest number that is a factor of them both.

EXAMPLE

The factors of 18 are: 1, 2, 3, 6, 9, 18.
The factors of 45 are: 1, 3, 5, 9, 15, 45.

The common factors of 18 and 45 are: 1, 3 and 9.

The highest common factor of 18 and 45 is 9.

$$18 \times 1 = 18 \qquad 45 \times 1 = 45$$
$$9 \times 2 = 18 \qquad 15 \times 3 = 45$$
$$6 \times 3 = 18 \qquad 9 \times 5 = 45$$

Exercise 6.3   Do not use a calculator.

1 Find the lowest common multiple of:
(a) 8 and 12   (b) 5 and 32   (c) 10 and 20   (d) 15 and 18
(e) 30 and 45   (f) 4, 6 and 8   (g) 5, 8, 10   (h) 45, 90 and 105

2 Find the highest common factor of:
(a) 12 and 66   (b) 8 and 24   (c) 16 and 18   (d) 20 and 36
(e) 33 and 88   (f) 16, 20 and 28   (g) 15, 39 and 45   (h) 45, 90 and 105

3 The table shows the highest common factors of pairs of numbers.

(a) Copy and extend the table up to at least 15 in each direction.
(b) Complete the table.
(c) Describe any patterns you see in the table.

	1	2	3	4	5	6	7
1	1						
2							
3							1
4		2					
6			3				

4 (a) Find the value of x when $2^2 \times 3^x = 108$.
(b) Write 162 as a product of prime factors.
(c) What is the highest common factor of 108 and 162?
(d) What is the lowest common multiple of 108 and 162?

5 (a) Write 216 as a product of prime factors.
(b) Write 288 as a product of prime factors.
(c) What is the highest common factor of 216 and 288?
(d) What is the lowest common multiple of 216 and 288?

6 The bell at St. Gabriel's church rings every 6 minutes.
At St. Paul's, the bell rings every 9 minutes.
Both bells ring together at 9.00 am. When is the next time both bells ring together?

What you need to know

- **Multiples** of a number are found by multiplying the number by 1, 2, 3, 4, . . .
  For example: the multiples of 8 are $1 \times 8 = 8$, $2 \times 8 = 16$, $3 \times 8 = 24$, $4 \times 8 = 32$, . . .

- You can find **all** the **factors** of a number by finding all the multiplication facts that give the number.
  For example: the factors of 6 are 1, 2, 3 and 6.

- A **prime number** is a number with only two factors, 1 and the number itself.
  The first few prime numbers are: 2, 3, 5, 7, 11, 13, 17, 19, 23, 29, 31, . . .

- The **prime factors** of a number are those factors of the number which are themselves prime numbers.

- The **Lowest Common Multiple** of two numbers is the smallest number that is a multiple of them both.

- The **Highest Common Factor** of two numbers is the largest number that is a factor of them both.

You should be able to:
- find multiples of a number.
- find **all** the factors of a number.
- find prime numbers. You should learn the prime numbers less than 50.
- find the prime factors of a number.
- write a number as the product of its prime factors – using powers.
- find the Lowest Common Multiple of two (or more) numbers.
- find the Highest Common Factor of two (or more) numbers.

IDEAS FOR INVESTIGATION

❶ 12 written as the product of its prime factors is $2^2 \times 3$.

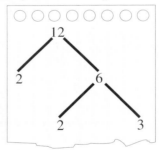

12 has 6 factors.
1, 2, 3, 4, 6, 12

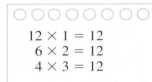

$12 \times 1 = 12$
$6 \times 2 = 12$
$4 \times 3 = 12$

Find the number of factors of some more numbers of the form $a^2 \times b$ where a and b are prime numbers.
What do you notice?

Investigate the number of factors of other numbers with just two prime factors.
What about numbers with any number of prime factors?

❷

> 20 written as the product of its prime factors is $2^2 \times 5$.
> The factors of 20 are 1, 2, 4, 5, 10 and 20.
> Multiples of 20 are 20, 40, 60, 80, 100, 120, 140, 160, 180, 200, …

> 18 written as the product of its prime factors is 2×3^2.
> The factors of 18 are 1, 2, 3, 6, 9 and 18.
> Multiples of 18 are 18, 36, 54, 72, 90, 108, 126, 144, 162, 180, 198, …

The highest common factor of 18 and 20 is 2.   The lowest common multiple of 18 and 20 is 180.
180 as the product of its prime factors is $2^2 \times 3^2 \times 5$.

Investigate the highest common factors and the lowest common multiples
of numbers written as the product of their prime factors.

Do not use a calculator.

1 Find all the factors of:
(a) 15   (b) 30   (c) 50
(d) 96   (e) 107   (f) 120

2
20   21   22   23   24
25   26   27   28   29

Which of the above numbers:
(a) are multiples of 3,
(b) are multiples of 7,
(c) is a multiple of 2 and 3,
(d) are factors of 13 800,
(e) are factors of 2 268,
(f) are factors of 5 500?

3 The table shows the factors of different numbers.

Number	Factors
2	1, 2
3	1, 3
4	1, 2, 4
5	1, 5
6	1, 2, 3, 6

What is the smallest number which has only five factors?

SEG 1996

4 (a) Write down the multiples of 3 which are less than 50.
(b) Write down all the multiples of 8 between 100 and 150.
(c) Write down all the factors of 50.
(d) Write down the factors of 96 which are less than 50.
(e) Write down all the prime numbers between 50 and 100.

5 (a) Find the highest common factor of:
(i) 6 and 81,
(ii) 40 and 88,
(iii) 108 and 120.

(b) Find the lowest common multiple of:
(i) 4 and 12,
(ii) 18 and 30,
(iii) 60 and 80.

6 James groups some counters in 6's with no remainder.
Tim groups the same counters in 4's with no remainder.
Mary groups them in 5's with no remainder.
What is the smallest possible number of counters?

7 Consider the numbers: 8, 9, 11, 17 and 121.
(a) Write down all the factors of these numbers.

(b) (i) Which of the numbers have only two factors?
(ii) What special name is given to these numbers?

(c) (i) Which of these numbers have exactly 3 factors?
(ii) What special name is given to these numbers?

8 (a) Write as a product of prime factors:
(i) 126, (ii) 90, (iii) 210

(b) What is the smallest number that has 90 and 210 as factors?
(c) What is the highest common factor of 90 and 126?

9 (a) Find the value of p when
$2^p \times 3 = 48$.
(b) Write 72 as a product of prime factors.
(c) What is the highest common factor of 48 and 72?
(d) What is the lowest common multiple of 48 and 72?

SEG 1998

10 $x = 63$ and $y = 36$.
(a) Write $21x$ as a product of its prime factors.
(b) Write xy as a product of its prime factors.
(c) What is the lowest square number which has x as a factor?
(d) What is the smallest number that y must be multiplied by to make it a cube number?

11 A blue light flashes every 18 seconds and a green light flashes every 30 seconds.
The two lights flash at the same time.
After how many seconds will the lights next flash at the same time?

6

Multiples, Factors and Primes

CHAPTER 7

Standard Index Form

Standard index form is a shorthand way of writing very small and very large numbers. Standard index form is often called **standard form** or **scientific notation**.

Very large numbers

Scientists who study the planets and the stars work with very large numbers. Approximate distances from the Sun to some planets are:

Mercury	58 000 000 km
Venus	108 000 000 km
Earth	149 000 000 km
Mars	228 000 000 km
Pluto	5 898 000 000 km

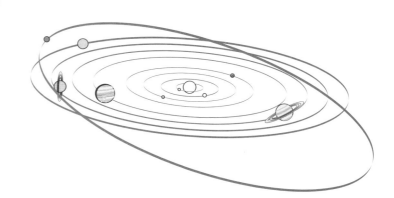

Distances to the stars are far greater.

Alpha Centauri is about 40 350 000 000 000 km from the Sun.
Alpha Cygni is about 15 300 000 000 000 000 km from the Sun.

What is the largest number your calculator can handle?

Large numbers and your calculator

A scientific calculator displays very large numbers in **standard form**.

3 000 000 × 25 000 000 = 75 000 000 000 000

Do this calculation on your calculator and write down the display.

The same calculation can also be done using powers of ten.

Ordinary number	Power of 10	Standard form
3 000 000	3 × 1 000 000	3×10^6
25 000 000	2.5 × 10 000 000	2.5×10^7

1 000 000
$= 10 \times 10 \times 10 \times 10 \times 10 \times 10$
$= 10^6$

$$3\,000\,000 \times 25\,000\,000 = (3 \times 10^6) \times (2.5 \times 10^7)$$
$$= 3 \times 2.5 \times 10^6 \times 10^7$$
$$= 7.5 \times 10^{13}$$

When **multiplying** the powers are **added**.
$10^6 \times 10^7 = 10^{6+7} = 10^{13}$

A number written in standard form has **two** parts.
The first part must be a number between 1 and 10.
The second part is a power of 10.
The two parts are connected by a multiplication sign.

Exercise 7.1

Use a calculator for question 2 only.

1 Copy the table and fill in all the different forms of each number.

	Ordinary number	Power of 10	Standard form
	300 000	3 × 100 000	3×10^5
(a)	75 000	7.5 × 10 000	
(b)		8 × 100 000 000	
(c)			3.5×10^{13}
(d)	62 300 000 000 000		
(e)			5.4×10^9
(f)		6.93 × 10 000 000	
(g)	453 100 000 000		
(h)			6.97×10^5
(i)	453 120		
(j)		1.097 × 100 000	

2 Use your calculator to work out each of the following. Write each of the answers:
(i) on your calculator display, (ii) in standard form, (iii) as an ordinary number.

(a) 300 000 × 200 000 000   (b) 120 000 × 80 000 000
(c) 15 000 × 700 000 000   (d) 65 000 × 2 000 000 000
(e) 480 000 × 500 000 000   (f) 50 000 × 50 000 000
(g) 352 000 000 × 40 000 000   (h) 35 200 × 6 500 000 000
(i) 3450 × 5200 × 45 000   (j) 550 000 × 8000 × 250 000

3 Write each of these numbers in standard form.
(a) 300 000 000 000   (b) 80 000 000   (c) 700 000 000   (d) 2 000 000 000
(e) 42 000 000   (f) 21 000 000 000   (g) 3 700 000 000   (h) 630
(i) 3 219 000 000   (j) 654 120 000   (k) 897 213   (l) 42 670 000 000

4 Change each of these numbers to an ordinary number.
(a) 6×10^5 (b) 2×10^3 (c) 5×10^7 (d) 9×10^8
(e) 3.7×10^9 (f) 2.8×10^1 (g) 9.9×10^{10} (h) 7.1×10^4
(i) 3.97×10^2 (j) 8.172×10^2 (k) 7.4312×10^6 (l) 1.234×10^9

Very small numbers

Scientists who study microbiology work with numbers that are very small.
The smallest living cells are bacteria which have a diameter of
about 0.000 025 cm.
Blood cells have a diameter of about 0.000 75 cm.

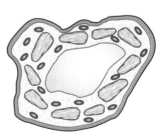

There are plenty of examples of other very small quantities.

A hydrogen atom has a diameter of about 0.000 000 2 mm.
The mumps virus has a diameter of about 0.000 225 mm.
The thickness of one page in the Yellow Pages is approximately 0.006 5 cm.
The fastest computers take about 0.000 000 000 8 seconds to perform one operation.

What is the smallest number your calculator can handle?

Small numbers and your calculator

A scientific calculator displays small numbers in **standard form**. It does this in the same sort of way that it does for large numbers.

$0.000\,003 \times 0.000\,25 = 0.000\,000\,000\,75$

Do this calculation on your calculator and write down the display.

To write small numbers in **standard form** you need to use the powers of ten for **negative** powers.

Ordinary number	Power of 10	Standard form
0.000 003 0.000 25	$3 \times 0.000\,001$ $2.5 \times 0.000\,01$	3×10^{-6} 2.5×10^{-4}

$$0.000\,001 = \frac{1}{1\,000\,000}$$
$$= \frac{1}{10 \times 10 \, 10 \times 10 \times 10 \times 10}$$
$$= \frac{1}{10^6} = 10^{-6}$$

$$\begin{aligned}0.000\,003 \times 0.000\,25 &= (3 \times 10^{-6}) \times (2.5 \times 10^{-4})\\ &= 3 \times 2.5 \times 10^{-6} \times 10^{-4}\\ &= 7.5 \times 10^{-10}\end{aligned}$$

When multiplying the powers are added.
$10^{-6} \times 10^{-4} = 10^{-6\,+\,-4} = 10^{-6-4} = 10^{-10}$

Standard form

In a **standard form** a number is written as:

a number between 1 and 10 × a power of 10

In standard form:
a **large** number has a **positive power**.
Eg $160\,000\,000 = 1.6 \times 10^8$
a **small** number has a **negative power**.
Eg $0.000\,000\,06 = 6 \times 10^{-8}$

Exercise 7.2

Do questions 1 to 5 without using a calculator.

1 Write down the power of 10 for each of these numbers.
(a) 0.1
(b) 0.00 001
(c) 0.000 000 001
(d) 0.001
(e) 0.000 000 000 01
(f) 0.000 000 000 000 1

2 Copy and complete the following to change each small number to standard form.
(a) 0.000 03 $\qquad = \qquad 3 \times 0.000\,01 \qquad = 3 \times 10^{-5}$
(b) 0.0075 $\qquad = \qquad 7.5 \times 0.001 \qquad =$
(c) 0.000 008 75 $\qquad = \qquad 8.75 \times 0.000\,001 \qquad =$
(d) 0.000 000 003 5 $\qquad = \qquad\qquad =$
(e) 0.000 000 000 006 23 $\quad =\qquad\qquad =$
(f) 0.000 000 5 $\qquad = \qquad\qquad =$
(g) 0.000 000 047 25 $\qquad = \qquad\qquad =$
(h) 0.05 $\qquad = \qquad\qquad =$
(i) 0.000 007 85 $\qquad = \qquad\qquad =$

3 Change each of these numbers in standard form to a small number:
(a) 3.5×10^{-1}
(b) 5×10^{-4}
(c) 7.2×10^{-5}
(d) 6.1×10^{-3}
(e) 1.17×10^{-10}
(f) 8.135×10^{-7}
(g) 6.462×10^{-2}
(h) 4.001×10^{-9}

4 Write each of these numbers in standard form.
  (a) 0.007   (b) 0.04   (c) 0.000 000 005
  (d) 0.000 8   (e) 0.000 000 002 3   (f) 0.000 000 045
  (g) 0.023 4   (h) 0.000 000 002 34   (i) 0.006 7
  (j) 0.3   (k) 0.000 000 073 95   (l) 0.000 000 000 000 34

5 Change each of these numbers in standard form to a large or a small number:
  (a) 5.5×10^{-6} (b) 6.5×10^{-8} (c) 3.2×10^{7} (d) 2.9×10^{2}
  (e) 3.167×10^{-11} (f) 1.115×10^{4} (g) 1.412×10^{-5} (h) 4×10^{1}

6 Use your calculator to work out each of the following. Write each of the answers:
  (i)   on the calculator display,   (ii) in standard form,   (iii) as a small or large number.

  (a) $0.000\ 03 \times 0.000\ 000\ 2$ (b) $0.000\ 045 \times 0.000\ 003$
  (c) $0.000\ 75 \times 0.000\ 000\ 04$ (d) $0.002\ 3 \times 0.000\ 000\ 05$
  (e) $0.053 \times 0.000\ 000\ 08$ (f) $0.000\ 006\ 4 \times 0.000\ 015\ 2$
  (g) $0.59 \times 0.000\ 000\ 7^{2}$ (h) $0.067\ 5 \div 15\ 000^{2}$
  (i) $6\ 330\ 000 \div 0.000\ 06$ (j) $7400 \div 0.002^{3}$

Using large and small numbers with a calculator

Scientific calculator

Calculations with large and small numbers can be done on a scientific calculator by:
  (i)   changing the numbers to standard form,
  (ii) entering the numbers into the calculator using the [Exp] button.

If your calculator works in a different way refer to the instruction booklet supplied with the calculator or ask someone for help.

EXAMPLES

1 Calculate the value of $62\ 500\ 000\ 000 \times 0.000\ 000\ 003$
Give your answer both as an ordinary number and in standard form.

$62\ 500\ 000\ 000 \times 0.000\ 000\ 003 = (6.25 \times 10^{10}) \times (3 \times 10^{-9})$

To do the calculation enter the following sequence into your calculator.

Giving:
$6\ 250\ 000\ 000 \times 0.000\ 000\ 03$
$= 187.5$ (ordinary number)
$= 1.875 \times 10^{2}$ (standard form)

Some calculators display this result as: 187.5
Other calculators give this display: 1.875 *02*

2 Calculate the value of $0.000\ 000\ 000\ 05^{4}$. Give your answer in standard form.

$(0.000\ 000\ 000\ 05)^{4} = (5 \times 10^{-11})^{4}$

To do the calculation enter the following sequence into your calculator.

[5] [Exp] [1] [1] [+/-] [x^y] [4] [=]

This gives the calculator display:
$0.000\ 000\ 000\ 05^{4} = 6.25 \times 10^{-42}$

| 6.25 | -42 |

Remember: The calculator display **must** be changed to either **standard form** or an **ordinary number**.

Solving problems involving large and small numbers

Problems can involve numbers given in standard form.

EXAMPLE

3 The following figures refer to the population of China and the USA in 1993.

China 1.01×10^9 USA 2.32×10^8

(a) By how much did the population of China exceed that of the USA in 1993?

(b) Calculate the total population of the two countries in 1993.

$1.01 \times 10^9 > 2.32 \times 10^8$
The greater the power . . .
. . . the bigger the number

(a) You need to work out $1.01 \times 10^9 - 2.32 \times 10^8$
To do the calculation enter the following sequence into your calculator.

| 1 | . | 0 | 1 | Exp | 9 | − | 2 | . | 3 | 2 | Exp | 8 | = |

Giving: $1.01 \times 10^9 - 2.32 \times 10^8 = 778\,000\,000 = 7.78 \times 10^8$

(b) You need to work out $1.01 \times 10^9 + 2.32 \times 10^8$
Enter the following sequence into your calculator.

| 1 | . | 0 | 1 | Exp | 9 | + | 2 | . | 3 | 2 | Exp | 8 | = |

Giving: $1.01 \times 10^9 + 2.32 \times 10^8 = 1.242 \times 10^9$

*Try this example **without** a calculator.*

Exercise 7.3

Use the Exp button on your calculator to answer these questions.

1 Give the answer to the following calculations as a large or small number.
(a) $(5.25 \times 10^9) \times (5 \times 10^{-5})$ (b) $(5.25 \times 10^9) \div (5 \times 10^{-5})$
(c) $(8.5 \times 10^6)^2$ (d) $(5 \times 10^{-3})^3$
(e) $(7.2 \times 10^5) \div (2.4 \times 10^{-5})$ (f) $(9.5 \times 10^6) \div (1.9 \times 10^{-7})^2$

2 Give the answer to the following calculations in standard form.
(a) $33\,500\,000\,000 \times 2\,800\,000\,000$ (b) $0.000\,000\,000\,2 \times 80\,000\,000\,000$
(c) $15\,000\,000\,000\,000^2$ (d) $0.000\,000\,000\,000\,5^3$
(e) $48\,000\,000\,000 \div 0.000\,000\,000\,2$ (f) $25\,000\,000\,000 \div 500\,000\,000\,000$

3 (a) In 1992 about $1\,400\,000\,000$ steel cans and about $688\,000\,000$ aluminium cans were recycled.
What was the total number of cans that were recycled in 1992?
Give your answer in standard form.

(b) Alpha Centauri is about $40\,350\,000\,000\,000$ km from the Sun.
Alpha Cygni is about $15\,300\,000\,000\,000\,000$ km from the Sun.
How much further is it from the Sun to Alpha Cygni than from the Sun to Alpha Centauri?
Give your answer in standard form.

4 Here are the diameters of some planets.
Saturn 1.42×10^5 km   Jupiter 1.2×10^5 km   Pluto 2.3×10^3 km

(a) List the planets in order of size starting with the smallest.
(b) What is the difference between the diameters of the largest and smallest planets?
Give your answers in standard form and as an ordinary number.

5 Here are the areas of some of the world's largest deserts.

The Sahara desert in North Africa	$8.6 \times 10^6 \, km^2$
The Gobi desert in Mongolia and North East China	$1.166 \times 10^6 \, km^2$
The Patagonian desert in Argentina	$6.73 \times 10^5 \, km^2$

(a) What is the total area of the Sahara and Patagonian deserts?
(b) What is the difference in area between the Gobi and the Patagonian desert?
Give your answers in standard form.

6 The mass of an oxygen atom is 2.7×10^{-23} grams.
The mass of an electron at rest is approximately 30 000 times smaller than this.
Estimate the mass of an electron at rest.

7 The modern human appeared on the earth about 3.5×10^4 years ago.
The earth has been in existence for something like 1.3×10^5 times as long as this.
(a) Estimate the age of the earth.

Reptiles appeared on the earth about 2.3×10^8 years ago.
(b) How many times longer than the modern human have reptiles been alive?
Give your answers in standard form.

Standard form calculations without a calculator

In some standard form problems the calculations can be handled without using a calculator.

EXAMPLES

1 Calculate the value of $(3 \times 10^2) + (4 \times 10^3)$.
Give your answer in standard form.

$3 \times 10^2 = 300 \qquad 4 \times 10^3 = 4000$
$(3 \times 10^2) + (4 \times 10^3) = 300 + 4000$
$= 4300$
$= 4.3 \times 10^3$

When adding or subtracting numbers in standard form without a calculator change to an ordinary number first.

2 Calculate the value of ab where
$a = 8 \times 10^3$ and $b = 4 \times 10^5$

$ab = (8 \times 10^3) \times (4 \times 10^5)$
$= 8 \times 4 \times 10^3 \times 10^5$
$= 32 \times 10^8$
$= 3.2 \times 10 \times 10^8$
$= 3.2 \times 10^9$

When **multiplying** the powers are **added**.
$10^3 \times 10^5 = 10^{3+5} = 10^8$
$10 \times 10^8 = 10^{1+8} = 10^9$

3 Calculate the value of x^2 where $x = 7 \times 10^{-8}$

$x^2 = (7 \times 10^{-8})^2$
$= 49 \times 10^{-16}$
$= 4.9 \times 10 \times 10^{-16}$
$= 4.9 \times 10^{-15}$

Remember:
$(7 \times 10^{-8})^2 = 7^2 \times (10^{-8})^2$
$10 \times 10^{-16} = 10^{1-16} = 10^{-15}$

4 Calculate the value of $(1.2 \times 10^3) \div (4 \times 10^{-8})$

$(1.2 \times 10^3) \div (4 \times 10^{-8}) = (1.2 \div 4) \times (10^3 \div 10^{-8})$
$= 0.3 \times 10^{11}$
$= 3 \times 10^{-1} \times 10^{11}$
$= 3 \times 10^{10}$

When **dividing** the powers are **subtracted**.
$10^3 \div 10^{-8} = 10^{3--8} = 10^{11}$

Do not use a calculator.

1 For each of the following calculate the value of $p + q$. Give your answers in standard form.
  (a) $p = 5 \times 10^3$ and $q = 2 \times 10^2$
  (b) $p = 4 \times 10^5$ and $q = 8 \times 10^6$
  (c) $p = 3.08 \times 10^4$ and $q = 9.2 \times 10^3$
  (d) $p = 4.25 \times 10^4$ and $q = 7.5 \times 10^3$
  (e) $p = 4.854 \times 10^5$ and $q = 4.6 \times 10^3$
  (f) $p = 3.955 \times 10^7$ and $q = 4.5 \times 10^5$

2 For each of the following calculate the value of $p - q$. Give your answers in standard form.
  (a) $p = 3 \times 10^3$ and $q = 2 \times 10^2$
  (b) $p = 9.05 \times 10^5$ and $q = 5 \times 10^3$
  (c) $p = 3.05 \times 10^7$ and $q = 5 \times 10^5$
  (d) $p = 9.545 \times 10^8$ and $q = 4.5 \times 10^6$
  (e) $p = 6.455 \times 10^6$ and $q = 5.5 \times 10^4$
  (f) $p = 7.326 \times 10^9$ and $q = 7.6 \times 10^7$

3 For each of the following calculate the value of $p \times q$. Give your answers in standard form.
  (a) $p = 4 \times 10^3$ and $q = 2 \times 10^4$
  (b) $p = 2 \times 10^4$ and $q = 3 \times 10^3$
  (c) $p = 4 \times 10^5$ and $q = 6 \times 10^2$
  (d) $p = 9 \times 10^9$ and $q = 3 \times 10^5$
  (e) $p = 6.5 \times 10^{-2}$ and $q = 2 \times 10^5$
  (f) $p = 8 \times 10^7$ and $q = 4.5 \times 10^{-2}$

4 For each of the following calculate the value of $p \div q$. Give your answers in standard form.
  (a) $p = 6 \times 10^5$ and $q = 2 \times 10^2$
  (b) $p = 9 \times 10^5$ and $q = 3 \times 10^2$
  (c) $p = 2.5 \times 10^5$ and $q = 5 \times 10^3$
  (d) $p = 4 \times 10^8$ and $q = 2 \times 10^{-3}$
  (e) $p = 1.2 \times 10^3$ and $q = 3 \times 10^{-3}$
  (f) $p = 1.5 \times 10^{-5}$ and $q = 5 \times 10^{-3}$

5 $x = 3 \times 10^4$ and $y = 5 \times 10^{-5}$.
  Work out the value of each of these expressions. Give your answers in standard form.
  (a) xy (b) x^3 (c) x^2y (d) y^3 (e) $10y^4$
  (f) $10\,000xy$ (g) $25x^2$ (h) xy^2 (i) $100x^2y^2$ (j) x^3y^2

6 Find the value of each of the following. Give your answers in standard form.
  (a) $(5 \times 10^6) \times (3 \times 10^4)$
  (b) $(8 \times 10^{-5}) \times (3 \times 10^7)$
  (c) $(7 \times 10^{-5}) \times (6 \times 10^{-4})$
  (d) $(8 \times 10^3)^2$
  (e) $(5 \times 10^3)^4$
  (f) $(6 \times 10^{-5})^3$
  (g) $(4 \times 10^5) \div (8 \times 10^3)$
  (h) $(1.8 \times 10^3) \div (6 \times 10^{-7})$
  (i) $(5 \times 10^{-7}) \div (8 \times 10^{-2})$
  (j) $(2 \times 10^4) \div (8 \times 10^{-1})$

7 Write each of these sets of numbers in order lowest to highest.
  (a) 4.5×10^{-1} 3.5×10^{-3} $0.000\,75$ 1.25×10^{-2} 7.05×10^{-4}
  (b) 5.6×10^{-5} 4.05×10^{-2} 9.31×10^{-4} $0.000\,050\,612$ 4.15×10^{-5}

What you need to know

- **Standard index form**, or **standard form**, is a shorthand way of writing very large and very small numbers.

- In **standard form** a number is written as: **a number between 1 and 10 × a power of 10**
  Large numbers (ten, or more) have a **positive** power of 10.
  Small numbers (less than one) have a **negative** power of 10.

You should be able to:
- Change both large and small numbers to and from standard form.
- Read numbers displayed in standard form on your calculator.
- Enter numbers in standard form into your calculator.
- Do calculations in standard form, both with and without a calculator.
- Solve problems involving very large and/or very small numbers.

Review Exercise   Try to do questions 1 to 4 without using your calculator.

1 Change each of the following numbers to standard form.
(a) 2 400
(b) 52 600
(c) 8 000 000
(d) 0.000 000 002 4
(e) 0.000 012 6
(f) 0.000 000 000 234

2 Write each of these numbers as an ordinary number.
(a) 3.4×10^3
(b) 1.46×10^7
(c) 8.312×10^5
(d) 1.714×10^{-4}
(e) 9.213×10^{-8}
(f) 7.35×10^7

3 Calculate the value of:
(a) $(6 \times 10^4) + (5 \times 10^3)$ (b) $(5 \times 10^5) - (5 \times 10^4)$ (c) $(2.7 \times 10^8) + (3 \times 10^7)$
(d) $(2.95 \times 10^4) - (5 \times 10^3)$ (e) $(8.46 \times 10^9) + (5.4 \times 10^8)$ (f) $(3.3 \times 10^9) - (5 \times 10^7)$
Give each of your answers in standard form.

4 In each of these questions give your answer in standard form.
(a) Find the value of pq,   where $p = 6 \times 10^5$ and $q = 5 \times 10^{-3}$.
(b) Find the value of x^2,   where $x = 5 \times 10^{-6}$.
(c) Find the value of y^3,   where $y = 6 \times 10^{-9}$.
(d) Find the value of abc,   where $a = 3 \times 10^7$, $b = 5 \times 10^{-3}$ and $c = 6 \times 10^{-4}$.
(e) Find the value of $p \div q$,   where $p = 8 \times 10^8$ and $q = 2 \times 10^{-5}$.

5 Use a calculator to do these calculations giving your answers in standard form.
(a) $(3 \times 10^7) \times (5.6 \times 10^{12})$ (b) $(2.3 \times 10^{-3}) \times (5.63 \times 10^8)$
(c) $(8.1 \times 10^{-5}) \div (6.6 \times 10^{-6})$ (d) $(5.013 \times 10^{-9}) \div (1.002 \times 10^{-7})$
(e) $(2 \times 10^2)^3$ (f) $(2 \times 10^2)^{-3}$ (g) $(2 \times 10^{-2})^3$ (h) $(2 \times 10^{-2})^{-3}$

6 In 1984, income from foreign tourists in Britain was $\$5.55 \times 10^9$.
British tourists spent $\$5.96 \times 10^8$ more than this when they were abroad.
Calculate how much British tourists spent abroad, giving your answer in standard form.
SEG 1997

7 In 1992/93, the British Government collected a total of $£2.02 \times 10^{11}$ from taxes.
Of this total, $£7.35 \times 10^{10}$ was collected from income tax.
How much was collected from other taxes?
Give your answer in standard form.
SEG 1996

8 (a) 9×10^9 red blood cells are made by one person every hour.
How many million red blood cells are made by one person every hour?

(b) 4×10^6 bacteria cells put end to end in a line have a length of 1 metre.
What is the average length of a bacteria cell in standard form?

(c) The length of a red blood cell is 30 times as big as the length of a bacteria cell.
What is the length of a red blood cell in standard form?
SEG 1996

9 A magazine is made from 36 sheets of paper.
The number of magazines printed is 3.3×10^6.
(a) Calculate how many sheets of paper are needed to print these magazines.
Give your answer in standard form.

Each sheet of paper is 9.6×10^{-3} cm thick.
(b) If all the magazines are piled on top of each other, how high would the pile be?

10 The fastest computers take about 8×10^{-10} seconds to perform one operation.

(a) How long does it take the fastest computers to perform 10 million operations?
(b) How many operations can the fastest computers do in one minute?

CHAPTER 8

Fractions

What fraction of this rectangle is shaded?

The rectangle is divided into **eight** squares.
The squares are all the same size.
Three of the squares are shaded.

$\frac{3}{8}$ of the rectangle is shaded.

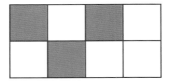

In a fraction:
The top number is called the **numerator**.
The bottom number is called the **denominator**.

Activity

What fraction of each of these shapes is shaded?

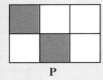 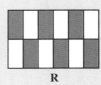 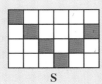

P   Q   R   S

Which rectangles have the same fraction shaded?

Equivalent fractions

Fractions which are equal are called **equivalent fractions**.

Rectangle Q has $\frac{3}{12}$ shaded, $\frac{3}{12} = \frac{1}{4}$.

Rectangle S has $\frac{6}{24}$ shaded, $\frac{6}{24} = \frac{1}{4}$.

Each of the fractions $\frac{1}{4}$, $\frac{3}{12}$, $\frac{6}{24}$, represent the same fraction written in different ways.

These fractions are all equivalent to $\frac{1}{4}$.

Write down two more fractions equivalent to $\frac{1}{4}$.

To write an equivalent fraction:
Multiply the numerator and denominator by the **same** number.

For example. $\quad \frac{1}{4} = \frac{1 \times 3}{4 \times 3} = \frac{3}{12}$

$\frac{1}{4} = \frac{1 \times 6}{4 \times 6} = \frac{6}{24}$

EXAMPLES

 Write down three fractions equivalent to $\frac{5}{7}$.

The numerators are any multiples of 5.
For example: 5, 10, 15, …

The denominators are the same multiples of 7: 7, 14, 21, …

This gives the fractions: $\frac{5}{7}$, $\frac{10}{14}$, $\frac{15}{21}$, …

 The fraction $\frac{2}{3}$ is equivalent to the fraction $\frac{n}{12}$.
Find the value of n.

3 has been multiplied by 4 to get 12.
So 2 must also be multiplied by 4 to get n.
So $n = 8$.

Simplifying fractions

Fractions can be simplified if the numerator and denominator have a common factor.
In its **simplest form**, the numerator and denominator of a fraction have no common factor other than 1.

To write a fraction in its simplest form divide the numerator and denominator of the fraction by their highest common factor.
This is sometimes called **cancelling** a fraction.

The numerator and denominator of $\frac{15}{25}$ have a highest common factor of 5.

$$\frac{15}{25} = \frac{15 \div 5}{25 \div 5} = \frac{3}{5}$$

3 and 5 have no common factors, other than 1.

$$\frac{15}{25} = \frac{3}{5} \text{ in its simplest form.}$$

Remember:
Multiplication and division are inverse (opposite) operations.
Equivalent fractions can also be made by dividing the numerator and denominator of a fraction by the same number.

EXAMPLES

1 Simplify $\frac{24}{30}$

The highest common factor of 24 and 30 is 6.

$$\frac{24}{30} = \frac{24 \div 6}{30 \div 6} = \frac{4}{5}$$

2 In a class of 28 pupils there are 12 boys.
What fraction of the pupils are boys?
Write this fraction in its simplest form.

There are 12 out of 28 boys.
The fraction of boys $= \frac{12}{28}$

$$\frac{12}{28} = \frac{12 \div 4}{28 \div 4} = \frac{3}{7}$$

$$\frac{12}{28} = \frac{3}{7} \text{ in its simplest form.}$$

3 Write 42 as a fraction of 70.

42 as a fraction of 70 is $\frac{42}{70}$

2 is a common factor of 42 and 70.

$$\frac{42}{70} = \frac{42 \div 2}{70 \div 2} = \frac{21}{35}$$

7 is a common factor of 21 and 35.

$$\frac{21}{35} = \frac{21 \div 7}{35 \div 7} = \frac{3}{5}$$

$$\frac{42}{70} = \frac{3}{5} \text{ in its simplest form.}$$

We could have divided by 14.

$$\frac{42}{70} = \frac{42 \div 14}{70 \div 14} = \frac{3}{5}$$

Exercise 8.1

Do not use a calculator in this exercise.

1 What fraction of each of these shapes is shaded?

(a)   (b)   (c)   (d)

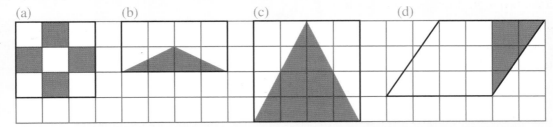

2 Write three equivalent fractions for the shaded part of this rectangle.
What is the simplest form of the shaded fraction?

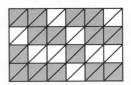

Fractions . . . Fractions . . . Fractions . . . Fractions . . .

3 Look at these diagrams.

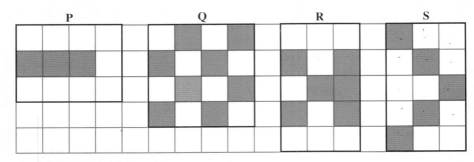

(a) Which diagram has $\frac{3}{12}$ shaded?

(b) Which diagram has $\frac{1}{4}$ shaded?

(c) Which diagram has $\frac{6}{15}$ shaded?

(d) Which diagram has $\frac{2}{5}$ shaded?

(e) Which diagram has $\frac{1}{2}$ shaded?

(f) Which diagram has $\frac{1}{3}$ shaded?

4 What fraction of each of these shapes is shaded?
Give your answers in their simplest form.

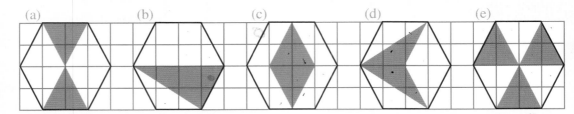

5 Write down three fractions equivalent to:

(a) $\frac{1}{3}$ (b) $\frac{2}{9}$ (c) $\frac{5}{8}$

(d) $\frac{4}{5}$ (e) $\frac{3}{10}$ (f) $\frac{7}{12}$

6 Each of these pairs of fractions are equivalent.
In each case find the value of n.

(a) $\frac{1}{3}, \frac{n}{6}$ (b) $\frac{n}{8}, \frac{6}{16}$ (c) $\frac{5}{n}, \frac{15}{18}$

(d) $\frac{n}{4}, \frac{12}{16}$ (e) $\frac{24}{64}, \frac{3}{n}$ (f) $\frac{n}{12}, \frac{56}{96}$

7 Write each of these fractions in its simplest form.

(a) $\frac{6}{8}$ (b) $\frac{12}{15}$ (c) $\frac{18}{27}$ (d) $\frac{22}{99}$

(e) $\frac{50}{75}$ (f) $\frac{16}{40}$ (g) $\frac{12}{50}$ (h) $\frac{52}{65}$

8 Write the first number as a fraction of the second.
Write the fractions in their simplest form.

(a) 4, 20   (b) 3, 12   (c) 8, 12

(d) 24, 60   (e) 60, 105

9 Mr Jones plans a car journey.

(a) The journey is 50 km long.
Mr Jones plans to stop after 35 km.
What fraction of the total distance is this?
Give your answer in its simplest form.

(b) The journey takes 60 minutes which includes a 12 minute stop.
For what fraction of the total time does Mr Jones stop on his journey?
Give your answer in its simplest form.

10 A group of students were asked some questions about how they travelled to school.
$\frac{1}{2}$ of the students said they walked.

$\frac{1}{3}$ of the students said they travelled by bus.

In the group there were more than 20 students and less than 30.

(a) How many students were in the group?

The rest of the group came by car.

(b) What fraction of the group came by car?
Give your answer in its simplest form.

Types of fractions

This diagram shows that when 5 cakes are shared equally between 2 people they get $2\frac{1}{2}$ cakes each.

This diagram shows that when 5 cakes are shared equally between 4 people they get $1\frac{1}{4}$ cakes each.

This diagram shows that when 5 cakes are shared equally between 3 people they get $1\frac{2}{3}$ cakes each.

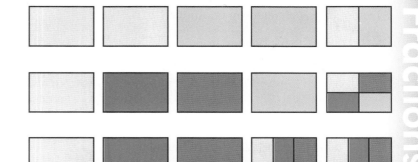

Numbers like $2\frac{1}{2}$, $1\frac{1}{4}$ and $1\frac{2}{3}$ are called **mixed numbers** because they are a mixture of whole numbers and fractions.

Mixed numbers can be written as **improper** or '**top heavy**' fractions.

These are fractions where the numerator is larger than the denominator.

EXAMPLES

1 Write $3\frac{4}{7}$ as an improper fraction.

$3\frac{4}{7} = 1 + 1 + 1 + \frac{4}{7}$

$= \frac{7}{7} + \frac{7}{7} + \frac{7}{7} + \frac{4}{7}$

$= \frac{25}{7}$

Alternative method

$3\frac{4}{7} = \frac{(3 \times 7) + 4}{7} = \frac{21 + 4}{7} = \frac{25}{7}$

2 Write $\frac{32}{5}$ as a mixed number.

$\frac{32}{5} = \frac{5}{5} + \frac{5}{5} + \frac{5}{5} + \frac{5}{5} + \frac{5}{5} + \frac{5}{5} + \frac{2}{5}$

$= 1 + 1 + 1 + 1 + 1 + 1 + \frac{2}{5}$

$= 6\frac{2}{5}$

Alternative method

$32 \div 5 = 6$ remainder 2.

$\frac{32}{5} = 6\frac{2}{5}$

Finding fractions of quantities

EXAMPLES

3 Find $\frac{3}{10}$ of 100.

Divide 100 into 10 equal parts.
$100 \div 10 = 10$.

10	10	10	10	10	10	10	10	10	10

Each of these parts is $\frac{1}{10}$ of 100.

Three of these parts is $\frac{3}{10}$ of 100.

10	10	10	10	10	10	10	10	10	10

So $\frac{3}{10}$ of $100 = 3 \times 10 = 30$.

4 Find $\frac{2}{5}$ of £65.

Divide £65 into 5 equal parts.
£65 ÷ 5 = £13.

13	13	13	13	13

Each of these parts is $\frac{1}{5}$ of £65.

Two of these parts is $\frac{2}{5}$ of £65.

13	13	13	13	13

So $\frac{2}{5}$ of £65 = 2 × £13 = £26.

Do not use a calculator in questions 1 to 3.

1 Change the following improper fractions to mixed numbers:

(a) $\frac{13}{10}$　　(b) $\frac{3}{2}$　　(c) $\frac{17}{8}$

(d) $\frac{15}{4}$　　(e) $\frac{23}{5}$　　(f) $\frac{34}{7}$

2 Change the following mixed numbers to improper fractions:

(a) $2\frac{7}{10}$　　(b) $1\frac{3}{5}$　　(c) $5\frac{5}{6}$

(d) $3\frac{3}{20}$　　(e) $4\frac{5}{9}$　　(f) $7\frac{4}{7}$

3 Calculate:

(a) $\frac{3}{10}$ of 30　　(b) $\frac{2}{7}$ of 42

(c) $\frac{5}{9}$ of 36　　(d) $\frac{2}{3}$ of 39

(e) $\frac{3}{8}$ of 56　　(f) $\frac{5}{6} \times 30$

(g) $\frac{4}{5} \times 85$　　(h) $\frac{11}{5} \times 25$

(i) $\frac{17}{6} \times 42$　　(j) $\frac{23}{7} \times 63$

4 A coat costing £138 is reduced by $\frac{1}{3}$. Find the new price of the coat.

5 A publisher offers a discount of $\frac{3}{20}$ for orders of more than 100 books. How much would a shop pay for an order of 250 books costing £3.50 each?

6 In a sale of electrical goods all items are reduced by $\frac{3}{8}$. What is the sale price of a microwave which was originally priced at £212?

7 Andy, Bill and Chris share two chocolate bars. Each chocolate bar has 30 squares. Andy eats $\frac{2}{3}$ of one chocolate bar. Bill eats $\frac{5}{12}$ of both chocolate bars. Chris eats $\frac{2}{5}$ of one chocolate bar.

(a) (i) How many squares has Andy eaten?
　　(ii) How many squares has Bill eaten?

(b) What fraction of **both** chocolate bars have Andy, Bill and Chris eaten altogether? Give your answer both as a mixed number and as an improper fraction in its simplest form.

Adding and subtracting fractions

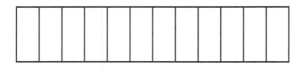

There are 12 sweets in a packet.

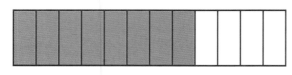

Alena eats $\frac{2}{3}$ of the sweets in the packet.
$\frac{2}{3}$ of $12 = 8$　　　$\frac{2}{3} = \frac{8}{12}$

Sead eats $\frac{1}{4}$ of the sweets in the packet.
$\frac{1}{4}$ of $12 = 3$　　　$\frac{1}{4} = \frac{3}{12}$

Together Alena and Sead eat $\frac{2}{3} + \frac{1}{4}$ of the packet.
$\frac{2}{3} + \frac{1}{4} = \frac{8}{12} + \frac{3}{12} = \frac{11}{12}$

Together Alena and Sead eat $\frac{11}{12}$ of the packet.

Fractions must have the same denominator before addition (or subtraction) can take place.

EXAMPLES

1 Calculate $\frac{3}{5} + \frac{17}{30}$

Multiples of 5: 5, 10, 15, 20, 25, 30, …
The lowest common multiple of 5 and 30 is 30.

$$\frac{3}{5} \text{ of } 30 = 18 \qquad \frac{3}{5} = \frac{18}{30}$$

$$\frac{3}{5} + \frac{17}{30} = \frac{18}{30} + \frac{17}{30} = \frac{35}{30} = \frac{7}{6} = 1\frac{1}{6}$$

2 Calculate $\frac{5}{8} - \frac{7}{12}$

Multiples of 8: 8, 16, 24, …
Multiples of 12: 12, 24, …
The lowest common multiple of 8 and 12 is 24.

$$\frac{5}{8} \text{ of } 24 = 15 \qquad \frac{5}{8} = \frac{15}{24}$$
$$\frac{7}{12} \text{ of } 24 = 14 \qquad \frac{7}{12} = \frac{14}{24}$$

$$\frac{5}{8} - \frac{7}{12} = \frac{15}{24} - \frac{14}{24} = \frac{1}{24}$$

How to add and subtract fractions

Calculate $1\frac{7}{10} + \frac{5}{6}$

Change mixed numbers to improper ('top heavy') fractions. $1\frac{7}{10} = \frac{17}{10}$

The calculation then becomes $\frac{17}{10} + \frac{5}{6}$

Find the **lowest** common multiple of the denominators (bottom numbers). Lowest common multiple of 10 and 6 is 30.

Change the original fractions to equivalent fractions using the lowest common multiple as the new denominator. $\frac{17}{10} = \frac{51}{30}$ and $\frac{5}{6} = \frac{25}{30}$

Add or subtract the new numerators. Keep the new denominator the same. $\frac{51}{30} + \frac{25}{30} = \frac{51 + 25}{30} = \frac{76}{30}$

Write the answer in its simplest form. $\frac{76}{30} = 2\frac{16}{30} = 2\frac{8}{15}$

Remember:
You can add or subtract fractions **only** when the denominators are the **same**.
*What happens if you use a common multiple that is **not** the lowest?*

EXAMPLES

3 Calculate $3\frac{3}{10} - 1\frac{5}{6}$
$$3\frac{3}{10} = \frac{33}{10}$$
$$1\frac{5}{6} = \frac{11}{6}$$

The lowest common multiple of 10 and 6 is 30.

$$\frac{33}{10} = \frac{99}{30} \qquad \frac{11}{6} = \frac{55}{30}$$
$$3\frac{3}{10} - 1\frac{5}{6} = \frac{99}{30} - \frac{55}{30} = \frac{44}{30}$$
$$\frac{44}{30} = \frac{22}{15} = \frac{15}{15} + \frac{7}{15} = 1\frac{7}{15}$$

4 In Jimmy's class:
$\frac{3}{10}$ of the pupils have blue eyes.
$\frac{7}{15}$ of the pupils have brown eyes.
What fraction of the pupils do not have blue or brown eyes?

$\frac{3}{10} + \frac{7}{15}$ of the pupils have either blue or brown eyes.

$$\frac{3}{10} = \frac{9}{30} \qquad \frac{7}{15} = \frac{14}{30}$$
$$\frac{3}{10} + \frac{7}{15} = \frac{9}{30} + \frac{14}{30} = \frac{23}{30}$$

$\frac{23}{30}$ of the pupils have either blue or brown eyes.
$1 - \frac{23}{30}$ have neither blue nor brown eyes.
$\frac{7}{30}$ have neither blue nor brown eyes.

1 Calculate:

(a) $\frac{1}{2} + \frac{1}{8}$ (b) $\frac{1}{4} + \frac{1}{5}$

(c) $\frac{1}{2} + \frac{1}{7}$ (d) $\frac{3}{8} + \frac{1}{4}$

(e) $\frac{3}{10} + \frac{1}{5}$ (f) $\frac{2}{5} + \frac{3}{7}$

(g) $\frac{1}{4} + \frac{2}{3}$ (h) $\frac{3}{10} + \frac{2}{3}$

(i) $\frac{1}{3} + \frac{3}{4}$ (j) $\frac{5}{12} + \frac{7}{18}$

(k) $\frac{5}{8} + \frac{3}{4}$ (l) $\frac{2}{3} + \frac{3}{5}$

2 Calculate:

(a) $\frac{3}{4} - \frac{1}{8}$ (b) $\frac{5}{8} - \frac{1}{2}$

(c) $\frac{1}{3} - \frac{1}{4}$ (d) $\frac{13}{15} - \frac{1}{3}$

(e) $\frac{5}{6} - \frac{5}{24}$ (f) $\frac{7}{9} - \frac{2}{5}$

(g) $\frac{7}{8} - \frac{2}{3}$ (h) $\frac{13}{16} - \frac{5}{12}$

3 Calculate:

(a) $2\frac{3}{4} + 1\frac{1}{2}$ (b) $1\frac{1}{2} + 2\frac{1}{3}$

(c) $1\frac{3}{4} + 2\frac{5}{8}$ (d) $2\frac{1}{4} + 3\frac{3}{5}$

(e) $4\frac{3}{5} + 1\frac{5}{6}$ (f) $3\frac{3}{10} + 2\frac{3}{20}$

4 Calculate:

(a) $2\frac{1}{2} - 1\frac{2}{5}$ (b) $1\frac{2}{3} - 1\frac{1}{4}$

(c) $3\frac{3}{8} - 2\frac{3}{4}$ (d) $5\frac{2}{5} - 2\frac{1}{10}$

(e) $4\frac{3}{10} - 2\frac{5}{8}$ (f) $3\frac{3}{16} - 2\frac{5}{24}$

5 Both Billy and Mary have a packet of the same sweets.

Mary eats $\frac{2}{5}$ of her packet.

Billy eats $\frac{3}{4}$ of his packet.

(a) Find the difference between the fraction Mary eats and the fraction Billy eats.

Billy gives his remaining sweets to Mary.

(b) What fraction of a packet does Mary now have?

6 A school has pupils in Years 7 to 13.
$\frac{7}{12}$ of its pupils are in Years 7 to 9.
$\frac{3}{10}$ of its pupils are in Years 10 and 11.
What fraction of the pupils in the school are in Years 12 and 13?

7 Only Andy, Billy and Cathy are candidates in a school election.
Andy got $\frac{7}{20}$ of the votes.
Billy got $\frac{5}{16}$ of the votes.

(a) What fraction of the votes did Cathy get?
(b) Which candidate won the election?

Multiplying fractions

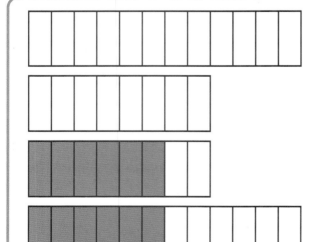

There are 12 sweets in a packet.

Alena give $\frac{2}{3}$ of the sweets in the packet to Sead.
$\frac{2}{3}$ of 12 = 8

Sead eats $\frac{3}{4}$ of the sweets that Alena gives him.
$\frac{3}{4}$ of 8 = 6

Sead eats $\frac{6}{12}$ of the whole packet.
So ... $\frac{2}{3}$ of $\frac{3}{4} = \frac{6}{12} = \frac{1}{2}$

This shows that $\frac{2}{3} \times \frac{3}{4} = \frac{2 \times 3}{3 \times 4} = \frac{6}{12} = \frac{1}{2}$

How to multiply fractions

Calculate $2\frac{2}{5} \times 3\frac{1}{4}$

Change mixed numbers to improper ('top heavy') fractions. $2\frac{2}{5} = \frac{12}{5}$ $3\frac{1}{4} = \frac{13}{4}$

The calculation then becomes $\frac{12}{5} \times \frac{13}{4}$

Multiply the numerators.
Multiply the denominators. $\frac{12 \times 13}{5 \times 4} = \frac{156}{20}$

$$\frac{156}{20} = \frac{156 \div 4}{20 \div 4} = \frac{39}{5}$$

$$7 \times 5 + 4 = 39$$

Write the answer in its simplest form. $\frac{156}{20} = 7\frac{4}{5}$

EXAMPLES

1 Multiply $1\frac{3}{5}$ by $1\frac{1}{2}$.

$$1\frac{1}{2} \times 1\frac{3}{5}$$

Change mixed numbers to improper fractions.

$$1\frac{1}{2} = \frac{2 \times 1 + 1}{2} = \frac{2 + 1}{2} = \frac{3}{2}$$

$$1\frac{3}{5} = \frac{5 \times 1 + 3}{5} = \frac{5 + 3}{5} = \frac{8}{5}$$

The calculation becomes $\frac{3}{2} \times \frac{8}{5}$

Multiply the numerators.
Multiply the denominators.

$$\frac{3 \times 8}{2 \times 5} = \frac{24}{10}$$

$$\frac{24}{10} = \frac{12}{5} = 2\frac{2}{5}$$

$$1\frac{1}{2} \times 1\frac{3}{5} = 2\frac{2}{5}$$

2 Calculate $\frac{5}{12}$ of $4\frac{1}{5}$.

$$\frac{5}{12} \times 4\frac{1}{5}$$

Change mixed numbers to improper fractions.

$$4\frac{1}{5} = \frac{5 \times 4 + 1}{5} = \frac{20 + 1}{5} = \frac{21}{5}$$

The calculation becomes $\frac{5}{12} \times \frac{21}{5}$

Multiply the numerators.
Multiply the denominators.

$$\frac{5 \times 21}{12 \times 5} = \frac{105}{60}$$

$$\frac{105}{60} = \frac{7}{4} = 1\frac{3}{4}$$

$$\frac{5}{12} \text{ of } 1\frac{3}{5} = 1\frac{3}{4}$$

Exercise 8.4

Do not use a calculator in this exercise.

1 Calculate:

(a) $\frac{1}{2} \times \frac{1}{4}$ (b) $\frac{1}{4} \times \frac{1}{3}$

(c) $\frac{1}{5} \times \frac{1}{6}$ (d) $\frac{2}{3} \times \frac{1}{2}$

(e) $\frac{3}{10} \times \frac{1}{8}$ (f) $\frac{2}{5} \times \frac{1}{7}$

(g) $\frac{3}{4} \times \frac{2}{3}$ (h) $\frac{3}{10} \times \frac{5}{6}$

(i) $\frac{1}{4} \times \frac{2}{9}$ (j) $\frac{5}{8} \times \frac{4}{15}$

2 Calculate:

(a) $1\frac{1}{2} \times \frac{3}{4}$ (b) $1\frac{1}{2} \times 1\frac{1}{3}$

(c) $2\frac{1}{4} \times 1\frac{2}{3}$ (d) $2\frac{3}{4} \times 1\frac{2}{5}$

(e) $1\frac{1}{2} \times 3\frac{1}{4}$ (f) $1\frac{3}{5} \times 1\frac{1}{6}$

(g) $6\frac{3}{10} \times 2\frac{2}{9}$ (h) $3\frac{3}{4} \times 3\frac{3}{5}$

(i) $1\frac{1}{4} \times 2\frac{4}{25}$ (j) $2\frac{5}{8} \times 3\frac{1}{3}$

3 Calculate:

(a) $\frac{4}{5}$ of $3\frac{1}{4}$ (b) $\frac{2}{3}$ of $5\frac{1}{4}$

(c) $\frac{3}{4}$ of $7\frac{1}{5}$ (d) $\frac{4}{5}$ of $3\frac{1}{8}$

(e) $\frac{3}{8}$ of $3\frac{5}{9}$ (f) $\frac{5}{6}$ of $4\frac{2}{7}$

(g) $\frac{5}{8}$ of $1\frac{1}{15}$ (h) $\frac{3}{10}$ of $4\frac{4}{9}$

4 Andy eats $\frac{1}{5}$ of a bag of sweets. He shares the remaining sweets equally among Bob, Cathy and David.

(a) What fraction of the bag of sweets does Bob get?

(b) What is the smallest possible number of sweets in the bag?

Dividing fractions

Activity

The diagram shows $1\frac{1}{2}$ divided into $\frac{1}{6}$'s.

Use the diagram to explain why …

(a) $1\frac{1}{2} \div \frac{1}{6} = 9$

(b) $1\frac{1}{2} \div \frac{1}{3} = 4\frac{1}{2}$

(c) $1\frac{1}{2} \div \frac{2}{3} = 2\frac{1}{4}$

Think of each of these as …

(a) How many $\frac{1}{6}$'s in $1\frac{1}{2}$?

(b) How many $\frac{1}{3}$'s in $1\frac{1}{2}$?

(c) How many $\frac{2}{3}$'s in $1\frac{1}{2}$?

How to divide fractions

The method normally used when one fraction is divided by another is to change the division to a multiplication. The fractions can then be multiplied in the usual way.

Calculate $1\frac{7}{25} \div 3\frac{1}{5}$

Change mixed numbers to improper ('top heavy') fractions.

$1\frac{7}{25} = \frac{32}{25}$ $\qquad$ $3\frac{1}{5} = \frac{16}{5}$

Change the division to a multiplication.

$\frac{32}{25} \div \frac{16}{5} = \frac{32}{25} \times \frac{5}{16}$

Multiply the numerators.
Multiply the denominators.

$\frac{32}{25} \times \frac{5}{16} = \frac{32 \times 5}{25 \times 16} = \frac{160}{400}$

Write the answer in its simplest form.

$\frac{160}{400} = \frac{2}{5}$

$\frac{160}{400} = \frac{160 \div 80}{400 \div 80} = \frac{2}{5}$

Exercise 8.5

Do not use a calculator in this exercise.

1 Calculate:

(a) $\frac{1}{5} \div \frac{1}{3}$ $\qquad$ (b) $\frac{1}{8} \div \frac{1}{2}$

(c) $\frac{3}{5} \div \frac{1}{4}$ $\qquad$ (d) $\frac{2}{5} \div \frac{3}{10}$

(e) $\frac{3}{8} \div \frac{9}{16}$ $\qquad$ (f) $\frac{7}{12} \div \frac{7}{18}$

(g) $\frac{4}{9} \div \frac{2}{3}$ $\qquad$ (h) $\frac{7}{10} \div \frac{3}{5}$

(i) $\frac{9}{20} \div \frac{3}{10}$ $\qquad$ (j) $\frac{21}{25} \div \frac{7}{15}$

2 Calculate:

(a) $2\frac{3}{4} \div 4\frac{1}{8}$ $\qquad$ (b) $1\frac{1}{2} \div 1\frac{1}{11}$

(c) $1\frac{3}{5} \div 1\frac{2}{5}$ $\qquad$ (d) $6\frac{3}{10} \div 1\frac{7}{20}$

(e) $3\frac{3}{4} \div \frac{5}{18}$ $\qquad$ (f) $1\frac{1}{4} \div 1\frac{9}{16}$

(g) $3\frac{1}{5} \div 2\frac{2}{15}$ $\qquad$ (h) $2\frac{1}{4} \div 1\frac{4}{5}$

(i) $4\frac{2}{7} \div 1\frac{7}{8}$ $\qquad$ (j) $5\frac{2}{5} \div 1\frac{2}{3}$

3 A shelf is $40\frac{3}{4}$ cm long.

(a) How many CD's of width $1\frac{9}{10}$ cm can be stored on the shelf?

(b) How many videos of width $1\frac{3}{4}$ cm can be stored on the shelf?

In each case how much space is left on the shelf?

4 (a) $3\frac{3}{4}$ is multiplied by a number to give $2\frac{2}{3}$. What is the number?

(b) The product of two numbers is 4. One of the numbers is $1\frac{2}{3}$. What is the other number?

5 A jug contains $1\frac{3}{4}$ litres of milk. Mrs Jones makes a rice pudding with $1\frac{1}{3}$ litres of the milk in the jug. What fraction of the milk in the jug does Mrs Jones use to make the rice pudding?

Problems involving fractions

EXAMPLES

1 Jenny spends $\frac{3}{5}$ of her money.
She has £1.40 left.
How much money did she start with?

Jenny has $1 - \frac{3}{5}$ of her money left.

$$1 - \frac{3}{5} = \frac{2}{5}$$

$\frac{2}{5}$ of Jenny's money is £1.40.

$\frac{1}{5}$ of Jenny's money is £1.40 ÷ 2.

Jenny started with 5 × £0.70 = £3.50.

2 In an experiment a weight is added to a spring.
The length of the spring increases by $\frac{2}{5}$.
The new length of the spring is 21 cm.
What was the length of the spring before the weight was added?

$$1 + \frac{2}{5} = \frac{7}{5}$$

$\frac{7}{5}$ of the original length is 21 cm.

$\frac{1}{5}$ of the original length is 21 ÷ 7.

The original length is 5 × 3 = 15 cm

Exercise 8.6

Do not use a calculator in this exercise.

1 Ben spends $\frac{5}{8}$ of his pocket money.
He has £1.20 left.
How much pocket money did Ben get?

2 A cyclist travels from A to B in two stages.
Stage 1 is 28 km which is $\frac{2}{7}$ of the total journey.
How long is stage 2?

3

Music Sale
$\frac{1}{4}$ off all CD's

Billy pays £9.60 for a CD in the sale.
How much did he save?

4 Sara's hourly wage is increased by $\frac{1}{10}$.
Her new hourly wage is £5.50.
What was her original hourly wage?

5 A young tree is $\frac{3}{8}$ taller in August than it was in May.
In August it is 132 centimetres tall.
How tall was it in May?

6 A factory produced 231 sofas in May, $\frac{2}{9}$ more than the number of sofas it produced in April.
How many sofas did the factory produce in April?

Fractions on a scientific calculator

Fraction calculations can be done quickly using the fraction button on a scientific calculator.
On most scientific calculators the fraction button looks like this …

EXAMPLES

1 Use a scientific calculator to calculate $4\frac{3}{5} \div 2\frac{1}{4}$

This can be calculated with this calculator sequence.

$$\boxed{4} \ \boxed{a^b/_c} \ \boxed{3} \ \boxed{a^b/_c} \ \boxed{5} \ \boxed{\div} \ \boxed{2} \ \boxed{a^b/_c} \ \boxed{1} \ \boxed{a^b/_c} \ \boxed{4} \ \boxed{=}$$

This gives the answer $2\frac{2}{45}$.

2 Calculate $\frac{7}{12}$ of 32.

This can be calculated with this calculator sequence.

$$\boxed{7} \ \boxed{a^b/_c} \ \boxed{1} \ \boxed{2} \ \boxed{\times} \ \boxed{3} \ \boxed{2} \ \boxed{=}$$

This gives the answer $18\frac{2}{3}$.

Use a scientific calculator to check your answers to some of the questions in Exercises 8.3 to 8.6.

- The top number of a fraction is called the **numerator**, the bottom number is called the **denominator**.

- To write **equivalent fractions**, the numerator and denominator of a fraction are multiplied (or divided) by the **same** number.
  e.g. $\frac{3}{8} = \frac{3 \times 4}{8 \times 4} = \frac{12}{32}$

- In its **simplest form**, the numerator and denominator of a fraction have no common factor, other than 1.

- $2\frac{1}{2}$ is an example of a **mixed number**. It is a mixture of whole numbers and fractions.

- $\frac{5}{2}$ is an **improper** (or '**top heavy**') fraction.

You should be able to:
- Write improper fractions as mixed numbers in their simplest form.
- Change mixed numbers to improper fractions.
- Find a fraction of a quantity.
- Add, subtract, multiply and divide fractions.
- Solve problems involving fractions.
- Use the fraction button on a scientific calculator.

Review Exercise

Questions 1 to 9.
Do not use a calculator to answer these questions. Show your working clearly.

1 5 cakes are shared equally between 8 people.
What fraction of one cake does each person get?

2 20 cakes are shared equally between 3 people.
How much does each person get?

3 Each of these pairs of fractions are equivalent.
In each case find the value of n.
(a) $\frac{5}{8}, \frac{15}{n}$ (b) $\frac{n}{20}, \frac{5}{n}$ (c) $\frac{n}{20}, \frac{3}{15}$

4 Write each of these fractions in its simplest form.
(a) $\frac{50}{85}$ (b) $\frac{24}{84}$ (c) $\frac{91}{143}$

5 Change these improper fractions to mixed numbers written in their simplest form:
(a) $\frac{50}{35}$ (b) $\frac{80}{15}$ (c) $\frac{60}{8}$

6 Change the following mixed numbers to improper fractions:
(a) $2\frac{5}{8}$ (b) $3\frac{4}{5}$ (c) $7\frac{3}{4}$

7 Calculate:
(a) $2\frac{1}{4} + 3\frac{5}{6}$ (e) $3\frac{3}{4} \times 1\frac{1}{5}$
(b) $2\frac{5}{7} + 1\frac{4}{9}$ (f) $2\frac{2}{3} \times 3\frac{3}{4}$
(c) $3\frac{3}{5} - 1\frac{1}{2}$ (g) $3\frac{3}{5} \div 2\frac{1}{10}$
(d) $4\frac{3}{10} - 1\frac{2}{3}$ (h) $5\frac{1}{4} \div 2\frac{1}{10}$

8 A shirt costing £15.30 is reduced by $\frac{1}{3}$.
Find the new price of the shirt.

9 The price of a coat is reduced by $\frac{2}{5}$ to £48.
What was the original price of the coat?

Questions 10 to 16.
You may use a calculator to answer these questions.

10

Flyway Tours undertake short distance, medium distance and long distance flights.
Last year $\frac{1}{4}$ of their flights were short distance and $\frac{2}{3}$ were medium distance.

(a) What fraction of Flyway Tours' flights were long distance?
Write your answer as a fraction in its simplest form.

Flyway Tours flew 630 long distance flights. The destination of $\frac{2}{5}$ of the long distance flights was Canada and $\frac{1}{3}$ of these were to the city of Vancouver in Canada.

(b) Calculate the number of flights to Vancouver last year.

SEG 1995

11 One kilometre is approximately five eighths of a mile.
The distance by car between Southampton and Birmingham is 130 miles.
What is the distance in kilometres? /

SEG 1997

12 36 girls and 24 boys applied to go on a rock climbing course.
$\frac{2}{3}$ of the girls and $\frac{3}{4}$ of the boys went on the course.
What fraction of the 60 students who applied went on the course?
Write the fraction in its simplest form.

13 The length of a rectangle is $\frac{2}{3}$m.
The width of the rectangle is $\frac{3}{8}$m.

(a) What is the perimeter of the rectangle?

(b) What is the area of the rectangle?

14 Jill wants to buy a Mini H-Fi system. She notices two advertisements for it.

FIRM A

Recommended Price £411

OUR PRICE $\frac{1}{3}$ OFF

FIRM B

OUR PRICE $\frac{3}{4}$ of the recommended price

Recommended Price £399

In each case find the final cost of the Hi-Fi system.

SEG 1994

15 The ancient Egyptians, who were the first to use fractions, only used fractions with a numerator of 1.
For fractions like $\frac{3}{4}$ they wrote $\frac{1}{2} + \frac{1}{4}$.
Copy and complete the following to show how the ancient Egyptians wrote the fractions $\frac{3}{8}$, $\frac{7}{12}$, $\frac{7}{10}$, $\frac{8}{15}$ and $\frac{47}{60}$.

(a) $\frac{1}{4} + \frac{1}{?} = \frac{3}{8}$

(b) $\frac{1}{2} + \frac{1}{?} = \frac{7}{12}$

(c) $\frac{1}{?} + \frac{1}{?} = \frac{7}{10}$

(d) $\frac{1}{?} + \frac{1}{?} = \frac{8}{15}$

(e) $\frac{1}{3} + \frac{1}{?} + \frac{1}{?} = \frac{47}{60}$

16 In a school $\frac{8}{15}$ of the pupils are girls.
$\frac{3}{16}$ of the girls are left handed.
What fraction of the pupils in the school are left handed girls?

Percentages

The meaning of a percentage

'Per cent' means 'out of 100'.
The symbol for per cent is %.
A percentage can be written as a fraction with denominator 100.

> 10% means 10 out of 100.
> 10% can be written as $\frac{10}{100}$.
> 10% is read as '10 percent'.

Changing percentages to fractions and decimals

EXAMPLES

1 Write 38% as a fraction in its simplest form.

38% means '38 out of 100'.

This can be written as $\frac{38}{100}$.

$\frac{38}{100} = \frac{38 \div 2}{100 \div 2} = \frac{19}{50}$

$38\% = \frac{19}{50}$

> **Remember**
> To simplify a fraction divide the **numerator** (top number) and the **denominator** (bottom number) of the fraction by their highest common factor.

2 Write 72% as a fraction in its simplest form.

$72\% = \frac{72}{100} = \frac{72 \div 4}{100 \div 4} = \frac{18}{25}$

> **Remember**
> To change a fraction to a decimal divide the numerator by the denominator.

3 Write 42.5% as a decimal.

$42.5\% = \frac{42.5}{100} = 42.5 \div 100 = 0.425$

Changing fractions and decimals to percentages

EXAMPLE

1 Change $\frac{3}{5}$ to a percentage.

Method 1
Multiply the fraction by 100.
$\frac{3}{5} \times 100 = \frac{300}{5} = 60$

Method 2
Write $\frac{3}{5}$ as a fraction with denominator 100.
$\frac{3}{5} = \frac{3 \times 20}{5 \times 20} = \frac{60}{100} = 60\%$

Method 3
Change the fraction to a decimal and then multiply by 100.
$\frac{3}{5} = 3 \div 5 = 0.6$
$0.6 \times 100 = 60\%$

> Both method 1 or method 2 can be used when the denominator of the fraction is a factor or multiple of 100.

> **Remember**
> To change a fraction to an **equivalent** fraction multiply or divide the numerator and denominator by the same number.

> Method 3 is useful when the denominator of the fraction is not a factor or a multiple of 100 and a calculator is available.

Percentages

EXAMPLES

2 Change $\frac{27}{400}$ to a percentage.

Write $\frac{27}{400}$ as a fraction with denominator 100.

$\frac{27}{400} = \frac{27 \div 4}{400 \div 4} = \frac{6.75}{100}$

$\frac{27}{400} = 6.75\%$

3 Write $\frac{7}{12}$ as a percentage.

$\frac{7}{12} = 7 \div 12 = 0.58333...$

$0.58\dot{3} \times 100 = 58.\dot{3}\%$

$\frac{7}{12} = 58.\dot{3}\%$

Remember
Some decimals have recurring digits. These are shown by:

a single dot above a single recurring digit.
For example:
$0.\dot{3}$ means 0.3333333 …

a dot above the first and last digit of a set of recurring digits.
For example:
$0.\dot{1}2\dot{3}$ means 0.123123123 …

Comparing fractions

Fractions can be compared by first writing them as percentages.

EXAMPLE

Ben scored 17 out of 20 in a Maths test and 21 out of 25 in a History test. Which is Ben's best mark?

Change each mark to a percentage.
Maths: $\frac{17}{20} = \frac{85}{100} = 85\%$ History: $\frac{21}{25} = \frac{84}{100} = 84\%$
So Ben's best mark was his Maths mark of 85%.

Exercise 9.1

Do not use a calculator in questions 1 to 5.

1 Copy and complete this table to work out the percentage equivalents of the fractions given.

Fraction	Equivalent fraction with a denominator of 100	Percentage
$\frac{1}{10}$	=	
$\frac{1}{5}$	=	
$\frac{1}{4}$	$\frac{1 \times 25}{4 \times 25} = \frac{25}{100}$	25%
$\frac{3}{10}$	=	
$\frac{2}{5}$	=	
$\frac{1}{2}$	$\frac{1 \times 50}{2 \times 50} = \frac{50}{100}$	50%
$\frac{3}{5}$	=	
$\frac{7}{10}$	=	
$\frac{3}{4}$	=	
$\frac{4}{5}$	=	
$\frac{9}{10}$	=	

2 Change these fractions to a percentage.
(a) $\frac{17}{50}$ (b) $\frac{12}{25}$ (c) $\frac{30}{200}$
(d) $\frac{4}{5}$ (e) $\frac{135}{500}$ (f) $\frac{13}{20}$

3 Change these percentages to fractions in their simplest form.
(a) 18%   (b) 52%   (c) 23%
(d) 12.5%   (e) 28.5%   (f) 72.5%

4 Change these decimals to a percentage.
(a) 0.45   (b) 0.32   (c) 0.125
(d) 0.07   (e) 1.12   (f) 0.015

5 Change these percentages to decimals.
(a) 80%   (b) 15%   (c) 47%
(d) 72%   (e) 87.5%   (f) 150%

6 Change these fractions to percentages.
(a) $\frac{2}{3}$ (b) $\frac{3}{8}$ (c) $\frac{2}{9}$
(d) $\frac{17}{45}$ (e) $\frac{42}{90}$ (f) $1\frac{5}{12}$

7 Write in order of size, lowest first.
$\frac{17}{40}$ 0.42 $\frac{13}{30}$ 43%

8 Write in order of size, lowest first.
$\frac{2}{7}$ 28% $\frac{57}{200}$ 0.2805

9 Change each of these marks to a percentage.
  (a) Maths: 27 out of 30.
  (b) French: 34 out of 40.
  (c) Science: 22 out of 25.
  (d) Art: 48 out of 60.

10 Which rectangle has the greatest percentage shaded?

A

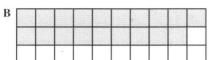

B

11 In an ice hockey competition Team A won 8 out of the 11 games they played whilst Team B won 5 of their 7 games.

Which team has the better record in the competition?

Finding a percentage of a quantity

Finding a percentage of a quantity is similar to finding a fraction of a quantity.
It can be done either by changing the percentage to a fraction or to a decimal.

EXAMPLES

1 Find 20% of £56.

Write 20% as a fraction.
20% of £56 is the same as $\frac{20}{100}$ of £56.
$56 \div 100 \times 20 = 0.56 \times 20 = 11.2$
20% of £56 is £11.20.

> To find $\frac{20}{100}$ of a quantity:
> find $\frac{1}{100}$ by dividing by 100,
> then multiply by 20 to find $\frac{20}{100}$.

Alternative method
Write 20% as a decimal.
20% of £56 is the same as $0.2 \times$ £56.
$0.2 \times 56 = 11.2$
20% of £56 is £11.20.

> To multiply by 0.2:
> multiply by 2, then divide by 10.

2 A shirt normally priced at £24 is reduced by 15% in a sale.
How much does this cost in the sale?

Reduction in price = 15% of £24
          = $\frac{15}{100}$ of £24
$24 \div 100 \times 15 = 0.24 \times 15 = 3.6$
15% of £24 = £3.60
The shirt costs £24 − £3.60 = £20.40.

Alternative method
$15\% = \frac{15}{100} = 15 \div 100 = 0.15$
$1 - 0.15 = 0.85$
$0.85 \times 24 = 20.4$
The shirt costs £20.40.
Explain why this method works.

3 There are 440 g in a normal packet of Rice Crunchies. A special offer packet contains 30% more than the normal packet.
How many grams of Rice Crunchies are there in the special offer packet?

Extra contents = 30% of 440 g
        = $\frac{30}{100}$ of 440
        = 132 g
$440 + 132 = 572$
There are 572 g in a special offer packet.

Alternative method
$30\% = \frac{30}{100} = 30 \div 100 = 0.3$
$1 + 0.3 = 1.3$
$1.3 \times 440 = 572$
There are 572 g in a special offer packet.
Explain why this method works.

Exercise 9.2

Do not use a calculator in this exercise.

1 Find

(a)	20% of £80	(b)	75% of £20
(c)	30% of £220	(d)	15% of £350
(e)	5% of £500	(f)	20% of £150
(g)	9% of £300	(h)	20% of 20 m
(i)	30% of 80 kg	(j)	35% of 800
(k)	45% of £25	(l)	60% of 20

2 Increase:

(a)	£50 by 60%	(b)	£10 by 30%
(c)	£15 by 10%	(d)	£50 by 15%

3 Decrease:

(a)	£600 by 15%	(b)	£55 by 90%
(c)	£42 by 20%	(d)	£63 by 35%

4 Tim invests £400 in a building society.
He earns 5% interest per year.
How much interest does he get in
one year?

5 There are 450 seats in a theatre.
60% of the seats are in the stalls.
How many seats are in the stalls?

6 A salesman earns a bonus of 3% of his
weekly sales.
How much bonus does the salesman earn
in a week when his sales are:
(a) £1400,   (b) £2350?

7 Jenny gets a 15% discount on a theatre
ticket.
The normal cost is £13.
How much does she save?

8 A mobile telephone company offers a
20% discount on calls made in March.
The normal cost of a peak time call is
50 pence per minute.
How much does a peak time call cost in
March?

9 A dozen biscuits weigh 720 g.
The amount of flour in a biscuit is 40%
of the weight of a biscuit.
What is the weight of flour in **each**
biscuit.

10 A packet of breakfast cereal contains
660 g.
A special offer packet contains an
extra 15%.
How many grammes of breakfast cereal
are in the special offer packet?

11 Abdul earns £200 per week.
He gets a wage rise of 7.5%.
What is his new weekly wage?

12 In a school of 1200 pupils 45% are
boys.
(a) How many are girls?

30% of the girls are under 13.
(b) How many girls are under 13?

13 35% of a magazine is pictures.
In the magazine there are 60 pages.
Each page is 25 cm long and
16 cm wide.
What is the area of pictures in the
magazine?

Expressing one quantity as a percentage of another

This involves writing a fraction and then changing it to a percentage.
The units of any quantities in the numerator and denominator of the fraction must be the same.

EXAMPLES

1 Express 30 p as a percentage of £2.

$\frac{30\,p}{£2} = \frac{30\,p}{200\,p} = \frac{30}{200}$

$\frac{30}{200} = \frac{30 \div 2}{200 \div 2} = \frac{15}{100} = 15\%$

This means that 30 p is 15% of £2.

2 A newspaper contains 48 pages, 6 of which are
Sports pages.
What percentage of the pages are Sports pages?

6 out of 48 pages are Sports pages.

$\frac{6}{48} = 6 \div 48 = 0.125$

$0.125 \times 100 = 12.5$

12.5% of the pages are Sports pages.

Do not use a calculator in questions 1 to 5.

1 What is
  (a) 64 pence as a percentage of £2,
  (b) 15 km as a percentage of 120 km,
  (c) 30 cm as percentage of 600 mm,
  (d) £3600 as a percentage of £4000,
  (e) 18 pence as a percentage of £0.60?

2 A school has 800 pupils of which 160 are in Year 11.
What percentage of pupils are in Year 11?

3 James saved £30 and then spent £9.
What percentage of his savings did he spend?

4 240 people took part in a survey.
30 of them were younger than 18.
What percentage were younger than 18?

5 A bar of chocolate has 32 squares.
Jane eats 12 of the squares.
What percentage of the bar does she eat?

6 What is
  (a) £2 as a percentage of £6,
  (b) 80 km as a percentage of 120 km,
  (c) 20 cm as a percentage of 180 cm,
  (d) £1530 as a percentage of £3600,
  (e) £105.09 as a percentage of £186?

7 A new car costs £13 500.
The dealer offers a discount of £1282.50.
What is the percentage discount?

8 Billy earns £3.50 per hour.
He gets a wage rise of 28 pence per hour.
What is his percentage wage rise?

9 There are 600 pupils in Years 9 to 13 of a High school.
360 of the pupils are in Years 10 and 11.
15% of the pupils are in Years 12 and 13.
What percentage of the pupils are in Year 9?

More complicated percentage problems

Problems involving percentages can involve more complicated calculations.

EXAMPLES

1 A salesman earns a bonus which is calculated as a percentage of the value of his weekly sales.
He earns 3% on the first £1500 of his weekly sales and 4.5% on any sales more than £1500.
How much bonus does the salesman earn when his weekly sales are
  (a) £1400, (b) £3455?

  (a) The salesman earns:
  3% of £1400
  $0.03 \times 1400 = 42$
  The salesman's bonus is £42.00.

  (b) The salesman earns:
  3% of £1500 + 4.5% of £1955.
  $0.03 \times 1500 + 0.045 \times 1955 = 132.975$
  The salesman's bonus is £132.98.

2 (a) Calculate 4×10^6 as a percentage of 2×10^8.
  (b) Calculate 30% of 8×10^4.

  (a) $\dfrac{4 \times 10^6}{2 \times 10^8} = 0.02$
  $0.02 \times 100 = 2\%$

  (b) $0.3 \times 8 \times 10^4 = 24\,000$

3 1.2×10^{10} steel cans were used in 1992.
1.4×10^9 of these were recycled.
Calculate the percentage of steel cans that were **not** recycled in 1992.

$\dfrac{1.4 \times 10^9}{1.2 \times 10^{10}} = 0.1166 \ldots$

$0.1166 \times 100 = 11.66 \ldots$
$= 11.7$ to 3 significant figures.
Percentage recycled = 11.7%
$100 - 11.7 = 88.3$
Percentage not recycled = 88.3%

Use a calculator in this exercise.
Where appropriate give your answers to
3 significant figures.

1 Prices in a sale are reduced by 18%.
The normal price of a shirt is £22.50.
Calculate its sale price.

2 A computer costs £980 plus VAT.
VAT is paid at the rate of 17.5%.
How much VAT is paid on the computer?

3 The prices of these items exclude VAT.
Calculate the VAT at 17.5% for each item.

(a) £425 for a 26 inch TV set.
(b) £1850 for a 3 piece suite.
(c) £23.50 for an electric kettle.

4 A refrigerator costs £220 plus VAT at
17.5%.
What is the total cost of the refrigerator?

5 (a) The price of a gold watch is £278.
What does it cost with a
12% discount?
(b) The price of a used car is £5200.
What does it cost with a 9.5%
discount?
(c) The price of a new kitchen is £3650.
What does it cost with a
35% discount?

6 A 5 litre can of paint covers an area
of 28 m².
James buys 3 cans of paint to cover 70 m².
What percentage of the paint does he use?

7 A rectangle has length 12 cm and
width 8.5 cm.
The length is increased by 8.5% and the
width decreased by 13.5%.

(a) Calculate the change in the area of
the rectangle.
(b) Find the change in area as a percentage
of the original area of the rectangle.

8 Jane's salary of £14 050 is increased by
3.5%.
(a) Calculate her new salary.

Jane pays tax at the rate of 23%.
(b) How much extra tax does she pay as a
result of her increase in salary?

9 A car was valued at £13 500 when new.
After one year it lost 22% of its value.
At the end of two years it was sold for
£8200.
(a) What was the value of the car after
one year?
(b) What percentage of its original
value did the car lose in its
second year?

10 Tim invests £650 in a building society.
He earns 5.25% interest in the
first year.
(a) How much interest does he earn?

Tim leaves his original £650 plus the
interest he has earned in the building
society.
He earns 6.05% in the second year.
(b) How much interest does Tim earn
in the second year?

11 There are 633 pupils in a school.
230 of the pupils walk to school, 212
travel by bus and 150 come by car.
(a) What percentage walk to school?
(b) What percentage come by car?

18% of the pupils who normally come
by car start to travel on a new bus
route.
(c) What percentage of the pupils now
travel by bus?

12 The volume of water on Earth is
approximately 1.436×10^9 km³.
About 94% of this is contained in the
Earth's oceans.
Use these figures to estimate the
volume of water in the Earth's oceans.

13 The area of the surface of the Earth is
about 5.095×10^9 square miles.
Approximately 29.2 % of this is land.
Use these figures to estimate the area of
land surface on Earth.

14 The planet Pluto is 5.914×10^9 km
from the Sun.
The Earth is 1.496×10^8 km from the
Sun.
Express the distance of the Earth from
the Sun as a percentage of the distance
of Pluto from the Sun.

Compound interest

When money is invested it **grows** according to interest it earns.
For example, an investment of 5% per annum means that the amount invested earns £5 for every £100 invested for one year.
So, after the first year of the investment, every £100 invested becomes £100 + 5% of £100.
£100 + 5% of £100 = £100 + £5 = £105

When investments are made for longer periods the interest earned is **compounded**.
This means that interest is given on both the interest earned **and** the original amount invested.
So, after the second year of the investment, every £100 of the original investment becomes £105 + 5% of £105.
£105 + 5% of £105 = £105 + £5.25 = £110.25

Interest earned in this way is called **compound interest**.

EXAMPLES

 Faye invests £300 in a building society which pays 6% interest per annum.
Find the value of her investment after 3 years.

Method 1
6% of 300 = 300 ÷ 100 × 6
          = 18
300 + 18 = 318
Value after 1 year = £318

6% of 318 = 318 ÷ 100 × 6
          = 19.08
318 + 19.08 = 337.08
Value after 2 years = £337.08

6% of 337.08 = 337.08 ÷ 100 × 6
            = 20.2248
337.08 + 20.2248 = 357.3048
Value after 3 years = £357.30

Method 2
After year 1
Faye's investment will have the value
£300 + 6% of £300
300 × 1.06 = £318

After year 2
Faye's investment will have the value
£318 + 6% of £318
318 × 1.06 = £337.08

After year 3
Faye's investment will have the value
£337.08 + 6% of £337.08
337.08 × 1.06 = £357.30

Method 3
After 3 years Faye's investment has the value:
£300 × 1.06^3 = £357.30
Explain why this method works.

Compound **decrease** is also possible.

 A car is valued at £15 000 when new.
Its value decreases at the rate of 9% each year.
Find its value after 3 years.

Method 1
9% of 15 000 = 15 000 ÷ 100 × 9
            = 1350
15 000 − 1350 = 13 650
Value after 1 year = £13 650

9% of 13 650 = 13 650 ÷ 100 × 9
            = 1228.50
13 650 − 1228.50 = 12 421.50
Value after 2 years = £12 421.50

9% of 12 421.50 = 12 421.50 ÷ 100 × 9
              = 1117.935
12 421.50 − 1117.935 = 11 303.565
Value after 3 years = £11 303.57

Method 2
Value after 1 year
£15 000 − 9% of £15 000
15 000 × 0.91 = £13 650

Value after 2 years
£13 650 − 9% of £13 650
13 650 × 0.91 = £12 421.50

Value after 3 years
£12 421.50 − 9% of £12 421.50
12 421.50 × 0.91 = £11 303.57

Method 3
After 3 years the car has the value:
£15000 × 0.91^3 = £11303.57

Exercise 9.5

Do questions 1 to 3 without a calculator. Where appropriate give your answers to 3 significant figures.

1 Jenny invests £200 at 10% per annum compound interest.
What is the value of her investment after 2 years?

2 Jenny invests £300 at 5% per annum compound interest.
What is the value of her investment after 2 years?

3 Which of the following investments earn most interest?
(a) £200 for 3 years at 5% compound.
(b) £300 for 2 years at 5% compound.

4 £10 000 is to be invested for 3 years.
Calculate the final value of the investment if the interest rate per annum is:
(a) 5%   (b) 6%
(c) 7%   (d) 8%

5 A man buys a new car for £13 000.
The car loses value at the rate of 14% per annum.
(a) (i) What is its value after 3 years?
    (ii) Express its value after 3 years as a percentage of its original value.
(b) Repeat (a) for a new car originally valued at £20 000.
(c) What do you notice about your answers to (a) and (b)?

6 The population of a Latin American country is approximately 1.5×10^8.
The population grows at the rate of 3% per annum.
What is the population after 3 years?

7 Interest on a loan of £2000 is charged at the rate of 21% per annum. Interest is calculated on the outstanding loan at the **start** of each year.
(a) How much is owed immediately the loan is taken out?
Repayments are £600 per year.
(b) How much is owed at the **start** of the third year of the loan?

8 The Amazonian rainforest covers an area of $7 \times 10^6 \, \text{km}^2$.
This area decreases at the rate of 7% per year.
What is the area of the rainforest after 3 years?

Percentage increase and decrease

Sadik and Chandni took Maths tests in October and June.

My mark went up from 54% to 72%.

My mark went up from 42% to 60%.

Who has made the most improvement?

They have both improved by a score of 18% so by one measure they have both improved equally.

Another way of comparing their improvement is to use the idea of a percentage increase.

$$\text{Percentage increase} = \frac{\text{actual increase}}{\text{initial value}} \times 100\%$$

Comparing percentage increases is the best way to decide whether Sadik or Chandni has made the most improvement.
Explain why.

Remember
To calculate
% increase or % decrease always use the initial value.

For Sadik
% increase = $\frac{18}{54} \times 100\% = 33.3\%$

For Chandni
% increase = $\frac{18}{42} \times 100\% = 42.9\%$

Both calculations are correct to one decimal place.

A percentage decrease can be calculated in a similar way.

$$\text{Percentage decrease} = \frac{\text{actual decrease}}{\text{initial value}} \times 100\%$$

1 A sample of soil is dried in an oven.
Its mass reduces from 65 g to 45 g.
Find the percentage decrease in the mass?

Actual decrease = $65 - 45 = 20$ g
% decrease = $\frac{20}{65} \times 100$
= 30.8%, correct to one decimal place.

2 A shop buys pens for 15 pence
and sells them for 21 pence.
What is their percentage profit?

Actual profit = $21 - 15$
= 6 pence

% increase = $\frac{6}{15} \times 100 = 40\%$

Exercise 9.6

Do questions 1 to 5 without a calculator.

1 A school buys calculators for £5 and
sells them for £6. Find the percentage
profit.

2 Sara's wages of £7.50 per hour are
increased to £9.00 per hour.
Find the percentage increase in her
earnings.

3 A man buys a car for £3500 and sells it
for £2625. Find his percentage loss.

4 In October, Sam scored 50% in an
English test. In January he improved
to 66%.
In the same tests, Becky scored 40%
and 56%.
Who has made the most improvement?
Explain your answer.

5 During 1998 the rent on Karen's flat
increased from £80 to £90 per week.
(a) Find the percentage increase in her
rent.
In the same period Karen's wages
increased from £250 per week to
£280 per week.
(b) Find the percentage increase in her
wages.
Comment on your answers.

6 A book goes up in price from £5.99
to £6.99.
What is the percentage increase in the
price?

7 John's weekly wage rises from £150
to £168.
What is John's percentage wage rise?

8 The value of car A when new was
£13 000.
The value of car B when new was
£16 500.
After one year the value of car A is
£11 200 and the value of car B is
£13 500.
Calculate the percentage loss in the
values of cars A and B after one year.

9 In a school the number of pupils
increased as shown in the table:

Year	1995	1996	1997	1998	1999
Number	554	605	643	679	734

In which year is the percentage
increase in the number of pupils the
greatest?

10 During 1995 the population of a village
decreased from 323 to 260.
Find the percentage decrease in the
population.

11 Between 1980 and 1990 the population
of the UK increased from 5.7×10^7 to
5.9×10^7.
Find the percentage increase in the
population of the UK between 1980 and
1990.

12 At the start of May a flower was
12.3 cm high.
In May it grew by 14.5%.
At the start of July it was 16.7 cm high.
What was its percentage growth during
June?

Reverse percentage problems

EXAMPLES

1 A 15% discount on a TV set is worth £82.50.
How much does the TV normally cost?

Method 1
15% of normal cost = £82.50
1% of normal cost = £82.50 ÷ 15
$\qquad$ = £5.50
So normal cost = £5.50 × 100
$\qquad$ = £550

Method 2
15% of normal cost = £82.50
0.15 × normal cost = 82.50
So normal cost = 82.50 ÷ 0.15
$\qquad$ = £550

2 A shop sells videos with a 20% discount.
Petra buys a video and pays £10.
How much does the video normally cost?

Method 1
Discount price is normal price less 20%.
So 80% of normal price = £10.
So 1% of normal price = £10 ÷ 80
$\qquad$ = £0.125
So normal price = £0.125 × 100
$\qquad$ = £12.50

Method 2
Discount price is 80% of normal price.
So £10 = 0.8 × normal price.
So normal price = £10 ÷ 0.8
$\qquad$ = £12.50

3 Tara gets a 5% wage rise.
Her new wage is £126 per week.
What was Tara's wage before her wage rise?

Method 1
New wage = old wage + 5%
So 105% of old wage = £126
1% of old wage is 126 ÷ 105 = £1.20
Old wage = 1.2 × 100 = £120

Method 2
105% of old wage is £126.
126 ÷ 1.05 = 120
Old wage = £120

4 A computer costs £1233.75 including VAT at 17.5%.
How much of the cost is VAT?

Method 1
Cost = cost without VAT + 17.5% VAT.
£1233.75 = 117.5% of cost without VAT.
1% of cost without VAT is given by
£1233.75 ÷ 117.5 = £10.50
VAT = 17.5% of cost without VAT.
So VAT = £10.50 × 17.5 = £183.75

Method 2
117.5% of cost without VAT is £1233.75
1233.75 ÷ 1.175 = 1050
1233.75 − 1050 **or** 1050 × 0.175
So VAT = £183.75

Exercise 9.7

Do questions 1 to 4 without a calculator.

1 A special bottle of pop contains 10% more than a normal bottle.
The special bottle contains 660 ml.
How much does the normal bottle contain?

2 Tim saves 15% of his monthly salary.
Each month he saves £90.
What is his monthly salary?

3 Mary gets a 20% wage rise.
Her new wage is £264 per week.
What was Mary's wage before her wage rise?

4 Mary and Sam take a History and a Geography test.
(a) Sam scored 60 marks in History.
Sam's score was 20% better than his score in Geography.
What was Sam's score in Geography?
(b) Mary scored 72 marks in History.
Mary's score was 20% worse than her score in Geography.
What was Mary's score in Geography?

5 30 grams of a breakfast cereal provides 16.2 mg of vitamin C.
This is 24% of the recommended daily intake.
What daily intake of vitamin C is recommended?

6 A gas bill of £33.60 includes VAT at 5%.
How much VAT is paid?

7 VAT at 17.5% on a washing machine is £43.75.
What is the price of the washing machine including VAT?

8 Tom gets a 3% increase in his salary.
His new salary is £1462.60 per month.
What was Tom's salary before his wage rise?

9 A one year old car is worth £1344.
This is a decrease of 16% of its value from new.
What was the price of the new car?

10 Here is some data about the changes in the number of pupils in schools A and B.
School A's numbers increased by 4% to 442.
School B's numbers decreased by 6% to 423.
How many pupils were in schools A and B before the change in numbers?

11 Billy sells his computer to Sam and makes a 15% profit.
Sam then sells the computer to Tom for £391.
Sam makes a 15% loss.
How much did Billy pay for the computer?
Explain why it is not £391.

12 Kim sells her bike to Sara.
Sara sells it to Tina for £121.50.
Both Kim and Sara make a 10% loss.
How much did Kim pay for the bike?
Explain why it is not 20% more than £121.50.

What you need to know

- 'Per cent' means 'out of 100'.
  The symbol for per cent is %.

- A percentage can be written as a fraction with denominator 100.
  10% can be written as $\frac{10}{100}$.

- A fraction can be changed to a percentage using:

  Method 1: Multiply the fraction by 100.
  $$\frac{3}{5} = \frac{3}{5} \times 100 = \frac{300}{5} = 60\%$$

  Method 2: Write the fraction with denominator 100.
  $$\frac{3}{5} = \frac{3 \times 20}{5 \times 20} = \frac{60}{100} = 60\%$$

  Method 3: Change the fraction to a decimal, then multiply by 100.
  $$\frac{3}{5} = 0.6 \quad 0.6 \times 100 = 60 \quad \frac{3}{5} = 60\%$$

- To change a percentage to a fraction, write the percentage as a fraction with denominator 100.
  Where possible simplify the fraction.
  $$38\% = \frac{38}{100} = \frac{19}{50}$$

- Percentage increase $= \dfrac{\text{actual increase}}{\text{initial value}} \times 100\%$ Percentage decrease $= \dfrac{\text{actual decrease}}{\text{initial value}} \times 100\%$

You should be able to:
- Find a percentage of a quantity.
- Express one quantity as a percentage of another quantity.
- Solve problems involving percentages in a variety of situations, including those involving compound interest and reverse percentage problems.

IDEAS FOR INVESTIGATION

Increasing and decreasing

200 increased by 10% and then decreased by 10%
200 → +10% → −10% → 198
200 → ×1.1 → ×0.9 → 198
The combined result is a 1% depreciation or −1%

500 decreased by 10% and then increased by 30%
500 → −10% → +30% → 585
500 → ×0.9 → ×1.3 → 585
The combined result is a 17% growth or +17%

Investigate increasing and decreasing different quantities by different percentages. You might find a spreadsheet useful.

Review Exercise

Questions 1 to 12.
Do not use a calculator.

1 Change these fractions to percentages.
(a) $\frac{9}{20}$ (b) $\frac{12}{40}$ (c) $\frac{12}{32}$

2 Change these percentages to fractions in their simplest form.
(a) 16% (b) 56% (c) 22.5%

3 Change these decimals to percentages.
(a) 0.31 (b) 0.05 (c) 0.025

4 Write in order of size, lowest first.
0.41 $\frac{83}{200}$ 41.05% $\frac{2}{5}$ 0.405

5 Find:
(a) 15% of £60 (b) 55% of £12
(c) 30% of £350 (d) 8% of £120

6 A train has 1200 seats.
85% of the seats are occupied.
How many seats are empty?

7 How much interest is earned in 1 year:
(a) on £600 invested at an interest rate of 8%,
(b) on £350 invested at an interest rate of 5%?

8 What is:
(a) 64 pence as a percentage of £4,
(b) 18 km as a percentage of 120 km?

9 Rolls of wallpaper are on sale at Fermants store at a reduced price.
The normal price of a roll of wallpaper is £8.

There is a 30% discount on the normal price.
How much money will be saved on each roll bought?

SEG 1995

10 A roll of carpet is 20 m long.
A customer buys 18 m of carpet from the roll.
What percentage of the roll did the customer buy?

11 (a) Sam invests £500 at 10% per annum compound interest.
What is the value of his investment after 2 years?

(b) Jane invests £2000 at 5% per annum compound interest.
What is the value of her investment after 3 years?

12 The price of a new car is increased by 10%.
The new price of the car is £12 100.
What was the price of the car before the price increase?

9

Percentages . . . Percentages . . . Percentages . . .

85

13 In a nine carat gold ring $\frac{9}{24}$ of the weight is pure gold.
What percentage of the weight of the ring is pure gold?

SEG 1994

14 A holiday week-end in a hotel costs £126 per person.
Next year the cost will increase by 15%.
What will be the new cost of the holiday week-end?

SEG 1995

15 The price of a coat was £59. This is reduced by 12%.
(a) What is the price reduction?
(b) What is the new price?

SEG 1995

16 (a) A year ago Martin was 1.60 m tall.
He is now 4% taller.
Calculate his height now.
Give your answer in centimetres.
(b) Martin now weighs 58 kg.
A year ago he weighed 51 kg.
Calculate the percentage increase in his weight.
Give your answer to an appropriate degree of accuracy.

SEG 1998

17 (a) In the men's long jump, Leroy improved on his first jump of 8.15 m by 8%.
What was the length of this improved jump?

(b) In the women's long jump, Sabrina improved her jump from 6.40 m to 7.36 m.
What was the percentage increase in her jump?

SEG 1996

18 An estate agent makes the following charge for the sale of a house.

SALE PRICE OF HOUSE	CHARGE BY ESTATE AGENT
up to £50 000	3% of the sale price
over £50 000	3% of the first £50 000 plus 2% on the remainder

Calculate the charge made by the estate agent for a house sold for £89 000.

SEG 1998

19

In 1990 Elm Tree House was bought for £88 000.
(a) In 1992 Elm Tree House was sold at a loss of 12.5%
What was the sale price?

(b) In 1996 Elm Tree House was sold again.
The sale price was 1.5% higher than its value in 1990.
By how much had the value of the house increased between 1992 and 1996?

SEG 1997

20 James has a 4% wage rise.
His new wage is £220.80 per week.
What was his weekly wage before his wage rise?

21 Matthew buys a new car for £12 800.
Its value depreciates at the rate of 12% per year.
Express its value after 3 years as a percentage of its original value.

22 Supertyres are having a sale in which all prices are reduced by 20%.
Mr. Driver buys 2 tyres.
The original price of each tyre is £29.50.
(a) What is the sale price of one tyre?

Mr. Driver gets an extra 7.5% discount because he is a member of a motoring club.
(b) What does Mr. Driver pay for the tyres?

23 The population of a colony of rats is growing at the rate of 20% per month.
At the beginning of July there are 210 rats.
How many rats are there:
(a) at the beginning of August,
(b) at the beginning of October?

Ratio

 Some faces are SMILERS.

Some faces are GLUMS.

In a group of 10 faces the **ratio** of SMILERS to GLUMS is 3 : 2.
This means that for every three SMILERS there are two GLUMS.

For the ratio 3 : 2 say 3 to 2.

In the group there are 6 SMILERS and 4 GLUMS.

Exercise **10.1**

1 (a) Draw 10 faces where the ratio of SMILERS to GLUMS is 4 : 1

(b) Draw 12 faces where the ratio of SMILERS to GLUMS is:
(i) 2 : 1
(ii) 1 : 3

(c) Draw 20 faces where the ratio of SMILERS to GLUMS is
(i) 4 : 1
(ii) 2 : 3

2 The ratio of GLUMS to SMILERS is 2 : 5.

(a) How many SMILERS are there when there are …
(i) 30 GLUMS,
(ii) 80 GLUMS?

(b) How many GLUMS are there when there are …
(i) 30 SMILERS,
(ii) 80 SMILERS?

(c) How many FACES are there when there are …
(i) 40 SMILERS,
(ii) 40 GLUMS?

3 The ratio of SMILERS to GLUMS is 4 : 3

(a) How many SMILERS are there when there are …
(i) 12 GLUMS,
(ii) 60 GLUMS?

(b) How many GLUMS are there when there are …
(i) 12 SMILERS,
(ii) 60 SMILERS?

(c) How many FACES are there when there are …
(i) 48 SMILERS,
(ii) 48 GLUMS?

4 How many SMILERS and how many GLUMS are there when …

(a) the ratio of SMILERS to GLUMS is 7 : 3 and there are:
(i) 20 faces,
(ii) 50 faces?

(b) the ratio of SMILERS to GLUMS is 3 : 2 and there are:
(i) 15 faces,
(ii) 50 faces?

Equivalent ratios

Ratios are used only to **compare** quantities.
They do not give information about actual values.

For example
A necklace is made using red beads and white beads in the ratio **3 : 4**.
This gives no information about the actual numbers of beads in the necklace.
The ratio **3 : 4** means that for every 3 red beads in the necklace there are 4 white beads.
The **possible** numbers of beads in the necklace are shown in the table.

Red beads	White beads	Total beads
3	4	7
6	8	14
9	12	21
12	16	28
18	24	42
…	…	…

Make similar tables when the ratio of red beads to white beads in the necklace is:

(a)   4 : 5   (b)   2 : 3   (c)   3 : 1

The ratios   3 : 4   6 : 8   9 : 12   … are different forms of the **same** ratio.
They are called **equivalent** ratios.
They can be found by multiplying or dividing each part of the ratio by the **same** number.

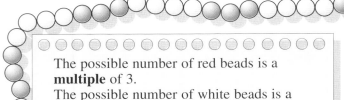

The possible number of red beads is a **multiple** of 3.
The possible number of white beads is a **multiple** of 4.
The possible total of beads is a **multiple** of 7.

Simplifying ratios

A ratio in its **simplest form** has only whole numbers that have no common factor other than 1.

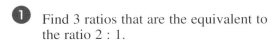

EXAMPLES

1   Find 3 ratios that are the equivalent to the ratio 2 : 1.

To find equivalent ratios multiply both numbers in the ratio by the same number.
$$2 \times 2 : 1 \times 2 = 4 : 2$$
$$2 \times 3 : 1 \times 3 = 6 : 3$$
$$2 \times 4 : 1 \times 4 = 8 : 4$$
3 ratios equivalent to the ratio 2 : 1 are 4 : 2, 6 : 3 and 8 : 4.

2   The ratio of boys to girls in a school is 3 : 4.
There are 72 boys.
How many girls are there?

$72 \div 3 = 24$
To find a ratio equivalent to 3 : 4 where the first number in the ratio is 72 multiply each number in the ratio by 24.
$$3 \times 24 : 4 \times 24 = 72 : 96$$
The number of girls = 96.

3   Write the ratio 15 : 9 in its simplest form.

The highest common factor of 15 and 9 is 3.
Divide both parts of the ratio by 3.
$15 \div 3 : 9 \div 3 = 5 : 3$
The ratio 15 : 9 in its simplest form is 5 : 3.

4   Write the ratio 2 cm : 50 mm in its simplest form.

This ratio compares two quantities with different units.
In its simplest form a ratio contains **only** whole numbers. There are **no units**.
In order to simplify the ratio both quantities in the ratio must be in the **same units**.

2 cm : 50 mm = 20 mm : 50 mm = 20 : 50
Divide both parts of the ratio by 10.
$20 \div 10 : 50 \div 10 = 2 : 5$
The ratio 2 cm : 50 mm in its simplest form is 2 : 5.

Do not use a calculator in this exercise.

1 Give three ratios equivalent to the ratio:
(a) 6 : 1 (b) 7 : 2 (c) 3 : 5

2 Give the simplest form of each of these ratios.
(a) 3 : 6   (b) 9 : 27
(c) 9 : 12   (d) 10 : 25
(e) 30 : 40   (f) 22 : 55
(g) 9 : 21   (h) 18 : 8
(i) 36 : 81   (j) 35 : 15

3 Each of these pairs of ratios are equivalent.
(a) 3 : 4 and 9 : n.
(b) 2 : 7 and 8 : n.
(c) 8 : n and 2 : 25.
(d) 25 : n and 5 : 4.
In each case calculate the value of n.

4 The heights of two friends are in the ratio 7 : 9.
The shorter of the friends is 154 cm tall.
What is the height of the taller of the friends?

5 Sugar and flour are mixed in the ratio 2 : 3.
How much sugar is used with 600 g of flour?

6 The ratio of boys to girls in a school is 4 : 5.
There are 80 girls.
How many boys are there?

7

I earn £800 per month.

I earn £720 per month.

The amounts Jenny and James earn is in the ratio of their ages.
Jenny is 20 years old.
How old is James?

8 A necklace contains 30 black beads and 45 gold beads.
What is the simplest form of the ratio of black beads to gold beads on the necklace?

9 Sam spends 45p a week on comics.
Tom spends £2 a week on comics.
Write the ratio of the amounts Tom and Sam spend on comics in its simplest form.

10 Denise draws a plan of the classroom.
On her plan Denise uses 2 cm to represent 5 m.
Write the scale as a ratio in its simplest form.

11 On a map a pond is 3.5 cm long.
The pond is actually 52.5 m long.
Write the scale as a ratio in its simplest form.

12 Write each of these ratios in its simplest form.
(a) £2 : 50p   (b) 20p : £2.50
(c) £2.20 : 40p   (d) 6 m : 240 cm
(e) 2 kg : 500 g   (f) 1 kg : 425 g
(g) 90 cm : 2 m   (h) 1500 mm : 2 m
(i) 3 litres : 600 ml (j) 3 cm² : 75 mm²
(k) 20 seconds : 5 minutes
(l) $\frac{1}{2}$ minute : 15 seconds

13 A hairdresser uses shampoo and conditioner in the ratio 5 : 2

At the start of the day the hairdresser opens a 500 ml bottle of conditioner. During the day she uses 1 litre of shampoo.
(a) How much conditioner is left in the bottle at the end of the day?
(b) Write the ratio of the amount of conditioner **used** to the amount of conditioner **left** in the bottle in its simplest form.

Sharing in a given ratio

EXAMPLES

1 A necklace is made using red beads and gold beads in the ratio 7 : 5.
A total of 36 beads are used in the necklace.

Calculate the number of red beads and gold beads used to make the necklace.

For every 7 red beads used to make the necklace 5 gold beads are used.
So the necklace is made using sets of 7 red beads and 5 gold beads.
$7 + 5 = 12$
In each set there is a total of 12 beads.
$36 ÷ 12 = 3$
To make the necklace 3 sets are needed.
$7 × 3 = 21$ and $5 × 3 = 15$.
There are 21 red beads and 15 gold beads.

Another method
7 red : 5 gold   Total beads = 12
14 red : 10 gold Total beads = 24
21 red : 15 gold Total beads = 36

2 Pip and Sue share £57.75 in the ratio 5 : 6.
How much do they each get?

Add the numbers in the ratio.
$5 + 6 = 11$.
For every £11 shared:
Pip gets £5,
Sue gets £6.
$57.75 ÷ 11 = 5.25$.
Pip gets £5 × 5.25 = £26.25,
Sue gets £6 × 5.25 = £31.50.

The number of shares is not always a whole number.

3 In 1901, the total population of England and Wales was 32 528 000. The ratio of the population of England to the population of Wales was 15 : 1.
What was the population of Wales in 1901?

Add the numbers in the ratio.
$15 + 1 = 16$
$32\ 528\ 000 ÷ 16$
$= 2\ 033\ 000$
The population of Wales is 2 033 000 (nearest 1000).

This ratio is an approximation

4 A box contains red, white and blue buttons in the ratio 1 : 2 : 5.
There are 104 buttons in the box.
How many of them are blue?

Add the numbers in the ratio.
$1 + 2 + 5 = 8$
$104 ÷ 8 = 13$ $5 × 13 = 65$
There are 65 blue counters in the box.

Exercise 10.3

1
(a) Share 35 in the ratio 2 : 3.
(b) Share 56 in the ratio 4 : 3.
(c) Share 5.5 in the ratio 7 : 4.

2
(a) Share £81.90 in the ratio 11 : 3.
(b) Share £97.50 in the ratio 5 : 8.
(c) Share £111 in the ratio 7 : 5.
(d) Share £54.45 in the ratio 7 : 4.

3 A necklace contains 80 beads.
The ratio of red beads to blue beads is 5 : 3.
How many red beads are on the necklace?

4 On a necklace for every 10 black beads there are 4 red beads.
(a) What is the ratio of black beads to red beads in its simplest form?
(b) If the necklace has 15 black beads how many red beads are there?
(c) If the necklace has a total of 77 beads how many black beads are there?
(d) Why can't the necklace have a total of 32 beads?

5 What is the difference between the larger and smaller shares when £39 200 is shared in the ratio 7 : 9?

6 Jenny and Tim each have 40 counters. Tim gives Jenny some counters so that the ratio of the number of counters they each have is 9 : 7. How many counters does Tim give Jenny?

7 In the UK there are 240 939 km² of land. The ratio of agricultural land to non-agricultural land is approximately 7 : 3. Estimate the area of land used for agriculture?

8 To make concrete a builder mixes gravel, sand and cement in the ratio 4 : 2 : 1. The builder wants 350 kg of concrete. How much gravel does the builder need?

9 The angles of a triangle are in the ratio 2 : 3 : 4. Calculate each angle.

10 The sides of a triangle are in the ratio 4 : 6 : 9. The perimeter of the triangle is 38 cm. Calculate the length of each side of the triangle.

Ratio and proportion

Some situations involve comparing **different** quantities.
For example, when a motorist buys fuel the more he buys the greater the cost.
In this situation the quantities can change but the ratio between the quantities stays the same.
When two different quantities are in the **same ratio** they are said to be in **proportion**.

EXAMPLES

1 4 cakes cost £1.20.
Find the cost of 7 cakes.

4 cakes cost £1.20
1 cake costs £1.20 ÷ 4 = 30p
7 cakes cost 30p × 7 = £2.10
So 7 cakes cost £2.10.

This is sometimes called the **unitary method**.
(a) **Divide** by 4 to find the cost of **1** cake.
(b) **Multiply** by 7 to find the cost of 7 cakes.

2 A holiday in France costs £660 for 3 weeks.
How much will the holiday cost for 4 weeks?

3 weeks costs £660
1 week costs £660 ÷ 3 = £220
4 weeks cost £220 × 4 = £880
The holiday will cost £880 for 4 weeks.

This assumes that cost is **proportional** to time.
So the different ratios of **cost : time** are equivalent.
660 : 3 = 220 : 1 = 880 : 4

3 A breakfast cereal can be bought in these ways:

400 g packet	£1.52
500 g packet	£1.80
Two 300 g packets	£2.20

What is the 'best buy'?

400 : 152 is equivalent to 1 : 0.38
500 : 180 is equivalent to 1 : 0.36
600 : 222 is equivalent to 1 : 0.37

These ratios each give the cost of 1 g of cereal.
In the 500 g packet, 1 g costs the least.
So the 500 g packet is the 'best buy'.

This example is about comparing three **different** ratios, amount : cost.
Each ratio has to be changed to an equivalent ratio where one of the numbers is the **same**.

1 9 metres of stair carpet cost £41.85. How much does 96 metres cost?

2 192 francs is about the same as £20. Sue spends 310 francs. How many pounds is this?

3 Mary phones her uncle in New York.

Phone calls to New York are charged at the rate of £1.10 for a 5 minute call.
(a) How much would a 7 minute call to New York cost?
(b) Mary's call cost £2.64. How long was her call?

4 This recipe makes Macaroni cheese for 4 people.

Macaroni	120 g
Cheese	72 g
Flour	30 g
Milk	850 ml

(a) How much cheese is needed to make macaroni cheese for 10 people?
(b) How much milk is needed to make macaroni cheese for 3 people?
(c) How much macaroni is needed to make macaroni cheese for 7 people?

5 A car travels 6 miles in 9 minutes? If the car travels at the same speed:
(a) how long will it take to travel 8 miles,
(b) how far will it travel in 24 minutes?

6 5 litres of paint covers an area of 30m².
(a) What area will 2 litres of paint cover?
(b) How much paint is needed to cover 72m²?

7 A school is organising three trips to the zoo.

Our trip is on Monday. There are 45 people going. The total cost is £234.

Our trip is on Tuesday. 25 students are going.

Our trip is on Wednesday. The total cost is £166.40.

(a) How much does Tuesday's trip cost?
(b) How many students are going to the zoo on Wednesday?

8 A 42 litre paddling pool is filled at the rate of 12 litres of water every 5 minutes. How long will it take to fill the pool?

9

Foodstuffs Instant Coffee 400 g £7.35

Foodstuffs Instant Coffee 125 g £2.45

Foodstuff's supermarket sell their own brand of instant coffee in two sizes of jar. Which jar is the better value?

10 *Two-cup* tea bags are sold in two sizes of box.
A large box of 320 tea bags costs £2.90.
A standard box of 250 tea bags costs £1.90.
Which box gives the best value?

11 50 g of flour and 90 ml of milk make 8 biscuits.
(a) How much flour is needed to make 27 biscuits?
(b) How many biscuits can be made with 225 g of flour?
Some biscuits are made with 300 g of flour.
(c) How much milk is needed?

Ratio, fractions and percentages

The following examples illustrate the connection between ratio, fractions and percentages.

EXAMPLES

1 In a school the ratio of the number of boys to the number of girls is 3 : 5. What fraction of the pupils in the school are girls?

$3 + 5 = 8$.
For every 8 pupils there are 5 girls.
So 5 out of every 8 pupils are girls.
$\frac{5}{8}$ of the pupils in the school are girls.

2 An alloy is made of tin and zinc. 40% of the alloy is tin. What is the ratio of tin : zinc in its simplest form?

If 40% is tin then 60% is zinc.
So the ratio of tin to zinc is 40 : 60.
The highest common factor of 40 and 60 is 20.
$40 \div 20 : 60 \div 20 = 2 : 3$
The ratio of tin : zinc in its simplest form is 2 : 3.

3 John is 12 years old and Sara is 13 years old. They share some money in the ratio of their ages. What percentage of the money does John get?

Method 1
Find the fraction of the total amount of money that John gets.
Then change this fraction to a percentage.

For every £25 shared, John gets £12.
So John gets $\frac{12}{25}$ of the money.
$\frac{12}{25} = 12 \div 25 = 0.48$ $0.48 \times 100 = 48$
So John gets 48% of the money.

Method 2
Share 100 in the ratio 12 : 13.

$12 + 13 = 25$
$100 \div 25 = 4$
$12 \times 4 = 48$ $13 \times 4 = 52$
So an equivalent ratio is 48 : 52.
For every £100 shared, John gets £48.
So John gets 48% of the money.

Exercise 10.5

1 (a) A box contains red beads and black beads in the ratio 1 : 3.
    (i) Find the fraction of red beads in the box.
    (ii) Find the fraction of black beads in the box.
    (iii) Find the percentage of red beads in the box.

  (b) Repeat part (a) for different boxes containing red beads and black beads in the following ratios.
    (i) 1 : 4
    (ii) 3 : 7
    (iii) 7 : 13
    (iv) 17 : 23

2 45% of the pupils in a school are boys. What is the ratio of the number of boys to the number of girls in the school in its simplest form?

3 32% of the beads on a necklace are red.
The remaining beads are white.
What is the ratio of the number of red beads on the necklace to the number of white beads on the necklace in its simplest form?

4 The ratio of non-fiction books to fiction books in a library is 9 : 5. Find the percentage of fiction books in the library to an accuracy of 3 significant figures.

5 A bag contains some red, green and black sweets.
30% of the sweets are red.
The ratio of the numbers of green sweets to black sweets is 5 to 9.
What percentage of the total number of sweets are black?

6 Alan, Beth and Catrina share some money in the ratio 1 : 3 : 4.
(a) What percentage of the money do they each receive?
(b) What fraction of Beth's share is Alan's share?
(c) What fraction of Alan and Catrina's share is Beth's share?

Scales on maps and drawings

Scales on maps and drawings are normally expressed as a ratio written in the form 1 : n.
This means that 1 unit on the map stands for n units on the 'ground'.

EXAMPLE

The scale of a map is 1 : 10 000.
On the map the distance between two villages is 8.5 cm.
(a) What is the actual distance between the two villages?

A field is 75 m long.
(b) How long is this on the map?

(a) 1 cm on the map is 10 000 cm on the 'ground'.
$8.5 \times 10\ 000 = 85\ 000$
8.5 cm on the map is 85 000 cm on the 'ground'.
$85\ 000 \text{ cm} = 85\ 000 \div 100\ 000 = 0.85 \text{ km}$.
The actual distance between the two villages is 0.85 km.

(b) $75 \text{ m} = 75 \times 100 = 7500 \text{ cm}$.
$7500 \div 10\ 000 = 0.75$.
So the field is 0.75 cm long on the map.

Exercise 10.6

Do this exercise without a calculator.

1 The scale of a map is 1 : 200.
(a) On a map a house is 3.5 cm long. How long is the actual house?
(b) A field is 60 m wide. How wide is the field on the map?

2 On a map a pond is 0.5 cm long. The actual pond is 20 m long.
(a) What is the scale of the map?
(b) On the map a church is 1.2 cm long. How long is the actual church?
(c) A playground is 36 m wide. How wide is the playground on the map?

3 Roy draws a plan of a boat using a scale of 125 : 2.
On Roy's plan the width of the boat is 20 cm.
What is the actual width of the boat?

4 Claire draws a diagram for a printed circuit board in the ratio 20 : 1.
On Claire's diagram the distance between two components is 35 mm.
What is the actual distance between the components?

5 Helen drew a plan of her classroom using a scale of 5 cm to represent 1 m.
    (a)   Write the scale Helen used in the form $1 : n$.
    (b)   On the plan, the length of the classroom is 29 cm.
         What is the actual length of the classroom?
    (c)   The actual width of the classroom is 4.5 m.
         What is the width of the classroom on the plan?

6 Javed drew a plan of the children's playground in the local park using a scale of 1 : 400.
    (a)   The actual distance between the swings and the slide is 20 m.
         What is the distance between the swings and the slide on the plan?
    (b)   On the plan, the roundabout is 25 cm from the gate.
         What is the actual distance from the roundabout to the gate?

What you need to know

- The ratio 3 : 2 is read '3 to 2'.

- A ratio is used only to compare quantities.
  A ratio does not give information about the exact values of quantities being compared.

- In its **simplest form**, a ratio contains whole numbers which have no common factor other than 1.
  All quantities in a ratio must have the **same units** before the ratio can be simplified.
  For example, £2.50 : 50p = 250p : 50p = 5 : 1.

- When two different quantities are always in the **same ratio** the two quantities are in **proportion.**
  For example, the amount and cost of fuel bought by a motorist.

You should be able to:
- Write equivalent ratios and use them to solve problems.
- Write a ratio in its simplest form.
- Share a quantity in a given ratio.
- Solve problems when the quantities involved are in proportion.
- Solve problems involving the connection between ratio, fractions and percentages.

Do the squares fit?
Square P has side 3 cm and square Q has side 4 cm.
Square Q is cut into four **equal** pieces, as shown, where the ratio $a : b$ on each side is 7 : 1.

Show how square P and the four pieces of Q fit together exactly to make another square.

Repeat when square P has side 2 cm and square Q has side 6 cm.

Investigate.

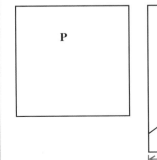

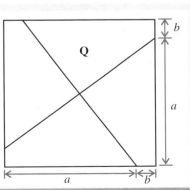

Questions 1 to 9. Do not use a calculator.

1 These ratios are in their simplest form:
(a) 3 : 4   (b) 7 : 20
(c) 2 : 9   (d) 6 : 5
Write three equivalent ratios for each of them.

2 In a class of 30 students the ratio of students with dark hair to those with light hair is 3 : 2.
How many dark haired students are there in the class?

3 The ratio of Billy's height to Samantha's height is 5 : 4.
Billy is 155 cm tall.
How tall is Samantha?

4 During a money raising appeal for charity 367 290 metal cans were collected for recycling.
The ratio of steel cans collected to aluminium cans collected was 8 : 1.
How many steel cans were collected?

5 Jane paints her room orange.
To make orange paint she mixes red and yellow paint in the ratio 5 : 3.
She needs 2.4 litres of orange paint.
How much red and yellow paint should she use?

6 A test is taken by 28 pupils.
The ratio of the number of boys to the number of girls is 3 : 4.
How many boys take the test?

SEG 1997

7 (a) A bag contains 3 black counters and 2 white counters.

Another bag contains 30 counters.
There is the same **ratio** of black counters to white counters.
How many black counters are in the bag?

(b) Another bag contains black counters and white counters in the ratio 7 to 13.
What percentage of the counters are black?

SEG 1996

8 (a) Peter and Jane share £36 in the ratio 5 : 7.
What is Peter's share?

(b) A bag contains 5p coins and 1p coins in the ratio 2 : 3.
What percentage of the coins are 5p coins?

9 A bag of carrots weighs 3 kg and costs £1.25.
An economy sack of carrots weighs 30 kg and costs £11.70.
Which purchase gives the best value?

10 Three friends start up a minicab service and agree to divide their income in the ratio of the distance that each of them drives. In one week, Anne drives 350 miles, Carl drives 280 miles and Lee drives 210 miles. Their week's income is £1360.80. How much does each person receive?

SEG 1996

11 This magnifying glass makes things look larger.
It enlarges in the ratio 1 : 4.

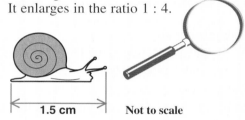

1.5 cm   **Not to scale**

(a) How long will the snail look under the magnifying glass?
The moth looks 2.4 cm wide under the magnifying glass.

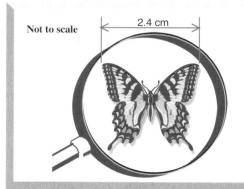

Not to scale   2.4 cm

(b) What is the actual width of the moth?

SEG 1994

12 This recipe is for 20 scones.

| 500 g flour | 100 g dried fruit |
| 250 g butter | water to mix |

(a) How much dried fruit would you need for 5 scones?
(b) How much flour would you need for 30 scones?

SEG 1994

13 Two students are talking about their school outing.

My class went to Tower Bridge last week. There are 30 people in my class. The total cost was £52.50

There are 45 people in my group. What will be the total cost for my group?

S94/2410/34

14 Two pints of milk cost 58p. What is the cost of 5 pints of milk at the same price per pint?

SEG 1994

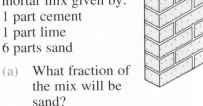
58p
MILK
2 Pints

15 Annabel and Henry are planning a party for 20 children. They have a shopping list of items for a party of 6 children. For the 6 children this includes
12 balloons
24 sausage rolls
9 jellies
4 packets of biscuits
Rewrite this shopping list for a party of 20 children.

SEG 1994

16 Jack is building a brick wall for a garage. He decides to use a mortar mix given by:
1 part cement
1 part lime
6 parts sand

(a) What fraction of the mix will be sand?
(b) What percentage of the mix will be cement?
(c) He uses 1200 cm³ of sand for the mix. What volume of lime will he need?

SEG 1994

17 On a map the distance between two houses is 19 mm. The actual distance between the houses is 3.8 km. What is the scale of the map?

18 The plan of a house has been drawn using a scale 1 : 20.
(a) On the plan, the length of the lounge is 25cm. What is the actual length of the lounge in metres?
(b) The actual kitchen is 2.6 m wide. Estimate, in feet, the width of the actual kitchen.

SEG 1995

19 A school badge is made in two sizes.

Not to scale

The width of the small size is 3 cm. The large size is an enlargement of the small size in the ratio 2 : 3. Calculate the width of the large size badge.

SEG 1994

Time and Money

The time of day is given in terms of hours, minutes and sometimes seconds. There are 24 hours in each day, 60 minutes in each hour and 60 seconds in each minute.

24-hour clock and 12-hour clock times

The time can be given using the 12-hour clock or the 24-hour clock.

The watch and the digital clock both show the same time.
The time on the watch is 5.45 pm using 12-hour clock time.
The digital clock shows 5.45 pm as 1745 using 24-hour clock time.

12-hour clock times	**24-hour clock times**
Times before midday are given as am. Times after midday are given as pm.	The first two figures give the hours. The last two figures give the minutes.

Explain how to change between 12-hour clock times and 24-hour clock times.

EXAMPLE

A motorist left Liverpool at 10.50 am and arrived in Birmingham at 1.20 pm.
How long did the journey take?

Method 1 (subtraction)

```
1 3.2 0     1.  Write the times as 24-hour clock times.
1 0.5 0     2.  Subtract the minutes.
_____        20 − 50 cannot be done.
                Exchange 1 hour for 60 minutes.
_____        60 + 20 − 50 = 30 minutes.
     2  6  0
1 3̶.2 0     3.  Subtract the hours.
1 0.5 0         12 − 10 = 2.
_____
   2.3 0
```

Method 2 (adding on)

10.50 to 11.00 =	10 minutes
11.00 to 13.00 = 2 hours	
13.00 to 13.20 =	20 minutes
Total time = 2 hours 30 minutes	

The journey took 2 hours 30 minutes.

Exercise 11.1

1 Write these 12-hour clock times in 24-hour clock time.
   (a) 10.30 am   (b) 10.30 pm   (c) 1.45 am   (d) 1.45 pm   (e) 7.50 am

2 Write these 24-hour clock times in 12-hour clock time.
   (a) 1415   (b) 0525   (c) 2320   (d) 1005   (e) 0940

3 A coach left Poole at 1340 and arrived in Swansea at 1428.
   (a) What was the arrival time in 12-hour clock time?
   (b) How many minutes did the journey take?

4 A train left Paddington at 1315 and arrived in Exeter at 1605.
   (a) At what time did the train leave in 12-hour clock time?
   (b) How long did the journey take?

5 A coach leaves Bournemouth at 10.50 am to travel to London.
   The journey takes 2 hours 40 minutes.
   At what time does the coach reach London?
   Give your answer in   (a) 24-hour clock time,   (b) 12-hour clock time.

6 A motorist leaves York at 2.35 pm to travel to Scarborough.
   The journey takes 50 minutes.
   At what time does the motorist reach Scarborough?
   Give your answer in   (a) 24-hour clock time,   (b) 12-hour clock time.

Timetables

Bus and rail timetables are usually given in 24-hour clock time.
Here is part of a rail timetable.

Kidderminster	1035	1115	1155	1240	1325	1410	1455	1540
Bewdley	1050	1130	—	1300	—	1430	—	1600
Arley	1105	1148	—	1318	1403	1448	—	1618
Highley	1114	1158	—	1328	—	1458	—	1628
Hampton Loade	1125	1210	—	1340	1425	1510	—	1640
Bridgnorth	1140	1225	1310	1355	1440	1525	1610	1655

Some trains do not stop at every station. This is shown by a dash on the timetable.

How many minutes does the journey take on the 1403 train from Arley to Bridgnorth?

Alex lives in Bewdley.
What is the latest train he can catch to keep an appointment in Bridgnorth at 1.15 pm?

A train takes 1 hour 10 minutes to complete the journey from Kidderminster to Bridgnorth.
At what time does the train arrive at Bridgnorth?

Exercise 11.2

1 The times of some trains from Hastings to Charing Cross are shown.

Hastings	0702	0802	0857	0900	0957	1102	1257
Crowhurst	—	—	0908	—	1008	—	1308
Battle	0715	0815	0912	—	1012	—	1312
Tunbridge Wells	0745	0845	0943	0940	1043	1141	1342
Sevenoaks	0805	0905	1003	—	1103	1201	1403
Charing Cross	0834	0934	1032	1025	1132	1230	1432

   (a) John catches the 0745 from Tunbridge Wells to Charing Cross.
       How many minutes does the journey take?

   (b) Aimee catches the 0857 from Hastings to Charing Cross.
       How long does the journey take?

   (c) Sarah catches the 1257 from Hastings to Tunbridge Wells.
       What is her arrival time using the 12-hour clock?

   (d) Keith wants to be in Charing Cross by 1030.
       What is the latest train he can catch from Battle?

2 Some of the rail services from Manchester to Birmingham are shown.

Manchester	0925	1115	1215	1415	1555
Stockport	0933	—	1223	—	1603
Stoke	1007	1155	1255	1459	1636
Stafford	1027	—	1318	—	1656
Wolverhampton	1056	1234	1336	1535	1716
Birmingham	1121	1257	1359	1558	1742

(a) David has to be in Wolverhampton by 2 pm.
What is the time of the latest train he can catch from Manchester?

(b) Pam catches the 0933 from Stockport to Birmingham.
How long does the journey take?

(c) What time does the 1555 from Manchester arrive in Birmingham in 12-hour clock time?

3 Some of the rail services from Poole to Waterloo are shown.

Poole	0544	0602	—	0640	—	0740	0825	0846
Bournemouth	0558	0616	—	0654	0715	0754	0839	0900
Brockenhurst	0619	0639	—	0722	0738	0823	0841	0921
Southampton	0634	0655	0714	0738	0754	0838	0908	0938
So'ton Parkway	0642	0703	0722	0746	0802	0848	0916	0947
Eastleigh	0646	—	—	0750	—	0852	—	0951
Winchester	0656	0715	0733	0759	0812	0901	0929	1001
Basingstoke	0716	—	0753	0816	—	0918	—	1020
Woking	0738	—	0815	0845	—	0938	—	1044
Waterloo	0804	0810	0844	0901	0908	1005	1018	1112

(a) Sid arrives at Bournemouth station at 0830.
What is the time of the next train to Eastleigh?

(b) Paul catches the 0654 from Bournemouth to Southampton.
How many minutes does the journey take?

(c) Emma catches the 0544 from Poole to Waterloo.
How long does the journey take?

4 Some of the coach services from Woking to Heathrow airport are shown.

Woking	0610	0650	0720	0750	0820	Then	1830	1900	2000
Terminal 1	0650	0730	0800	0830	0900	every	1900	1930	2030
Terminal 2	0655	0735	0805	0835	0905	30	1905	1935	2035
Terminal 3	0700	0740	0810	0840	0910	mins	1910	1940	2040
Terminal 4	0710	0750	0820	0850	0920	until	1920	1950	2050

(a) How long does the coach take to complete the journey from Woking to Terminal 1 in the morning?

(b) Helen arrives at Woking at 3pm.
She catches the next coach to Heathrow.
(i) At what time does it leave Woking?
(ii) At what time does it arrive at Terminal 3?

(c) Leroy needs to be at Terminal 2 at 6pm.
What is the latest time he can catch a coach from Woking?

5 The table shows the train services from Oxford to Birmingham.

Oxford	1109	1204	1313	1413	1503	1628	1736
Banbury	1142	1239	1337	—	1521	1652	1800
Leamington	1201	1300	1359	1454	1542	1713	1822
Coventry	1218	1317	1416	1512	1559	1730	1839
Birmingham	1247	1345	1445	1540	1635	1758	1911

(a) Carol catches the 1142 from Banbury to Coventry.
How long does the journey take?

(b) Arnold needs to be in Birmingham before ten to five in the afternoon.
What is the latest train he can catch from Oxford?

(c) Debbie arrives at Leamington station at 4.30 pm.
What time is the next train to Birmingham?

Wages

Hourly pay

Many people are paid by the hour for their work. In most cases they receive a **basic hourly rate** for a fixed number of hours and an **overtime rate** for any extra hours worked.

EXAMPLE

A car-park attendant is paid £3.20 per hour for a basic 40 hour week.
Overtime is paid at time and a half.
One week an attendant works 48 hours.
How much does he earn?

Basic Pay: £3.20 × 40 = £128.00
Overtime: 1.5 × £3.20 × 8 =   £38.40
              Total pay = £166.40

Overtime paid at 'time and a half' means 1.5 × normal hourly rate.
In this example, the hourly overtime rate is given by:
1.5 × £3.20

Common overtime rates are 'time and a quarter', 'double time', etc.

Commission

As an incentive for their employees to work harder some companies pay a basic wage (fixed amount) plus commission. The amount of commission is usually expressed as a percentage of the value of the sales made by the employee.

EXAMPLE

An estate agent is paid a salary of £11 000 per year plus commission of 0.5% on the sales of all houses.
In 1998 the estate agent sold houses to the value of £2 040 500.
How much did the estate agent earn?

Annual salary: £11 000
Commission: 0.005 × £2 040 500 = £10 202.50
              Total pay = £21 202.50

Remember:
$0.5\% = \frac{0.5}{100} = 0.005$

1 A chef is paid £5.60 per hour for a basic 38 hour week.
Overtime is paid at time and a half.
How much does the chef earn in a week in which she works 50 hours?

2 A mechanic is paid £6.40 per hour for a basic 40 hour week.
Overtime is paid at time and a quarter.
One week the mechanic works 42 hours. How much does he earn?

3 A hairdresser is paid £4.80 per hour for a basic 35 hour week.
One week she works two hours overtime at time and a half and $3\frac{1}{2}$ hours overtime at time and a quarter.
How much is she paid that week?

4 A furniture salesperson is paid an annual salary of £9600 plus commission of 2% on sales.
In 1998 the salesperson sold £300 000 worth of furniture.
How much did the salesperson earn?

5 A car salesperson is paid an annual salary of £10 200 plus commission of 1.5% on sales.
How much does the salesperson earn in a year in which cars to the value of £868 000 are sold?

6 A double glazing salesperson is paid £480 per month plus commission of 5% on sales.
How much does he earn in a month in which he makes sales of £12 600?

Income tax

The amount you earn for your work is called your **gross pay**.
Your employer will make deductions from your gross pay for income tax, National Insurance, etc. Pay after all deductions have been made is called **net pay**.

The amount of **income tax** you pay will depend on how much you earn. Everyone is allowed to earn some money which is not taxed, this is called a **tax allowance**. Any remaining money is your **taxable income**.

> The rates of tax and the bands (ranges of income) to which they apply vary.

EXAMPLE

George earns £6800 per year. His tax allowance is £4195 per year and he pays tax at 20p in the £ on his taxable income.
How much income tax does George pay per year?

Taxable income: £6800 − £4195 = £2605
Income tax: £2605 × 0.20 = £521

George pays income tax of £521 per year.

> An income tax rate of 20% is often expressed as '20p in the pound (£)'.

11

Exercise **11.4**

1 Lyn earns £8600 per year. Her tax allowance is £4195 per year and she pays tax at 20p in the £ on her taxable income.
How much income tax does she pay per year?

2 Sam earns £10 140 per year. His tax allowance is £6095 per year and he pays tax at 20p in the £ on his taxable income.
How much income tax does he pay per year?

3 Julie earns £685 per month. Her tax allowance is £4195 per year and she pays tax at 20p in the £ on her taxable income.
How much income tax does she pay per month?

4 Jim is paid £156 per week for 52 weeks a year. His tax allowance is £4195 per year and he pays tax at 20p in the £ on his taxable income.
How much income tax does he pay per week?

5 Kay has an annual salary of £23 700. Her tax allowance is £4195 per year. She pays tax at 20p in the £ on the first £4300 of her taxable income and tax at 23p in the £ on the remainder.
How much income tax does she pay per year?

6 Les has an annual salary of £18 600. His tax allowance is £6095 per year. He pays tax at 20p in the £ on the first £4300 of his taxable income and tax at 23p in the £ on the remainder.
He is paid monthly. How much income tax does he pay per month?

7 Alex has an annual salary of £28 240. Her tax allowance is £6095 per year. She pays tax at 20p in the £ on the first £4300 of her taxable income and tax at 23p in the £ on the remainder.
She is paid monthly. How much income tax does she pay per month?

8 Alf's income is £19 850 per year.
He pays 9% of his gross income into a company pension scheme on which he does not pay tax.
Alf also has a tax allowance of £6420 per year.
He pays tax at 20p in the £ on the first £4300 of his taxable income and tax at 23p in the £ on the remainder.
Calculate how much income tax he pays per year.

Household bills

The cost of living includes many bills for services provided to our homes. Electricity, gas and telephone charges are all examples of **quarterly bills** which are sent out four times a year. Each bill is made up of two parts:
A fixed (standing) charge, for providing the service.
A charge for the quantity of the service used (amount of gas/electricity, duration of telephone calls, etc.)

Other household bills include taxes payable to the local council, water charges and the cost of the insurance of the house (structure) and its contents.

1 Last year the Evans family received four quarterly gas bills.

March	£134.26
June	£52.00
September	£33.49
December	£80.25

(a) What was their total bill for the year?

(b) The family can pay for their gas by 12 equal monthly instalments.
How much would each instalment be?

2 Mrs Cotton uses 1064 units of electricity during one quarter.
Find the cost of her electricity bill if each unit costs 6.16 pence and the quarterly charge is £9.30.

3 Mr Jones receives an electricity bill for £59.20
The bill includes a quarterly charge of £9.30 and the cost per unit is 6.16 pence.
Calculate to the nearest whole number, the number of units he has used.

4 Mrs Madan receives a gas bill for £179.53. The bill includes a standing charge and the cost of the gas used. During the quarter the gas used is equivalent to 13 377 kWh at 1.295 pence per kWh.
How much is the standing charge?
Give your answer to an appropriate degree of accuracy.

5 Mr Peters has an annual community charge of £1123.05.
He pays the community charge in 10 instalments.
The first instalment is £115.05 and the remaining amount is payable in 9 instalments of equal value.
How much is the second instalment?

6 Mrs Dear checks her water bill.
She has used 46 cubic metres of water at 77.76 pence per cubic metre and there is a standing charge of £11.
How much is her bill?

7 The table on the right shows the premiums charged by an insurance company to insure a house and its contents.

(a) Mrs Adams has a flat valued at £38 000.
What premium would she pay to insure the flat?

(b) Jim has bought a house valued at £54 000.
How much would he pay to insure the house?

(c) The cost for Mr Brown to insure his house is £124.
What is the value of his house?

Buildings and Contents Insurance		
	Buildings	Contents
Annual premium for each £1000 insured.	£1.50	£5.00
	Minimum £20 per year	

(d) Mrs Crow insures the contents of her house for £18 500.
What is the annual premium?

(e) Mr Rowe insures his house valued at £74 000 and its contents valued at £22 300.
What is the total cost of the insurance premium?

(f) Andy insures his flat valued at £12 000 and its contents valued at £9500.
Calculate the total cost of the insurance premium.

VAT

Some goods and services are subject to a tax called **value added tax**, or **VAT**, which is calculated as a percentage of the price or bill.

Total amount payable = cost of item or service + VAT

For most purchases the rate of VAT is 17.5%.
For gas and electricity the rate of VAT is 5%.
Some goods are exempt from VAT.

EXAMPLE

A bill at a restaurant is £24 + VAT at 17.5%.
What is the total bill?

VAT: £24 × 0.175 = £4.20

Total bill: £24 + £4.20 = £28.20

The total bill is £28.20

Remember:
$17.5\% = \frac{17.5}{100} = 0.175$

Exercise 11.6

1. A washing machine costs £340 plus VAT at 17.5%.
   (a) Calculate the amount of VAT charged.
   (b) What is the total cost of the washing machine?

2. A car service costs £90 plus VAT at 17.5%.
   (a) Calculate the amount of VAT charged.
   (b) What is the total cost of the service?

3. Jim buys a ladder for £145 plus VAT at 17.5%.
   What is the total cost of the ladder?

4. A mountain bike costs £248 plus VAT at 17.5%.
   What is the total cost of the bike?

5. Mrs Swan receives a gas bill for £179.53.
   VAT at 5% is added to the bill.
   (a) How much VAT does she have to pay?
   (b) What is the total bill?

6. Joyce buys a greenhouse for £184 plus VAT. VAT is charged at 17.5%.
   What is the total cost of the greenhouse?

7. James receives a telephone bill for £37.56 plus VAT at 17.5%.
   How much is the total bill?

8. George buys vertical blinds for his windows.
   He needs three blinds at £65 each and two blinds at £85 each.
   VAT at 17.5% is added to the cost of the blinds.
   How much do the blinds cost altogether?

9. Sarah hired a car when she was on holiday.

CAR HIRE CHARGES
£25 per day
plus 10p for every mile driven.

   She hired the car for two days and drove 90 miles.
   VAT at 17.5% was added to the car charges.
   How much did it cost to hire the car altogether?

When shopping we often have to make choices between products which are packed in various sizes and priced differently. If we want to buy the one which gives the better value for money we must compare prices using the same units.

EXAMPLE

Peanut butter is available in small or large jars, as shown.
Which size is the better value for money?

Compare the number of grams per penny for each size.
Small: $250 \div 58 = 4.31\ldots$ grams per penny.
Large: $454 \div 106 = 4.28\ldots$ grams per penny.

The small size gives more grams per penny and is better value.

Exercise 11.7

1 Milk is sold in 1 pint, 2 pint and 4 pint containers.
The cost of a 1 pint container is 28p, the cost of a two pint container is 55p and the cost of a 4 pint container is 89p.
  (a) How much per pint is saved by buying a 2 pint container instead of two 1 pint containers?
  (b) How much per pint is saved by buying a 4 pint container instead of two 2 pint containers?

2 Jars of pickled onions are sold at the following prices: 460 g at 65p or 700 g at 98p. Which size is better value for money?

3 Honey is sold in two sizes.
A large pot of honey costs £1.28 and weighs 454 g.
A small pot of honey costs 56p and weighs 185 g.
Which pot of honey is better value for money?

4 Toothpaste is sold in small, medium and large sizes.
The small size contains 72 ml and costs 58p.
The medium size contains 125 ml and costs 98p.
The large size contains 180 ml and costs £1.44.
Which size is the best value for money? You must show all your working.

5 Cottage cheese costs 85p for 120 g, £1.55 for 250 g and £6 for 1 kg.
Which size is the best value for money? You must show all your working.

6 Hazel wants to buy a microwave oven. She looks at three different advertisements.

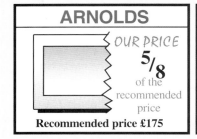

In each case find the total cost of the microwave oven.

SEG 1994

7   Sport is sold in two different sized bottles.

Which of these bottles of Sport drink is the better value for money?
You must show all your working.

Savings

Money invested in a savings account or a bank or building society earns **interest**, which is usually paid once a year.

With **Simple Interest**, the interest is paid out each year and not added to your account.
The amount of Simple Interest an investment earns can be calculated using:

Simple Interest = $\dfrac{\text{Amount}}{\text{invested}} \times \dfrac{\text{Time in}}{\text{years}} \times \dfrac{\text{Rate of interest}}{\text{per year}}$

With **Compound Interest**, the interest earned each year is added to your account and also earns interest the following year.

Banks and building societies advertise the **yearly rates** of interest payable.
For example, 6% per year.

Interest, usually calculated annually, can also be calculated for shorter periods of time.

EXAMPLES

1   Find the Simple Interest paid on £600 invested for 6 months at 8% per year.

Simple Interest = $600 \times \frac{6}{12} \times \frac{8}{100}$
$= 600 \times 0.5 \times 0.08$
$= £24$

The Simple Interest paid is £24.

Note:
Interest rates are given 'per year'.
The length of time for which an investment is made is also given in years.

6 months = $\frac{6}{12}$ years.

Explain why.

2   Find the Compound Interest paid on £600 invested for 3 years at 6% per year.

1st year	Investment	= £600
	Interest: £600 × 0.06	= £ 36
	Value of investment after one year	= £636
2nd year	Investment	= £636
	Interest: £636 × 0.06	= £ 38.16
	Value of investment after two years	= £674.16
3rd year	Investment	= £674.16
	Interest: £674.16 × 0.06	= £ 40.45
	Value of investment after three years	= £714.61

Remember:
$6\% = \frac{6}{100} = 0.06$

Compound Interest = Final value − Original value
$= £714.61 - £600$
$= £114.61$

Exercise 11.8

1 Find the simple interest on:
   (a) £1000 invested for 1 year at 7% per year,
   (b) £800 invested for 9 months at 8% per year,
   (c) £6000 invested for 6 months at 7.5% per year,
   (d) £10 000 invested for 3 months at 9% per year.

2 Find the simple interest paid on an investment of £8000 at 7.4% per year after
   (a) 6 months,   (b)   1 year.

3 Find the compound interest on:
   (a) £200 invested for 2 years at 6% per year,
   (b) £5000 invested for 2 years at 8% per year.

4 Find the compound interest on:
   (a) £400 invested for 3 years at 5% per year,
   (b) £3000 invested for 3 years at 7% per year.

5 Sarah invests £8000 at 6% per year. The interest is added to the investment at the end of each year. What is the value of her investment after 2 years?

6 John invests £5000 at 8% per year. The interest is added to the investment at the end of each year. What is the value of his investment after 3 years?

Foreign currency

When we go abroad we have to pay for goods and services in the currency of the country we are visiting. We therefore need to change pounds (£) into other currencies. The rate of exchange varies from day to day.

The table below shows the exchange rate in May 1998.

EXAMPLE

EXCHANGE RATE	
Each £1 will buy	
France	9.47 francs
Germany	2.84 marks
Greece	498 drachmas
Italy	2816 lira
Spain	239 pesetas
USA	1.61 dollars

What is the value, in £'s and pence, of 35 200 lira?

2816 lira = £1.
35 200 lira = 35 200 ÷ 2816
            = £12.50
35 200 lira = £12.50

Exercise 11.9

Use the table of exchange rates to answer these questions.

1 How much will I receive if I change £150 into
   (a) French francs,   (b) German marks,
   (c) Greek drachmas,   (d) Italian lira,
   (e) Spanish pesetas, (f) USA dollars?

2 How much would each of these items cost in £'s?
   (a) A vase for 90 francs.
   (b) A wallet for 1250 pesetas.
   (c) A radio for 71 marks.
   (d) A pair of jeans for 35 dollars.
   (e) A pair of shoes for 112 000 lira.
   (f) A meal for 9000 drachmas.

3 Sue changes £500 into dollars for a trip to the USA.
   (a) How many dollars will she receive?
   (b) On holiday she spends 680 dollars. She changes the remaining dollars back into £.
       There is a £3 charge for changing the money.
       How much, in £'s and pence, will she receive?

4 Jeff has just returned from France. He needs to change 1280 francs back into £.
   There is a £3 charge for changing the money.
   How much, in £'s and pence, will he receive?

- Time can be given using either the **12-hour clock** or the **24-hour clock**.
  When using the 12-hour clock:
  times **before** midday are given as am,
  times **after** midday are given as pm.

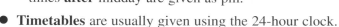

- **Timetables** are usually given using the 24-hour clock.

- **Hourly pay** is paid at a **basic rate** for a fixed number of hours.
  Overtime pay is usually paid at a higher rate such as time and a half, which means each hour's work is worth 1.5 times the basic rate.

- Everyone is allowed to earn some money which is not taxed.
  This is called a **tax allowance**.

- Tax is only paid on income earned in excess of the tax allowance.
  This is called **taxable income**.

- **Value added tax**, or **VAT**, is a tax on some goods and services and is added to the bill.

- Gas, electricity and telephone bills are paid **quarterly**. The bill consists of a standing charge plus a charge for the amount used.

- When considering a **best buy**, compare quantities by using the same units. For example, find which product gives more grams per penny.

- Money invested in a savings account at a bank or building society earns **interest**, which is usually paid once a year.
  With **Simple Interest**, the interest is paid out each year and not added to your account.

$$\text{Simple Interest} = \frac{\text{Amount}}{\text{invested}} \times \frac{\text{Time in}}{\text{years}} \times \frac{\text{Rate of interest}}{\text{per year}}$$

  With **Compound Interest**, the interest earned each year is added to your account and also earns interest the following year.

- **Exchange rates** are used to show what £1 will buy in foreign currencies.

Review Exercise

1 Some of the programmes on a Wednesday evening on Channel 4 are shown.
Balbino records the programme starting at 1830 on his video.
What programme does he record?

SEG 1992

Channel 4	
6 00	The Wonder Years
6 30	Tonight with Jonathon Ross
7 00	Channel Four News
7 50	Party Political Broadcast
8 00	Brookside
8 30	Dispatches
9 15	Short and Curlies
9 30	Free For All
10 00	The Golden Girls
10 30	Vic Reeves Big Night Out

2 Four boys were in a team for a relay race.
Jason ran the first lap of the race in 79.31 seconds.
Harry ran the fourth lap in 74.53 seconds.
The second and third laps were each run in 80.67 seconds

(a) What was the total time for the four laps of the relay race
   (i) in seconds,
   (ii) in minutes and seconds?
(b) By how many seconds was Harry faster than Jason?

SEG 1996

3 Sheila travelled from London to stay with relatives in Bournemouth.
She caught a train which left London at 1535.
The journey took 1 hour 40 minutes.
At what time did she arrive in Bournemouth?

SEG 1991

4 The times of some early evening television programmes are shown.

Neighbours is shown twice as day five days a week.
All programmes of Neighbours are the same length.
For how many hours and minutes is Neighbours shown each week?

BBC 1	
5 00	Newsround
5 10	Blue Peter
5 35	Neighbours
6 00	News

SEG 1996

5 A railway timetable is shown.

Bournemouth	0558	0616	0642	0654	0715	0754	0839	0900
Brockenhurst	0619	0639	0646	0722	0738	0823	0841	0921
Southampton	0634	0655	0714	0738	0754	0838	0908	0938
So'ton Parkway	0642	0703	0722	0746	0802	0848	0916	0947
Eastleigh	0646	0707	—	0750	—	0852	—	0951
Winchester	0656	0716	0733	0759	0812	0901	—	1001
Basingstoke	0716	0733	0753	0816	—	0918	—	1020
Woking	0738	—	0815	0845	0851	0938	—	1044
Waterloo	0804	0819	0844	0901	0917	1005	1018	1112

(a) David intends to catch a train from Eastleigh to Waterloo.
He has to be in Waterloo by 9.30am.
What is the time of the last train he can catch?

(b) Elisa misses the 0839 train from Bournemouth to Waterloo and catches the 0900 train instead.
How much longer, in hours and minutes, does the journey take?

SEG 1998 S

6 Angela is paid £3.80 per hour as her basic rate of pay.
One week she works 2 hours 45 minutes overtime at time and a half and $3\frac{1}{2}$ hours overtime at time and a quarter.
How much did Angela earn in overtime that week?

7 Francis is paid £4.80 per hour for a basic 35 hour week.
One week Francis also works overtime at time and a half.
His total pay that week was £196.80.
How many hours overtime did he work that week?

8 Victoria earns £101.40 per week. She has a tax allowance of £3445.
(a) What is her taxable income?

She pays tax at the rate of 20p in the £ on her taxable income.
(b) How much tax does Victoria pay per month?

SEG 1994

9 Leroy has an income of £1580 per month.
He has a tax allowance of £3445.
(a) What is his taxable income?

The rates of tax are:
20% of the first £2500 of taxable income.
25% of any remaining taxable income.
(b) Calculate how much tax Leroy pays per year.

SEG 1994

10 Samantha earns £508.30 per month. Her tax allowance is £3445 and she pays tax at the rate of 20p in the £ on her taxable income.
How much tax does Samantha pay per year?

SEG 1995

11 Mostafa has an income of £1720 per month.
He has a tax allowance of £3765.

(a)   What is his taxable income?

The rates of income tax are:
20% of the first £3900 of taxable income.
24% of any remaining taxable income.

(b)   Calculate how much income tax Mostafa pays per year.

SEG 1996

12 Mr England insures his house for £68 000 and its contents for £17 000.
The annual premiums for the insurance are:
Buildings: 16p for every £100 of cover;
Contents: 98p for every £100 of cover.
What is the total annual cost for Mr England to insure his house and contents?

SEG 1994

13 The gas board gives the following rule for changing units of gas to therms.

> MULTIPLY THE NUMBER OF UNITS BY 1032 AND DIVIDE BY 1000

Syd checks the cost of his quarterly gas bill.
He has used 450 units.
(a)   How many therms has Syd used?
(b)   The cost of gas is 45p per therm.
Find the cost of the therms used.
(c)   To calculate the total amount of the gas bill, an additional £9.80 standing charge is added.
Find the total amount of Syd's bill.

SEG 1993

14 (a)   Mr Gray receives an electricity bill for £42.91.
The bill includes a quarterly charge of £10.33 and the cost per unit is 7.49 pence.
He uses the following formula to calculate how many units of electricity he has used.

$$\text{Units used} = \frac{(42.91 - 10.33) \times 100}{7.49}$$

Calculate, to the nearest whole number, how many units he has used.

(b)   In the next quarter he used 578 units.
The cost of the quarterly charge is the same and the cost per unit is the same.
Calculate the quarterly bill.

SEG 1995

15 The recommended price of a calculator is £9.60.
Two shops have special offers.

At which shop is the calculator cheaper?

By how much?
You must show all your working.

SEG 1998 S

16 William saw two identical sweatshirts.

Work out which sweatshirt will cost less to buy.
You must show all
your working.

 £19.80

 £15.00

In the shop they said
"You can have it at $\frac{2}{3}$
of the marked price."

At the market they said
"You can have 20% off
the marked price."

SEG 1995

17 Jam is sold in two sizes.
A large pot of jam costs 88p and weighs 822 g.
A small pot of jam costs 47p and weighs 454 g.
Which pot of jam is better value for money?
You must show all your working.

SEG 1995

18 The size and selling price of small and medium
sauce is shown.
Which size of sauce gives better value for money?
You must show all your working.

Small size
285 g
35p

Medium size
567 g
68p

19 Hannah invests £360 in a building society account at 4.8% per year.
Find the simple interest paid on her investment after 4 months.

20 Shane invests £2000 at 7% per annum compound interest.
Calculate the value of his investment after 3 years.

21 Leroy changes £475.60 into guilders for a holiday in Holland.
The exchange rate is £1 = 2.68 guilders.
There is a £5 charge for changing the money.
How many guilders should he receive?

SEG 1995

22 In 1997 the rate of exchange was 2.84 German marks to the £.

(a) A tourist changes £25 into marks.
How many marks does she receive?

(b) She pays 42 marks for a gift to bring home.
What is the cost of the gift in pounds and pence?

Speed and Other Compound Measures

Activity

Over short distances the cheetah is the fastest mammal on land, taking about 4 seconds to travel 100 metres.
A cheetah running at this speed for 1 hour would travel 90 km.

A sprinter runs 100 metres in about 10 seconds.
(a) How many times faster than this does the cheetah run?
(b) If a sprinter could run at this speed for 1 hour what distance would he cover?

On average, Concorde travels 25 times faster than a cheetah.
(c) On average, how far does Concorde travel in 1 second?

Speed

Speed is a measure of how fast something is travelling.
Speed is a **compound measure** because it involves two other measures, **distance** and **time**.
The formula for speed is:

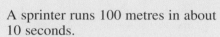

$$\text{Speed} = \frac{\text{Distance}}{\text{Time}}$$

> **Speed** can be thought of as the **distance** travelled in **one unit of time** (1 hour, 1 second, …)

Average speed

When the speed of an object is **constant** it means that the object doesn't slow down or go faster.
However, in many situations, speed is not constant.
For example:

A sprinter needs time to start from the starting blocks and is well into the race before running at top speed.
Concorde changes speed as it takes off and lands.

> **Average speed** can be thought of as the **average distance** travelled in **one unit of time** (1 hour, 1 second, …)

In situations like this it is more common to use **average speed**.
The formula for average speed is:

$$\text{Average speed} = \frac{\text{Total distance travelled}}{\text{Total time taken}}$$

113

1 A cheetah takes 4 seconds to cover 100 metres.
Assuming that this speed remains constant for 1 hour the cheetah would cover 90 kilometres.
What is the speed of the cheetah:
(a) in kilometres per hour,
(b) in metres per second?

(a) The cheetah would travel 90 km in 1 hour so its speed in km/hour is 90 km/hour.

(b) The cheetah covers 100 m in 4 seconds.

$$\text{Speed} = \frac{\text{Distance}}{\text{Time}} = \frac{100}{4} = 25$$

The cheetah's speed is 25 m/s.

2 The Scottish Pullman travels from London to York, a distance of 302.8 km in 1 hour 45 minutes.
It then travels from York to Edinburgh, a distance of 334.7 km in 2 hours 30 minutes.
Calculate the average speed of the train between London and Edinburgh.

Total distance travelled = 302.8 + 334.7
$$= 637.5 \text{ km}$$
Total time taken = 1 hr 45 mins + 2 hr 30 mins
$$= 4 \text{ hr } 15 \text{ mins} = 4.25 \text{ hours}$$

Average speed $= \frac{637.5}{4.25} = 150$

Average speed = 150 km/hour.

Exercise 12.1

Do not use a calculator in questions 1 to 6.

1 John cycles 16 miles in 2 hours.
What is his average speed in miles per hour?

2 Sue runs 24 km in 3 hours.
What is her average speed in kilometres per hour?

3 Joe swims 100 m in 4 minutes.
What is his average speed in metres per minute?

4 Laura walks 2 km in 20 minutes.
What is her average speed in kilometres per hour?

5 Arnold runs 400 m in 1 minute.
(a) What is his average speed in metres per hour?
(b) What is his average speed in kilometres per hour?

6 A car travels 115 km in 2 hours.
(a) What is its average speed in km/hour?
(b) How many hours would the car take to travel 115 km if it had gone twice as fast?

7 A car travels 140 km in 2 hours 30 minutes.
(a) What is its average speed in kilometres per hour?
The car takes 2 more hours to travel a further 130 km.
(b) What is its average speed for the whole journey?

8 Here are some Olympic records for track events:

Men's 200 m	19.73 secs
Women's 200 m	21.34 secs
Men's 400 m	43.50 secs
Women's 400 m	48.64 secs
Men's 800 m	1 min 43.00 secs
Women's 800 m	1 min 53.50 secs

What was the average speed, in metres per second, of each of the record holders in these races.

9 In a 4 × 400 metres relay the split times of the runners for each leg of the winning team were:

First leg	45.13 secs
Second leg	44.71 secs
Third leg	44.64 secs
Fourth leg	44.23 secs

Calculate, in metres per second,
(a) the average speed of each runner,
(b) the average speed of the relay team.

The formula linking speed, distance and time can be rearranged and remembered as:

(average) **speed** = (total) **distance** ÷ (total) **time**	$S = D \div T$
(total) **distance** = (average) **speed** × (total) **time**	$D = S \times T$
(total) **time** = (total) **distance** ÷ (average) **speed**	$T = D \div S$

EXAMPLES

1 A car travels at a constant speed of 10 m/sec.
How far does the car travel in 30 seconds?

In 1 second the car travels 10 m.
In 30 seconds the car travels
$$30 \times 10 = 300 \text{ m}.$$

3 John runs from A to B and then from B to C.
The distance from A to B is 30 km.
John's average speed from A to B is 15 km/hour.

(a) Calculate the time it takes John to run from A to B.

John takes 30 minutes to run from B to C.
John's average speed from B to C is 10 km/hour.

(b) Calculate the distance John runs from B to C.

(c) Calculate John's average speed over the whole of the distance that he runs from A to B to C.

(a) Time = Distance ÷ Speed
Time = $30 \div 15 = 2$
John takes 2 hours to run from A to B.

(b) Distance = Speed × Time
Distance = $10 \times 0.5 = 5$
The distance from B to C is 5 km.

(c) Total distance John runs = $30 + 5$
$= 35$ km.
Total time John takes = $2 + 0.5$
$= 2.5$ hours.

Average speed = $\dfrac{\text{Total distance travelled}}{\text{Total time taken}}$

Average speed = $\frac{35}{2.5} = 14$ km/hour

2 A car travels at a constant speed of 40 km/hour.
How long does it take the car to travel 80 km.
The car travels 40 km in 1 hour.
The car travels 80 km in $80 \div 40 = 2$ hours.

4 Angela, Ben and Cathy drive from London to Glasgow.
Angela takes 12 hours 30 minutes driving at an average speed of 64 km/hour.
Ben drives at an average speed of 100 km/hour.
(a) How long does Ben take?
Cathy takes 7 hours 12 minutes.
(b) At what average speed does Cathy drive?
Give your answer to 3 significant figures.

Angela takes 12.5 hours at 64 km/h.
Distance = Speed × Time
$= 12.5 \times 64 = 800$
The distance from London to Glasgow is 800 km.

(a) Time = Distance ÷ Speed
$= 800 \div 100 = 8$
Ben takes 8 hours.

(b)

12 minutes = $\frac{12}{60}$ hours
$\frac{12}{60} = 12 \div 60 = 0.2$
12 minutes = 0.2 hours

Speed = $\dfrac{\text{Distance}}{\text{Time}}$

$= \frac{800}{7.2}$

$= 111.111...$

Cathy drives at a speed of 111 km/hour to 3 significant figures.

Do not use a calculator in questions 1 to 8.

1 Beverley walks for 2 hours at an average speed of 4 km/h.
How many kilometres does she walk?

2 Sam runs at 6 km/h for 30 minutes.
How far does he run?

3 Penny cycles to work at 18 km/h.
She takes 20 minutes.
How far does she cycle to work?

4 Bristol is 40 miles from Gloucester.
(a) How long does it take to cycle from Bristol to Gloucester at 16 miles per hour?
(b) How long does it take to drive from Bristol to Gloucester at 48 miles per hour?

5 The table shows details of 5 different journeys.

Journey	(a)	(b)	(c)	(d)	(e)
Total distance	200 m			200 km	250 m
Total time	25 secs	2 hours	10 min		
Average speed		50 km/h	1.2 cm/min	200 km/h	250 m/s

Copy and complete the table.
State the units of each answer.

6 Cars A, B, C and D travelled from London to Newcastle.
Details are given in this table.

Car	A	B	C	D
Time (hours)	5		6	4.2
Average speed (km/h)	84	105		

Copy and complete the table.

7 Jenny sets out on a journey at 10.20 a.m.
She completes her journey at 1.05 p.m.
She travels a total distance of 27.5 km.
Calculate her average speed in kilometres per hour.

8 Billy drives for 40 km at an average speed of 60 km/h.
He starts his journey at 9.50 a.m.
At what time does his journey end?

9 Sally cycles 38 km at an average speed of 23 km/h.
She starts her journey at 9.30 a.m.
At what time does she finish?
Give your answer to the nearest minute.

10 Ron runs 400 m in 1 minute 23.2 seconds.
Calculate his average speed in metres per second.

11 Chandni runs from Newcastle to Whitley Bay and then from Whitley Bay to Blyth.
Newcastle to Whitley Bay
    Time taken: 1 hr 20 min.
    Distance: 20 km.
Whitley Bay to Blyth
    Average speed: 0.2 km/min.
    Distance: 12 km.
Calculate Chandni's average speed over the whole journey.

12 The distance from the Sun to the Earth is about 1.5×10^8 km.
It takes light from the Sun about 500 seconds to reach the Earth.
Calculate the speed of light in metres per second.

13 Coaches A and B are based in Leeds.
Coach A goes on a return trip to Scarborough.
Coach B goes on a return trip to Blackpool.
Here are details of the journeys.
Coach A
    Leeds to Scarborough
    Time taken: 1 hr 30 min.
    Average speed: 80 km/hour.
    Scarborough to Leeds
    Average speed: 75 km/hour.
Coach B
    Leeds to Blackpool
    Time taken: 1 hr 20 min.
    Distance: 135 km.
    Blackpool to Leeds
    Average speed: 90 km/hour.
Which coach travels:
(a) for the longest distance - by how much?
(b) for the longest time - by how much?
(c) at the fastest average speed - by how much?

EXAMPLES

❶ The graph shows a bus journey.
   (a) How many times does the bus stop?
   (b) On which part of the journey does the bus travel fastest?
   (c) Find the average speed of the bus between the first and second stops.

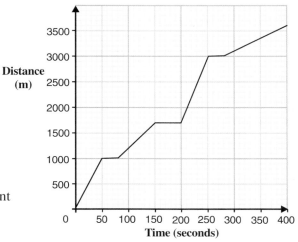

   (a) At zero speed the distance-time graph is horizontal.
       So the bus stops 3 times.
   (b) The bus travels fastest when the gradient of the distance-time graph is steepest.
       So the bus travels fastest between the second and third stops.
   (c) Between the first and second stops the bus travels 700 m in 70 seconds.
       The average speed of the bus $= \frac{700}{70} = 10$ m/s.

> ⭘⭘⭘⭘⭘⭘⭘⭘⭘⭘⭘⭘⭘⭘⭘
> **Distance-time graphs**
> Speed = gradient of line
> The faster the speed the steeper the gradient.
> Zero gradient means zero speed.

❷ Dan walks around Bolam Lake. He starts and finishes his walk at the car park beside the lake. The distance-time graph shows his journey.

   (a) At what time did Dan start his walk?
   (b) At what time did Dan reach the furthest distance from the car park?
   (c) How many times did Dan stop during his walk?
   (d) Dan stopped for lunch at 1330. For how many minutes did he stop for lunch?
   (e) Between what times did Dan walk the fastest?
   (f) At what speed did Dan walk between 1530 and 1600?

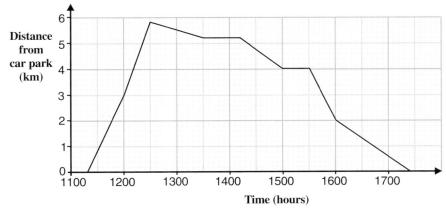

   (a) One small square represents 60 ÷ 10 = 6 minutes.
       So Dan starts his walk at 1118.
   (b) As soon as Dan walks past the furthest distance from the car park, his distance from the car park gets less. This occurs at 1230.
   (c) When Dan stops the graph is horizontal. This occurs twice.
   (d) Dan stops between 1330 and 1412. So Dan stops for 42 minutes.
   (e) The gradient of the distance-time graph is steepest between 1200 and 1230 when Dan walks 2.8 km.
   (f) Distance travelled = 2 km. Time taken = 30 minutes = 0.5 hours. So speed $= \frac{2}{0.5} = 4$ km/h.

Do not use a calculator.

1 What speed is shown by each of these distance-time graphs?

(a)
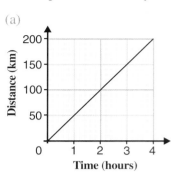

(b)
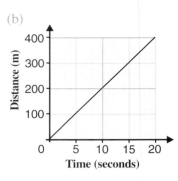

(c)
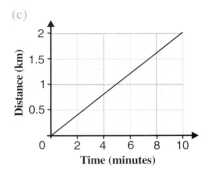

2 Amy, Ben, Cathy and Dan are pupils at the same school who live in the same street. This graph shows each of their journeys to school.

One of the pupils travels to school by car, one cycles, one walks and one comes by bus.

(a) How does each pupil come to school?

The average speed of the cyclist is 12 kilometres per hour.

(b) Find the average speed of all the other pupils.

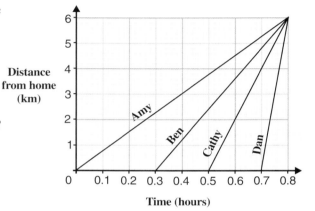

3 This distance-time graph shows a car journey.
During the journey the car has to stop at traffic lights.

(a) For how long does the car stop at traffic lights?
(b) What is the fastest speed that the car travels on the journey?

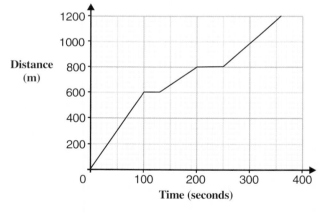

4 This graph shows what happens when Ben leaves home to catch a bus.

(a) At what speed does Ben start to walk to the bus stop?
(b) Does Ben catch the bus? Use the graph to explain your answer.

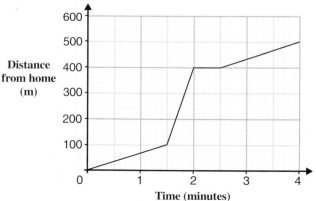

5 This graph shows the progress made by a runner during the first 20 km of a marathon race.

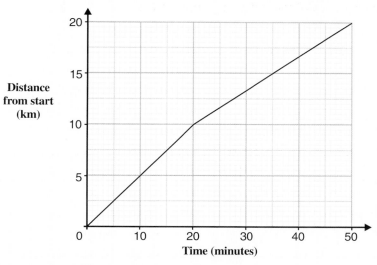

Find the average speed of the runner:
(a) during the first 10 km of the race,
(b) during the second 10 km of the race,
(c) during the first 20 km of the race.

6 Lisa went on a cycling holiday.
The following graph shows her journey for the first day.

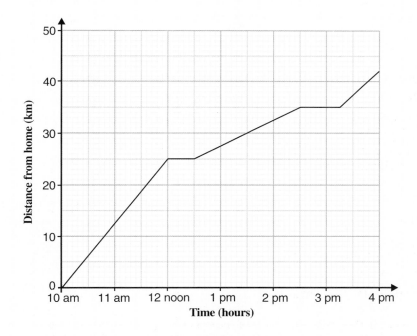

(a) (i)   How many times did she stop before 4 pm?
     (ii) For how long did she stop at 2.30 pm?

(b) (i)   What was her speed between 10 am and noon?
     (ii) What was her average speed for the whole journey?
     (iii) Between what times was she travelling fastest?

SEG 1994

7 The graph shows the journey of a business woman.

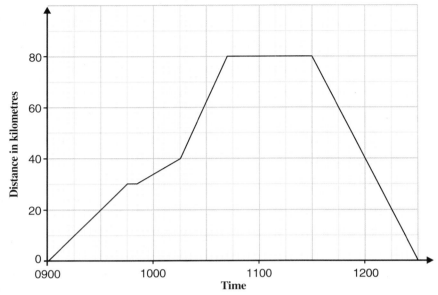

(a) At what time did the woman first stop on her journey?
(b) Between what times did the woman travel the fastest?
(c) Calculate the speed at which the woman was travelling on her return journey?

SEG 1995

8 This graph shows Jenny's walk from Corfe Castle to Wareham and back again.

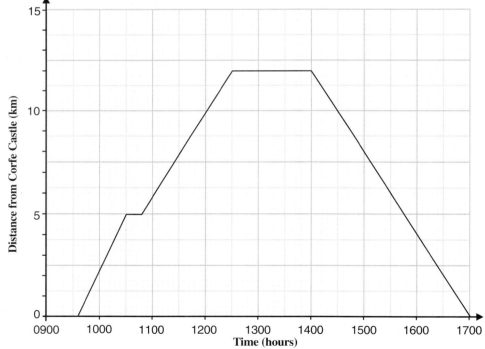

(a) At what time did Jenny leave Corfe Castle?
(b) How far was Jenny from Wareham when she made her first stop?
(c) Jenny had lunch at Wareham.
    How many minutes did she stop for lunch?
(d) At what average speed did Jenny walk back from Wareham to Corfe Castle?

SEG 1994

9 Billy has a 10 km journey to school.
He leaves home at 8.05 a.m. and takes
10 minutes to walk 1 km to Jane's
house.
Billy gets a lift with Jane's mum at
8.20 a.m.
Billy arrives at school at 8.45 a.m.

(a) Using 1 cm for 5 minutes on the
time axis and 1 cm for 1 km on the
distance axis draw a distance time
graph for Billy's journey.

(b) Find Billy's average speed for his
whole journey in km/hour?

10 Billie and Angie run along the same
track starting from the same point.
Angie runs at an average speed of
2 km/second.
Billie starts 10 seconds after Angie and
runs at an average speed of
3 km/second.

(a) Using 1 cm for 5 seconds on the
time axis and 1 cm for 10 m on the
distance axis draw a distance-time
graph to show both Angie's and
Billie's runs.

(b) Use your graph to find how long it
takes for Billie to overtake Angie.

11 Mary leaves home at 1500 and walks at
a constant speed from her house to a
shop, a distance of 1 km.
She takes 20 minutes to walk to the
shop and 5 minutes to do her shopping.
She then walks home at a constant
speed arriving home at 1550.

(a) Using 1 cm for 5 minutes on the
time axis and 1 cm for 100 m on
the distance axis, draw a distance-
time graph for her journey.

(b) Find Mary's average speed for her
whole journey.

12 An athlete runs two laps of a 400 metre
track.
The athlete runs:
the first 200 metres at 8 m/s,
the next 400 metres at 10 m/s,
the last 200 metres at 8 m/s.
Using a scale of 1 cm for 10 seconds on
the time axis and 1 cm for 50 m on the
distance axis, draw a graph to show the
distance of the athlete from the start-
finish line during the run.

13 At Newcastle, Sam gets on a coach for
London.
The coach travels from Newcastle to
London in two stages.
Stage 1: The coach leaves Newcastle
at 0830 and travels 270 km to a
service station at an average speed of
90 km/hour.
Stage 2: The coach leaves the service
station and travels a further 180 km to
London arriving at 1500.
The coach stops at the service station
for 30 minutes.

(a) Using 2 cm for 1 hour on the
time axis and 1 cm for 50 km on
the distance axis, draw a
distance-time graph for the coach
journey.

(b) Find the average speed of the
coach on Stage 2 of the journey.

Tom leaves London at 1000 and
travels by car on the route to
Newcastle.
Tom and Sam meet each other at the
service station.

(c) What is the slowest average
speed that Tom drives?

14 Emby and Ashwood are two towns
14 km apart.
Kim leaves Emby at 1000 and walks
at a steady pace of 6 km/hour towards
Ashwood.
Ray leaves Ashwood at 1040 and
cycles towards Emby.
Ray travels at a steady speed of
21 km/hour for the first 20 minutes
and then at a slower steady speed for
the rest of his journey
Ray arrives at Emby at 1130.

(a) On the same diagram and using a
scale of 1 cm for 10 minutes on
the time axis and 1 cm for 1 km
on the distance axis, draw a
distance-time graph to show both
journeys.

(b) Use your diagram to find:
(i) the time that Kim arrives at
Ashwood,
(ii) the time that Kim and Ray
pass each other,
(iii) Ray's speed for the slower
part of his journey.

Density

Density is a compound measure because it involves two other measures, **mass** and **volume**.
The formula for density is:

$$\text{Density} = \frac{\text{Mass}}{\text{Volume}}$$

For example, if a metal has a density of $2500\,\text{kg/m}^3$ then $1\,\text{m}^3$ of the metal weighs $2500\,\text{kg}$.

The formula linking density, mass and volume can be rearranged and remembered as:

$$\text{Volume} = \frac{\text{Mass}}{\text{Density}}$$

$$\text{Mass} = \text{Density} \times \text{Volume}$$

EXAMPLES

1 A block of metal has mass $500\,\text{g}$ and volume $400\,\text{cm}^3$.
Calculate the density of the metal.

$\text{Density} = \frac{500}{400} = 1.25\,\text{g/cm}^3$

2 The density of a certain metal is $3.5\,\text{g/cm}^3$.
A block of the metal has volume $1000\,\text{cm}^3$.
Calculate the mass of the block.

$\text{Mass} = 3.5 \times 1000 = 350\,\text{g}$.

3 Metal A has density $3\,\text{g/cm}^3$ and metal B has density $2\,\text{g/cm}^3$.
$600\,\text{g}$ of metal A and $300\,\text{g}$ of metal B are melted down and mixed to make an alloy which is cast into a block.
(a) Calculate the volume of the block.
(b) Calculate the density of the alloy.

(a) Volume of metal A $= \frac{600}{3} = 200\,\text{cm}^3$.
Volume of metal B $= \frac{300}{2} = 150\,\text{cm}^3$.
Total volume $200 + 150 = 350\,\text{cm}^3$.

(b) Density $= \frac{900}{350} = 2.57\,\text{g/cm}^3$.

Population density

Population density is a measure of how populated an area is.
The formula for population density is:

$$\text{Population density} = \frac{\text{Population}}{\text{Area}}$$

EXAMPLE

4 The population of the county of Cumbria is 4.897×10^5.
The area of the county of Cumbria is $6824\,\text{km}^2$.
The population of the county of Surrey is 1.036×10^6.
The area of the county of Surrey is $1677\,\text{km}^2$.
Which county has the greater population density?

The population densities are:

Cumbria $\frac{4.897 \times 10^5}{6824} = 71.8$ people/km^2.

Surrey $\frac{1.036 \times 10^6}{1677} = 617.8$ people/km^2.

Surrey has the greater population density.

Exercise 12.4

You may use a calculator in this exercise.

1 A metal bar has a mass of 960 g and a volume of 120 cm³.
Find the density of the metal in the bar.

2 A block of copper has a mass of 2160 g.
The block measures 4 cm by 6 cm by 10 cm.
What is the density of copper?

3 A silver necklace has a mass of 300 g.
The density of silver is 10.5 g/cm³.
What is the volume of the silver?

4 A rectangular can measuring 30 cm by 15 cm by 20 cm is full of oil.
The density of oil is 0.8 g/cm³.
What is the mass of the oil?

5 A rectangular pane of glass measures 60 cm by 120 cm by 0.5 cm.
The density of glass is 2.6 g/cm³.
What is the mass of the glass?

6 A bag of sugar has a mass of 1 kg.
The average density of the sugar in the bag is 0.5 g/cm³.
Find the volume of sugar in the bag.

7 A block of concrete has dimensions 15 cm by 25 cm by 40 cm.
The block has a mass of 12 kg.
What is the density of the concrete?

8 A bottle holds 450 cm³ of water and has a mass of 550 g.
The density of water is 1 g/cm³.
What is the mass of the empty bottle?

9 The population of Northern Ireland is 1.595×10^6.
The area of Northern Ireland is 13 483 km².
Calculate the population density of Northern Ireland.

10 The table shows the total population, land area and the population densities for some countries in Europe.

	Country	Area km²	Population	Population density
(a)	Belgium	?	9.97×10^6	326.6
(b)	France	543 960	5.67×10^7	?
(c)	UK	244 090	?	235.2

Calculate the missing figures in the table.

What you need to know

- **Speed** is a compound measure because it involves **two** other measures.
- **Speed** is a measure of how fast something is travelling. It involves the measures **distance** and **time**.
  $$\text{Speed} = \frac{\text{Distance}}{\text{Time}}$$
- In situations where speed is not constant, **average speed** is used.
  $$\text{Average speed} = \frac{\text{Total distance travelled}}{\text{Total time taken}}$$
- The formula linking speed, distance and time can be rearranged and remembered as:
  (average) **speed** = (total) **distance** ÷ (total) **time**
  (total) **distance** = (average) **speed** × (total) **time**
  (total) **time** = (total) **distance** ÷ (average) **speed**
- **Distance-time graphs** are used to illustrate journeys.
  On a distance-time graph: speed can be calculated from the gradient of a line,
  the faster the speed the steeper the gradient,
  zero gradient (horizontal line) means zero speed.
- Two other commonly used compound measures are **density** and **population density**.
- **Density** is a compound measure which involves the measures **mass** and **volume**.
  $$\text{Density} = \frac{\text{Mass}}{\text{Volume}}$$
- **Population density** is a measure of how populated an area is.
  $$\text{Population density} = \frac{\text{Population}}{\text{Area}}$$

You may use a calculator in this exercise.

1 Jane runs 1800 m in 9 minutes.
Tom runs 100 m in 12 seconds.
Sam runs 400 m in 1 minute 40 seconds.
Calculate the speed of each of Jane, Tom and Sam in metres per second.

2 (a) Ben runs 600 m at an average speed of 4.2 m/s.
How long does Ben take in seconds?
(b) Tim runs for 1 minute at an average speed of 4.2 m/s.
How far does Tim run in metres?

3 Part of a bus timetable is shown.

Bournemouth	0630	0730	0750	0810
Westbourne	0638	0738	0758	0818
Parkstone	0645	0745	0805	0825
Poole	0654	0754	0814	0834

The bus journey from Bournemouth to Poole is 8 km.
(a) When the bus is 6 minutes late what is the average speed of the bus in km/hour?
(b) When the bus is on time what is the average speed of the bus in km/hour?

SEG 1995

4 An aeroplane flies from New York to Los Angeles, a distance of 2475 miles, at an average speed of 427 miles per hour.
How long does the flight take in hours and minutes?

SEG 1997

5 The distance from London to Newcastle is 285 miles.
Derek takes $4\frac{1}{2}$ hours to drive this distance.
(a) Calculate the average speed of Derek's car.
A train takes 3 hours 20 minutes to travel this distance.
(b) Calculate the average speed of the train.

SEG 1995

6 The distance from the earth to the moon is 2.38×10^5 miles.
Light travels at a speed of 3.0×10^8 m/sec.
1 mile $= 1.609 \times 10^3$ metres.
How long does it take a beam of light to travel from the earth to the moon?

SEG 1994

7 Hannah goes to the shop to buy a loaf of bread.
The shop is 800 m from her house.
She leaves home at 1512 and walks to the shop at a steady speed.
She takes 16 minutes to reach the shop and then 5 minutes to buy a loaf of bread.
She then walks home at a steady speed arriving at 1548.
Draw a distance-time graph to represent her journey.

SEG 1996

8 Billy makes a journey to college and back on his bicycle.
The journey is shown on the distance-time graph.

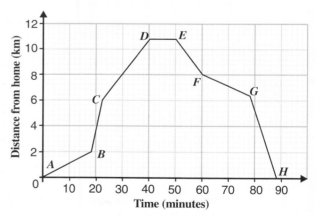

(a) Between which two points on his journey is Billy:
  (i) cycling downhill,
  (ii) resting,
  (iii) cycling towards his starting point?
(b) Calculate Billy's average speed between:
  (i) points B and C,
  (ii) points E and F,
  (iii) points F and H.

9 The distance from Ashby to Banborough is 16 km.
The distance from Banborough to Calby is 8 km.
John leaves Ashby at noon.
He walks towards Banborough for 1 hour at an average speed of 6 km/h and then rests for 20 minutes.
John then runs the remaining distance to Banborough at an average speed of 10 km/h.
At Banborough John talks to a friend for 20 minutes and borrows his bicycle.
He then cycles to Calby at an average speed of 16 km/h.
John leaves Calby at 1600.
He cycles home over the same route arriving at 1650.
Using a scale of 1 cm for 20 minutes and 1 cm for 2 km draw a distance-time graph for John's journey.

10 The distance-time graph shows the journey of a man travelling from home to work.

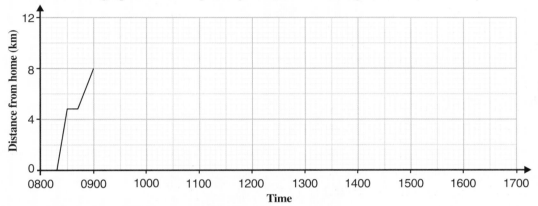

The man left work at 1612 to return home.
He travelled without stopping.
The journey took 24 minutes.
(a) Copy and complete the graph.
(b) What was the average speed of the man on his journey home?

SEG 1996

11 The table gives some information about various materials.
Calculate the missing figures in the table.
State the units of each answer.

Metal	Volume	Mass	Density
Steel	120 cm³	300 g	?
Concrete	?	12 kg	7.5 g/cm³
Foam	4000 cm³	?	0.05 g/cm³

12 Population density = $\frac{\text{Population}}{\text{Area}}$

Which of these two continents has the larger population density?
You **must** show all your working.

SEG 96

Continent	Population	Area (km²)
Europe	6.82×10^8	1.05×10^{10}
Asia	2.96×10^9	4.35×10^{10}

13 Brass is an alloy made from zinc and copper.
The ratio of the volume of zinc to the volume of copper in the alloy is 1 : 3.
The density of zinc is 2.5 g/cm³.
The density of copper is 3 g/cm³.
A block of brass in the shape of a cuboid has dimensions 10 cm by 10 cm by 40 cm.
Calculate the mass of the block.

Questions 1 to 17.
Do not use a calculator.

1 John pays £2.60 for 200 g of jelly babies and 300 g of toffees.
100 g of jelly babies cost 37p.
What is the cost of 100 g of toffees?

2 How many minutes are there in 1 week?

SEG 1994

3 The temperature is recorded inside a house and outside a house.

Inside temperature	Outside temperature
16°C	−8°C

How many degrees warmer was it inside the house than outside?

SEG 1994

4 Sanjay's class wants to buy a colour printer.

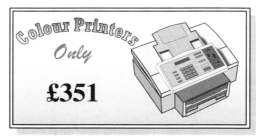

There are 27 students in the class.
They share the cost equally.
How much should each student pay?
Your **must** show all your working.

SEG 1996

5 Pork should be cooked for 70 minutes per kilogram plus 35 minutes.
A joint of pork weighs 2 kg.
It is placed in the oven at 10.30 am.
At what time of day will it be cooked?

SEG 1997

6 Rhianna measures her pencil and says,
'It is 13.6 cm long.'
She knows that her measurement is correct to 1 decimal place.
Which two of the following lengths could **not** be the actual length of the pencil?
       13.649   13.7   13.61   13.55   13.66

SEG 1995

7 An athletics event is watched by 253 people.
They each pay an entrance fee of 45p.
(a)   Find the total amount of money paid by these people.
       You **must** show all your working.
(b)   It costs £1.35 for an adult to sit in the grandstand.
       A child pays $\frac{3}{5}$ of this adult cost to sit in the grandstand.
       How much does it cost for a group of six children to sit in the grandstand?

SEG 1996

8 Georgina buys a bar of chocolate.
The bar is divided into 18 equal pieces.

(a) Georgina eats three pieces of chocolate.
What fraction of the bar has she eaten?

(b) Later in the day Georgina eats $\frac{3}{5}$ of the pieces that are left.
How many pieces of chocolate have been eaten altogether?

(c) What percentage of the bar has **not** been eaten?

SEG 1995

9 (a) Work out 20% of £4.80.

(b) Find $\frac{2}{5}$ of £170.

SEG 1996

10 The number of people who watch a hockey match is 25 936.
Write this number to an appropriate degree of accuracy for a newspaper headline.
State what degree of accuracy you have chosen.

SEG 1997

11

There are 250 ml of Cola in the small can.
The large can contains 30% **more** than the small can.
How much Cola does the large can contain?

SEG 1995

12 Here is a recipe for American Indian bread.

> 2 cups of flour
> 2 teaspoons of baking powder
> $\frac{1}{2}$ teaspoon of salt
> 140 ml of milk
> 200 ml of water

This recipe makes enough for 4 people.
You are cooking for 10 people.

(a) What quantity of flour would you need?

(b) What quantity of milk would you need?

SEG 1995

13 In 1990 a fruit corner yogurt cost 20p.

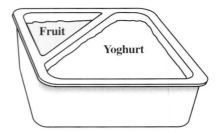

(a) In 1991 a fruit corner yogurt cost 15% more than in 1990.
How much more did one of these yogurts cost in 1991?

(b) In 1992 a fruit corner yogurt cost 24 pence.
Calculate the percentage increase in the price of one of these yogurts from 1990 to 1992.

(c) A fruit corner yogurt weighs 175 g altogether.
The ratio of the **weight of fruit** to the **weight of yogurt** is 2 : 5.
Calculate the weight of the fruit.

SEG 1995

14 The weights of two tins of fruit are in the ratio 3 : 5.
Find the weight of the smaller tin as a percentage of the weight of the larger tin.

SEG 1994

15 Two newspapers write about a rock concert.
Both newspapers estimate the number of people in the audience.

> According to *The Post*, 3000 fans attended.
> *The Post* make their estimate to **the nearest 1000**.

> *The Chronicle* said there were 2500 fans in the audience.
> Their estimate is to **the nearest 100**.

What are the largest and smallest possible sizes of the audience?

SEG 1997

16 A number x written as the product of its prime factors is $2^3 \times 3^2 \times 7$.
A number y written as the product of its prime factors is $2^2 \times 3^3 \times 7$.

(a) Calculate the values of x and y
(b) Write the number xy as the product of its prime factors.
(c) Write the number $7x$ as the product of its prime factors.
(d) Write the number $9y$ as the product of its prime factors.
(e) Write $14x$ as the product of its prime factors and explain why it is a square number.

17 $A = 3 \times 10^4$
$B = 5 \times 10^{-2}$

(a) Calculate $A \times B$
Give your answer in standard form.
(b) Calculate $A \div B$.
Give your answer in standard form.

18 Jonathan is paid £4.20 per hour as his basic wage. In one week he works five hours twenty minutes overtime at time and a half. How much does Jonathan earn in overtime that week?

SEG 1994

19 The distance from London to Taunton is 150 miles.
A coach averaged 60 miles per hour for the journey.
(a) How long did the coach journey take?

The coach left London at 1530 for the journey to Taunton.
(b) What was its arrival time in   (i)   24-hour clock time,
                                     (ii)   12-hour clock time?   SEG 1993

20 Write this set in order lowest first.
$$0.32 \qquad \frac{4}{13} \qquad 32.5\% \qquad \frac{11}{35} \qquad 0.315$$

21 Find:
(a) 3.4% of £12.60,   (b) 24.6% of £12.

22 When 15 oranges are bought individually the total cost is £1.20.
When 15 oranges are bought in a pack the cost is £1.14.

(a) What is the percentage saving by buying the pack?
(b) A special offer pack of thee oranges has 20% extra free.
How many extra oranges are in the special offer pack?
(c) What fraction of the oranges in the special offer pack are free?   SEG 1994

23 (a) Three students took a French exam.
Claire scored $\frac{2}{3}$ of the total marks.

Ranjit scored $\frac{3}{5}$ of the total marks.

Nicola scored $\frac{5}{8}$ of the total marks.

Which student scored the highest mark?
You **must** show all your working.
(b) In a Hindi exam the ratio of Dilip's mark to Thomas' mark was 3 : 2.
Dilip's mark was 42.
Calculate Thomas' mark.   SEG 1995

24 Gary is using a calculator to work out $\dfrac{241}{55.8 + 0.35}$
What answer should he get?   SEG 1997

25 A formula for converting degrees Celsius (C) into degrees Fahrenheit (F) is
$$F = \frac{9}{5}\left(C + 17\tfrac{7}{9}\right).$$
Calculate the Fahrenheit equivalent of −9 degrees Celsius.   SEG 1997

26 Alan scored 24 marks in a test.
(a) The test was marked out of 75.
Calculate Alan's percentage mark.
(b) The marks were increased in the ratio 2 : 3.
(i) Calculate Alan's new mark.
(ii) After the marks were increased, Indira's new mark was 46.5.
Calculate her original mark in the test.   SEG 1996

27 Darren drives 38 km at an average speed of 63 km per hour.
(a) Calculate how long his journey takes.
Give your answer in minutes.
(b) Without using a calculator, show how to check that your answer is of the right
order of magnitude.   SEG 1995

28 Billy goes on a bike ride in three stages.
Stage 1
Billy cycles for 16 km at an average speed of 20 km/hour.
Stage 2
Billy cycles for 45 minutes at an average speed of 24 km/hour.
Stage 3
Billy cycles 15 km in 20 minutes.
Calculate Billy's average speed on his ride.

29 Javed split his garden into three parts.

	Area
Vegetable plot	10 m^2
Flower beds	8 m^2
Rockery	7 m^2

(a) He spread 60 kg of compost over the three parts in the ratio of their areas.
How much was spread over the vegetable plot?
(b) What percentage of the compost was spread over the rockery?
(c) The following year Javed is told that the vegetable plot should have twice as much compost per square metre as the other two parts of his garden.
Javed spread more compost over his garden.
What fraction of the compost should be spread over his vegetable plot?
(d) Jane split her garden into three parts.

Vegetable plot	$\frac{3}{5}$
Flower beds	$\frac{1}{4}$
Rockery	

Calculate what fraction of the garden is occupied by the rockery.

SEG 1996

30 Work out the value of $\dfrac{7^5 + 2^4}{5^7}$.

SEG 1996

31 (a) Calculate the value of $\dfrac{6.73 + 4.23}{8.41 - \sqrt{9.71}}$

(b) The cost, £C, of moving a load, M kilograms, a distance, D miles, is given by the formula
$$C = 22 + 0.47(2M + D).$$
(i) Find C when $M = 61.8$ and $D = 317$.
(ii) Sarah calculates the value of C when $M = 53$ and $D = 198$.
She gets an answer of £26.98.
Use estimates to check whether Sarah's answer is of the correct order of magnitude.
You **must** show all your working.

SEG 1997

32 (a) Calculate the value of 2×5^9

(b) (i) Calculate $\dfrac{28.3 + \sqrt{0.512}}{(18.9 - 2.75)^2}$.

(ii) Paul gives his answer to (i) correct to 5 significant figures.

Give one reason why this is **not** an appropriate degree of accuracy.

SEG 1996

130

33 (a) Calculate $\dfrac{3.82}{\sqrt{46}} + \dfrac{\sqrt{0.731}}{2.87}$.

Write down all the figures shown on your calculator.

(b) Andy correctly works out $\sqrt{\dfrac{271\,000 + 680}{283 \times 39.4}}$.

Each number in this calculation is correct to three significant figures. Give Andy's answer correct to an appropriate degree of accuracy.

SEG 1997

34 Calculate the value of $(2.34 \times 10^{-2})^{\frac{1}{2}}$.

SEG 1996

35 A 'Travel Saver Card' entitles the holder to 40% off the normal price of a journey.
(a) A particular journey normally costs £28.50.
How much would it cost with a Travel Saver Card?
(b) The Travel Saver Card price for another journey is £18.60.
What is the normal price of this journey?

SEG 1998

36 (a) The approximate population of the United Kingdom is given in standard form as 5.2×10^7.
Write this as an ordinary number.
(b) The thickness of grade A paper is 6.0×10^{-2} cm. Grade B paper is twice as thick as grade A.
Calculate, in centimetres, the thickness of grade B paper.
Write your answer in standard form.

SEG 1994

37 In Britain there are 5.8×10^7 people.
8.8% of the people in Britain live in Scotland.
How many people live in Scotland?

38 (a) A town has a population of 645 166 people.
The ratio of retired people to the rest of the population is 1 : 3.
How many people are retired?
Give your answer correct to three significant figures.

(b) In Britain there are 5.80×10^7 people.
The number of retired people is 1.04×10^7.
What percentage of people in Britain are retired?
Give your answer to an appropriate degree of accuracy.

SEG 1998

39 $P = a^m \times b^n$, where a and b are prime numbers and m and n are whole numbers.
(a) What can you say about the values of m and n when P is a square number?
(b) What can you say about the values of m an n when P is a cube number?
(c) Write 54 as the product of its prime factors.
(d) (i) What is the smallest square number that has 54 as a factor?
(ii) What is the smallest cube number that has 54 as a factor?

40 (a) (i) Calculate the value of $3 \times 10^{-4} \times 7 \times 10^6$. Give your answer in standard form.
(ii) Give your answer to part (i) as a product of prime numbers.

(b) Calculate the value of $(7 \times 10^6)^3$.
Give your answer in standard form.

SEG 1996

CHAPTER 13

Introduction to Algebra

Algebra is sometimes called the language of Mathematics.
Algebra uses letters in place of numbers

> A class of children line up.
> I cannot see how many there are because of the tree.
> Imagine there are n children in the line.

The letter n is used in place of an unknown number.

Three more children join the line.
There are now $n + 3$ children.

Start again with a class of n children in a line.
Another class of n children lines up beside them.

There are now $n + n$ children or $2 \times n$ children.

The simplest way to write this is $2n$.

Exercise **13.1**

1
  (a)   I start with n children in a queue. 4 more join the queue. How many children are in the queue now?

  (b)   I start with n children. 3 leave the queue. How many children are left in the queue?

  (c)   There are 3 classes with n children in each class. How many children are there altogether?

2
  (a)   I have n marbles in a bag. I put in another 6 marbles. How many marbles are now in the bag?

  (b)   I have n marbles. I lose 12 marbles. How many marbles have I now?

  (c)   I have 8 bags. Each bag contains n marbles. How many marbles do I have altogether?

3
  (a)   I have p pencils in a pencil case. I take one pencil out. How many pencils are left in the pencil case?

  (b)   I have p pencils in a pencil case. I put in another 5. How many pencils are now in the pencil case?

  (c)   I have 25 pencil cases. There are p pencils in each pencil case. How many pencils do I have altogether?

4
   I have 6 keyrings. There are k keys on each keyring. How many keys do I have altogether?

5
   What is the cost of n biscuits costing 5 pence each?

6
   There are 48 toffees in a tin. How many toffees are there in
  (a)   2 tins,   (b)   10 tins,   (c) t tins?

Writing expressions and formulae

Algebra can be used in lots of situations.

> An **expression** is just an answer using letters and numbers.
>
> A formula is an algebraic rule. It always has an equals sign.

EXAMPLES

1 A fence is L metres long.
An extra 50 metres is put on one end.
Write an **expression** for the total length of the fence.

The fence is now $(L + 50)$ metres long.

2 Boxes of matches each contain 48 matches.
Write down a **formula** for the number of matches, M, in N boxes of matches.

$M = 48 \times N$

This could be written as $M = 48N$.

Exercise 13.2

1 Egg boxes hold 12 eggs each.
How many eggs are there in e boxes?

2 A child is making a tower with toy bricks.
He has b bricks in his tower.

Write an expression for the number of bricks in the tower after he takes 3 bricks from the top.

3 I am a years old.
(a) How old will I be in 1 years time?
(b) How old was I four years ago?
(c) How old will I be in n years time?

4 John is h cm tall.
Sue is 12 cm taller than John.
Write down an expression for Sue's height in terms of h.

5 John has d CDs.
(a) Carol has twice as many CDs as John.
Write down an expression for the number of CDs that Carol has in terms of d.

(b) Fred has 5 more CDs than Carol.
Write down an expression for the number of CDs that Fred has in terms of d.

6

A packet of biscuits costs y pence.
Write down a formula for the cost, P pence, of another packet which costs
(a) five pence more than the first packet,
(b) two pence less than the first packet,
(c) twice the cost of the first packet,
(d) three pence more than twice the price of the first packet,
(e) a penny less than three times the cost of the first packet.

7 David is d years old.
Copy and complete this table to show the ages, A, of these people.

Name	Clue	Age
Alec	3 years older than David.	$A = d + 3$
Ben	2 years younger than David.	
Charlotte	Twice as old as David.	
Erica	Half David's age.	
Frank	5 years younger than three times David's age.	
Gillian	Next year she will be three times as old as David.	

Simplifying

Addition and subtraction

You can add and subtract **terms** with the same letter.

$w + 4w = 5w$
$5k + 3k - 2k = 6k$
$2a + 4b$ cannot be simplified.
$6 + a$ cannot be simplified.
$3p + 5 + p - 1 = 4p + 4$

Multiplication

$6 \times a = 6a$
$a \times b = ab$
$x \times x = x^2$

Note that:
A simpler way to write $1d$ is just d.

$-1d$ can be written as $-d$.

$0d$ is the same as 0.

Just as with ordinary numbers you can add terms in any order.
$a - 2a + 5a = a + 5a - 2a = 4a$

EXAMPLE   Three girls were given this question.

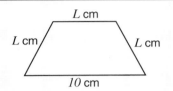

Write down the formula for the perimeter, P, of this shape in terms of L.

Their answers were:

Jaqui: $P = L + L + L + 10$
Fionna: $P = L \times 3 + 10$
Suzanne: $P = 3L + 10$

All three formulae are correct . . .
. . . but Suzanne's formula is the simplest.

Exercise 13.3

1 Write simpler expressions for the following.

(a) $c + c + c$
(b) $x + x + x + x + x$
(c) $p + p + p + p + p + p + p$
(d) $2y + 3y$
(e) $5g + g + 4g$
(f) $5z + 4z + z + 3z$
(g) $2m + 5m + m$
(h) $5r - 3r$
(i) $7t - 2t$
(j) $5j + 2j - 4j$
(k) $9c - 2c - 3c$
(l) $12w - 7w - 4w$
(m) $5d + 7d - 12d$
(n) $3x - 8x$
(o) $2a - 5a - 12a + a$

2 Write down the simplest possible expression for the perimeters of these shapes.

(a)
(b)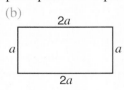
(c)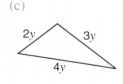
(d)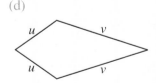

3 Write in a simpler way, wherever possible.

(a) $5x + 3x$
(b) $3v - v$
(c) $2x + 3y$
(d) $7u - v$
(e) $p + 3q + q$
(f) $3d + 5d + 4d$
(g) $a + b + 2c$
(h) $3m + n + m + 2n$
(i) $5c + 4c - c$
(j) $2x + y - x$
(k) $-p + 4p + 3p$
(l) $5k - 9k + 4k$

4 Simplify where possible.

(a) $a + 2a + 5$
(b) $3x + 5y - x - 2y$
(c) $m + 2m - n + 3n$
(d) $a + 6$
(e) $p + 2q + 2p + q$
(f) $2d + 5 - d - 2$
(g) $3a - 5a$
(h) $a - 2a + 7 + a$
(i) $2c + d + 4 - c - 2d + 7$
(j) $f + g - f - g$
(k) $2v + w - 3w + v$
(l) $7 - 2t - 9 - 3t$

5 Write down a formula for the perimeter, P, for each shape in terms of the other letters.

(a)

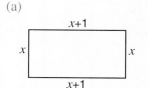

(b)

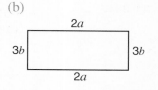

(c)

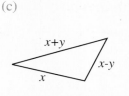

(d)

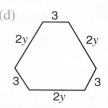

Brackets

Some expressions and formulae contain brackets.
One example you may have seen is the two formulae for finding the perimeter of a rectangle.

$$P = 2(L + W) \qquad \text{and} \qquad P = 2L + 2W$$

These two formulae both mean the same thing.
$2(L + W)$ means $2 \times (L + W)$.
Use both formulae to find the value of P when $L = 3$ and $W = 5$.
You should get the same answer.

You can multiply out brackets in an expression, or formula, either by using a diagram or by expanding.

EXAMPLES

1 Multiply out the bracket $2(x + 3)$.

Diagram method
$2(x + 3)$ means $2 \times (x + 3)$.
This can be shown using a rectangle.

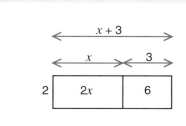

The areas of the two parts are $2x$ and 6.
The total area is $2x + 6$.
$2(x + 3) = 2x + 6$

Expanding
$2(x + 3) = 2 \times x + 2 \times 3$
$\qquad\qquad = 2x + 6$

2 Multiply out the bracket $3(4a + 5)$ using a diagram and by expanding.

Diagram method

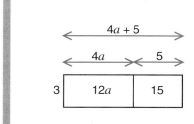

$3(4a + 5) = 12a + 15$

Expanding
$3(4a + 5) = 3 \times 4a + 3 \times 5$
$\qquad\qquad = 12a + 15$

3 Expand $3(2x - 5)$.

$3 \times 2x = 6x$
$+3 \times -5 = -15$
$3(2x - 5) = 6x - 15$

1 Use the diagrams to multiply out the brackets.

(a)

2 | x + 5 |

$2(x + 5) = \ldots$

(b)

a + 6

3 | |

$3(a + 6) = \ldots$

2 Draw your own diagrams to multiply out these brackets.

(a) $3(x + 2)$ (b) $4(r + 7)$ (c) $2(y + 5)$
(d) $3(2t + 1)$ (e) $5(4z + 7)$ (f) $2(x + y)$

3 Multiply out the brackets by expanding.

(a) $2(x + 4)$ (b) $4(b + 1)$ (c) $3(p + 6)$
(d) $5(a + 7)$ (e) $4(2x + 1)$ (f) $2(3a + b)$
(g) $3(t - 2)$ (h) $4(5 - a)$ (i) $3(2 - 4p)$
(j) $6(b + 2c)$ (k) $3(2m - 5n)$ (l) $7(a + b + c)$

4 Match the pairs of cards.

| $2(q + 2)$ | $2(q - 1)$ | $2(2q + 1)$ | $2(2 - q)$ |

| $4q + 2$ | $4 - 2q$ | $2q + 4$ | $2q - 2$ |

Remember:
Always remove brackets first, then simplify by collecting like terms together.

$3(t + 4) + 2$ Remove the brackets
$= 3t + 12 + 2$ Simplify
$= 3t + 14$

5 Multiply out the brackets and simplify where possible.

(a) $2(x + 1) + 3$ (b) $3(a + 2) + 5$ (c) $6(w + 4) + 7$
(d) $4(z + 2) + z$ (e) $5(t + 3) + 3t$ (f) $3(c - 2) - c$
(g) $4(2a + 5) + 3$ (h) $2x + 4(x - 5)$ (i) $3(p - 5) - p + 4$

6 Remove the brackets and simplify.

(a) $2(x + 1) + 3(x + 2)$ (b) $3(a + 1) + 2(a + 5)$
(c) $4(y + 2) + 5(y + 3)$ (d) $2(3a + 1) + 3(a + 1)$
(e) $3(2t + 5) + 5(4t + 3)$ (f) $3(z + 5) + 2(z - 1)$
(g) $7(q - 2) + 5(q + 6)$ (h) $5(x + 3) + 6(x - 3)$
(i) $8(2e - 1) + 4(e - 2)$ (j) $2(5d + 4) - 2(d - 1)$

Multiplying terms

Further multiplication

$a \times b = ab$ $3x \times y = 3xy$
$a \times a = a^2$ $5c \times 4c = 20c^2$
$3a \times 2b = 6ab$ $b \times b \times b = b^3$

Work logically.
Multiply the numbers and then letters in alphabetical order.
$3e \times 5d = 15de$
$4a^2b \times 3abc^2 = 12a^3b^2c^2$
$(4 \times 3 = 12, a^2 \times a = a^3, b \times b = b^2, c^2)$

EXAMPLES

1 Find the area of this rectangle.

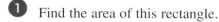

Area $= 3d \times d$

The simplest way to write the area is $3d^2$.

2 Find the volume of this cuboid.

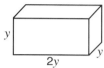

Volume $= 2y \times y \times y$

The simplest way to write the volume is $2y^3$.

Exercise 13.5

1 Simplify.

(a) $3 \times y$ (b) $5 \times p$ (c) $x \times y$
(d) $a \times a$ (e) $2 \times a \times a$ (f) $4 \times a \times a$
(g) $h \times h \times h$ (h) $w \times w^2$ (i) $2 \times d \times d \times d$
(j) $2m \times m^2$ (k) $2x \times 3x \times x$ (l) $3a \times 2a$

2 Write the area of each shape in the simplest way.

(a)   (b)   (c)   (d)

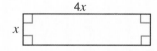 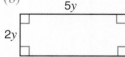 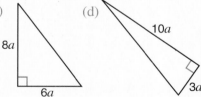

3 Find simplified expressions for the volumes of these cuboids.

(a)   (b)   (c)

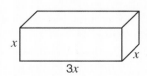 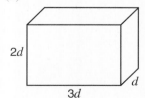 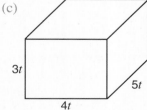

4 Simplify the following.

(a) $f \times g$ (b) $4 \times 5c$ (c) $4d \times e$
(d) $2 \times a \times b$ (e) $3x \times 4y$ (f) $4a \times 2b$
(g) $2h \times h \times j$ (h) $y \times 5w$ (i) $2m \times 7p^2$
(j) $2x \times 3y \times x^2$ (k) $3a^2b \times 7ab^2$ (l) $5e^2f \times 3f^3g^2$

Using formulae

You have already seen the formula for the perimeter of a rectangle,
$P = 2L + 2W$.
By **substituting** values for the length, L, and the width, W, you
can calculate the value of P.

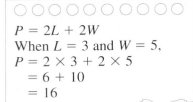

$P = 2L + 2W$
When $L = 3$ and $W = 5$,
$P = 2 \times 3 + 2 \times 5$
$\quad = 6 + 10$
$\quad = 16$

EXAMPLES

1 A joiner earns £W for working H hours.
Her boss uses the formula
$W = 5H + 35$ to calculate her wage.
Find her wage if she works for 40 hours.

$W = 5 \times 40 + 35$
$\quad = 200 + 35$
$\quad = £235$

2 $H = 3(4x - y)$. Find the value of H
when $x = 5$ and $y = 7$.

$H = 3(4x - y)$
$\quad = 3(4 \times 5 - 7)$
$\quad = 3(20 - 7)$
$\quad = 3(13)$
$\quad = 39$

3 The cost, £C, of a bus journey depends on the number of miles, m, travelled.
The cost is calculated using the formula $C = 0.35m + 0.25$
Calculate the cost of bus journeys of length (a) 1 mile, (b) 3.6 miles.

(a) $C = 0.35 \times 1 + 0.25$
$\quad = 0.35 + 0.25$
$\quad = £0.60$ or 60 pence

(b) $C = 0.35 \times 3.6 + 0.25$
$\quad = 1.26 + 0.25$
$\quad = £1.51$

Exercise 13.6

1 Find the value of $x + 3$ when
(a) $x = 2$ (b) $x = 12$ (c) $x = 25$

2 Find the value of $4a$ when
(a) $a = 5$ (b) $a = 14$ (c) $a = 2.5$

3 Find the value of $2p + 3$ when
(a) $p = 4$ (b) $p = 9$ (c) $p = 0$

4 Find the value of $7 - 2d$ when
(a) $d = 2$ (b) $d = 1$ (c) $d = 5$

5 $F = v + 6$. Find F when $v = 9$.

6 $V = 2x + 7$. Find V when $x = 12$.

7 $P = 2(d + 5)$. What is P when $d = 6$?

8 $C = 8(p + q)$. Calculate C if $p = 5$ and $q = 13$.

9 $S = ax + 4$. Find the value of S when $a = 12$ and $x = 0.4$.

10 $S = a(x + 4)$. Find the value of S when $a = 12$ and $x = 0.4$.

11 $S = 2a^2$. Find the value of S when
(a) $a = 3$ (b) $a = -3$

12 $S = (2a)^2$. Find the value of S when
(a) $a = 3$ (b) $a = -3$

13 $S = \frac{1}{2}p^2$. Find the value of S when
(a) $p = 4$ (b) $p = -6$

14 $S = (\frac{1}{2}p)^2$. Find the value of S when
(a) $p = 4$ (b) $p = -6$

15 The number of matches, M, needed to
make a pattern of P pentagons is given
by the formula $M = 4P + 1$.
Find the number of matches needed to
make 8 pentagons.

16 The distance, d, metres travelled by a
lawn mower in t minutes is given by the
formula: $d = 24t$.
Find the distance travelled by the lawn
mower in:
(a) 4 minutes,
(b) 30 minutes,
(c) 90 seconds.

138

Solving equations

A formula for the perimeter, P, of this rectangle is $P = 2x + 6$.
If the perimeter is 20, then we can write the equation $2x + 6 = 20$.
Then we can find out what x is by asking:

*"A certain number, when doubled and added to 6, gives 20.
What is the number?"*

Or, we can write $2 \times \square + 6 = 20$ and ask the question:

"What number goes in the box to make the statement true?"

The answer is $x = 7$.

This is called **solving** an equation.
The **solution** of the equation $2x + 6 = 20$ is $x = 7$.

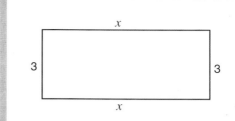

EXAMPLES

1 The time, T minutes, needed to bake a fish of weight w pounds is given by $T = 4w + 5$.
(a) Write down an equation in w for a fish which needs 17 minutes to cook.
(b) Solve your equation to find the weight of the fish.

(a) $4w + 5 = 17$ (b) $w = 3$ (because $4 \times 3 + 5 = 17$)

2 Solve the following equations.
(a) $3a + 4 = 10$ (b) $2t - 6 = 14$ (c) $3(x + 1) = 12$

$a = 2$ $t = 10$ $x = 3$
$(3 \times 2 + 4 = 10)$ $(2 \times 10 - 6 = 14)$ $(3 \times (3 + 1) = 12)$

Exercise 13.7

1 What number should be put in the box to make each of these statements correct.
(a) $\square + 4 = 7$ (b) $15 - \square = 11$ (c) $13 = \square - 4$
(d) $3 \times \square = 18$ (e) $24 = \square \times 4$ (f) $\square \div 2 = 7$
(g) $2 \times \square + 6 = 12$ (h) $15 - 3 \times \square = 9$ (i) $29 = 4 \times \square - 3$

2 What is the value of x in the following?
(a) $x - 2 = 6$ (b) $11 - x = 4$ (c) $2x = 10$
(d) $28 = 4x$ (e) $3x + 1 = 10$ (f) $25 - 4x = 17$
(g) $7 = 31 - 6x$ (h) $2(x + 3) = 24$ (i) $12 = 3(5 - x)$

3 Solve the following equations.
(a) $3y + 2 = 8$ (b) $2d - 4 = 6$ (c) $8a + 7 = 79$ (d) $6(a + 1) = 60$

4 (a) I think of a number, double it and add 4. The answer is 16. What is my number?
(b) I think of a number, multiply it by 5 and then add 2. The answer is 17. What is my number?
(c) I think of a number, add 4 then double the result. The answer is 24. What is my number?
(d) I think of a number, multiply it by 3 and then subtract 5. The answer is 7. What is my number?
(e) I think of a number, double it and add 3, then multiply the result by 4. The answer is 52. What is my number?

What you need to know

You should be able to:

- Write simple algebraic expressions and formulae.

- Simplify expressions and rules by collecting the terms together,
  e.g. $2d + 3d = 5d$ and
  $3x + 2 - x + 4 = 2x + 6$

- Multiply out brackets in expressions and formulae.
  e.g. $2(x - 5) = 2x - 10$

- Multiply simple expressions together.
  e.g. $2a \times a = 2a^2$, $y \times y \times y = y^3$
  and $2a \times 3b^2 = 6ab^2$

- Substitute numbers in simple formulae to solve problems.

- Solve simple equations by inspection.
  e.g. $x + 2 = 5$, $x - 3 = 7$,
  $2x = 10$, $x \div 4 = 12$

Review Exercise

1 (a) Aimee is n years old. Her brother Ben is two years younger. Write down Ben's age in terms of n.

(b) Aimee's mother is three times as old as Aimee. Write down her mother's age in terms of n.

(c) Aimee's father is four years older than her mother. Write down her father's age in terms of n.

(d) Write an expression for the combined ages of all four members of the family. Simplify your answer.

SEG 1994

2 Books of postage stamps contain n stamps.

(a) John buys a book of postage stamps. Each stamp costs 25p. Write an equation for the cost, in pence, of the stamps.

(b) Claire buys a book of postage stamps. Each stamp costs 19p. How much less than John did Claire pay for her n stamps?

SEG 1994

3 In the triangle ABC, the side AB has length x units.
AC is twice the length of AB.
BC is three units shorter than AC.

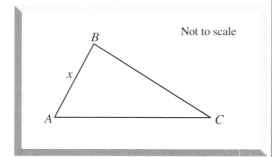

Not to scale

(a) Write expressions in terms of x, for
(i) AC,
(ii) BC.

(b) Write an expression for the perimeter of the triangle, in terms of x. Give your answer in its simplest form.

SEG 1996

4

I think of a number
I call it x
Multiply by 3
Take away 5

(a) Write down an expression for Sam's rule in terms of x.

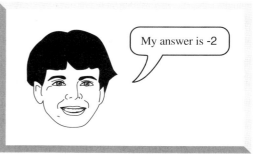

My answer is -2

(b) Find Sam's starting number.

SEG 1996

5 p, q and r are positive whole numbers.

> p is an even number,
> q is an odd number,
> r can be either even or odd.

For each of the following calculations, state whether the answer results in an even number, an odd number or either.
(a) $pq + r$
(b) $pr + q$
(c) $p(q + r)$

SEG 1996

6 Sam organises a football league. She uses this formula to calculate the total number of matches m for a given number of teams t.
> $m = (t - 1) \times t$.

(a) Work out the number of matches for ten teams.
(b) In one league there are 210 matches. Work out how many teams there are.

SEG 1994

7 Electrical fuses are available as shown.

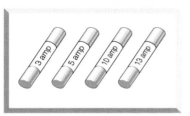

The correct fuse can be calculated using this formula:

> $I = \frac{P}{240}$
>
> I = Fuse in amps
>
> P = Power rating in watts

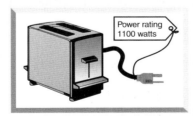

(a) Which fuse should be fitted to this toaster?
(b) A fire needs a 13 amp fuse. What is the largest power rating it may have?

SEG 1996

8 Peter buys p "Dead Rockin" CDs and q "Street Mania" CDs.

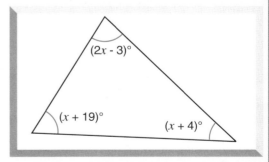

Write down an expression for the total cost of these CDs.

SEG 1997

9 In Segford town there is a badminton league. A team scores w points for a win, and two points for a draw. Pauline's team has won seven games, drawn four games, and has scored 43 points. We can write
> $7w + (4 \times 2) = 43$

(a) Solve this equation to find w.

Last year the points system was different. There were y points for a win and z points for a draw.
Last year Pauline's team won nine games and drew five games.
(b) Write down an expression, containing y and z, for the number of points scored by Pauline's team last year.

SEG 1996

10 The angles of a triangle are $(2x - 3)°$, $(x + 4)°$ and $(x + 19)°$.

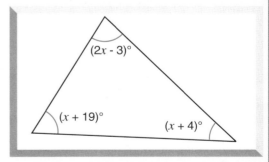

(a) Write an expression, in terms of x, for the sum of the angles. Write your answer in its simplest form.

The sum of the angles is 180°.
(b) (i) Write down an equation in x.
  (ii) Solve your equation to find the size of the **smallest** angle in the triangle.

SEG 1998

CHAPTER 14

Solving Equations

Activity

Can you solve these puzzles?

- **Nueve** is a Spanish number.
  If you add 1 to **nueve** you get 10.
  What is **nueve**?

- What number must be put in each shape to make the statements correct?

  $\square + 3 = 8$ $\hexagon \times 3 = 30$ $2 \times \bigcirc - 3 = 7$

- a, b and c stand for three numbers in a code.
  Use these clues to work out what a, b and c are.

  $a - 2 = 5$ $\frac{1}{2} b = 7$ $3 \times (c + 1) = 30$

Equations such as these can be solved using a method known as **inspection**.
Solving an equation means finding the numerical value of the letter which fits the equation.

EXAMPLES   Solve these equations by inspection.

1 $x - 2 = 6$

$x = 8$

Reason:
8 $- 2 = 6$

2 $2y = 10$

$y = 5$

Reason:
$2 \times$ **5** $= 10$

3 $6(n + 1) = 60$

$n = 9$

Reason:
$6 \times ($**9**$ + 1) = 60$

Remember:
A letter or a symbol stands
for an unknown number.
$2y$ means $2 \times y$.
$6(n + 1)$ means $6 \times (n + 1)$.

Exercise 14.1

1 Solve these equations by inspection.
  (a) $x + 2 = 6$
  (b) $a + 7 = 15$
  (c) $y - 4 = 4$
  (d) $6 + t = 12$
  (e) $h - 1.8 = 2.4$
  (f) $d + \frac{1}{2} = 5$
  (g) $z - 175 = 250$
  (h) $p + 2.6 = 7$
  (i) $c + 1 = 1000$

2 Solve by inspection.
  (a) $2a = 18$
  (b) $4c = 20$
  (c) $6e = 42$
  (d) $6t = 360$
  (e) $5y = 450$
  (f) $12g = 60$
  (g) $\frac{1}{2} d = 7$
  (h) $\frac{1}{3} d = 2$
  (i) $\frac{h}{5} = 8$

The balance method

It is not always easy to solve equations by inspection.
Many equations are harder to solve than those in Exercise 14.1.
To solve harder equations a better method has to be used.
Here is a method that works a bit like a balance.

These scales are balanced.

You can add the same amount to both sides
and they still balance.

You can subtract the same amount from both sides
and they still balance.

You can double (or halve) the amount on both
sides and they still balance.

Equations work in the same way.
If you do the same to both sides of an equation, it is still true.

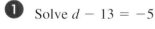 Use the balance method to solve these equations. Explain what you are doing.

1. Solve $d - 13 = -5$

   $d - 13 = -5$
   Add 13 to both sides.
   $\quad d = 8$

2. Solve $-4a = 20$

   $-4a = 20$
   Divide both sides by -4.
   $\quad a = -5$

> The aim is to find the numerical
> value of the letter, by ending up
> with **one letter** on one side of the
> equation and a **number** on the
> other side of the equation.

3. Solve $5 - 4n = -1$

   $5 - 4n = -1$
   Subtract 5 from both sides.
   $\quad -4n = -6$
   Divide both sides by -4.
   $\quad\quad n = 1.5$

4. Solve $\frac{1}{2}x - 7 = -1$

   $\frac{1}{2}x - 7 = -1$
   Add 7 to both sides.
   $\quad \frac{1}{2}x = 6$
   Multiply both sides by 2.
   $\quad\quad x = 12$

Look at the examples carefully.
The steps taken to solve the equations are explained.
Notice that:
Doing the same to both sides means:
  adding the **same number** to both sides.
  subtracting the **same number** from both sides.
  dividing both sides by the **same number**.
  multiplying both sides by the **same number**.

Exercise 14.2

1 Use the balance method to solve the equations. Write down the steps that you use to solve the equations.

(a) $y + 4 = 7$ (b) $m - 2 = -18$ (c) $f + 16 = -34$
(d) $14 + b = 21$ (e) $x - 42 = -28$ (f) $t - 1.5 = -13$

2 Use the balance method to solve the equations. Explain each step of your working.

(a) $3c = -12$ (b) $5a = 75$ (c) $-4f = 64$
(d) $8h = 20$ (e) $\frac{1}{2}p = 4$ (f) $\frac{1}{3}t = -0.3$

3 Use the balance method to solve the equations. Explain what you are doing.

(a) $4x + 3 = 11$ (b) $3n - 1 = 8$ (c) $2a + 7 = 7$
(d) $2d - 7 = 8$ (e) $8c + 3 = 15$ (f) $3 + 2a = -17$
(g) $-6p - 1 = 8$ (h) $2w + 6 = 4$ (i) $4m + 8 = 2$
(j) $\frac{1}{2}z + 2 = 7$ (k) $\frac{1}{4}t - 1 = 4$ (l) $1 - \frac{x}{6} = 4$

4 Solve these equations. There is no need to explain your working if you are confident of what you are doing.

(a) $2p + 1 = 9$ (b) $4t - 1 = 11$ (c) $3h - 7 = 14$
(d) $5d - 8 = 42$ (e) $3 + 2b = 15$ (f) $\frac{1}{2}x - 3 = 2$
(g) $8y - 14 = 26$ (h) $2.5z + 6 = 26$ (i) $\frac{n}{4} + 1 = 7$

5 Solve these equations.

(a) $p + 3 = -7$ (b) $6a = 15$ (c) $32 - 3t = 11$
(d) $-3 = 17 - 5n$ (e) $0.8c + 4 = 3.6$ (f) $1.2h + 1.7 = -3.1$
(g) $3 + 5x = 18$ (h) $0.5y + 6 = 2$ (i) $-\frac{1}{2}y + 13 = 7$
(j) $-2 = 5m + 13$ (k) $\frac{t}{3} + 21 = 15$ (l) $12 - \frac{v}{3} = 15$

Equations with letters on both sides

In some questions letters appear on both sides of the equation.
This is no problem. You can still use the balance method.

EXAMPLES   Solve the following equations using the balance method.
Explain what you are doing.

1 Solve $3x + 1 = x + 7$

$3x + 1 = x + 7$
Subtract 1 from both sides.
  $3x = x + 6$
Subtract x from both sides.
  $2x = 6$
Divide both sides by 2.
  $x = 3$

2 Solve $2a - 3 = 9 - a$

$2a - 3 = 9 - a$
Add 3 to both sides.
  $2a = 12 - a$
Add to both sides.
  $3a = 12$
Divide both sides by 3.
  $a = 4$

144

EXAMPLES

3 Solve $2p + 3 = 4 + 5p$

$2p + 3 = 4 + 5p$
Subtract 3 from both sides.
$2p = 1 + 5p$
Subtract $5p$ from both sides.
$-3p = 1$
Divide both sides by -3.
$p = -\frac{1}{3}$

4 Solve $\frac{1}{2}x - 7 = \frac{1}{4}x + 1$

$\frac{1}{2}x - 7 = \frac{1}{4}x + 1$
Add 7 to both sides.
$\frac{1}{2}x = \frac{1}{4}x + 8$
Subtract $\frac{1}{4}x$ from both sides.
$\frac{1}{2}x - \frac{1}{4}x = \frac{1}{4}x$
$\frac{1}{4}x = 8$
Multiply both sides by 4.
$x = 32$

As you become more confident you will not need to write down the steps you use to solve equations.
If you get confused, think of a balance and write down the steps needed to keep it balanced as you solve
the equation.

Exercise 14.3

1 Solve:
(a) $4x + 1 = x + 7$
(b) $3a + 5 = a + 7$
(c) $5p + 2 = p + 10$
(d) $6m - 1 = m + 9$
(e) $2y - 3 = 6 - y$

(f) $3t - 5 = 7 - t$
(g) $8n + 1 = 10 - n$
(h) $2c + 1 = 8 + c$
(i) $h - 2 = 2 - h$
(j) $3d - 4 = 5 + d$

(k) $7k + 3 = 3k + 7$
(l) $x + 2 = \frac{1}{2}x + 5$
(m) $4a + 3 = a$
(n) $3x - 2 = x$

2 Solve:
(a) $3c - 5 = c + 9$
(b) $2p + 1 = 10 - p$
(c) $3a + 1 = 16 - 2a$
(d) $6t - 1 = 15 - 2t$

(e) $6h - 16 = h + 4$
(f) $13 + 2u = 7 + 5u$
(g) $4b - 3 = 8b - 7$

(h) $3 - 5d = d + 18$
(i) $3n + 2 = n$
(j) $7x = 12 + 3x$

3 Solve:
(a) $4t + 3 = t - 12$
(b) $3y + 1 = 9 - y$
(c) $12s = 2s + 5$

(d) $3q = 12 - q$
(e) $6a - 2.5 = a + 6.5$
(f) $8c + 0.7 = 1.8 - 2c$

(g) $4 - 1\frac{1}{2}p = \frac{1}{2}p - 6$
(h) $x = \frac{1}{2}x - 3$

Equations with brackets

Equations can include brackets.
Before using the balance method any brackets must be
simplified by multiplying out.
This is called **expanding**.
Once the brackets have been removed the balance method
can be used as before.

Remember:
$2(x + 3) = 2 \times x + 2 \times 3$
$= 2x + 6$

$3(4a - 5) = 12a - 15$

EXAMPLES   Solve the following equations.

1 Solve $3(x + 2) = 12$

$3(x + 2) = 12$
Expand the brackets.
$3x + 6 = 12$
$3x = 6$
$x = 2$

2 Solve $4(3 + 2x) = 5(x + 2)$.

$4(3 + 2x) = 5(x + 2)$
$12 + 8x = 5x + 10$
$8x = 5x - 2$
$3x = -2$
$x = -\frac{2}{3}$

3 Solve $5(x + 2) + 2(2x - 1) = 7(x - 4)$

$5(x + 2) + 2(2x - 1) = 7(x - 4)$
Expanding.
$\qquad 5x + 10 + 4x - 2 = 7x - 28$
Gather like terms.
$\qquad\qquad 9x + 8 = 7x - 28$
Subtract 8 from both sides.
$\qquad\qquad 9x = 7x - 36$
Subtract $7x$ from both sides.
$\qquad\qquad 2x = -36$
Divide both sides by 2.
$\qquad\qquad x = -18$

Gathering terms
There are four terms in the expression.
$\qquad 5x + 10 + 4x - 2$
The x terms are **like** terms.
$\qquad 5x + 4x = 9x$
The number terms are **like** terms.
$\qquad 10 - 2 = 8$
So, $5x + 10 + 4x - 2 = 9x + 8$

Exercise 14.4

1 Solve:
  (a) $\ 2(x + 3) = 12$
  (b) $\ 4(a + 1) = 12$
  (c) $\ 6(c - 2) = 24$
  (d) $\ 3(p - 2) = 9$

  (e) $\ 4(2d - 1) = 20$
  (f) $\ 5(4 + 2t) = 50$
  (g) $\ 3(6 - a) = 15$
  (h) $\ 2(2 - 3t) = 10$

2 Solve:
  (a) $\ 3(n + 5) + n = 23$
  (b) $\ 3(2z - 5) = z + 15$
  (c) $\ 4(2w + 3) + 7 = 43$
  (d) $\ m + 2(m + 1) = 14$
  (e) $\ 2(3h - 4) = 3(h + 1) - 5$

  (f) $\ 2(3 - 2x) = 2(6 - x)$
  (g) $\ 2(3w - 1) + 4w = 28$
  (h) $\ 2(y + 4) + 3(2y - 5) = 5$
  (i) $\ 3(2v + 3) = 5 - 4(3 - v)$
  (j) $\ 5c - 2(4c - 9) = 5 + 5(2 - c)$

Equations with fractions

You have already met some equations with fractions in Exercise 14.2.
This section deals with harder equations with fractions.
For example: $\frac{3}{4} x = \frac{2}{5}$
With equations like this, it is easier to get rid of the fractions first.
To do this multiply both sides of the equation by the lowest common multiple of the denominators of the fractions.

What part of the fraction is the denominator?

The multiples of 4 are: 4, 8, 12, 16, **20**, . . .
The multiples of 5 are: 5, 10, 15, **20**, . . .
The lowest common multiple of 4 and 5 is 20.
So, the first step is to multiply both sides of the equation by 20.

$$\frac{3}{4} x \times 20 = \frac{2}{5} \times 20$$
This is the same as:
$$x \times \frac{3}{4} \times 20 = \frac{2}{5} \times 20$$
$$15x = 8$$

Divide both sides by 5.
$$x = \frac{8}{15}$$

Remember:
$\frac{3}{4} \times 20$ is the same as $\frac{3}{4}$ of 20.
To find $\frac{3}{4}$ of 20:
$\qquad 20 \div 4 = 5$ gives $\frac{1}{4}$ of 20.
$\qquad 5 \times 3 = 15$ gives $\frac{3}{4}$ of 20.
So, $\frac{3}{4} \times 20 = 15$.

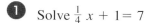

EXAMPLES

1 Solve $\frac{1}{4} x + 1 = 7$

$\frac{1}{4} x + 1 = 7$
Multiply both sides by 4.
$4 \times \frac{1}{4} x = x, \quad 4 \times 1 = 4$
$x + 4 = 28$
$x = 24$

2 Solve $\frac{2}{5} x = 6$

$\frac{2}{5} x = 6$
Multiply both sides by 5.
$5 \times \frac{2}{5} x = 5 \times 6$
$2x = 30$
$x = 15$

3 Solve $\frac{x + 3}{4} = 2$

$\frac{x + 3}{4} = 2$
Multiply both sides by 4.
$4 \times \frac{(x + 3)}{4} = 4 \times 2$
$x + 3 = 8$
$x = 5$

4 Solve $\frac{x - 1}{3} = \frac{x + 1}{4}$

$\frac{x - 1}{3} = \frac{x + 1}{4}$
Multiply both sides by 12.
Explain why?
$4(x - 1) = 3(x + 1)$
$4x - 4 = 3x + 3$
$4x = 3x + 7$
$x = 7$

Exercise 14.5

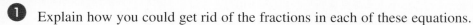

1 Explain how you could get rid of the fractions in each of these equations.

(a) $\frac{3}{4} a = \frac{2}{3}$ (b) $\frac{5}{8} = \frac{3}{4} b$ (c) $\frac{2}{7} c + 4 = 5$ (d) $\frac{x + 3}{5} = \frac{x - 7}{3}$

2 Solve these equations. Explain each step of your working.

(a) $\frac{2}{3} x = 4$ (b) $\frac{3}{4} w = 6$ (c) $\frac{5}{6} n = 20$

(d) $\frac{4}{5} a = \frac{3}{8}$ (e) $\frac{3}{4} p = \frac{4}{7}$ (f) $\frac{2}{3} b = \frac{5}{9}$

3 Solve these equations.

(a) $\frac{1}{4} y - 2 = 5$ (d) $\frac{1}{4} t - 1 = 5$ (g) $\frac{2(4x - 3)}{5} = -6$

(b) $\frac{a}{3} - 1 = 7$ (e) $\frac{h + 1}{4} = 3$ (h) $\frac{a - 1}{2} = \frac{a + 1}{3}$

(c) $\frac{a}{4} - 1 = 5$ (f) $\frac{7 - 2x}{3} = 5$ (i) $\frac{x + 2}{5} = \frac{3 - x}{4}$

Writing equations

So far, in this chapter, you have been given equations and asked to solve them.
The next step is to **write equations** (or **form equations**) using the information given in a problem.
The equations can then be solved in the usual way.
You may also be asked to use the solution to the equation to answer questions related to the initial problem.

Remember:
An **expression** is just an answer using letters and numbers.
An **equation** is similar to a formula. It always has an equal sign.
You first met these in Chapter 13.

EXAMPLES

1

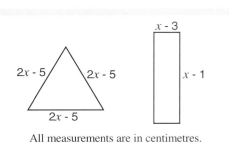

All measurements are in centimetres.

(a) Write down simplified expressions for the following, in terms of x.
 (i) The perimeter of the triangle.
 (ii) The perimeter of the rectangle.
(b) The perimeter of the triangle is equal to the perimeter of the rectangle.
 (i) Write down an equation in x.
 (ii) Use your equation to find the length of a side of the triangle.

(a) (i) The perimeter of the triangle is given by:
$3(2x - 5)$ cm
$= 6x - 15$ cm
 (ii) The perimeter of the rectangle is given by:
$2 \times$ length $+ 2 \times$ breadth
$= 2(x - 1) + 2(x - 3)$ cm
$= 2x - 2 + 2x - 6$
$= 4x - 8$ cm

(b) (i) The perimeter of the triangle is the same (equal to) as the perimeter of the rectangle.
$6x - 15 = 4x - 8$
$6x = 4x + 7$
$2x = 7$
$x = 3.5$
 (ii) The length of a side of the triangle is given by:
$(2x - 5)$ cm
Substitute $x = 3.5$
$2 \times 3.5 - 5$
$= 7 - 5$
$= 2$
The length of a side of the triangle is 2 cm.

2 John has x CDs in his collection.
Sarah has five times as many CDs as John.
John and Sarah each collect another 12 CDs.
Now Sarah has twice as many CDs as John.
 (a) Write down an expression, in terms of x, for the number of CDs Sarah has now.
 (b) Form an equation and solve it to find how many CDS Sarah has now.

 (a) John started with x CDs.
Sarah started with five times as many, $5x$ CDs.
After collecting another 12, Sarah now has $5x + 12$ CDs.

 (b) John started with x CDs.
He now has $x + 12$ CDs.
Sarah has twice as many CDs as John.
This means that:
$2 \times$ number of CDs John has now = number of CDs Sarah has now
$2(x + 12) = 5x + 12$
$2x + 24 = 5x + 12$
$2x + 12 = 5x$
$12 = 3x$
$x = 4$
The number of CDs Sarah has now is given by: $5x + 12$
Substitute $x = 4$
$5 \times 4 + 12$
$= 20 + 12$
$= 32$
Sarah has 32 CDs now.

1 (a) Write down a simplified expression, in terms of x, for the perimeter of the triangle.
(b) The perimeter of the triangle is 59 cm. Write down an equation and solve it to find the value of x.
(c) Use your answer to find the length of each side of the triangle.

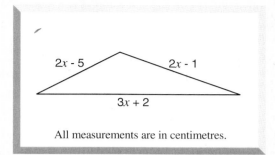

All measurements are in centimetres.

2 Geoffrey knows that the angles of a pentagon add up to 540°.
(a) Write down an equation in x.
(b) Use your equation to find the size of the largest angle.

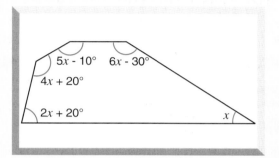

3 (a) Write down an expression, in terms of x, for the perimeter of the rectangle.
(b) The perimeter of the rectangle is equal to the perimeter of the square.
Form an equation and find the value of x.
(c) What is the perimeter of the rectangle, in centimetres?

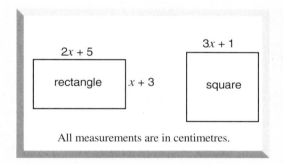

All measurements are in centimetres.

4 Claire is x years old now. Her father is six times as old as Claire.
(a) Write expressions for the following, in terms of x.
  (i) Claire's father's age now.
  (ii) Claire's age in 20 years time.
  (iii) Claire's father's age in 20 years time.
After 20 years Claire's father will be twice as old as Claire.
(b) Write an equation and solve it to find Claire's age now.

5 Alex has x marbles. Bert has 10 marbles fewer than Alex.
Each boy wins two extra marbles.
Alex then said to Bert, "I now have three times as many marbles as you have."
(a) Write expressions for the following, in terms of x.
  (i) The number of marbles Bert had to start with.
  (ii) The number of marbles Bert has now.
(b) (i) Using Alex's statement write down an equation.
  (ii) Solve your equation to find the number of marbles Alex had at the start.
  (iii) How many marbles does Bert have now?

What you need to know

- The solution of an equation is the value of the unknown letter that fits the equation.

You should be able to:
- Solve simple equations by inspection.
  e.g. $x + 2 = 5$, $x - 3 = 7$, $2x = 10$, $\frac{x}{4} = 12$
- Use the balance method to solve equations which are difficult to solve by inspection.
- Solve equations with unknowns on both sides of the equals sign.
  e.g. $3x + 1 = x + 7$
- Solve equations with brackets.
  e.g. $4(3 + 2x) = 5(x + 2)$
- Solve equations with fractions.
  e.g. $\frac{1}{4} x + 1 = 7$, $\frac{x + 3}{4} = 2$
- Write, or form, equations using the information given in a problem.

Review Exercise

1 Solve these equations.
   (a) $3 - 4q = 11$ (b) $2(s + 5) = 7$ (c) $3p - 2 = 6 - p$

   (d) $4(2t - 3) + 4t = 6$ (e) $7 + 2(3p - 7) = 29$ (f) $\frac{2x + 9}{5} = 6$

2 Solve the equation $\frac{x}{4} + 7 = 12$
                                                                   SEG 1996

3 Solve these equations.
   (a) $3x + 2 = 18 - 5x$ (b) $2(x + 3) = 18 - 6x$ SEG 1994

4 The lengths of the sides of a triangle are x cm, $(x + 3)$ cm and $(x - 2)$ cm.
   (a)   What is the perimeter of the triangle in terms of x?
   (b)   The triangle has a perimeter of 22 cm.
       (i)   Write down an equation in x.
      (ii)   Use your equation to find the length of each side of the triangle.
                                    SEG 1995

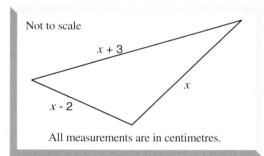

Not to scale

All measurements are in centimetres.

5 P and Q are rectangles.
The dimensions are given in centimetres.
   (a)   Write down a simplified expression for the area of P.

The two rectangles have the same perimeter.
The perimeter of P is $4x + 8$.
The perimeter of Q is $12x + 2$.

   (b)   (i)   Solve the equation $4x + 8 = 12x + 2$.
      (ii)   What is the perimeter of P in centimetres?
                               SEG 1997

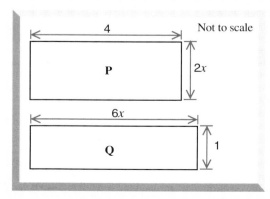

Not to scale

6 These rectangles are equal in area.
Solve $3(x + 2) = 2(5x - 4)$ to find the value of x.
Find the length and width of each rectangle.

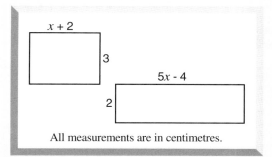

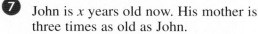

All measurements are in centimetres.

7 John is x years old now. His mother is three times as old as John.
(a) Write down expressions for the following, in terms of x.
   (i) John's age in 9 years time.
   (ii) John's mother's age in 9 years time.

After 9 years John's mother will be twice as old as John.
   (b) Form an equation and solve it to find John's age **now**.

SEG 1995

8

A party cup costs three pence. A party plate costs four pence.

(a) Write an expression, in terms of n, for the cost of n cups.
(b) Write an expression, in terms of n, for the cost of $n - 5$ plates.
(c) George buys n cups and $n - 5$ plates.
He pays 85 pence.
   (i) Form an equation in n.
   (ii) Solve your equation to find the number of cups bought.

SEG 1995

9 Suzi is wheeling two bags of compost in a trolley.
Mike is carrying five bags of compost in a basket.

An empty trolley weighs 10 kg and an empty basket weighs 1 kg.
A bag of compost weighs c kilograms.
Suzi's trolley and compost weigh $2c + 10$ kg.

(a) Write down an expression for the weight of Mike's basket and compost

Suzi's trolley and compost weigh the same as Mike's basket and compost.
(b) (i) Form an equation from the two expressions.
   (ii) Solve your equation to find the weight of a bag of compost.

SEG 1995

10 A bottle of lemonade costs x pence.
A bottle of cola costs 7 pence more than a bottle of lemonade.

(a) Write down, in terms of x,
   (i) the cost of a bottle of cola,
   (ii) the total cost of three bottles of lemonade and one bottle of cola.

(b) The total cost of the three bottles of lemonade and one bottle of cola is £2.75.
Form an equation in x and solve it to find the cost of a bottle of lemonade.

SEG 1997

Sequence of numbers from shape patterns

Activity

These patterns are made using squares.

Pattern 1
3 squares

Pattern 2
5 squares

Pattern 3
7 squares

How many squares are used to make Pattern 4?
How many squares are used to make Pattern 10?
How many squares are used to make Pattern 100?
Which pattern is made using 81 squares?

The number of squares used to make each pattern forms a **sequence**.

Pattern 4 is made using 9 squares.
You could have answered this: by drawing Pattern 4 or,
by continuing the sequence of numbers 3, 5, 7, . . .
It is possible to do the same for Pattern 10, though it would involve a lot of work, but it would be unreasonable to use either method for Pattern 100.
Instead we can investigate how each pattern is made.

$2 \times 1 + 1 = 3$ **squares** $2 \times 2 + 1 = 5$ **squares** $2 \times 3 + 1 = 7$ **squares**

Each pattern is made using a **rule**.
The rule can be **described in words**.
To find the number of squares used to make a pattern use the rule:
"Double the pattern number and add 1."

Pattern number	Rule	Number of squares
4	$2 \times 4 + 1$	9
10	$2 \times 10 + 1$	21
100	$2 \times 100 + 1$	201

$81 = 2 \times 40 + 1$, so the 40th pattern is made using 81 squares.

The same rule can be **written using symbols**.
We can then answer a very important question:
How many squares are used to make Pattern n?

Pattern n will have $2 \times n + 1$ squares.
This can be written as $2n + 1$ squares.

152

1 Patterns are made using black and white counters.

(a) How many white counters are
there in a pattern with
(i)   5 black counters,
(ii) 10 black counters,
(iii) 100 black counters?

1 black
3 white

2 black
6 white

3 black
9 white

(b) How many white counters are there in a pattern with *n* black counters?

2 These patterns are made using matches.

(a) How many matches are used to make
(i)   Pattern 4,
(ii) Pattern 20?

(b) Which pattern uses 29 matches?

Pattern 1
5 matches

Pattern 2
9 matches

Pattern 3
13 matches

(c) How many matches are used to make Pattern *n*?

3 Fences are made by placing fence posts 1m apart and using 2 horizontal bars between them.

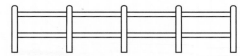

The fence above is 4m long. It has 5 posts and 8 bars.

(a) A fence is 50 m long.
(i)   How many posts does it have?
(ii) How many bars does it have?

(b) A fence is *x* metres long.
Write down expressions for
(i)   the number of posts,
(ii) the number of bars.

4 Cubes of side 1 cm are used to make rods.
This rod is made using 4 linking cubes.

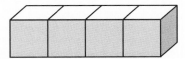

The surface area of the rod is 18 square centimetres.
(4 squares on each of the long sides plus one square at each end.)

(a) What is the surface area of a rod made using 5 linking cubes?

(b) What is the surface area of a rod made using 10 linking cubes?

(c) What is the surface area of a rod made using *n* linking cubes?

5 These patterns are made using matches.

(a) How many matches are used to make
Pattern 5?

Pattern 1

Pattern 2

Pattern 3

(b) Which pattern uses 37 matches?

(c) Find a formula for the number of matches, *m*, in Pattern *p*.

The first thing to consider when investigating a sequence is whether it is **linear** or **quadratic**.

Numbers in a sequence are called **terms**.

Linear sequences

These increase (or decrease) by the same amount from one term to the next.
That is they have a **common difference**.
For example, terms in the sequence 2, 8, 14, 20, 26, ... have a common difference of 6.
If a sequence is linear compare each term in the sequence with the counting numbers 1, 2, 3, 4, ...

Quadratic sequences

Terms in a quadratic sequence do not have a common difference, **but** the change in the differences between terms increases (or decreases) by the same amount each time.
For example, the sequence 3, 4, 6, 9, 13, ... has differences of 1, 2, 3, 4, ... which increase by 1 each time.
If a sequence is quadratic compare each term with the square numbers 1, 4, 9, 16, ...

EXAMPLES

Multiply the counting numbers by the common difference. In this example we multiply by 4.

1 Find the nth term of the sequence 5, 9, 13, 17, ...

First we have to decide whether the sequence is linear or quadratic. It is linear because the numbers go up by 4 each time.
Compare each term with 1, 2, 3, ...

1	2	3	4	...	n
↓	↓	↓	↓		
5	9	13	17	...	
$= 4 \times 1 + 1$	$= 4 \times 2 + 1$	$= 4 \times 3 + 1$	$= 4 \times 4 + 1 \ldots$		$4 \times n + 1$

So the nth term is $4 \times n + 1$ or $4n + 1$.

2 Find the nth term of the sequence 2, 5, 10, 17, ...

This is not a linear sequence as the numbers do not increase by the same amount each time. It is a quadratic sequence. The differences (3, 5, 7, ...) increase by 2 each time.
Compare each term with 1, 4, 9, 16, ...

1	2	3	4		n
↓	↓	↓	↓		↓
1	4	9	16	...	n^2
↓	↓	↓	↓		↓
2	5	10	17	...	
$= 1^2 + 1$	$= 2^2 + 1$	$= 3^2 + 1$	$= 4^2 + 1 \ldots$		$= n^2 + 1$

So the nth term is $n^2 + 1$.

EXAMPLE

3 What is the nth term of the sequence 3, 12, 27, 48, 75, . . .

This is a quadratic sequence because the differences go up by 6 each time (9, 15, 21, 27, . . .).

1	2	3	4	5	. . .	n
↓	↓	↓	↓	↓		↓
1	4	9	16	25	. . .	n^2
↓	↓	↓	↓	↓		
3	12	27	48	75		
$= 3 \times 1^2$	$= 3 \times 2^2$	$= 3 \times 3^2$	$= 3 \times 4^2$	$= 3 \times 5^2 \ldots$		$= 3 \times n^2$

So the nth term is $3 \times n^2$ or $3n^2$.

Exercise 15.2

1 The next number in this sequence is found by adding the last two terms.
1, 1, 2, 3, 5, 8, . . .

(a) Write down the next **three** terms in the sequence.
(b) What is the 12th term of the sequence?

2 A sequence begins 4, 7, 13, 25, . . .
The next number in the sequence can be found using the rule:
"Multiply the last term by 2 then subtract 1."

(a) Write down the next **two** terms in the sequence.
(b) The 11th term in the sequence is 3073. Use this information to find the 10th term in the sequence.

3 Find the next term in each sequence and state whether the sequence is linear or quadratic?

(a) 1, 4, 7, 10, 13, . . .
(b) 1, 3, 6, 10, 15, . . .
(c) 1, 7, 13, 19, 25, . . .
(d) 19, 16, 13, 10, 7, . . .
(e) 5, 10, 17, 26, 37, . . .
(f) 5, 9, 13, 17, . . .

4 These sequences are linear.
Find the nth term of each sequence.

(a) 4, 8, 12, 16, . . .
(b) 1, 3, 5, 7, 9, . . .
(c) 7, 11, 15, 19, 23, . . .
(d) 2, 7, 12, 17, 22, . . .
(e) 8, 12, 16, 20, . . .
(f) 6, 4, 2, 0, –2, . . .

5 These sequences are quadratic.
Find the nth term in each sequence by comparing it with 1, 4, 9, 16, . . .

(a) 0, 3, 8, 15, 24, . . .
(b) 4, 7, 12, 19, 28, . . .
(c) 2, 8, 18, 32, 50, . . .
(d) 2, 6, 12, 20, 30, . . .

6 Find the nth term in these sequences.

(a) 5, 8, 11, 14, 17, . . .
(b) 5, 8, 13, 20, . . .
(c) 8, 14, 20, 26, . . .
(d) 3, 12, 27, 64, . . .
(e) 3, 8, 13, 18, 23, . . .
(f) 3, 6, 11, 18, 27, . . .
(g) 0, 2, 6, 12, 20, . . .
(h) $\frac{1}{2}, \frac{2}{3}, \frac{3}{4}, \frac{4}{5}, \frac{5}{6}, \ldots$

Substituting into formulae

A formula is an algebraic rule.
Formulae can either be written in words or written using algebraic symbols.
For example,
$S = 2\pi r (r + h)$ is a formula used to find the total surface area, $S\,\text{cm}^2$, of a cylinder that has radius, $r\,\text{cm}$ and height, $h\,\text{cm}$.
By **substituting** values for π, r and h you can calculate the value of S.

Substitution into formulae was first covered in Chapter 13.
Here, the formulae are more complex.
Values to be substituted may include whole numbers, negative numbers, decimals, fractions, etc.

1 The population density of a country is given by the formula:

$$\text{population density} = \frac{\text{Population}}{\text{Area}}$$

Find the population density of Greenland, which has an area of 840 000 square miles and a population of 56 000.

$$\text{population density} = \frac{56\,000}{840\,000}$$

$$= 0.0666 \ldots$$
$$= 0.067$$

Population of Greenland = 0.067 people per square mile, correct to 3 decimal places.

2 The height, h metres, of a bullet after t seconds, is given by the formula $h = ut - \frac{1}{2}gt^2$, where u ms^{-1} is the initial vertical speed and g ms^{-2} is the acceleration due to gravity.
Find h when $u = 20$ and $t = 1\frac{3}{5}$.
Take $g = 9.8$

$$h = ut - \frac{1}{2}gt^2$$
$$= 200 \times 1.6 - \frac{1}{2} \times 9.8 \times 1.6^2$$

Notice that $1\frac{3}{5} = 1 + 3 \div 5 = 1.6$

$$= 320 - 12.544$$
$$= 307.456$$

h = 307 m, correct to 3 sig. fig.

Exercise 15.3

Questions 1 to 4.
Do not use a calculator.
Show your working clearly.

1 The approximate area of a circle, A, is given by the formula $A = 3r^2$, where r is the radius of the circle.
Find the value of A when $r = 5$.

2 The voltage, V volts, in a circuit with resistance R ohms, and current, I amps, is given by the formula $V = IR$.
Find the voltage in a circuit when $I = 12$ and $R = 20$.

3 A simple formula for the motion of a car is $F = ma + R$.
Find F when $m = 500$, $a = 0.2$ and $R = 4000$.

4 The formula $F = \frac{mv^2}{r}$ describes the motion of a cyclist rounding a corner.
Find F when $m = 80$, $v = 6$ and $r = 20$.

Questions 5 to 10.
You may use a calculator to answer these questions.

5 $T = 45W + 30$ is used to calculate the time in minutes needed to cook a joint of beef weighing W kilograms.
How many minutes are needed to cook a joint weighing 2.4 kg?

6 The formula $v = u + at$ gives the speed v of a particle, t seconds after it starts with speed u. Calculate v when $u = 7.8$, $a = -10$ and $t = \frac{3}{4}$.

7 The cost, £C, of n units of gas is calculated using the formula $C = 0.08n + 3.5$
Calculate the cost of 458 units of gas.

8 Temperatures in °F can be changed into °C using the formula:
$$C = \frac{5}{9}(F - 32)$$
(a) Calculate the value of C when $F = 59$.
(b) What temperature, in °C, is equivalent to 5°F?

9 The time T, for a pendulum to make a complete swing is given by the formula:
$$T = 2\pi\sqrt{\frac{l}{g}}$$
(a) Calculate the value of T when $l = 0.8$ and $g = 9.8$
(b) Calculate the value of T when $l = 1\frac{1}{2}$ and $g = 9.8$
Take π to be 3.14 or use the π key on your calculator.

10 Use the formula $v = \sqrt{u^2 + 2as}$
to calculate the value of v when
(a) $u = 2.4$, $a = 3.2$, $s = 5.25$
(b) $u = 9.1$, $a = -4.7$, $s = 3.04$
Give your answers correct to one decimal place.

Rearranging formulae

Sometimes it is easier to use a formula if you **rearrange** it first.

EXAMPLES

1 The formula $k = \frac{8m}{5}$ can be used to change distances in miles to distances in kilometres. Rearrange this to give a formula which can be used to change distances in kilometres into distances in miles.

$$k = \frac{8m}{5}$$

Multiply both sides by 5.

$$5k = 8m$$

Divide both sides by 8.

$$\frac{5k}{8} = m$$

We say we have **rearranged the formula**

$k = \frac{8m}{5}$ to make m the **subject** of the formula.

2 Make x the subject of $y = 2x + 8$

$$y = 2x + 8$$

Subtract 8 from both sides.

$$y - 8 = 2x$$

Divide both sides by 2.

$$\tfrac{1}{2} y - 4 = x$$

So we rearranged $y = 2x + 8$

to get $x = \tfrac{1}{2} y - 4$.

y is the subject of $y = 2x + 8$,

x is the subject of $x = \tfrac{1}{2} y - 4$

Exercise 15.4

1 Make x the subject of these formulae:

(a) $y = x + 5$ (b) $y = x - 2$

(c) $y = 4x$ (d) $y = \tfrac{1}{2}x$

(e) $y = 2x + 6$ (f) $y = 3x - 9$

(g) $4y = 2x - 5$ (h) $y = \tfrac{1}{2}(3x + 6)$

2 A formula for changing kilograms to pounds is $P = 0.45K$
Rearrange the formula to give K in terms of P.

3 $F = 1.8C + 32$ changes temperatures in °C to °F.
Rearrange the formula to give C in terms of F.

4 Match the pairs:

$y = x + 3$ $x = 3y$ $y = 3x + 1$

$x = y - 3$ $y = \tfrac{1}{3} x$ $x = \tfrac{1}{3} y$

$y = 3x$ $x = \tfrac{1}{3}(y - 1)$ $y = 3x - 1$

$x = \tfrac{1}{3} y + \tfrac{1}{3}$

5 Make v the subject of each of these formulae:

(a) $v + 3 = u$ (b) $v - u = r$

(c) $2v = r$ (d) $vi = u$

(e) $\frac{v}{x} = t$ (f) $v - u = at$

(g) $p = mv + d$ (h) $mv^2 = F$

6 The cost, £C, of hiring a car for n days is given by $C = 35 + 24n$.

(a) Find the cost of hiring a car for 3 days.

(b) A customer paid £251 to hire a car.
Make n the subject of the formula and use your new formula to find for how many days the customer had hired the car.

7 The area of a trapezium is given by $A = \tfrac{1}{2}h(a + b)$
Make a the subject of this formula.

8 Make the bold letter the subject of these formulae.

(a) $\frac{V}{I} = R$ (b) $E = \mathbf{m}c^2$

(c) $y = a\mathbf{x}^2 + b$ (d) $e = \tfrac{1}{2}m\mathbf{v}^2$

9 Make a the subject of these formulae.

(a) $b = a + c^2$ (b) $a^2 = b$

(c) $4a = 8b + c$ (d) $6a = 2b$

(e) $3a = \frac{4b}{5}$ (f) $b = \frac{2a}{3}$

(g) $b = \tfrac{1}{4} a^2$ (h) $3b = 2a^2 - 5$

Using graphs

Graphs are sometimes drawn to show real-life situations.
In most cases a quantity is measured over a period of time.

EXAMPLE

Craig drew a graph to show the amount of fuel in the family car as they travelled to their holiday destination. He also made these notes:

Part of Graph	Event
A	Leave home.
A to B	Motorway.
B to C	Car breaks down.
C to D	On our way again.
D to E	Stop for lunch.
E to F	Fill tank with fuel.
F to G	Country roads.
G	Arrive, at last!

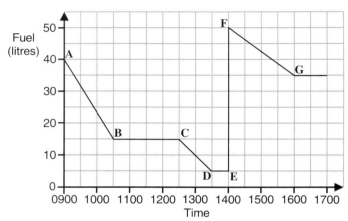

How much fuel was in the tank at the start of the journey?
At what time did the car break down?
How long did the family stop for lunch?
How much fuel was put into the tank at the garage?
At what time did the journey end?

Notice that in this example and others involving graphs against time.

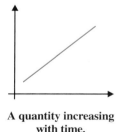

A quantity increasing with time.

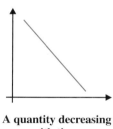

A quantity decreasing with time.

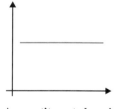

A quantity not changing, i.e. constant.

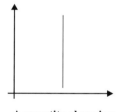

A quantity changing instantly.

Exercise 15.5

1 A climber pulls a rucksack up a vertical cliff face using a rope.
Which of the graphs below could represent the motion of the rucksack against time?

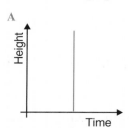

A

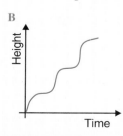

B

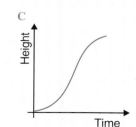

C

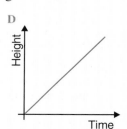

D

2 (a) Sketch a graph to show what is happening in this story:

"John leaves home at 8 am to go the shops. After 5 minutes he sees the bus coming and runs for 2 minutes. The bus has broken down so he waits for 3 minutes. He then walks slowly home, which takes 10 minutes."

(b) Write a similar story about your journey to school and draw a graph for it.

(c) Write a story for this graph.

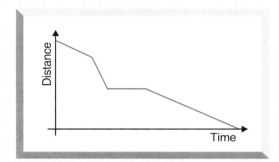

3 Match the graphs to the situations. In each graph, the horizontal axis represents time and the vertical axis represents speed.

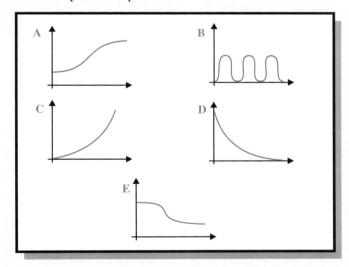

1 A runner starts from rest and begins to pick up speed.

2 A runner keeps having to stop and start.

3 A runner gets tired and has to slow down.

4 A runner sees the finish, builds up speed and sprints to the line.

4 Cans of drink can be bought from a vending machine in the school canteen.
At the start of the day the machine is three quarters full.
During break, from 10.45 to 11.00, drinks are bought from the machine at a steady rate.
By the end of the break the machine is one-quarter full.
At 12.00 the machine is filled.
The lunch break is from 12.30 to 1.30. Someone complains at 1.15 that the machine is empty.
The machine is filled at 2.00, ready for the afternoon break from 2.45 to 3.00.
At the end of the day the machine is three-quarters full.

Sketch a graph to show the number of drinks in the machine from 9.00 to 4.00.

5 Water is poured into some containers at a constant rate.
Copy the axes given and sketch the graph of the depth of the water against time for each container as it is filled.

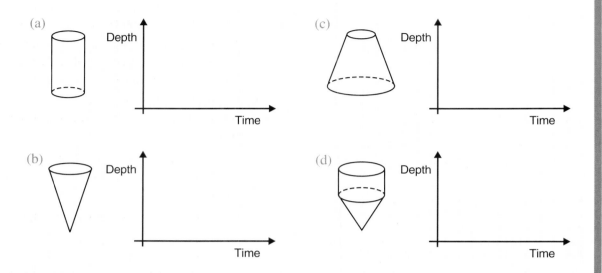

6 Water is drained from a hole in the bottom of a container.

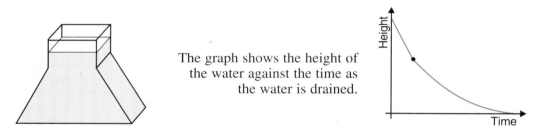

The graph shows the height of the water against the time as the water is drained.

Water is drained from these containers. Each graph shows the height of the water against time.
(a) Match the containers to the graphs.
(b) Draw a container for the graph which is not matched.

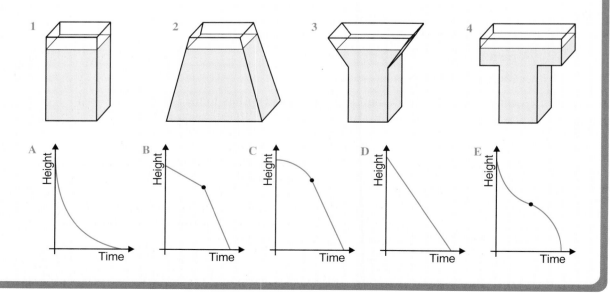

What you need to know

- Patterns of shapes can be drawn to represent **number sequences**.

  For example,

  represents the sequence, 3, 5, 7, …

- Patterns are made using **rules** which can either be described in words or written using symbols.

- Numbers in a sequence are called **terms**.

- **Linear sequences** increase (or decrease) by the same amount from one term to the next, i.e. they have a **common difference**.

- **Quadratic sequences** do not have a common difference, but the change in the differences between terms increases (or decreases) by the same amount each time.

- A **formula** is an algebraic rule which can be **rearranged** to make another letter (variable) the **subject**.

You should be able to:
- Draw patterns of shapes which represent number sequences.

- Continue a given number sequence.

- Find the expression for the nth term of a sequence.

- Substitute values into given formulae.

- Draw and interpret graphs which represent real-life situations.

Review Exercise

1 A sequence of patterns is formed using equilateral triangles.

 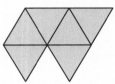 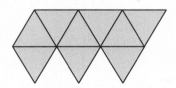

| Pattern 1 | Pattern 2 | Pattern 3 |

(a) How many triangles are in Pattern 10?
(b) Explain why a pattern in this sequence cannot have 40 triangles.
(c) Write an expression, in terms of p, for the number of triangles in Pattern p.

SEG 1997

2 Patterns of hexagons are made using matchsticks.
The first three patterns are drawn.

| Pattern 1 | Pattern 2 | Pattern 3 |

(a) Complete this table.

(b) A pattern has 36 sticks.
What is the number of this pattern?

(c) (i) How many sticks are needed to make Pattern 100?

Pattern (p)	1	2	3	4
Number of sticks (n)	6			

(ii) Write down a rule for finding the number of sticks used in Pattern p.

SEG 1996

3 (a) (i) Copy and complete this mapping.

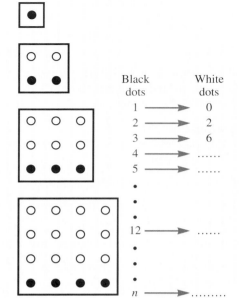

Black dots		White dots
1	⟶	0
2	⟶	2
3	⟶	6
4	⟶	......
5	⟶	......
.		
.		
.		
12	⟶	......
.		
.		
.		
n	⟶	....

(ii) In another of these rectangles the total number of dots is 74. Use the expression in (i) to find the length of this rectangle.

(b) Copy and complete this mapping.

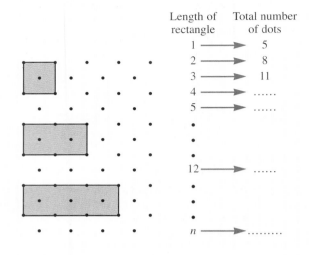

Length of rectangle		Total number of dots
1	⟶	5
2	⟶	8
3	⟶	11
4	⟶	......
5	⟶	......
.		
.		
.		
12	⟶	......
.		
.		
.		
n	⟶	....

SEG 1994

4 (a) Write down, in terms of n, the nth term of the sequence: 3, 7, 11, 15, ...

(b) Write down, in terms of n, the nth term of the sequence: $\frac{1}{3}, \frac{1}{9}, \frac{1}{27}, \frac{1}{81}, \ldots$

SEG 1995

5 The first two terms of a sequence are: 4, 8.

(a) Using the rule:

> ADD THE TWO PREVIOUS NUMBERS AND DIVIDE BY TWO

write down the third and fourth terms of the sequence.

(b) If the sequence had begun 8, 4 instead of 4, 8 would the third and fourth terms be the same as those in part (a)?
Give a reason for your answer.

SEG 1997

6 The rule for any term in a sequence is $\frac{n}{2n-1}$, where n is the number of the term.

(a) Use this rule to write down the first five terms of the sequence.

(b) The first five terms of a different sequence are

Term	1	2	3	4	5
Sequence	$\frac{1}{2}$	$\frac{2}{5}$	$\frac{3}{8}$	$\frac{4}{11}$	$\frac{5}{14}$

Write down the rule for the nth term of the sequence.

SEG 1995

7 Jeff is investigating rectangular patterns of crosses.
The first four patterns he draws are shown.

```
× ×      × × × ×      × × × × × ×      × × × × × × × ×
         × × × ×      × × × × × ×      × × × × × × × ×
                      × × × × × ×      × × × × × × × ×
                                       × × × × × × × ×
```

   Pattern 1   **Pattern 2**   **Pattern 3**   **Pattern 4**

More patterns are drawn.
(a) Copy and complete the statements.
   (i) The number of crosses in the 10th pattern is 10 by ……
   (ii) The number of crosses in the nth pattern is n by ……

(b) The number of crosses in each pattern form a sequence.
         2, 8, 18, 32, ……
   (i) Find the next **two** numbers in the sequence.
   (ii) When each number in this sequence is divided by two a new sequence
      1, 4, 9, 16, … is formed.
      Describe the new sequence of the numbers.
   (iii) The nth term of the sequence 1, 4, 9, 16, … is n^2.
      What is the nth term of the sequence 2, 8, 18, 32, … ?

SEG 1995

8 The cost of hiring a car can be calculated by using the formula
$$\text{Cost(£)} = 25d + \frac{12\,(m - 50d)}{100}$$

where d is the number of days the car is hired and m is the number of miles the car is driven.

A car is hired for 7 days and driven 476 miles.
Calculate the total cost of the car hire.

SEG 1996

9 You are given the formula $v = u + at$.
   (a) Work out the value of v when $u = 20$, $a = -6$ and $t = \frac{9}{5}$.
   (b) Rearrange the formula to give t in terms of v, u and a.

SEG 1998

10 When a person is 50 years old or more, the cost of joining the "Have Fun" Sports Club is calculated using the formula:
$$C = \tfrac{1}{2} \sqrt{(75 - x)}.$$

   C is the cost in pounds.

The age, in completed years, of the person joining is x.

(a) At what age does it become free to join the club?

Mary is more than 50 years old.
She paid £1.50 to join the club.
(b) Calculate Mary's age.

When a person is younger than 50 years of age, the cost of joining the Sports Club is given by the formula:
$$C = \tfrac{1}{3} \sqrt{(25 + y)}$$

where C is the cost in pounds and y is the age of the person joining.

(c) Express y in terms of C.

SEG 1996

11 Water flows into some containers at a constant rate.
  (a) Sketch the graphs of the depths of the water against time.

  (i)   (ii)

  (b) Sketch the cross-section of the container that generated this graph.

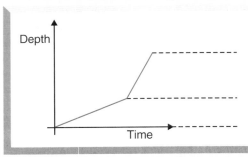

SEG 1995

12 Decide which graph matches each relationship.

Graph W 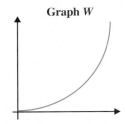   **Graph X** 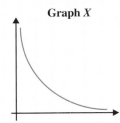   **Graph Y** 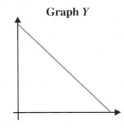   **Graph Z**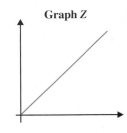

Relationships
A: The area of a circle plotted against its radius.
B: The circumference of a circle plotted against its radius.
C: The length of a rectangle of area 24 cm² plotted against its width.

SEG 1996

13 A builder wants to build houses on a triangular plot of land.
The plot has sides of length 125.5 metres, 106.3 metres and
144.2 metres.

The builder needs to work out the area of the plot.
The following method can be used to find the area
of a triangle when the sides are known.

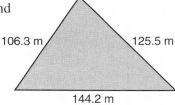

In any triangle with sides of length a, b and c, follow these steps to find the area.

  Step 1: calculate the semi-perimeter, s, from
  $$s = \frac{a + b + c}{2}$$

  Step 2: calculate the area, A, from
  $$A = \sqrt{s(s - a)(s - b)(s - c)}$$

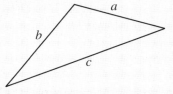

Use this method to calculate the area of the plot.

SEG 1997

CHAPTER 16

Straight Line Graphs

Number patterns and graphs

Look at these coordinates (1, 3), (2, 5), (3, 7), (4, 9).
Can you see any number patterns?

The same coordinates can be shown in a **table**.

x	1	2	3	4
y	3	5	7	9

The pairs of coordinates are part of a **linear sequence**.
    The x coordinate increases by 1.
    The y coordinate increases by 2.

A **rule** connects the x coordinate with the y coordinate.
This rule can be written, in **words**, as:
    "To find the y coordinate, multiply the
    x coordinate by 2 and add 1."
The same rule can also be written, using **symbols**, as:
    $y = 2x + 1$

The diagram shows the coordinates plotted on a **graph**.
The points all lie on a **straight line**.
All points on the line obey the rule $y = 2x + 1$.

Graphs don't just stop at the points that are plotted.
They go right through them and don't even stop at
the axes.

*How can you check that the points (1.5, 4) and
(−2, −3) lie on the line $y = 2x + 1$?*

Linear sequences were first
introduced in Chapter 15.

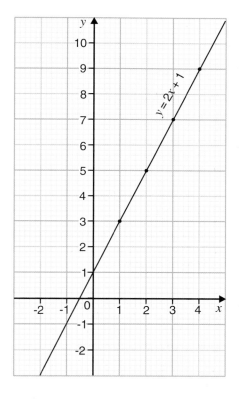

Activity
Describe each of these sets of coordinates in the same way and then show them on a graph.

1	2	3	4	5	6
(1, 0)	(0, 4)	(0, 0)	(1, 1)	(1, 7)	(1, 6)
(1, 2)	(1, 4)	(1, 1)	(2, 3)	(2, 6)	(2, 4)
(1, 4)	(2, 4)	(2, 2)	(3, 5)	(3, 5)	(3, 2)
(1, 6)	(3, 4)	(3, 3)	(4, 6)	(4, 4)	(4, 0)

What do you notice?

Drawing a graph from a rule

This diagram shows the graphs:

$x = 4$ $\quad$ $y = 3$
$x = -2$ $\quad$ $y = -5$

Notice that:
The graph of $x = 4$ is a **vertical** line.
All points on the line have x coordinate 4.

The graph of $y = 3$ is a **horizontal** line.
All points on the line have y coordinate 3.

$x = 0$ is the y axis.
$y = 0$ is the x axis.

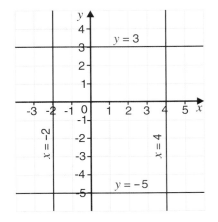

EXAMPLE

Draw the graph of the equation $y = 3x - 4$.

If values for x are not given in the question you must choose your own.

When $x = 0$, $y = 3 \times 0 - 4 = -4$.
This gives the point $(0, -4)$.

When $x = 1$, $y = 3 \times 1 - 4 = -1$.
This gives the point $(1, -1)$.

When $x = 3$, $y = 3 \times 3 - 4 = 5$.
This gives the point $(3, 5)$.

Why do you think these values of x have been chosen?
Could other values have been chosen?

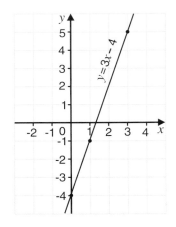

Exercise 16.1

1 Write down the equations of the lines labelled on this graph.

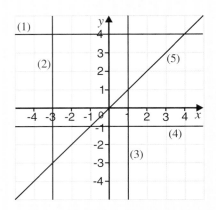

2

x	1	2	3
y			

Copy and complete a table like the one above for each of these equations.
(a) $y = x + 2$
(b) $y = 2x$
(c) $y = 6 - 2x$

3 On separate copies of this coordinate grid draw graphs for each of the equations in Question 2.

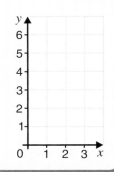

4 Draw tables and use them to draw graphs of:

(a) $y = x - 1$
Draw and label the x axis from -2 to 3 and the y axis from -4 to 3.

(b) $y = 3x - 2$
Draw and label the x axis from -2 to 3 and the y axis from -10 to 10.

5 Complete this table and use it to plot the straight line graph of $y = 4 - x$

x	-2	-1	0	1	2
y		5			2

Draw and label the x axis from -3 to 3 and the y axis from -1 to 6.

6 Draw the graphs of:

(a) $y = x - 3$ (d) $y = 6 - x$
(b) $y = 2x + 1$ (e) $y = 10 - 2x$
(c) $y = \frac{1}{4}x + 1$ (f) $y = 2(x - 1)$

7 (a) Draw these graphs **on the same diagram**:
(i) $y = x + 2$ (ii) $y = x + 1$
(iii) $y = x$ (iv) $y = x - 1$
Draw and label the x axis from 0 to 3 and the y axis from -1 to 5.

(b) What do they all have in common? What is different?

8 (a) Draw these graphs **on the same diagram**:
(i) $y = 2x + 2$ (ii) $y = 2x + 1$
(iii) $y = 2x$ (iv) $y = 2x - 1$
Draw and label the x axis from 0 to 3 and the y axis from -1 to 8.

(b) What do they all have in common? What is different?

9 (a) Draw these graphs **on the same diagram**:
(i) $y = 3x + 3$ (ii) $y = 2x + 3$
(iii) $y = x + 3$ (iv) $y = \frac{1}{2}x + 3$
Draw and label the x axis from -3 to 3 and the y axis from -6 to 12.

(b) What do they all have in common? What is different?

Gradient and intercept

Lines that are **parallel** have the same **slope** or **gradient**.

Gradient $= \frac{\text{distance up}}{\text{distance along}}$

The gradient of a straight line graph is found by drawing a right-angled triangle.

The gradient of a line can be positive, zero or negative.

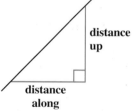

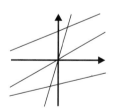

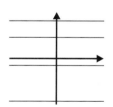

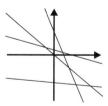

Positive gradients go "uphill".

Zero gradients are "flat".

Negative gradients go "downhill".

> **In general:**
> the graph of $y = mx + c$
> had **gradient** m and
> **intercept** c.

In Question 8 of Exercise 16.1, the graphs of
$y = 2x + 2$, $y = 2x + 1$, $y = 2x$, $y = 2x - 1$,
go 2 squares up for every 1 square along.
The graphs are all parallel and have a gradient of 2.

The point where a graph crosses the y axis is called the **intercept**.
In Question 9 of Exercise 16.1, the graphs of
$y = 3x + 3$, $y = 2x + 3$, $y = x + 3$, $y = \frac{1}{2}x + 3$,
all cross the y axis at the point (0, 3).
The graphs each have the same intercept, 3.

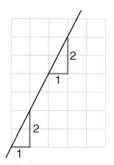

1 Write down the gradient and intercept for each of the following graphs.
(a) $y = 3x + 5$
(b) $y = 4x - 1$
(c) $y = 6 - x$

(a) Gradient = 3, intercept = 5.
(b) Gradient = 4, intercept = −1.
(c) Gradient = −1, intercept = 6.

2 Write down the equation of the straight line which has gradient −7 and cuts the y axis at the point (0, 4).

The general form for the equation of a straight line is $y = mx + c$.
The gradient, m = −7, and the intercept, c = 4.
Substitute these values into the general equation.
The equation of the line is $y = -7x + 4$.
This can be written as $y = 4 - 7x$.

3

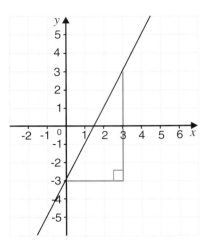

Find the equation of the line shown on this graph.

First, work out the gradient of the line. Draw a right-angled triangle.

Gradient = $\dfrac{\text{distance up}}{\text{distance along}}$

$= \dfrac{6}{3}$

$= 2$

The graph crosses the y axis at the point (0, −3), so the intercept is −3.
The equation of the line is $y = 2x - 3$.

Exercise 16.2

1 (a) Write down the gradient and intercept of $y = 3x - 1$.
  (b) Draw the graph of $y = 3x - 1$ to check your answer.

2 Which of the following graphs are parallel?

$y = 3x$

$y = x + 2$

$y = 2x + 3$

$y = 3x + 2$

3 Copy and complete this table.

Graph	gradient	intercept
$y = 4x + 3$	4	3
$y = 3x + 5$	3	
$y = 2x - 3$		
$y = 4 - 2x$		4
$y = \frac{1}{2}x + 3$		
$y = 2x$		
$y = 3$		
$y = 4 - \frac{1}{2}x$		

4 Match the following equations to their graphs.

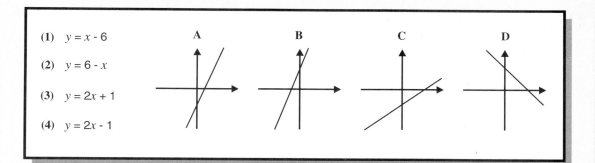

(1) $y = x - 6$

(2) $y = 6 - x$

(3) $y = 2x + 1$

(4) $y = 2x - 1$

5 (a) Write down the equation of the straight line which has gradient 5 and crosses the y axis at the point $(0, -4)$.

(b) Write down the equation of the straight line which has gradient $-\frac{1}{2}$ and cuts the y axis at the point $(0, 6)$.

6 Find the equations of the lines shown on the following graphs.

(a)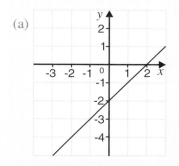

(b)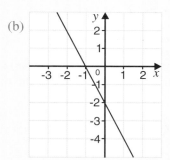

7 (a) Draw x and y axes from -8 to 8.

(b) Plot the points $A\ (-2, -6)$ and $B\ (8, 4)$.

(c) Find the gradient of the line which passes through the points A and B.

(d) Write down the coordinates of the point where the line crosses the y axis.

(e) Find the equation of the line which passes through the points A and B.

8 (a) Draw x and y axes from -8 to 8.

(b) Plot the points $P\ (-2, 3)$ and $Q\ (3, -7)$.

(c) Find the equation of the line which passes through the points P and Q.

Rearranging equations

The general equation for a straight line graph is $y = mx + c$.
When an equation is in this form the gradient and intercept are given by the values of m and c.

The equation for a straight line can also be written in the form $px + qy = r$.
To find the gradient and intercept of this line we must first **rearrange** the equation.

Equations of the form $px + qy = r$ are used in simultaneous equations. You will meet these in Chapter 17.

1 The graph of a straight line is given by the equation $4y - 3x = 8$.
Write this equation in the form $y = mx + c$.

$4y - 3x = 8$
Add $3x$ to both sides.
$\qquad 4y = 3x + 8$
Divide both sides by 4.
$\qquad y = \frac{3}{4}x + 2$

The line has gradient $\frac{3}{4}$ and intercept 2.

2 The equation of a straight line is $6x + 3y = 2$.
Write down the equation of another line which is parallel to this line.

Write the equation in the form $y = mx + c$.
$6x + 3y = 2$
Subtract $6x$ from both sides.
$\qquad 3y = -6x + 2$
Divide both sides by 3.
$\qquad y = -2x + \frac{2}{3}$

The gradient of the line is -2.
To write an equation of a parallel line keep the same gradient and change the value of the intercept.
For example: $y = -2x + 5$

Write the equations for two different lines which are parallel to this line.

3 Sketch the graph of the line given by the equation $4y - 3x = 12$.

Substitute $x = 0$ into the equation.
$4y = 12$.
$y = 3$

The line crosses the y axis at $(0, 3)$.

Substitute $y = 0$ into the equation.
$-3x = 12$
Divide both sides by -3.
$x = -4$

The line crosses the x axis at $(-4, 0)$.

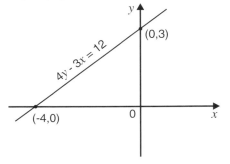

Exercise 16.3

1 The graph of a straight line is given by the equation $2y - 3x = 6$.
Write this equation in the form $y = mx + c$.

2 Write equations for the following lines in the form $y = mx + c$.
(a) $5y + 4x = 20$ (c) $4 - 3y = 2x$
(b) $2x - 7y = 14$ (d) $3(y - x) = 2$

3 The equation of a straight line is $2y + 3x = 4$.
Write down the equation of another line which is parallel to this line.

4 The equation of a line is given by $5y - 4x = 10$.
(a) Find the gradient of the line.
(b) Find the intercept of the line.
(c) Write down an equation of another line which has the **same** intercept but a **different** gradient.

5 A straight line has equation $3y + 5x = 15$.
(a) By substituting $x = 0$ find the coordinates of the point where the line crosses the y axis.
(b) By substituting $y = 0$ find the coordinates of the point where the line crosses the x axis.
(c) **Sketch** the graph of the line $3y + 5x = 15$.

6 Sketch the graphs of lines with the following equations, marking clearly the coordinates of the points where the lines cross the axes.
(a) $5y + 4x = 20$
(b) $4x - y = 2$
(c) $3y + 2x = 15$

Using graphs to solve equations

One way of solving the equation
$2x - 3 = 2$ is to use the **balance method**.
$$2x - 3 = 2$$
Add 3 to both sides.
$$2x = 5$$
Divide both sides by 2.
$$x = 2.5$$

Graphs can be used to solve equations.
The diagram shows two graphs:
$y = 2x - 3$
$y = 2$

At the point where the lines cross,
both $y = 2x - 3$ and $y = 2$ are true.
The value of x at this point is the solution
to the equation $2x - 3 = 2$.
Reading from the graph, $x = 2.5$.

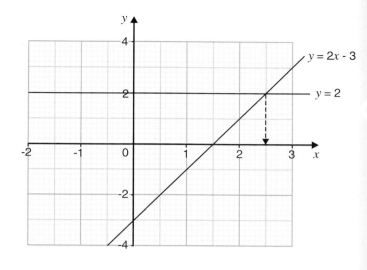

EXAMPLE

(a) Complete the tables for $y = x + 6$ and $y = 13 - x$.

x	1	2	3
$y = x + 6$			

x	1	2	3
$y = 13 - x$			

(b) Draw the graphs of $y = x + 6$ and $y = 13 - x$ on the same diagram.
(c) Use your graph to solve the equation $13 - x = x + 6$.

(a)

x	1	2	3
$y = x + 6$	7	8	9

x	1	2	3
$y = 13 - x$	12	11	10

(b)

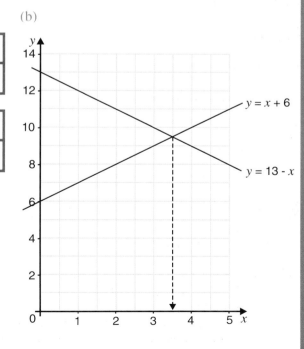

(c) Reading from the graph.
$$x = 3.5$$

Use the balance method to check the
graphical solution of the equation.

1 (a) Copy and complete the tables for $y = x + 2$ and $y = 5 - x$.

x	1	2	3
$y = x + 2$			

x	1	2	3
$y = 5 - x$			

(b) Draw the graphs of $y = x + 2$ and $y = 5 - x$ on the same diagram.
(c) Use your graphs to solve $x + 2 = 5 - x$.

2 (a) Draw the graphs of $y = 3x + 1$ and $y = x + 6$.
(b) Use your graphs to solve the equation $3x + 1 = x + 6$.

3 Draw suitable graphs to solve the following equations:
(a) $x - 1 = \frac{1}{2}x + 3$
(b) $2(x + 1) = x + 4$
(c) $\frac{1}{2}(x - 1) = 4 - x$.

4 (a) Draw the graph of $y = 3 + 2x$.
(b) What graph should be drawn to solve the equation $3 + 2x = 9$?
(c) Draw the graph and use it to solve the equation $3 + 2x = 9$.

5 A delivery firm charges £25 for delivering a package.
Another firm uses the formula $y = 10 + 2x$ to calculate the charge, in pounds, where x is the number of hours taken to make the delivery.

(a) Draw the graph of $y = 10 + 2x$.
(b) On the same axes draw another graph which could be used to solve the equation $10 + 2x = 25$.
(c) What does the solution to the equation in part (b) mean?

6 Two companies each use a formula to calculate the charge made for hiring out scaffolding.
Company A uses the formula $c = 20 + 5d$,
Company B uses the formula $c = 8d + 2$,
where c is the total charge, in pounds,
        d is the length of the hire period, in days.

(a) Draw the horizontal axis for d from 0 to 8 and the vertical axis for c from 0 to 60.
(b) Draw the graph of $c = 20 + 5d$.
(c) Draw the graph of $c = 8d + 2$.

Use your graph to answer the following.
(d) From which company is it cheaper to hire scaffolding for 2 days?
(e) From which company is it cheaper to hire scaffolding for 8 days?
(f) For what number of days do both companies make the same charge?

What you need to know

16

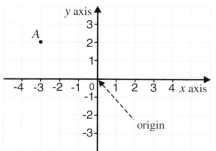

- **Coordinates** (involving positive and negative numbers) are used to describe the position of a point on a graph. For example, $A\,(-3, 2)$ is the point where the lines $x = -3$ and $y = 2$ cross.

- The general equation for a **straight line** graph is $y = mx + c$
  where m is the **gradient** (slope) of the line,
       c is the **intercept**, the point $(0, c)$.

The x axis crosses the y axis at the origin.

- The **gradient** of a line can be found by drawing a right-angled triangle.

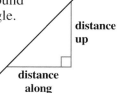

  Gradient $= \dfrac{\text{distance up}}{\text{distance along}}$

  Gradient can be positive, zero or negative.

- The points where a line crosses the axes can be found:
    by reading the coordinates from a graph,
    by substituting $x = 0$ and $y = 0$ into the equation of the line.

- Equations of the form $px + qy = r$ can be **rearranged** to the form $y = mx + c$.

Work in this chapter is essential to:
simultaneous equations,
inequalities.

You should be able to:
- Plot coordinates and draw graphs.
- Find the equation for a given line.
- Solve equations and problems involving straight line graphs.

Straight Line Graphs

Review Exercise

1 Which of these diagrams shows the graph of $y = 2x$?

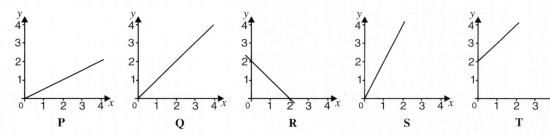

| P | Q | R | S | T |

2 The graph of a straight line is given by the equation $y - 2x = 7$.

(a) Write down the equation of one other straight line which is parallel to $y - 2x = 7$.

(b) Write down the equation of one other straight line which crosses the y axis at the same point as $y - 2x = 7$.
The graph of a different line is given by the equation $3y - 2x = -9$.

(c) Rearrange this equation into the form of $y = mx + c$.

SEG 1994

173

3 This diagram shows the graph of $y = 4 - x$.
Copy the graph onto squared paper.

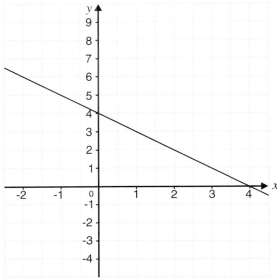

(a) Copy and complete this table for $y = 3x + 2$.

x	-2	-1	0	1	2
$y = 3x + 2$					

(b) Draw the graph of $y = 3x + 2$.

(c) Write down the coordinates of the point where the graph of $y = 4 - x$ crosses the graph of $y = 3x + 2$.

SEG 1997

4 The cost of removals includes a fixed amount and a charge per mile for the distance moved.
The graph shows the cost, in £, for removals up to a distance of 50 miles.

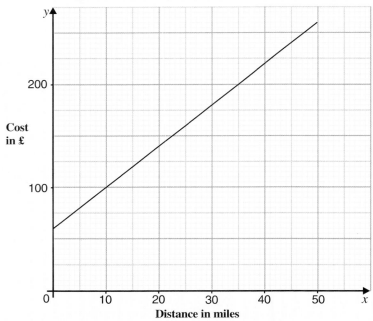

(a) Find the equation of the line in the form $y = ax + b$.

(b) Calculate the cost of removals for a distance of 100 miles.

SEG 2000 S

5 The graph of $y = \frac{1}{2}x + 2$ has been drawn for you. Copy the graph.

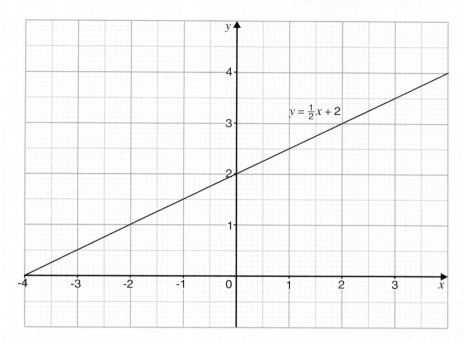

(a) Copy and complete this table of values and use it to draw the graph of $y = 2x + 5$.

x	-3	-2	-1	0	1
y	...	...	...	...	...

(b) Write down the coordinates of the point of intersection of $y = 2x + 5$ and $y = \frac{1}{2}x + 2$.

(c) Solve the equation $\frac{1}{2}x + 2 = 0$.

SEG 1997

6 On graph paper, draw x and y axes from -7 to 2.

(a) Plot the points $(-7, 2)$ and $(1, -6)$ and draw the straight line which passes through these points.

(b) Write down the coordinates of the points where your line crosses the two axes.

(c) Write down the equation connecting x and y.

SEG 1997

7 (a) Helen entered the equation $y = 1\frac{1}{2}x + 3$ into the computer and obtained this graph.

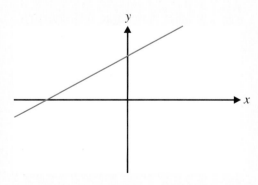

Roy entered the equation $2y - 3x = 6$ and got the same graph.
Rearrange Roy's equation to show that it is equivalent to Helen's.

(b) (i) What is the gradient of the graph of $2x + y = 10$?

(ii) Sketch the graph of $2x + y = 10$.

SEG 1995

8 At the village fête Debbie has £y in her purse and wants to buy some chocolate cakes at £x each.

She knows that if she buys 2 cakes she will have £1 left in her purse.
This can be written as the equation $y = 2x + 1$.

(a) (i) Copy and complete the table below for the line $y = 2x + 1$.

x	1	2	3	4	5
y		5			

(ii) Plot the above points on a graph and draw a line through them.

Debbie also knows that if she buys 3 cakes she will need £2 more than she has got in her purse.
This can be written as the equation $y = 3x - 2$.

(b) (i) Copy and complete the table below for the line $y = 3x - 2$.

x	1	2	3	4	5
y					13

(ii) Plot the above points on your graph and draw a line through them.

(c) **Use your graph** to find out
   (i) the cost of one cake, £x,
   (ii) the amount of money, £y, that Debbie has in her purse.

SEG 1994

9 It costs £3.50 for a badminton lesson.
As a special offer, the first lesson costs only £2.50.
The table shows the cost, £C, of n lessons.

Number of lessons (n)	1	2	3	4	5	6
Cost (£C)	2.50	6.00	9.50	13.00	16.50	20.00

Using the table, find a formula connecting C and n.

SEG 1996

10 Television repair charges depend on the length of time taken for the repair, as shown on the graph.
The charge is made up of a fixed amount plus an extra amount which depends on the time.

(a) What is the charge for a repair which takes 45 minutes?
(b) (i) Calculate the gradient of the line.
   (ii) What does the gradient represent?
(c) Write down the equation of the line.
(d) Mr Banks' repair will cost £84 or less. Calculate the maximum time which can be spent on the repair.

SEG 1994

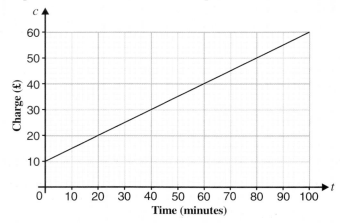

176

CHAPTER 17

Simultaneous Equations

$x + y = 10$ is an equation with two unknown quantities x and y.
Many pairs of values of x and y fit this equation.
For example.
$x = 1$ and $y = 9$, $x = 4$ and $y = 6$, $x = 2.9$ and $y = 7.1$, $x = 1.005$ and $y = 8.995$,   …
$x - y = 2$ is another equation with the **same** two unknown quantities x and y.
Again, many pairs of values of x and y fit this equation.
For example.
$x = 4$ and $y = 2$, $x = 7$ and $y = 5$, $x = 2.9$ and $y = 0.9$, $x = -1$ and $y = -3$,   …

There is only **one** pair of values of x and y which fit **both** of these equations ($x = 6$ and $y = 4$).
Pairs of equations like $x + y = 10$ and $x - y = 2$ are called **simultaneous equations**.

To solve simultaneous equations you need to find values which fit **both** equations simultaneously.
Simultaneous equations can be solved using different methods.

Using graphs to solve simultaneous equations

Consider the simultaneous equations $x + 2y = 5$ and $x - 2y = 1$.

Draw the graphs of $x + 2y = 5$ and $x - 2y = 1$.

For $x + 2y = 5$:
When $x = 1$, $y = 2$.
This gives the point $(1, 2)$.

When $x = 5$, $y = 0$.
This gives the point $(5, 0)$.

To draw the graph of $x + 2y = 5$
draw a line through the points
$(1, 2)$ and $(5, 0)$.

For $x - 2y = 1$:
When $x = 1$, $y = 0$.
This gives the point $(1, 0)$.

When $x = 5$, $y = 2$.
This gives the point $(5, 2)$.

To draw the graph of $x - 2y = 1$
draw a line through the points
$(1, 0)$ and $(5, 2)$.

Drawing straight line graphs was first covered in Chapter 16.

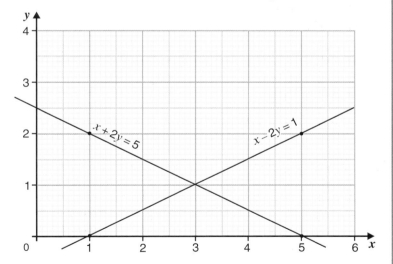

The values of x and y at the point where the lines cross give the solution to the simultaneous equations.

The lines cross at the point $(3, 1)$.

This gives the solution $x = 3$ and $y = 1$.

To solve a pair of simultaneous equations plot the graph of each of the equations on the same diagram.
The coordinates of the point where the two lines cross:
● fit **both equations** simultaneously,
● give the **graphical solution** of the equations.

Use a graphical method to solve this
pair of simultaneous equations:
$$5x + 2y = 20$$
$$y = 2x + 1$$

Find the points that fit the equations
$5x + 2y = 20$ and $y = 2x + 1$.

For $5x + 2y = 20$:

When $x = 0$, $y = 10$.
This gives the point $(0, 10)$.

When $y = 0$, $x = 4$.
This gives the point $(4, 0)$.

For $y = 2x + 1$:

When $x = 0$, $y = 1$.
This gives the point $(0, 1)$.

When $x = 4$, $y = 9$.
This gives the point $(4, 9)$.

The lines cross at the point $(2, 5)$.
This gives the solution
$x = 2$ and $y = 5$.

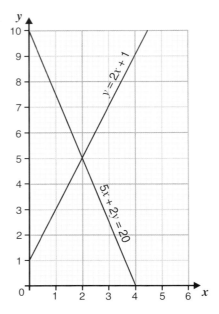

Check
You can check a graphical solution by substituting
the values of x and y into the original equations.
When $x = 2$ and $y = 5$
$$5x + 2y = 5 \times 2 + 2 \times 5 = 20$$
$$y = 2x + 1 = 2 \times 2 + 1 = 5$$

Exercise 17.1

Use a graphical method to solve each of these
pairs of simultaneous equations.
For each question use the sizes of axes given.
All solutions are positive whole numbers.

Drawing and labelling axes
$0 \le x \le 8$ means draw and label the
x axis from 0 to 8 inclusive.
What does $-3 \le y \le 7$ mean?

1 $x + y = 6$
$y = x - 2$
Axes $0 \le x \le 8$, $-3 \le y \le 7$

2 $x + y = 8$
$y - x = 2$
Axes $0 \le x \le 10$, $-3 \le y \le 10$

3 $x + 2y = 8$
$2x + y = 7$
Axes $0 \le x \le 10$, $0 \le y \le 8$

4 $3x + 2y = 12$
$y = x + 1$
Axes $0 \le x \le 5$, $0 \le y \le 8$

5 $x + 3y = 6$
$y = 2x - 5$
Axes $0 \le x \le 10$, $-6 \le y \le 4$

6 $3x + 4y = 24$
$2y = x + 2$
Axes $-4 \le x \le 10$, $-2 \le y \le 8$

Simultaneous equations with no solution

Some pairs of simultaneous equations do not have a solution.

EXAMPLE

Show that this pair of simultaneous equations do not have a solution.

$$y - 2x = 4$$
$$2y = 4x - 1$$

Method 1
Draw the graphs of each equation.

$y - 2x = 4$
When $x = 0$, $y = 4$.
This gives the point $(0, 4)$.
When $y = 0$, $x = -2$
This gives the point $(-2, 0)$.

$2y = 4x - 1$
When $x = 0$, $y = -0.5$.
This gives the point $(0, -0.5)$.
When $x = 2$, $y = 3.5$
This gives the point $(2, 3.5)$.

The two lines are **parallel**.
This means they never cross and there are no values of x and y which fit both equations.
So the simultaneous equations have no solution.

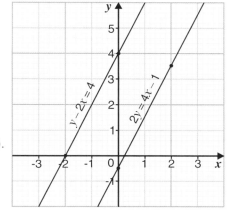

Method 2
Rearrange each equation to the form $y = mx + c$.

$y - 2x = 4$
Add $2x$ to both sides.
$y = 2x + 4$
The graph of this equation has a gradient (m) of 2 and an intercept (c) of 4.

$2y = 4x - 1$
Divide both sides by 2.
$y = 2x - 1$
The graph of this equation has a gradient (m) of 2 and an intercept (c) of -1.

Both lines have the same gradient (2) and different intercepts which shows that the lines are parallel.

Exercise 17.2

1 Draw graphs to show that each of these pairs of simultaneous equations have no solution.

(a) $x + y = 6$
  $y = 2 - x$

(b) $y - 4x = 8$
  $y = 4x + 2$

(c) $3x + 4y = 12$
  $8y = 24 - 6x$

(d) $5y - 2x = 10$
  $5y = 2x + 20$

2 By rearranging each of these pairs of simultaneous equations to the form $y = mx + c$ show that they do not have a solution.

(a) $2x + y = 6$
  $y = 3 - 2x$

(b) $2y - 4x = 7$
  $y - 2 = 2x$

(c) $5x - 2y = 8$
  $4y = 10x + 7$

(d) $4y + 12x = 5$
  $1 - 2y = 6x$

3 Two of these pairs of simultaneous equations have no solution.

(a) $5x + y = 6$
  $y - 5x = 2$

(b) $5x = 8 + y$
  $y - 5x = 2$

(c) $2y - 10x = 5$
  $4y + 20x = 5$

(d) $y + 1 = -5x$
  $2y + 10x = 5$

Use an appropriate method to find which ones.
Use a graphical method to solve the other two.

The elimination method

The graphical method of solving simultaneous equations can be quite time consuming. Sometimes, due to the equations involved, the coordinates of the points where the lines intersect can be difficult to read accurately.
For these reasons, other methods of solving simultaneous equations are often used.

Consider again the simultaneous equations $x + 2y = 5$ and $x - 2y = 1$.
Both equations have the same number of x's and the same number of y's.
If the two equations are added together the y's will be **eliminated** as shown.

$$x + 2y = 5$$
$$x - 2y = 1$$

Adding gives $2x = 6$
So $x = 3$

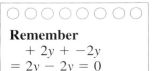

Remember
$+ 2y + -2y$
$= 2y - 2y = 0$

By **substituting** the value of this letter (x) into one of the original equations we can find the value of the other letter (y).

$$x + 2y = 5$$
$$3 + 2y = 5$$
$$2y = 2$$
$$y = 1$$

Remember:
If you do the same to both sides of an equation it is still true.

This gives the solution $x = 3$ and $y = 1$.

EXAMPLES

1 Use the elimination method to solve this pair of simultaneous equations:
$$2x - y = 1$$
$$3x + y = 9$$

Each equation has the **same number** of y's but the **signs** are **different**.
To eliminate the y's the equations must be **added**.

$$5x = 10$$
$$x = 2$$

Substitute $x = 2$ into $3x + y = 9$
$$3 \times 2 + y = 9$$
$$6 + y = 9$$
$$y = 3$$

The solution is $x = 2$ and $y = 3$.

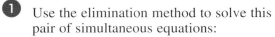

Check
Substitute $x = 2$ and $y = 3$ into
$$2x - y = 1$$
$$2 \times 2 - 3 = 1$$
$$4 - 3 = 1$$
$$1 = 1$$
The equation is true, so the solution
$x = 2$ and $y = 3$ is correct.

2 Use the elimination method to solve this pair of simultaneous equations:
$$2x + 3y = 9$$
$$2x + y = 7$$

Each equation has the **same number** of x's and the **signs** are the **same**.
To eliminate the x's one equation must be **subtracted** from the other.

Subtract $2x + y = 7$ from $2x + 3y = 9$.
$$2y = 2$$
$$y = 1$$

Substitute $y = 1$ into $2x + y = 7$
$$2x + 1 = 7$$
$$2x = 6$$
$$x = 3$$

The solution is $x = 3$ and $y = 1$.

Check
Substitute $x = 3$ and $y = 1$ into
$2x + 3y = 9$
Do this and make sure the solution is correct

Exercise 17.3

Use the elimination method to solve each of these pairs of simultaneous equations.

1 $3x - y = 1$
   $x + y = 3$

2 $2x - y = 2$
   $x + y = 7$

3 $4x + y = 9$
   $2x - y = 3$

4 $-x + 2y = 13$
   $x + y = 8$

5 $2x + y = 7$
   $x + y = 4$

6 $3x + y = 9$
   $2x + y = 7$

7 $2x + y = 12$
   $x + y = 7$

8 $x + 5y = 14$
   $x + 2y = 8$

9 $x + 2y = 13$
   $x + 4y = 21$

10 $x + 4y = 11$
   $x + y = 5$

11 $2x + 5y = 13$
   $2x + y = 9$

12 $5x + 3y = 26$
   $2x + 3y = 14$

13 $5x + 4y = 22$
   $5x + y = 13$

14 $2x - y = 10$
   $3x + y = 10$

15 $5x - 2y = 13$
   $3x + 2y = 3$

16 $x + 5y = 14$
   $-x + 2y = 7$

17 $2x + 3y = 8$
   $2x + y = -4$

18 $2x + y = 4$
   $4x - y = 11$

19 $3x + 4y = -8$
   $x + 4y = 4$

20 $3x + 2y = 6$
   $x - 2y = 6$

Further use of the elimination method

Look at this pair of simultaneous equations:
$$5x + 2y = 11$$
$$3x - 4y = 4$$

$5x + 2y = 11$ Equation A
$3x - 4y = 4$ Equation B

A useful technique is to use capital letters to label the equations.

These equations do not have the same number of x's or the same number of y's.

To make the number of y's the same we can multiply equation A by 2.

A × 2 gives $10x + 4y = 22$ Equation C
B × 1 gives $3x - 4y = 4$ Equation D

C + D gives $13x = 26$
    $x = 2$

The number of y's in equations **C** and **D** is the **same** but the **signs** are **different**. So, to eliminate the y's the equations must be **added**.

Substitute $x = 2$ into $5x + 2y = 11$
    $5 \times 2 + 2y = 11$
    $10 + 2y = 11$
    $2y = 1$
    $y = 0.5$

The solution is $x = 2$ and $y = 0.5$.

Check the solution by substituting $x = 2$ and $y = 0.5$ into $3x - 4y = 4$.

In this example eliminating the y's rather than the x's is less likely to produce an error.
Try to solve the equations by eliminating the x's.

Solve this pair of simultaneous equations: $3x + 7y = -2$
$4x + 9 = -3y$

Rearrange and label the equations as necessary.
$3x + 7y = -2$ A
$4x + 3y = -9$ B
These equations do not have the same number of x's or the
same number of y's.
So the multiplying method can be used.

> Both equations must be in
> the form $px + qy = r$ before
> the elimination method can
> be used.
> You may have to **rearrange**
> the equations you are given.
> $4x + 9 = -3y$ can be
> rearranged as $4x + 3y = -9$

Method 1
Eliminating the x's.

A $\times$ 4 gives $12x + 28y = -8$ C
B $\times$ 3 gives $12x + 9y = -27$ D

C $-$ D gives $19y = -8 - -27$
                            $19y = -8 + 27$
                            $19y = 19$
                             $y = 1$
Substitute $y = 1$ into $3x + 7y = -2$
    $3x + 7 \times 1 = -2$
        $3x + 7 = -2$
            $3x = -9$
             $x = -3$

The solution is $x = -3$ and $y = 1$.

Method 2
Eliminating the y's.

A $\times$ 3 gives $9x + 21y = -6$ C
B $\times$ 7 gives $28x + 21y = -63$ D

D $-$ C gives $19x = -63 - -6$
                            $19x = -63 + 6$
                            $19x = -57$
                             $x = -3$
Substitute $x = -3$ into $3x + 7y = -2$
    $3 \times -3 + 7y = -2$
        $-9 + 7y = -2$
            $7y = 7$
             $y = 1$

*Check the solution by substituting $x = -3$
and $y = 1$ into $4x + 9 = -3y$.*

Exercise 17.4

Solve each of these pairs of simultaneous equations.

1 $3x + 2y = 8$
        $2x - y = 3$

2 $x + y = 5$
        $5x - 3y = 1$

3 $2x + 3y = 9$
        $x + 4y = 7$

4 $x + 3y = 10$
        $2x + 5y = 18$

5 $5x + 2y = 8$
        $2x - y = 5$

6 $3x + y = 9$
        $x - 2y = 10$

7 $3x - 4y = 10$
        $x + 2y = 5$

8 $x + 6y = 0$
        $3x - 2y = -10$

9 $2x + 3y = 11$
        $3x + y = 13$

10 $2x + y = 10$
        $-x + 2y = 9$

11 $2x + 3y = 9$
        $4x - y = 4$

12 $2x + 3y = 8$
        $3x + 2y = 7$

13 $3x + 4y = 23$
        $2x + 5y = 20$

14 $2x - 3y = 8$
        $x - 5y = 11$

15 $3x + 4y = 5$
        $-2x + 5y = 12$

16 $3x - 2y = 4$
        $x + 4y = 6$

17 $-3x + 2y = 5$
        $4x + 3y = -1$

18 $3x + 4y = 6$
        $3y = 7 - x$

19 $5x + 3y = 16$
        $2y = 13 - x$

20 $5x - 4y = 24$
        $2x = y + 9$

21 $3y = 1 + 5x$
        $5y - 7 = 3x$

22 $4x - 7y = 15$
        $5x - 12 = 2y$

23 $8x + 3y = 2$
        $5x = 1 - 2y$

24 $9x = 4y - 20$
        $5x = 6y - 13$

The substitution method

For some pairs of simultaneous equations a method using **substitution** is sometimes more convenient.

EXAMPLE

Solve this pair of simultaneous equations: $5x + y = 9$
$$y = 4x$$

$5x + y = 9$ Equation A
$\quad y = 4x$ Equation B
Substitute $y = 4x$ into Equation A
$$5x + 4x = 9$$
$$9x = 9$$
$$x = 1$$

Substitute $x = 1$ into $y = 4x$.
$$y = 4 \times 1$$
$$y = 4$$

The solution is $x = 1$ and $y = 4$.

Check the solution by substituting
$x = 1$ and $y = 4$ into $5x + y = 9$.

Exercise 17.5

Use the substitution method to solve these pairs of simultaneous equations.

1 $2x + y = 10$
$\quad\quad y = 3x$

2 $3x - y = 9$
$\quad\quad\quad y = 2x$

3 $x + 5y = 18$
$\quad\quad\quad x = 4y$

4 $x + 2y = 15$
$\quad\quad\quad y = 2x$

5 $2x + y = 17$
$\quad\quad y = 6x + 1$

6 $3x + 2y = 4$
$\quad\quad\quad x = y - 2$

7 $5x + 6y = 34$
$\quad\quad\quad y = x + 2$

8 $5x - 2y = 23$
$\quad\quad\quad x = y + 1$

9 $5x - y = 12$
$\quad\quad y = 32 - 6x$

10 $x + 5y = 13$
$\quad\quad x = 3y + 9$

11 $5x - 3y = 26$
$\quad\quad\quad y = 2x + 14$

12 $x + 4y = 32$
$\quad\quad\quad x = 2y - 4$

Solving problems using simultaneous equations

EXAMPLE

Billy buys 5 first class stamps and 3 second class stamps at a cost of £1.93.
Jane buys 3 first class stamps and 5 second class stamps at a cost of £1.83.
Calculate the cost of a first class stamp and the cost of a second class stamp.

Let x pence be the cost of a first class stamp, and
let y pence be the cost of a second class stamp.
Billy's purchase of the stamps gives this equation.
$$5x + 3y = 193 \quad\quad \text{Equation A}$$
Jane's purchase of the stamps gives this equation.
$$3x + 5y = 183 \quad\quad \text{Equation B}$$
This gives a pair of simultaneous equations which can be solved using the elimination method.
$$5x + 3y = 193 \quad\quad \text{A}$$
$$3x + 5y = 183 \quad\quad \text{B}$$

A $\times$ 5 gives $25x + 15y = 965$ C
B $\times$ 3 gives $9x + 15y = 549$ D

C $-$ D gives $16x = 416$
$$x = 26$$

Substitute $x = 26$ into $5x + 3y = 193$.
$$5 \times 26 + 3y = 193$$
$$3y = 63$$
$$y = 21$$

So the cost of a first class stamp is 26 pence and the cost of a second class stamp is 21 pence.

Check the solution by substituting the values for x and y into the original problem.

1 Apples are x pence per kg. Oranges are y pence each.
5 kg of apples and 30 oranges cost £9.00.
10 kg of apples and 15 oranges cost £12.60.
Calculate x and y.

2 Standard eggs cost x pence per dozen. Small eggs cost y pence per dozen.
10 dozen standard eggs and 5 dozen small eggs cost £13.60.
5 dozen standard eggs and 8 dozen small eggs cost £11.31.
Calculate x and y.

3 A group of children and adults went on a coach trip to a theme park.
Ticket prices for the theme park were £10 for adults and £5 for children.
Ticket prices for the coach were £5 for adults and £2 for children.
The total cost of the tickets for the theme park was £190.
The total cost of the coach tickets was £79.
How many children and adults went on the trip?

4 Jenny types at x words per minute. Stuart types at y words per minute.
When Jenny and Stuart both type for 1 minute they type a total of 170 words.
When Jenny types for 5 minutes and Stuart types for 3 minutes they type a total of
710 words.
Calculate x and y.

5 At a café, John buys 3 coffees and 2 teas for £2.30 and Susan buys 2 coffees and 3 teas for £2.20.
Calculate the price of a coffee and the price of a tea.

6 Standard coaches hold x passengers and first class coaches hold y passengers.
A train with 5 standard coaches and 2 first class coaches carries a total of 1040 passengers.
A train with 7 standard coaches and 3 first class coaches carries a total of 1480 passengers.

(a) Write down two equations connecting x and y.
(b) Solve these simultaneous equations to find the values of x and y.

What you need to know

- A pair of **simultaneous equations** are linked equations with the same unknown letters in each equation.

- To solve a pair of simultaneous equations find values for the unknown letters that fit **both** equations.

- Simultaneous equations can be solved either **graphically** or **algebraically**.

- Solving simultaneous equations **graphically** involves:
  drawing the graph of both equations,
  finding the point where the graphs cross.
  When the graphs of both equations are parallel, the equations have no solution.

- Solving simultaneous equations **algebraically** involves using either:
  the **elimination** method, or
  the **substitution** method (if it is more convenient).

1 Use a graphical method to solve each of these simultaneous equations.
For each question use the size of axes given.

(a) $x + y = 10$
$y = 2x + 1$
Axes $0 \leqslant x \leqslant 11, 0 \leqslant y \leqslant 11$

(b) $x + 3y = 9$
$5y + x = 10$
Axes $0 \leqslant x \leqslant 10, 0 \leqslant y \leqslant 5$

(c) $5x + 6y = 30$
$2y = x - 2$
Axes $0 \leqslant x \leqslant 8, -3 \leqslant y \leqslant 8$

(d) $3x - 2y = 18$
$4x + y = 2$
Axes $0 \leqslant x \leqslant 8, -10 \leqslant y \leqslant 3$

2 Use an algebraic method to solve each of these simultaneous equations.
You must show all your working.

(a) $x + y = 3$
$x - y = 1$

(b) $2x + y = 8$
$x + y = 5$

(c) $7x + 3y = 19$
$2x + 3y = 14$

(d) $6x + 5y = 28$
$4x - 5y = 2$

(e) $2x + 3y = 4$
$x + 2y = 3$

(f) $3x + y = 10$
$x - 2y = 8$

(g) $7x + 2y = 17$
$3x + 4y = 1$

(h) $9x - 4y = 20$
$3x + 2y = 5$

(i) $3x + 5y = 21$
$2x + 7y = 25$

(j) $9x - 4y = 31$
$2x + 3y = 3$

(k) $3x - 5y = 11$
$2x + 7y = -3$

(l) $3y - 5x = 1$
$5y - 3x = 7$

(m) $3x + y = 13$
$y = 7 - x$

(n) $x + 3y = 5$
$y = 2x + 18$

(o) $3x - 2y = 26$
$x = 2y - 18$

(p) $x + 5y = 3$
$y = 3x + 7$

3 (a) Show that the simultaneous equations $y = 2x - 2$ and $2y - 4x = 3$ have no solution.
(b) Show that the simultaneous equations $4y = x + 1$ and $8y - 2x = 3$ have no solution.
(c) The simultaneous equations $y = 3x + 2$ and $y = ax + b$ have no solution.
What can you say about the values of a and b?
(d) The simultaneous equations $y = 3x + 2$ and $py + qx = r$ have no solution.
Find some possible values for p, q and r.

4 This graph shows the line $y - 2x = -1$.

Copy the graph.
By drawing another line, use the graph to solve
the simultaneous equations
$$y - 2x = -1$$
$$x + 2y = 4$$

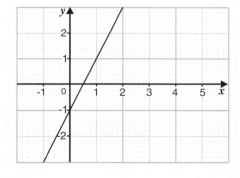

SEG 1997

5 In a competition, a win scores x points and a draw scores y points.
Nayeem has won one game, drawn three games and has 16 points.
Freda has won two games, drawn one game and has 17 points.
Find x and y, by solving the simultaneous equations
$$x + 3y = 16$$
$$2x + y = 17$$

SEG 1996

6 Peaches cost x pence each and bananas cost y pence per kilogram.
4 peaches and 1kg of bananas cost 72p.
6 peaches and 1kg of bananas cost 90p.

(a) Write down two equations connecting x and y.
(b) Solve these simultaneous equations to find the values of x and y.

More or Less

Activity

For all children who enter the competition we can say that
Age < 16 years

For anyone riding the Big Dipper we can say that
Height ⩾ 1.2 m

For all items sold in the store we can say that
Cost ⩽ £1

These are examples of inequalities.
Can you think of other situations where inequalities are used?

Inequalities

An **inequality** is a mathematical statement, such as $x > 1$ or $a \leqslant 2$.

In the following, x is an integer.

Sign	Meaning	Example	Possible values of x
<	is less than	$x < 4$	3, 2, 1, 0, -1, -2, -3, …
⩽	is less than or equal to	$x \leqslant 4$	4, 3, 2, 1, 0, -1, -2, -3, …
>	is greater than	$x > 6$	7, 8, 9, 10, …
⩾	is greater than or equal to	$x \geqslant 2$	2, 3, 4, 5, …

> You met equations in Chapter 13, and again in Chapter 14. Inequalities are similar to equations.

> An **integer** is a positive or negative whole number or zero.

Explain the difference between the meanings of the signs < and ⩽.
Explain the difference between the meanings of the signs > and ⩾.

Temperature

❶ We can compare temperatures in two ways:
$-5°C$ is a **lower** temperature than $-2°C$.
So we can write $-5 < -2$.

❷ $-2°C$ is a **higher** temperature than $-5°C$.
So we can write $-2 > -5$.

*A thermometer shows $-2°C$
The temperature rises by $3°C$.
What is the new temperature?
Write an inequality which compares the
new temperature with the previous temperature.*

Number lines

Inequalities can be shown on a **number line**.

```
-6  -5  -4  -3  -2  -1   0   1   2   3   4   5   6
```

As you move to the right, numbers get bigger.
As you move to the left, numbers get smaller.

Values of x which make an inequality true are said to **satisfy** the inequality.

EXAMPLES

Draw number lines to show the following inequalities.

1 $x < 1.5$

The circle is **not filled** because 1.5 is **not included**.

2 $x \geqslant -2$

The circle is **filled** because -2 is **included**.

3 $x \leqslant 4$ and $x > -1$.

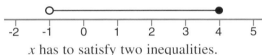

x has to satisfy two inequalities.

4 $3 \leqslant x < 8$

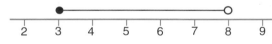

$3 \leqslant x < 8$ is a shorthand method of writing $3 \leqslant x$ **and** $x < 8$.

Exercise 18.1

1 Write down the following mathematical statements and say whether each is true or false.
  (a) $4 < 7$ (b) $3 > -3$ (c) $4 \geqslant 4$ (d) $-2 > -1$
  (e) $-8 \leqslant -8$ (f) $1.5 \geqslant 2.1$ (g) $3 \times 5 \leqslant 7 \times 2$ (h) $-4 \times (-2) > -4 - 4$

2 Write down an integer which could replace the letter.
  (a) $x < 6$ (b) $a \geqslant -2$ (c) $c + 2 < 8$ (d) $2d \leqslant 14$
  (e) $f - 3 > 7$ (f) $-2 < h < 0$ (g) $t \leqslant 5$ **and** $t > 4$ (h) $r \geqslant -6$ **and** $r < -1$

3 In this question x is an integer. Write down all the values of x which satisfy these inequalities.
  (a) $1 < x < 5$ (b) $-2 < x \leqslant 3$ (c) $-4 \leqslant x \leqslant -1$ (d) $-1 \leqslant x < 3$

4 Arrange these numbers in order of size, starting with the smallest.
  (a) $-2, -1, 4, -6, 0, 2, 1$
  (b) $1, -1, 2, -3, 4, -5, 6$
  (c) $2.5, 0.5, -3.5, -8.5, -6.0, 1.0, 3.5$

5 Write down a mathematical statement, using inequalities, for each of these diagrams.

(a)

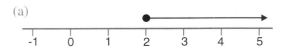

(b)

(c)

(d)

6

Draw number lines to show the following inequalities. For each part, draw and label a number line from −5 to 5.
(a) $-2 \leqslant x < 3$ (b) $x > -4$ (c) $x < -3$ and $x \geqslant 1$

Solving inequalities

Solve means to find the values of x which make the inequality true.
The aim is to end up with **one letter** on one side of the inequality and a **number** on the other side of the inequality.

EXAMPLES

1 Solve the inequality $5x - 3 < 27$

$5x - 3 < 27$
Add 3 to both sides.
   $5x < 30$
Divide both sides by 5.
    $x < 6$

This means that the inequality is **true** for all values of x which are less than 6.
Substitute $x = 5$ and $x = 7$ into the original inequality. What do you notice?

2 Solve the inequality $7a \geqslant a + 9$

$7a \geqslant a + 9$
Subtract a from both sides.
$6a \geqslant 9$
Divide both sides by 6.
 $a \geqslant 1.5$

This means that the inequality is true for all values of a which are equal to 1.5, or greater.
Substitute $a = 1.5$, $a = 2$ and $a = 1$ into the original inequality. What do you notice?

Exercise **18.2**

Solve the following inequalities. Show your working clearly.

1 $a + 3 < 7$

2 $b - 3 \geqslant -2$

3 $3 + a > 5$

4 $-2 + b \leqslant -1$

5 $3c > 15$

6 $2d < -6$

7 $\frac{1}{2}a \geqslant 3$

8 $\frac{1}{3}b < 5$

9 $2c + 5 \leqslant 11$

10 $3d - 4 > 8$

11 $2e + 5 \geqslant 9$

12 $4 + 3f < -2$

13 $8g - 1 \leqslant 3$

14 $5h < h + 8$

15 $6j \geqslant 2j + 10$

16 $7k > 3k - 16$

17 $4m + 2 > 2m - 11$

18 $7n - 3 \leqslant 13 - n$

19 $3p - 2 > 6 + 2p$

20 $4q + 5 > 12 - 3q$

21 $6r + 1 \geqslant 4r - 2$

22 $2t - 10 > t + 3$

23 $2(u - 5) \leqslant 8$

24 $3(4v + 1) < -15$

25 $\frac{1}{2}w + 3 > 7$

26 $\frac{1}{4}x - 5 \geqslant -6\frac{1}{2}$

Multiplying (or dividing) an inequality by a negative number

Activity

$-2 < 3$

Multiply both sides by -1.
$-2 \times (-1) = 2$ and $3 \times (-1) = -3$

$2 > -3$

To keep the statement true we have to reverse the inequality sign.

Multiply both sides of these inequalities by -1.

1 $3 > 2$

2 $3 > -2$

3 $-3 < -1$

4 $5 \geqslant 4$

5 $-4 \leqslant 5$

6 $-4 \geqslant -5$

The same rules for equations can be applied to inequalities, with one exception:
When you **multiply** (or **divide**) both sides of an inequality by a negative number the inequality is reversed.

Remember:
Division is the inverse (opposite) operation to multiplication.

EXAMPLES

1 Solve $-3x < 6$

Divide both sides by -3.
Because we are dividing by a negative number the inequality is reversed.
$x > -2$

2 Solve $3a - 2 \geqslant 5a - 9$

Subtract $5a$ from both sides.
$-2a - 2 \geqslant -9$
Add 2 to both sides.
$-2a \geqslant -7$
Divide both sides by -2.
$a \leqslant 3.5$

Solve the following inequalities. Show your working clearly.

1 $-4a > 8$

2 $-5b \leqslant -15$

3 $-3c \geqslant 12$

4 $-2d < 5$

5 $-3e \leqslant 4e + 14$

6 $-5f > 4f - 9$

7 $4g < 7g + 12$

8 $5 - 3h \leqslant h - 3$

9 $-5 - j \geqslant 12j - 18$

10 $3 - 5k < 2(3 + 2k)$

11 $3(m - 2) > 5m$

12 $3(2n - 1) < 8n + 5$

13 $3p \geqslant 5 - 6p$

14 $2(q - 3) < 5 + 7q$

Double inequalities

EXAMPLE

1 Find the values of x such that $-8 < 4x - 2 \leqslant 10$.

$-8 < 4x - 2 \leqslant 10$
Add 2 to each part of the inequality.
$-6 < 4x \leqslant 12$
Divide each part of the inequality by 4.
$-1.5 < x \leqslant 3$

Alternative method
Write the **double inequality** as two separate inequalities.
$\quad -8 < 4x - 2 \qquad$ and $\qquad 4x - 2 \leqslant 10$
Solve each inequality.
$\quad -8 < 4x - 2 \qquad\qquad\qquad 4x - 2 \leqslant 10$
Add 2 to both sides. $\qquad\qquad\qquad$ Add 2 to both sides.
$\quad -6 < 4x \qquad\qquad\qquad\qquad\quad 4x \leqslant 12$
Divide both sides by 4. $\qquad\qquad\quad$ Divide both sides by 4.
$\quad -1.5 < x \qquad\qquad\qquad\qquad\qquad x \leqslant 3$
$\qquad\qquad\qquad$ So $-1.5 < x \leqslant 3$

The double inequality $-1.5 < x \leqslant 3$ gives **all** the possible values of x.
This means that the inequality $-8 < 4x - 2 \leqslant 10$ is true for all the values of x from -1.5 (not included) up to 3 (included).

Inequalities involving integers

EXAMPLE

2 Find the integer values for n for which $-2 \leqslant 2n + 6 < 13$.

$-2 \leqslant 2n + 6 < 13$
Subtract 6 from each part.
$-8 \leqslant 2n < 7$
Divide each part by 2.
$-4 \leqslant n < 3.5$

Alternative method
$-2 \leqslant 2n + 6 \qquad\qquad\quad 2n + 6 < 13$
Subtract 6 from both sides. $\quad$ Subtract 6 from both sides.
$-8 \leqslant 2n \qquad\qquad\qquad\quad 2n < 7$
Divide both sides by 2. $\qquad$ Divide both sides by 2.
$-4 \leqslant n \qquad\qquad\qquad\qquad n < 3.5$
This can be written as the double inequality:
$\qquad\qquad -4 \leqslant n < 3.5$

Integer values of n which satisfy the inequality $-2 \leqslant 2n + 6 < 13$ are:
$-4, -3, -2, -1, 0, 1, 2, 3$.

Exercise **18.4**

1 Find the values of x such that:
(a) $5 < x + 4 \leqslant 9$
(b) $-3 \leqslant x - 2 < 7$
(c) $2 < 9 + x \leqslant 13$
(d) $2 < 2x \leqslant 6$
(e) $-6 \leqslant 3x < 12$
(f) $5 < 2x - 1 < 8$
(g) $-2 \leqslant 3x - 1 \leqslant 11$
(h) $12 < 5x + 2 \leqslant 27$
(i) $-9 \leqslant 4x + 3 < 27$
(j) $-16 < 7x - 2 < 12$
(k) $-1 \leqslant 3x - 10 < 8$
(l) $-4 \leqslant 5 + 2x \leqslant 3$

2 Find the integer values of n for which:
(a) $3 < n - 2 < 7$
(b) $-2 < n + 1 \leqslant 5$
(c) $-2 < 2n \leqslant 4$
(d) $5 \leqslant 2n - 3 < 13$
(e) $0 < 2n - 8 < 3$
(f) $5 < 4n + 1 \leqslant 13$
(g) $-4 \leqslant 5n + 6 < 11$
(h) $-4 < 3n + 2 \leqslant 11$
(i) $-5 \leqslant \frac{1}{2}n - 3 \leqslant 0$

Inequalities involving x^2, n^2, etc.

EXAMPLES

1 Find the integer values of n such that $n^2 \geqslant 16$.

Obviously n can be 4, or 5, or 6, or …
But there are some other answers.
Can you find them?

The square of a negative number is positive.
$(-4)^2 = 16$, $(-5)^2 = 25$, …
So n can also be -4, -5, -6, …

$n = 4, 5, 6, \ldots$ or $-4, -5, -6, \ldots$

2 Given that n is an integer, solve the inequality $n^2 < 8$.

The value of n can be 0, 1, or 2, but not 3 (because $3^2 > 8$).
It can also be -1 or -2.

$n = -2, -1, 0, 1, 2.$

3 Solve the inequality $x^2 > 36$.

$x < -6$ or $x > 6$

4 Find the values of x for which $x^2 \leqslant 4$.

The value of x must be 2, or less than 2.
It cannot be less than -2.
All the values from -2 to 2 satisfy the inequality.
We can write this as the double inequality:
$-2 \leqslant x \leqslant 2$

Exercise **18.5**

1 Find the values of x for which:
(a) $x^2 \geqslant 9$
(b) $x^2 < 36$
(c) $x^2 > 1$
(d) $x^2 \leqslant 25$
(e) $3x^2 < 12$
(f) $7 + x^2 \leqslant 56$
(g) $3x^2 - 8 > -5$
(h) $5 - 2x^2 \geqslant -3$

2 Find all the values of n, given that n is an integer, when:
(a) $n^2 \leqslant 3$
(b) $n^2 < 25$
(c) $n^2 > 9$
(d) $n^2 \geqslant 37$
(e) $n^2 + 3 < 12$
(f) $5n^2 > 23$
(g) $2n^2 - 6 \leqslant 66$
(h) $12 - 5n^2 \leqslant -31$

Activity

Line (A) has equation $y = 2$.

Describe the y coordinates of points **on** line A.
Describe the y coordinates of points **below** line A.
Describe the y coordinates of points **above** line A.

Above the line is the region $y > 2$.
Below the line is the region $y < 2$.

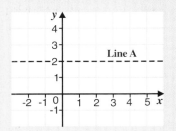

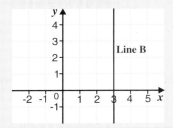

Use an inequality to describe the region to the right of line B.
Use an inequality to describe the region to the left of line B.

Regions

A line divides the graph into two **regions**.
The region $x \leq 2$ is to the **left** of the line $x = 2$, including the line itself.
The region $x \geq 2$ is to the **right** of the line $x = 2$, including the line itself.

The region $y < -3$ is **below** the line $y = -3$.
The region $y > -3$ is **above** the line $y = -3$.

A **solid line** is used when the points on the line are included.
A **broken line** is used when the points on the line are not included.

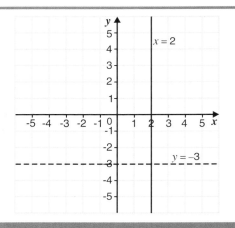

EXAMPLES

On a sketch, show the region where the inequalities
$x > -2$ and $y \leq 1$ are both true.
Label the region R.

To do this:
1 Draw the x and y axes.
2 Draw and label the line $x = -2$, using a broken line.
3 Show the region $x > -2$ by shading out the **unwanted** region.

4 Draw and label the line $y = 1$ using a solid line.
5 Show the region $y \leq 1$ by shading out the **unwanted** region.

6 Label the region, R, where $x > -2$ **and** $y \leq 1$.
Note that the region R extends for ever to the right and downwards.

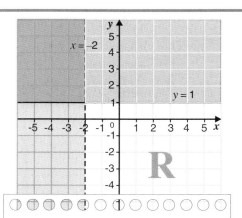

Shading regions on a graph
Unless you are told to do otherwise, always shade out the **unwanted** region.

Exercise 18.6

For each question, draw and label axes for x and y from -5 to 5. Shade the unwanted regions. Leave the given region unshaded and label it R.

1 $x > 2$ and $y \geqslant 1$

2 $x \geqslant -3$ and $y < 4$

3 $x \geqslant -2$, $x < 1$ and $y > 2$

4 $x < 5$, $x \geqslant -1$ and $y \leqslant 3$

5 $x \leqslant 2$, $x > -2$, $y < 3$ and $y \geqslant 1$

6 $x \geqslant -2$, $x \leqslant 0$, $y \geqslant 1$ and $y \leqslant 4$

7 $x \leqslant 1.5$, $y > -1$ and $y \leqslant 2.5$

8 $x > -2.5$, $x \leqslant 1.5$ and $y \leqslant 2.5$

Inequalities involving sloping lines

EXAMPLES

1 Show the region defined by the inequality $y \geqslant 2x - 3$.

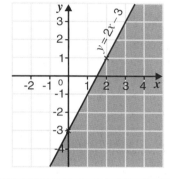

First draw the line with equation $y = 2x - 3$.
When $x = 0$, $y = -3$. Plot the point $(0, -3)$.
When $x = 2$, $y = 1$. Plot the point $(2, 1)$.

Next, draw the line through the two points.
Use a solid line because the inequality sign is $\geqslant$.

Now test a point above the line and a point below the line.

	Coordinates	Value of y	Value of $2x - 3$	Is $y \geqslant 2x - 3$?
Above	$(1, 3)$	3	-1	Yes
Below	$(4, -2)$	-2	5	No

The inequality $y \geqslant 2x - 3$ is true **above** the line, so we shade the unwanted region, below the line.

2 Show the region where the inequality $2x + 3y < 12$ is true.

First draw the line with equation $2x + 3y = 12$.
When $x = 0$, $y = 4$. Plot the point $(0, 4)$.
When $y = 0$, $x = 6$. Plot the point $(6, 0)$.

Next, draw the line through the two points.
Use a broken line because the inequality sign is $<$.

	Coordinates	Value of $2x + 3y$	Is $2x + 3y < 12$?
Above	$(3, 4)$	18	No
Below	$(2, 1)$	7	Yes

The inequality $2x + 3y < 12$ is true **below** the line, so we shade the unwanted region, above the line.

1 Draw graphs to show the following. Leave unshaded the regions where the inequalities are true.
- (a) $y \geqslant x$
- (b) $y < 2x$
- (c) $y > x + 1$
- (d) $y \leqslant 2x - 1$
- (e) $y < 3x + 1$ and $x < 2$
- (f) $y \geqslant \frac{1}{2}x + 2$, $x > -1$ and $y \leqslant 5$
- (g) $y > -2x + 4$, $y < 5$ and $y \geqslant -1$
- (h) $y \leqslant 5 - x$, $x \geqslant -1$ and $y < 3$
- (i) $y < x + 5$, $y < 5 - 2x$ and $y > 1$
- (j) $y > -3x - 4$, $y < \frac{1}{2}x + 1$ and $y > -1$

2 Draw graphs to show the following. Label with the letter R the region defined by the inequalities.
- (a) $2x + 5y \leqslant 10$
- (b) $3x + 4y > 12$
- (c) $4x + 3y \geqslant 6$ and $y > 2$
- (d) $x + 3y < 6$, $x > -1$ and $y > 1$
- (e) $2x + 3y > 9$, $x \geqslant 1$ and $x \leqslant 6$
- (f) $4x + 5y < 10$, $x \geqslant -1$ and $y > 0$
- (g) $3x + y < 9$, $y < 6x + 9$ and $y > -1$
- (h) $2x + 5y > 12$, $x + y < 6$ and $x > 0$
- (i) $3x + 2y \leqslant 8$, $2x + 3y > 6$ and $x > -1$

What you need to know

- Inequalities can be described using words or numbers and symbols.

Sign	Meaning
$<$	is less than
$\leqslant$	is less than or equal to
$>$	is greater than
$\geqslant$	is greater than or equal to

- Inequalities can be shown on a **number line**.

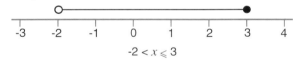

$$-2 < x \leqslant 3$$

The circle is:
> **filled** if the inequality is **included** (i.e. $\leqslant$ or $\geqslant$),
> **not filled** if the inequality is **not included** (i.e. $<$ or $>$).

- Solving inequalities
  Solve means find the values of x which make the inequality true.
  The same rules for equations can be applied to inequalities, with one exception:
  > When you **multiply** (or **divide**) both sides of an inequality by a negative number the inequality is reversed.

  For example, if $-3x < 6$ then $x > -2$.

- Inequalities can be shown on a graph.
  Replace the inequality sign by '$=$' and draw the line.
  For $>$ and $<$ the line is broken. For $\geqslant$ and $\leqslant$ the line is solid.
  Test a point on each side of the line to see whether its coordinates satisfy the inequality.
  Shade the **unwanted** region.

You should be able to do all these questions without a calculator

1 Solve these inequalities.
(a) $3x \geqslant -15$ (b) $3x < x + 6$
(c) $5x - 4 \leqslant 2x + 14$ (d) $5 - 3x < 11$

2 Draw number lines to show each of these inequalities.
(a) $x \leqslant -1$ (b) $4 < x \leqslant 9$
(c) $x < -2$ **and** $x > 5$

3 Find the integer values of n such that:
(a) $-4 < 2n \leqslant 8$
(b) $-3 \leqslant 3n + 6 < 12$
(c) $-4 \leqslant 5n + 6 \leqslant 1$

4 Find the values of a which satisfy the following inequalities.
(a) $a^2 > 9$ (b) $a^2 \leqslant 100$
(c) $3a^2 - 5 \leqslant 43$

5 Given that p is an integer, solve the following inequalities.
(a) $p^2 \leqslant 16$ (b) $p^2 > 30$
(c) $2p^2 < 20$

6 Show, on a graph, the region where the following inequalities are true.
(a) $x \leqslant 2$, $y > -3$ and $y < 1$
(b) $2x + 3y < 6$, $x > -1$ and $y \geqslant 0$
(c) $3x + 4y \leqslant 12$, $3x + y > 3$ and $y > -1$

7 Write down all the whole number values of x, such that $-3 \leqslant x < 4$.

8 Solve the inequality $-1 \leqslant 3x + 2 < 5$.
SEG 2000 S

9 List the values of n, where n is an integer, such that $3 \leqslant n + 4 < 6$
SEG 1998

10 Solve the inequality $5(a - 3) > 3a - 5$.
SEG 1996

11 (a) List all the possible values of x where x is an integer such that $-4 \leqslant x < 2$

(b) Solve (i) $4x - 5 < -3$,
          (ii) $y^2 \geqslant 25$.
SEG 1997

12 Match each of these inequalities to its **unshaded** region.
  A $2x + y < 4$ **B** $2x - y > 4$ **C** $y > 4 - 2x$ **D** $x + 2y < 4$

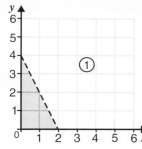 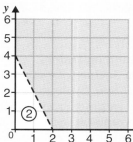 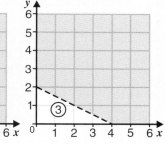 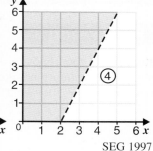

SEG 1997

13 This graph shows the lines $y = x + 4$ and $y = 9 - x$. Two points with whole number coordinates, satisfy the inequalities
$y < x + 4$,
$y < 9 - x$,
$y > 4$.
Write down the coordinates of these two points.

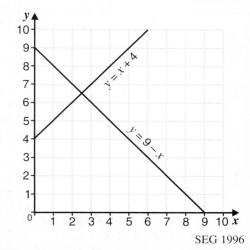

14 Draw and label axes for x from -3 to 8 and for y from 0 to 7.
(a) On your diagram draw and label the lines $y = 3$ and $x + y = 5$.
(b) Show clearly on your diagram the single region that is satisfied by all of these inequalities. $x \geqslant 0$, $y \geqslant 3$ and $x + y \leqslant 5$. Label this region R.
SEG 1996

CHAPTER 19

Quadratic and Other Equations

Brackets

Some expressions and formulae contain **brackets**. You can multiply out brackets, either by using a diagram or by expanding.

> Removing brackets was first covered in Chapter 13.

Diagram method

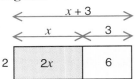

The areas of the two parts are $2x$ and 6.
The total area is $2x + 6$.
$2(x + 3) = 2x + 6$

Expanding

$2(x + 3) = 2 \times x + 2 \times 3$
$ = 2x + 6$

EXAMPLES

1 Expand $x(x + 3)$ by multiplying out the brackets.

$x(x + 3) = x \times x + x \times 3$
$ = x^2 + 3x$

2 Expand $3y(2x - 5y)$.

$3y(2x - 5y) = 3y \times 2x - 3y \times 5y$
$ = 6xy - 15y^2$

Factorising

Factorising is the opposite operation to removing brackets.
For example, $x^2 + 4x = x(x + 4)$.

> **Common factors**
> The **factors** of a number are all the numbers that will divide exactly in the number.
> Factors of 6 are 1, 2, 3 and 6.
> A **common factor** is a factor which will divide into two, or more numbers.

EXAMPLES

> You can check that you have factorised an expression correctly by multiplying out the brackets.

1 Factorise $8ab + 12bc$.

Each term has a factor of 4 and a factor of b.
So the **common factor** of $8ab$ and $12bc$ is $4b$.
$8ab + 12bc = 4b(2a + 3c)$

2 Factorise $6d^2 - 3d^3$

Each term has a factor of 3 and a factor of d^2.
So the **common factor** of $6d^2$ and $3d^3$ is $3d^2$.
$6d^2 - 3d^3 = 3d^2(2 - d)$

3 Factorise $e^3 + e$

$e^3 + e = e(e^2 + 1)$
and $e(e^2 + 1) = e^3 + e$

4 Factorise $4f^3 + 6f^2 - 2f$

$4f^3 + 6f^2 - 2f = 2f(2f^2 + 3f - 1)$
and $2f(2f^2 + 3f - 1) = 4f^3 + 6f^2 - 2f$

Exercise **19.1**

1 Multiply out the brackets by expanding.

(a) $3(a - 4)$
(b) $b(c - 3)$
(c) $d(d + 2)$
(d) $3e(e - 1)$
(e) $2f(3 - 2f)$
(f) $g(2g + 3h)$
(g) $5j(3k - 4j)$
(h) $2m(3 - 4m)$
(i) $3p(2p + 3q - 4)$
(j) $rs(r + s + 2)$

2 Copy and complete the following.

(a) $4a + 4b = 4(\ldots + \ldots)$
(b) $5c - 5d = 5(\ldots - \ldots)$
(c) $ef + eg = e(\ldots + \ldots)$
(d) $hj + jk = j(\ldots + \ldots)$
(e) $l^2 - l = l(\ldots - \ldots)$
(f) $m + m^2 = m(\ldots + \ldots)$
(g) $5n + 10p = 5(\ldots + \ldots)$

3 Factorise.

(a) $2a + 2b$
(b) $7c + 7d$
(c) $8e - 2f$
(d) $7g + 14h$
(e) $24j - 16k$
(f) $ab - a$
(g) $cd + de$
(h) $fg + fh$
(i) $4jk + 2j$
(j) $6l - 9lm$
(k) $a^2 - a$
(l) $b - b^2$
(m) $cd^2 + cd$
(n) $e^2f - e$
(o) $gh^2 - g^2h$

More brackets

We can use a diagram to multiply out the bracket $x(x + 3)$.

The areas of the two parts are x^2 and $3x$.
$x(x + 3) = x^2 + 3x$

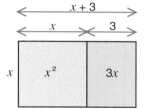

This method can be extended to multiply out $(x + 2)(x + 5)$.

The areas of the four parts are:
x^2, $5x$, and $2x$ and 10.

$(x + 2)(x + 5) = x^2 + 5x + 2x + 10$
Collect like terms and simplify (i.e. $5x + 2x = 7x$)
$\qquad\qquad = x^2 + 7x + 10$

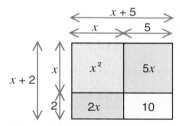

EXAMPLES

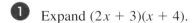

1 Expand $(2x + 3)(x + 4)$.

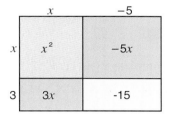

$(2x + 3)(x + 4) = 2x^2 + 8x + 3x + 12$
$\qquad\qquad\quad = 2x^2 + 11x + 12$

2 Expand $(x + 3)(x - 5)$.

The diagram method works with negative numbers.
$(x + 3)(x - 5) = x^2 - 5x + 3x - 15$
$\qquad\qquad\quad = x^2 - 2x - 15$

3 Expand $(2x - 5)^2$.

	$2x$	-5
$2x$	$4x^2$	$-10x$
-5	$-10x$	25

$$(2x - 5)^2 = (2x - 5)(2x - 5)$$
$$= 4x^2 - 10x - 10x + 25$$
$$= 4x^2 - 20x + 25$$

4 Expand $(x - 1)(2x + 3)$.
As you become more confident you may not need a diagram to expand the brackets.

$(x - 1)(2x + 3)$

1. $x \times 2x = 2x^2$
2. $x \times 3 = 3x$
3. $-1 \times 2x = -2x$
4. $-1 \times 3 = -3$

$$(x - 1)(2x + 3) = 2x^2 + 3x - 2x - 3$$
$$= 2x^2 + x - 3$$

Exercise 19.2

Questions 1 to 6.
Use diagrams to multiply out the brackets.

1 $(x + 3)(x + 4)$

2 $(x + 1)(x + 5)$

3 $(x - 5)(x + 2)$

4 $(2x + 1)(x - 2)$

5 $(3x - 2)(x - 6)$

6 $(2x + 1)(3x + 2)$

Questions 7 to 24.
Expand the following brackets. Only draw a diagram if necessary.

7 $(x + 8)(x - 2)$

8 $(x + 5)(x - 2)$

9 $(x - 1)(x + 3)$

10 $(x - 3)(x - 2)$

11 $(x - 4)(x - 1)$

12 $(x - 7)(x + 2)$

13 $(2x + 3)(x - 1)$

14 $(3x - 1)(x + 5)$

15 $(4x - 2)(3x + 5)$

16 $(x + 3)(x - 3)$

17 $(x + 5)(x - 5)$

18 $(x + 7)(x - 7)$

19 $(x - 10)(x + 10)$

20 $(x + 3)^2$

21 $(x + 5)^2$

22 $(x - 3)^2$

23 $(x - 7)^2$

24 $(2x - 3)^2$

Further factorising

$x^2 + 7x + 12$ and $x^2 - 25$ are examples of **quadratic expressions**.
You will need to be able to factorise such expressions in order to solve quadratic equations in the next section of this chapter.

The general form of a quadratic expression is $ax^2 + bx + c$, where a cannot be equal to 0.

1 Copy and complete $x^2 + 7x + 12 = (x + 4)(x + \ldots)$.

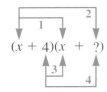

$(x + 4)(x + ?)$

1. $x \times x = x^2$
2. $x \times ? = \square$
3. $4 \times x = 4x$
4. $4 \times ? = 12$

$\square + 4x = 7x, \square = 3x$
So $? = 3$
Giving $? = 3$

$$x^2 + 7x + 12 = (x + 4)(x + 3)$$

2 Copy and complete $x^2 - 5x + 6 = (x - \ldots)(x - 2)$.

$\quad$ **1** $\quad x \times x = x^2$

$(x - ?)\ (x - 2)$

$\left.\begin{array}{l}\textbf{2} \quad x \times -2 = -2x \\ \textbf{3} \quad ? \times x = \boxed{}\end{array}\right\} \begin{array}{l} -2x + \boxed{} = -5x, \boxed{} = -3x \\ \text{So } ? = 3 \end{array}$

$\quad$ **4** $\quad -? \times -2 = 6 \quad$ Giving $? = 3$

$\qquad x^2 - 5x + 6 = (x - 3)(x - 2)$

3 Factorise $x^2 - 8x + 12$

$x^2 - 8x + 12 = (x - 6)(x - 2)$

Because $-6 \times -2 = 12$
and $-6 + -2 = -8$

4 Factorise $x^2 - 2x - 8$

$x^2 - 2x - 8 = (x + 2)(x - 4)$

Because $+2 \times -4 = -8$
and $+2 + -4 = -2$.

Difference of two squares

$(x + 2)(x - 2) = x^2 + 2x - 2x - 4$
$\qquad\qquad\qquad = x^2 - 4$

This result is called the **difference of two squares**.
$x^2 = x \times x$ and $4 = 2^2 = 2 \times 2$

Factorise $x^2 - 64$.

$x^2 - 64 = (x + 8)(x - 8)$

In general: $\quad a^2 - b^2 = (a - b)(a + b)$

Exercise 19.3

1 Copy and complete the following.

(a) $x^2 + 6x + 5 = (x + 5)(x + \ldots)$
(b) $x^2 + 9x + 14 = (x + 7)(x + \ldots)$
(c) $x^2 + 6x + 8 = (x + \ldots)(x + 4)$
(d) $x^2 + 9x + 18 = (x + \ldots)(x + 6)$
(e) $x^2 - 6x + 5 = (x - 5)(x - \ldots)$

(f) $x^2 - 7x + 10 = (x - 5)(x - \ldots)$
(g) $x^2 - 7x + 12 = (x - \ldots)(x - 3)$
(h) $x^2 + 3x - 4 = (x + 4)(x - \ldots)$
(i) $x^2 + 5x - 14 = (x + 7)(x - \ldots)$
(j) $x^2 - 4x - 5 = (x - 5)(x + \ldots)$

2 Factorise.
(a) $x^2 + 3x + 2$
(b) $x^2 + 8x + 7$
(c) $x^2 + 8x + 15$
(d) $x^2 + 8x + 12$
(e) $x^2 + 12x + 11$
(f) $x^2 + 9x + 20$
(g) $x^2 + 10x + 24$
(h) $x^2 + 13x + 36$

3 Factorise.
(a) $x^2 - 6x + 9$
(b) $x^2 - 6x + 8$
(c) $x^2 - 11x + 10$
(d) $x^2 - 7x + 10$
(e) $x^2 - 8x + 15$
(f) $x^2 - 10x + 16$
(g) $x^2 - 12x + 20$
(h) $x^2 - 11x + 24$

4 Factorise.
(a) $x^2 - x - 6$
(b) $x^2 - 5x - 6$
(c) $x^2 + 2x - 24$
(d) $x^2 + 5x - 24$
(e) $x^2 - 2x - 15$
(f) $x^2 + 3x - 18$
(g) $x^2 - 3x - 40$
(h) $x^2 - 4x - 12$

5 Factorise.
(a) $x^2 - 4x + 4$
(b) $x^2 + 11x + 30$
(c) $x^2 + 2x - 8$
(d) $x^2 - 4x - 21$
(e) $x^2 + 2x - 15$
(f) $x^2 + 8x + 12$
(g) $x^2 + 8x + 16$
(h) $x^2 - 2x + 1$

6 Factorise.
(a) $x^2 - 9$
(b) $x^2 - 25$
(c) $x^2 - 81$
(d) $100 - x^2$
(e) $36 - x^2$
(f) $x^2 - 1$

Solving quadratic equations

Activity

> I am thinking of two numbers.
> I multiply them together.
> The answer is zero.

Write down 2 numbers which could be Jim's numbers.
Now write down **four** more pairs.
What can you say about Jim's numbers?

You should have discovered that at least one of Jim's numbers must be **zero**.
We can use this fact to solve **quadratic equations**.

°EXAMPLES

1 Find x if

(a) $x(x - 2) = 0$
Either $x = 0$ or $x - 2 = 0$
Because one of them must be zero.
$x = 0$ or $x = 2$

(b) $(x - 3)(x + 2) = 0$
$x - 3 = 0$ or $x + 2 = 0$
Because one of them must be zero.
$x = 3$ or $x = -2$

2 Factorise the quadratic expression and so solve the equation.

(a) $x^2 - 5x + 6 = 0$
$(x - 2)(x - 3) = 0$
$x = 2$ or $x = 3$

(b) $x^2 - 9 = 0$
$(x - 3)(x + 3) = 0$
$x = 3$ or $x = -3$

(c) $y^2 + 7y = 0$
$y(y + 7) = 0$
$y = 0$ or $y + 7 = 0$
$y = 0$ or $y = -7$

(d) $a^2 + 4a - 5 = 0$
$(a - 1)(a + 5) = 0$
$a = 1$ or $a = -5$

Exercise 19.4

1 Solve these equations.

(a) $(x - 2)(x - 3) = 0$
(d) $x(x - 5)(x + 2) = 0$

(b) $(x + 4)(x + 6) = 0$
(e) $x(x - 4) = 0$

(c) $(x - 3)(x + 1) = 0$
(f) $3x(x + 2) = 0$

2 Solve.

(a) $x^2 - 3x + 2 = 0$
(d) $a^2 + a - 12 = 0$
(g) $k^2 + 8k + 15 = 0$
(j) $v^2 - 7v - 60 = 0$

(b) $y^2 + 7y + 12 = 0$
(e) $n^2 - 5n - 36 = 0$
(h) $c^2 + 15c + 56 = 0$
(k) $w^2 + 8w - 48 = 0$

(c) $m^2 - 2m - 8 = 0$
(f) $z^2 - 9z + 18 = 0$
(i) $b^2 + b - 20 = 0$
(l) $p^2 - p - 72 = 0$

3 Solve.

(a) $x^2 - 5x = 0$
(d) $4a - a^2 = 0$

(b) $y^2 + y = 0$
(e) $t^2 - 6t = 0$

(c) $p^2 + 3p = 0$
(f) $g^2 - 4g = 0$

4 Solve.

(a) $x^2 - 4 = 0$
(b) $y^2 - 144 = 0$
(c) $9 - a^2 = 0$
(d) $d^2 - 16 = 0$

Solving equations graphically

The graphs of **linear functions** are straight lines. The general equation of a straight line graph is $y = mx + c$. In this section we are going to look at the graphs of **quadratic** and **cubic** functions.

Quadratic graphs

The graph of a **quadratic function** is always smooth and is called a **parabola**. The general equation of a quadratic function is $y = ax^2 + bx + c$, where a cannot be equal to zero.

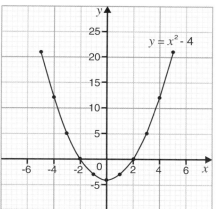

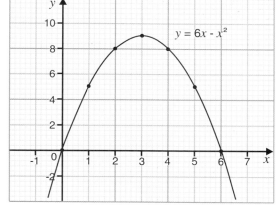

The graph of $y = x^2 - 4$ has a **minimum value** at the point $(0, -4)$.

The graph of $y = 6x - x^2$ has a **maximum value** at the point $(3, 9)$

The values of x where the graphs of quadratic functions cross (or touch) the x axis give the **solutions to quadratic equations**.

At the point where the graph $y = x^2 - 4$ crosses the x axis the value of $y = 0$.
$x^2 - 4 = 0$
The solutions of this quadratic equation can be read from the graph. $x = -2$ *and* $x = 2$.

Remember:
- Your graphs should never be flat or pointed.
- Quadratic graphs are always symmetrical.
- Join plotted points using smooth curves and not a series of straight lines.

Find the solutions of the equation $6x - x^2 = 0$ from the graph of $y = 6x - x^2$. Check the graphical solutions using the factorising method.

EXAMPLE

Draw the graph of
$y = x^2 + 3x - 2$ for values of x from -5 to 2.
Use the graph to find the solution of the equation $x^2 + 3x - 2 = 0$.
First make a table of values for $y = x^2 + 3x - 2$.

x	-5	-4	-3	-2	-1	0	1	2
y	8	2	-2	-4	-4	-2	2	8

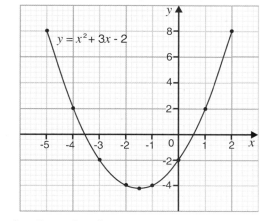

The graph has a **minimum value** between $x = -2$ and $x = -1$.
To find this value substitute $x = -1.5$ into the equation. $y = (-1.5 \times -1.5) + (3 \times -1.5) - 2$
$= 2.25 - 4.5 - 2$
$= -4.25$
Plot the point $(-2.5, -4.25)$.

$x^2 + 3x - 2 = 0$
To solve this equation, read the values of x where the graph of $y = x^2 + 3x - 2$ crosses the x axis. $x = -3.6$ and $x = 0.6$, correct to 1 d.p.

Cubic graphs

The general form of a **cubic function** is $y = ax^3 + bx^2 + cx + d$, where a cannot be equal to zero.
As for quadratic graphs, the solutions of cubic equations can be found in a similar way.

Exercise 19.5

1 (a) Copy and complete this table of values for $y = 2x^2$.

x	-2	-1	0	1	2
y					

    (b) Draw axes marked from -2 to 2 for x and from -2 to 8 for y. Draw the graph of $y = 2x^2$ on your axes.

    (c) Use your graph to solve the equation $2x^2 = 0$.

2 (a) Copy and complete this table of values for $y = x^2 + x$.

x	-3	-2	-1	0	1	2
y						

    (b) Draw axes marked from -3 to 2 for x and from -2 to 6 for y. Draw the graph of $y = x^2 + x$ on your axes.

    (c) Use your graph to solve the equation $x^2 + x = 0$.

    (d) Find the coordinates of the point at which the graph has a minimum value.

3 (a) Copy and complete this table of values for $y = x^2 - x - 1$.

x	-2	-1	0	1	2	3
y						

    (b) Draw axes marked from -2 to 3 for x and from -2 to 6 for y. Draw the graph of $y = x^2 - x - 1$ on your axes.

    (c) Use your graph to solve the equation $x^2 - x - 1 = 0$.

4 (a) Draw the graph of $y = x^2 + 2x - 3$ for values of x from -5 to 3.

    (b) Use your graph to solve the equation $x^2 + 2x - 3 = 0$.

5 (a) Copy and complete this table of values for $y = 10 - x^2$.

x	-4	-3	-2	-1	0	1	2	3	4
y									

    (b) Draw axes marked from -4 to 4 for x and from -6 to 10 for y. Draw the graph of $y = 10 - x^2$ on your axes.

    (c) Use your graph to solve the equation $10 - x^2 = 0$.

    (d) Find the coordinates of the point at which the graph has a maximum value.

6 (a) Copy and complete this table of values for $y = 15 - 2x^2$.

x	-3	-2	-1	0	1	2	3
y							

    (b) Draw axes marked from -3 to 3 for x and from -4 to 16 for y. Draw the graph of $y = 15 - 2x^2$ on your axes.

    (c) Use your graph to solve the equation $15 - 2x^2 = 0$.

7 Draw suitable graphs to solve the following equations.
    (a) $x^2 - 8 = 0$ (b) $5 - x^2 = 0$
    (c) $3x^2 = 0$ (d) $12 - 2x^2 = 0$

8 (a) Draw the graph of $y = x^3 - 3$ for values of x from -3 to 3.

    (b) Draw the graph of $y = x^3 + x$ for values of x from -3 to 3.

    (c) Draw the graph of $y = \frac{1}{x}$ for values of x from -4 to 4.

9 (a) Copy and complete this table of values for $y = x^3 + x^2 - 6x$.

x	-4	-3	-2	-1	0	1	2	3
y								

(b) Draw axes marked from -4 to 3 for x and from -25 to 20 for y.
Draw the graph of $y = x^3 + x^2 - 6x$ on your axes.

(c) Use your graph to solve the equation $x^3 + x^2 - 6x = 0$.

10 (a) Copy and complete this table of values for $y = x^3 - 5x + 6$.

x	-3	-2	-1	0	1	2	3
y							

(b) Draw axes marked from -3 to 3 for x and from -10 to 20 for y.
Draw the graph of $y = x^3 - 5x + 6$ on your axes.

(c) Use your graph to solve the equation $x^3 - 5x + 6 = 0$.

Trial and improvement methods

This method is mainly used to solve cubic equations. The accuracy of the value of the unknown letter is improved by **trial and improvement** until the required degree of accuracy is reached.
This can be a time consuming method of solving equations and is often used only as a last resort for solving equations which cannot be solved easily by algebraic or graphical methods.

EXAMPLE

1 Use a trial and improvement method to solve $2x^2 + 1 = 11$, correct to one decimal place.

First guess: $x = 5$
$2(5)^2 + 1 = 51$ Too big
We are trying to find a value for x which produces the answer 11.

Second guess: $x = 3$
$2(3)^2 + 1 = 19$ Too big
Try a smaller value.

Third guess: $x = 2$
$2(2)^2 + 1 = 9$ Too small
We know that the value of x is between 2 and 3. *Why?*

Fourth guess: $x = 2.2$
$2(2.2)^2 + 1 = 10.68$ Too small

Fifth guess: $x = 2.3$
$2(2.3)^2 + 1 = 11.58$ Too big
So the value of x is between 2.2 and 2.3.

Sixth guess: $x = 2.25$
$2(2.25)^2 + 1 = 11.125$ Too big
So x is nearer to 2.2 than to 2.3. *Why?*

So, $x = 2.2$, correct to one decimal place.

2 Use trial and improvement to solve $x^3 = 54$, correct to one decimal place.

The working can be shown in a table.

So, $x = 3.8$, correct to one decimal place.

x	x^3	
3	27	Too small
4	64	Too big
3.7	50.653	Too small
3.8	54.872	Too big
3.75	52.734	Too small

Exercise 19.6

You will need a calculator for this exercise.

1 $a^2 - 7a = 58$ has a solution between 11 and 12.
Use trial and improvement to find the solution to one decimal place.

2 Use trial and improvement to solve these equations.
Give your answers to one decimal place.

(a) $x^2 + 7 = 10$ (b) $3t^2 = 50$ (c) $c^2 - 4 = 91$

(d) $3p^2 + 4 = 150$ (e) $2(y^2 + 1) = 19$ (f) $\frac{1}{2} d^2 - 2 = 28$

3 Use trial and improvement to solve these cubic equations.

(a) $w^3 = 72$ (b) $4x^3 = 51$ (c) $2y^3 + y = 270$

What you need to know

- **Factorising** is the opposite operation to removing brackets.

- A **common factor** is a factor which divides into two, or more, numbers (or terms).
  For example: $8ab + 12bc = 4b(2a + c)$
  where $4b$ is a common factor of $8ab$ and $12bc$.

- Brackets, such as $(x + 2)(x + 5)$ can be multiplied out using:
  the **diagram method**,
  by **expanding**.

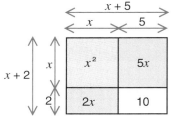

- **Difference of two squares**
  $a^2 - b^2 = (a - b)(a + b)$

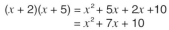

$(x + 2)(x + 5) = x^2 + 5x + 2x + 10$
$= x^2 + 7x + 10$

- **Quadratic equations** can be solved:
  by factorising,
  graphically,
  by trial and improvement.

- The general form for a **quadratic function** is $y = ax^2 + bx + c$,
  where a cannot be zero.
  The graph of a quadratic function is symmetrical and has a
  maximum or **minimum** value.

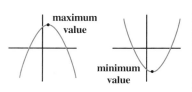

- The general form of a **cubic function** is $y = ax^3 + bx^2 + cx + d$,
  where a cannot be zero.
  Cubic equations can be solved graphically or by trial and improvement.

1 Factorise completely $6a^2 - 2a$

S96/2410/34 (adapted)

2 (a) Factorise $2ab - a$
(b) Factorise $3a^2 - 6a$

3 Multiply out the brackets and simplify your answer.
$(2x - 3)(x + 4)$

SEG 1994

4 Multiply out and simplify
$(3x + 4y)(2x - y)$.

5 (a) Multiply out and simplify
$(3p + 1)(p - 4)$.
(b) Simplify $3p^2 + 3p + 4 + 2(p - 2)$.
Write your answer in fully factorised form.

SEG 1997

6 Solve the equations:
(a) $2x + 3 = 15 - x$;
(b) $(x + 3)(x - 4) = 0$.

SEG 1998

7 (a) Factorise $x^2 - 3x - 10$
(b) Solve the equation $x^2 + 3x = 0$.

SEG 2000 S

8 These two rectangles have the same area.

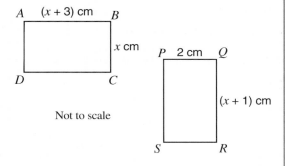

Not to scale

(a) Form an equation in x and show that is can be simplified to
$x^2 + x - 2 = 0$.
(b) Solve the equation $x^2 + x - 2 = 0$ to find the length of BC.

SEG 2000 S

9 Draw the graph of $y = x^2 - 3$ for values of x from 0 to 4.
Draw axes marked from 0 to 4 for x and from -4 to 14 for y.

SEG 1997

10 (a) Copy and complete the table of values for $y = x^2 - 2x - 2$.

x	-2	-1	0	1	2	3	4
y	6		-2			1	

(b) Draw the graph of $y = x^2 - 2x - 2$. Draw axes marked from -2 to 4 for x and from -4 to 6 for y.
(c) Use your graph to solve the equation $x^2 - 2x - 2 = 0$.

SEG 1998

11 (a) Copy and complete the table of values for $y = x^2 + 1$.

x	-3	-2	-1	0	1	2	3
y							

(b) Draw the graph of $y = x^2 + 1$. Draw axes marked from -3 to 3 for x and from 0 to 11 for y.
(c) By drawing a suitable line on your graph, use your graph to find the values of x when $x^2 + 1 = 9$. Give your answers correct to one decimal place.

SEG 1996

12 Use trial and improvement to find a solution of the equation $x^3 = 22$.
Start with $x = 2$ and show your trials in a table like the one below.
Give your answer correct to **one** decimal place.

x	$x3$
2	

SEG 1997

13 The equation $x^3 + x = 20$ has a solution between 2 and 3.
Use a trial and improvement method to find the solution correct to two decimal places.
Show all your working.

Section Review - Algebra

1 Simplify (a) $3a - 2 - a + 3$
(b) $y^2 - 2y + y^2 + y$

2 Solve (a) $8x + 4 = 20$
(b) $3x - 2 = 10$
(c) $\frac{1}{2}x + 2 = 8$

3 Kim thinks of a number.
She doubles it and adds 3.
The answer is 16.
What is her number?

4 Lucy said to Ben:

???

Think of a number.
Take away 4.
Multiply by 3.
Add 5.
Now tell me your answer.

Ben's answer was 26. What was the number he first thought of?

5 John thinks of a number.
He adds 2 to it and then doubles the result.
The answer is 18.
What was his number?

SEG 1997

6 (a) The diagram shows two rows of four tables
with a total of 56 seats.

This formula can be used to work out the
number of seats, S, in R rows of T tables.
$S = R \times (6T + 4)$
How many seats are there in 3 rows of
10 tables?

(b) Work out the value of c in the equation
$3a + 2b = 7c$ when $a = 9$ and $b = 4$.

(c) x, y and z are **different** numbers in this list.
2   3   4   5   6   7   8   9
x and y are prime numbers.
z is a square number.
$x + y = z$
Work out the values of x, y and z.

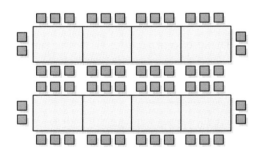

SEG 2000 S

7 Patterns are formed using black squares and white squares.
The first three patterns are shown.

(a) How many black squares has Pattern 4?
(b) How many more black squares has
Pattern 8 than Pattern 7?
(c) Pattern n has a total of 100 squares.
(i) What is the value of n?
(ii) How many of these squares are black?

Pattern 1   Pattern 2   Pattern 3

SEG 1996

8 Hexagons are used to make a sequence of patterns as shown.

 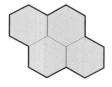 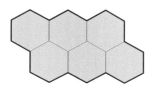

Pattern 1	**Pattern 2**	**Pattern 3**
10 outside edges	14 outside edges	18 outside edges

(a) How many outside edges has Pattern 8?
(b) Write down a rule to find the number of outside edges for Pattern n.

SEG 1997

9 The diagram shows a rectangle of length x and width w.

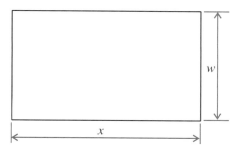

(a) Write an expression for the area of the rectangle, in terms of x and w.
(b) Write an expression for the perimeter of the rectangle, in terms of x and w.
(c) When the perimeter of the rectangle is 48 cm the width is half of the length.
Use your answer to (b) to form an equation and solve it to find the length x.

SEG 1995

10 (a) The perimeter of a rectangle is $8x$ cm.

Not to scale

The length of the shorter side is x cm.
Write an expression, in terms of x, for the length of one of the longer sides.

(b) The perimeters of these triangles are equal.

Not to scale

 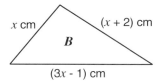

(i) Triangle A is equilateral. Its perimeter is $3(x + 2)$ cm.
Multiply out $3(x + 2)$.
(ii) Solve the equation $3(x + 2) = x + (x + 2) + (3x - 1)$.
(iii) Calculate the perimeter of triangle B.

SEG 1996

11 Solve the equations   (a) $3(x - 1) = 6$

                                  (b) $30 + 12(n - 1) = 102$

12 Solve the equation $6x + 7 = 2x - 3$.

SEG 1997

13

> **CAR HIRE RATES**
>
> Vauxhall Nova
> per day: £25
> per mile: 12p

The total cost, £C, of hiring the car can be calculated from the formula

$$C = 25d + \frac{(12m - 50d)}{100}$$

where d = number of days hired, and m = number of miles driven.
A car is hired for 7 days, and is driven 476 miles.
Calculate the total cost of hiring the car.

SEG 1996

14 (a)   A sequence begins   1,   3,   7,   15, ...
          The next number in the sequence can be found by using the following rule.

> **MULTIPLY THE PREVIOUS NUMBER BY TWO AND ADD ONE**

        (i)   What is the next number in the sequence?
        The tenth number in the sequence is 1023.
        (ii)   Explain how you can use the tenth number in the sequence to find the ninth
             number in the sequence.

    (b)   (i)   Write down the next number in this sequence,
               $\frac{1}{2}$, $\frac{3}{4}$, $\frac{7}{8}$, $\frac{15}{16}$, ...
        (ii)   Explain how you found your answer.

    (c)   Another sequence begins   0,   3,   8,   15,   24, ...
          Write an expression, in terms of n, for the n th term of the sequence.

SEG 1997

15 Copy and complete the table.

	Sequence	Rule	Next three terms	10th term	n th term
(a)	10, 7, 4, ...	Take away 3	..... , ... , ...	.....	.....
(b)	2, 5, 10, 17, ...	Add 2 to the difference	..... , ... , ...	.....	.....

SEG 1997

16 The rule for any number in a sequence is $\frac{n}{n^2 + 1}$, where n is the number of the term.

    (a)   Use this rule to write down the first **five** numbers of the sequence.

The first five terms of a different sequence are
       $\frac{1}{3}$, $\frac{2}{5}$, $\frac{3}{7}$, $\frac{4}{9}$, $\frac{5}{11}$,   ...

    (b)   Write down the rule for the n th term of this sequence.

SEG 1995

17 Factorise   (a) $6p - 3$
                 (b) $p^2 + 2p$

18 Use a trial and improvement method to solve the equation $x^3 = 19$, correct to **one** decimal place.
You **must** show all your working.

SEG 1996

19 (a)   (i)   List all the whole number values of n which satisfy the inequality
                 $3 < 2n \leqslant 11$.
         (ii)   Solve the inequality $2x^2 < 19$.
    (b)   Use trial and improvement to solve the equation $x^3 + x = 24$.
         Start with $x = 3$.
         Give your final answer correct to **one** decimal place.
         You **must** show all your working.

SEG 1997

20 (a)   Draw the graphs of $y = 2x - 4$ and $y = -x^2$ for values of x from -4 to 4.
    (b)   Use the graphs to find the smallest value of x which gives the same value of y in both
         equations.

SEG 1996

21 (a)   (i)   Draw the graph of $y = 2x^2$ for values of x from 0 to 3.
         (ii)   Use your graph to find a value of x when $y = 12$.
    (b)   Solve the simultaneous equations
           $3x - 2y = 8$
           $x + 4y = 5$

SEG 1997

22 (a)   Solve the equation $\frac{1}{2}x + 3 = 2x + 9$.
    (b)   Solve these simultaneous equations.
           $3x + y = 7$
           $x + 2y = 1$

SEG 1996

23 (a)   Draw and label axes for x from -5 to 6 and for y from -3 to 6.
         On your diagram draw and label the following lines.
           $y = 2x$ and $x + y = 5$
    (b)   Explain how to use your graph to solve the equation $2x = 5 - x$.
    (c)   Show clearly the single region that is satisfied by **all** of these inequalities.
           $x + y \leqslant 5$ $y \geqslant 2x$ $x \geqslant 0$
         Label this region R.

SEG 1998

24 Two rival electrical firms have differing charges.
The cost, $£C$, of repairs with **WYREKARE** is $C = 20 + 6H$.
The cost, $£C$, of repairs with **VOLTMEND** is $C = 30 + 4H$.
H is the number of hours spent doing the repair.

    (a)   Solve the simultaneous equations to find the length of time taken and the cost for a
         repair which costs the same for both firms.
    (b)   Which would be the cheaper firm for a repair that takes longer than your answer to (a)?

SEG 1994

25 (a) Solve the simultaneous equations

$$3x + 2y = 7$$
$$5x - 4y = 8$$

(b) List all the integer values of n for which this inequality is true.

$$n^2 < 10$$

SEG 1997

26 (a) Solve the equation $3x - 2 = x + 7$.

(b) Solve the simultaneous equations

$$x + y = 4$$
$$15x + 25y = 76.$$

(c) Solve the inequality

$$2(3x - 2) < 11.$$

(d) Copy the graph below onto graph paper.
Label letter R, the single region which satisfies all of these inequalities.

$$y > 2, \qquad x + y > 4, \qquad 0 < x < 3$$

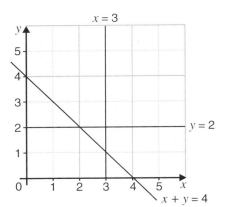

SEG 1995

27 (a) Draw and label axes for x from 0 to 20 and for y from 0 to 30.
On your diagram draw the appropriate boundary lines and carefully shade the area that contains all the points satisfying the inequalities

$$x > 5, y > 8 \text{ and } y < 30 - 2x.$$

(b) Solve the inequality

$$2(3x - 2) < 11.$$

28 (a) Draw two graphs to solve these simultaneous equations.

$$y - x = 2, \qquad 3x + 4y = 24$$

(b) (i) Label with the letter R the region where the inequalities

$$y - x \geqslant 2 \text{ and } 3x + 4y \leqslant 24 \text{ are satisfied.}$$

(ii) The values of x and y are whole numbers.
Write down one possible pair of values that satisfy these inequalities.

SEG 1996

29 (a) Use the formula $v = \sqrt{u^2 + 2as}$ to find the value of v when

$$u = 24, a = -9.8 \text{ and } s = 10\tfrac{1}{4}.$$

(b) **Without using a calculator**, use approximation to check that your answer to (a) is of the correct order of magnitude.
You **must** show all your working.

SEG 1996

30 (a) Simplify the expression
$$x(x + 2) - x(3x - 2).$$
(b) Factorise the expression
$$14xy^2 - 21y^3.$$
(c) Rearrange this formula to make d the subject.
$$A = \frac{\pi d^2}{4}$$
(d) Solve
$$x^2 \geqslant 25.$$

SEG 1996

 31 (a) List all the integer values of n for which
$$-4 < n + 1 \leqslant 2.$$
(b) Solve the inequality
$$3x + 5 < 1 - 2x.$$
(c) Make x the subject of the formula
$$A = \frac{5x^2 + 2}{3}$$

SEG 1996

 32 The formula for finding the total surface area of a cylinder is
$A = 2\pi r^2 + \pi rh$.

(a) Factorise the expression $2\pi r^2 + \pi rh$.
(b) Rearrange $A = 2\pi r^2 + \pi rh$ to make h the subject of the formula.

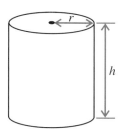

SEG 1995

 33 The volume of a sphere is given by the formula $V = \frac{4}{3}\pi r^3$.

(a) Rearrange the formula to give r, in terms of V.
(b) Find the value of r when $V = 75$.

SEG 1995

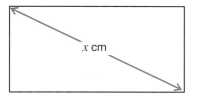 **34** A rectangular window has a diagonal of length x cm.
The width is 18 cm less than the diagonal.
The length is 9 cm less than the diagonal.

Show that the area of the rectangle can be represented by the expression $x^2 - 27x + 162$.

SEG 1997

 35 (a) Multiply out and simplify $(x - 3)(x - 2)$.
(b) Solve the equation $x^2 + 7x - 8 = 0$.

 36 A rectangle has length $(x + 2)$ cm and width $(x + 1)$ cm.

The rectangle has an area of 6 cm^2.
Form an equation and show that it can be simplified to $x^2 + 3x - 4 = 0$.

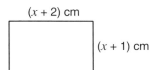

The diagram shows a stopwatch with a second hand.
Every minute the second hand will make one complete turn.
An **angle** is a measure of turn.
Angles are measured in **degrees**.
In one minute the second hand will turn through an angle of 360°.

Types and names of angles

Each of these diagrams shows a quarter-turn.

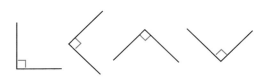

A quarter-turn is called a **right angle**.
A right angle is 90°.

An angle less than 90° is called an **acute** angle.
An angle between 90° and 180° is called an **obtuse** angle.
An angle greater than 180° is called a **reflex** angle.

Exercise **20.1**

1 Through what angle will a second hand turn in:

(a) half a minute,
(b) quarter of a minute,
(c) three-quarters of a minute,
(d) 15 seconds,
(e) 20 seconds,

(f) 1 second,
(g) 7 seconds,
(h) 2 minutes,
(i) $1\frac{1}{2}$ minutes,
(j) 135 seconds?

2 This clock shows 4.30.

(a) What size is the acute angle between the hands of the clock?

(b) What is the size of the reflex angle between the hands?

3 Through what angle will the hour hand of the clock turn between:
(a) 10.00 am and 11.30 am,
(b) 10.00 am and 10.00 pm?

4 Say whether each of the marked angles is acute, obtuse, reflex or a right angle.

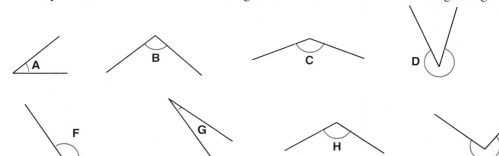

Measuring angles

To measure an angle accurately we need to use a **protractor**.

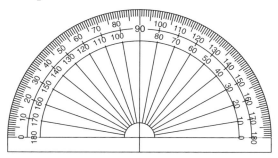

Some protractors have two scales. Look at the type of angle (acute/obtuse) you are measuring and use the correct scale.

To measure an angle, the protractor is placed so that its centre point is on the corner (vertex) of the angle, with the base along one of the arms of the angle as shown.

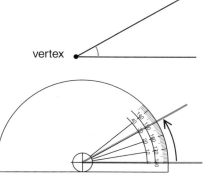

This angle measures 30°.

How can you measure the size of a reflex angle?

Drawing angles

Draw an angle of 74°.

Draw a line.
Mark the vertex of the angle.

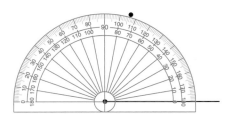

Position the protractor as if you were measuring an angle.
Mark a dot at 74°.

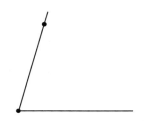

Draw a line from the vertex through the dot.

Exercise 20.2

1 Use a protractor to measure these angles.

(a)

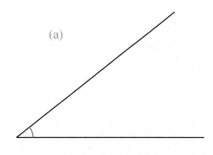

(b)

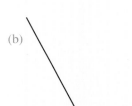

(c)

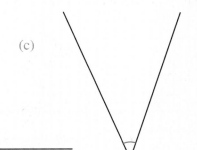

2 Use a protractor to measure these angles.

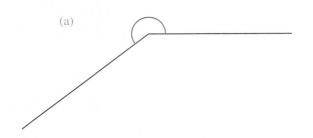

(a)

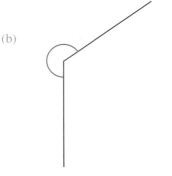

(b)

3 Draw these angles accurately.

   (a) 20°   (b) 85°   (c) 128°   (d) 205°   (e) 324°

Angles at a point

When angles meet at a point, the sum of all the angles is 360°.

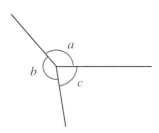

$$a + b + c = 360°$$

Complementary angles

When two angles add up to 90°, the angles are called **complementary**.

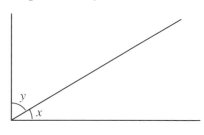

$$x + y = 90°$$

x and *y* are complementary angles.

Supplementary angles

Angles which can be placed together on a straight line add up to 180°.
When two angles add up to 180°, the angles are called **supplementary**.

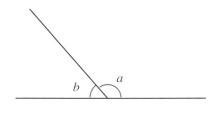

$$a + b = 180°$$

a and *b* are supplementary angles.

Vertically opposite angles

When two lines cross each other the angles between the lines make two pairs of equal angles.

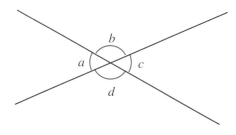

$$a = c \text{ and } b = d$$

a and *c* are vertically opposite angles.
b and *d* are vertically opposite angles.

214

EXAMPLES

1 Without measuring, work out the size of the angle marked *a*.

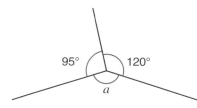

Angles at a point add up to 360°.
$a + 95 + 120 = 360$
$\qquad a = 360 - 95 - 120$
$\qquad a = 145°$

2 Calculate the sizes of the angles marked with letters.

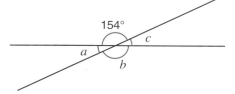

$b = 154°$ (vertically opposite angles)

$a + 154 = 180$ (supplementary angles)
$\qquad a = 180 - 154$
$\qquad a = 26°$

$c = 26°$

$a = 26°, b = 154°, c = 26°$

Exercise **20.3**

1 Without measuring, work out the size of the angles marked with letters.

(a)

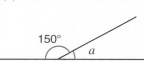

(b)

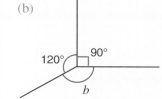

(c)

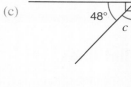

(d)

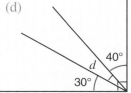

(e)

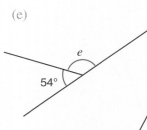

(f)

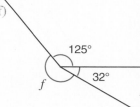

(g)

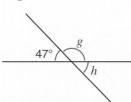

(h)

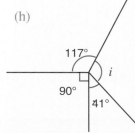

(i)

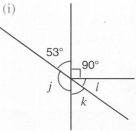

(j)

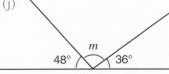

(k)

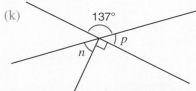

2 These diagrams are not drawn accurately. Without measuring, work out the value of x in each diagram.

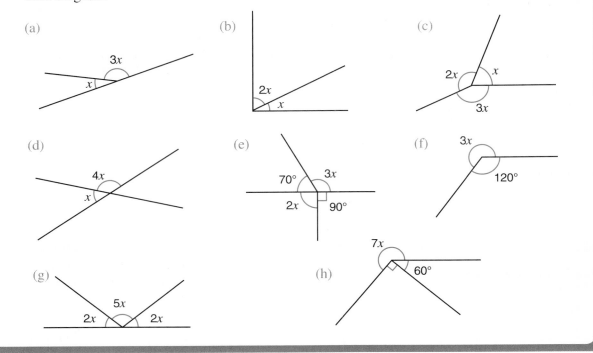

(a)

(b)

(c)

(d)

(e)

(f)

(g)

(h)

Parallel lines

Which of the following pairs of lines are parallel?

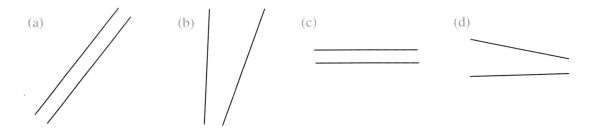

(a)

(b)

(c)

(d)

Parallel lines are lines which never meet.
The pairs of lines in (a) and (c) are parallel.

The diagram, in the activity below, shows two parallel lines crossed by another straight line called a **transversal**.

Activity

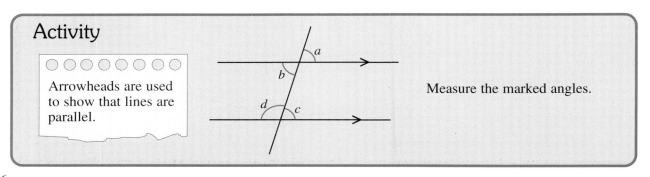

Arrowheads are used to show that lines are parallel.

Measure the marked angles.

Corresponding angles

Angles *a* and *c* are equal. They are called **corresponding** angles.
Corresponding angles are always equal.
Here are some examples of corresponding angles.

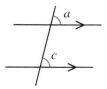 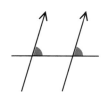 

Corresponding angles are always on the same side of the transversal.

Alternate angles

Angles *b* and *c* are equal. They are called **alternate** angles.
Alternate angles are always equal.
Here are some examples of alternate angles.

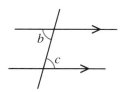 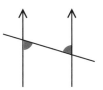 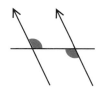

Alternate angles are always on opposite sides of the transversal.

Allied angles

Angles *b* and *d* add up to 180°. They are called **allied** angles.
Allied angles are supplementary, they always add up to 180°.
Here are some examples of allied angles.

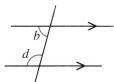 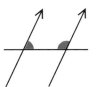 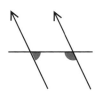

Allied angles are always between parallels on the same side of the transversal.

$b + d = 180°$

EXAMPLE

Without measuring, work out the size of the angles marked with letters.

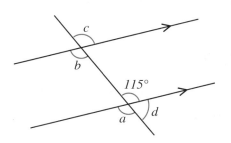

$a = 115°$ (vertically opposite angles)

$b = 115°$ (alternate angles)

$c = 115°$ (corresponding angles)

$d + 115 = 180$ (supplementary angles)
$$d = 180 - 115$$
$$d = 65°$$

Exercise **20.4**

The diagrams in this exercise are not drawn accurately.

1 Without measuring, work out the sizes of the angles marked with letters.

(a)

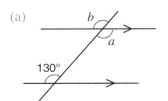

(b)

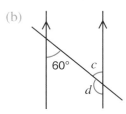

(c)

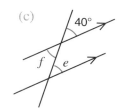

(d)

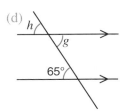

(e)

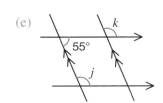

(f)

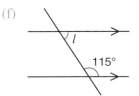

(g)

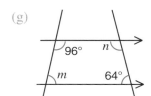

(h)

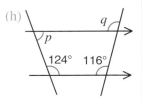

2 Calculate the sizes of the angles marked with letters.

(a)

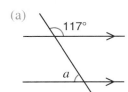

(b)

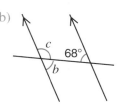

(c)

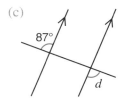

(d)

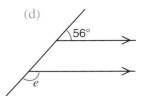

(e)

(f)

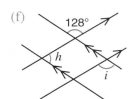

(g)

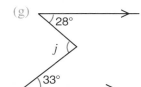

(h)

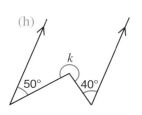

Naming angles

Up to now we have used small letters to name angles. This is not always convenient.
Another method is to use three capital letters.

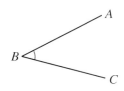

angle *ABC*
∠*ABC*

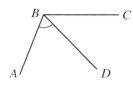

angle *ABD*
∠*ABD*

○○○○○○○○○○○○○○○○○○○○○○○○

∠ means 'angle'.

∠*CBA* is the same as ∠*ABC*.
We usually write the letters either side of the
vertex (shown by the middle letter) in
alphabetical order.

Notice that the middle letter is where the angle is made.

218

1 Use three letters to name the angles marked with small letters in this diagram.

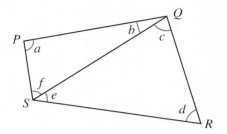

2 Use your protractor to measure accurately the size of these angles.

    (a) ∠ABH

    (b) ∠HGF

    (c) ∠BCD

    (d) ∠AJE

    (e) ∠GFJ

    (f) reflex ∠GFJ

    (g) reflex ∠BHG

    (h) reflex ∠DEJ

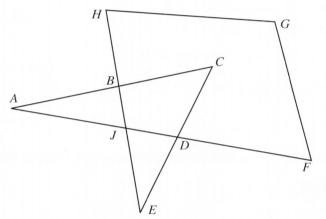

3 These diagrams are not drawn accurately. Work out the sizes of the required angles.

(a)

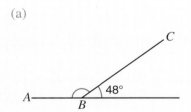

Find ∠ABC.

(b)

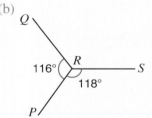

Find ∠QRS.

(c)

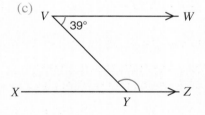

Find ∠ZYV.

(d)

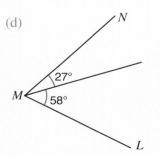

Find ∠LMN.

(e)

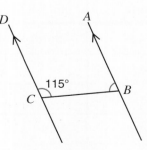

Find ∠ABC.

(f)

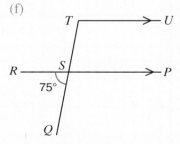

Find ∠QSP and ∠STU.

4 These diagrams are not drawn accurately. Work out the sizes of the required angles.

(a)

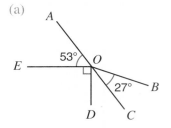

Find ∠AOB and ∠COD.

(b)

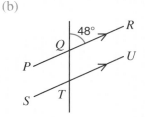

Find ∠QTU and ∠QTS.

(c)

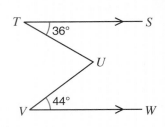

Find reflex angle TUV.

Compass points

The diagram shows the points of the compass.

The angle between North and East is 90°.

The angle between North and North-East is 45°.

Do you know the names of any other compass points?

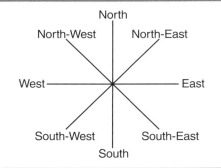

Exercise **20.6**

1 (a) What is the angle between North and North-West?
(b) What is the angle between South and North-West?
(c) What is the angle between South-West and South-East?
(d) What is the angle between North-West and South-West?
(e) What is the angle between South-East and North-West?

2 (a) Claire is facing South. In which direction will she face after turning clockwise through an angle of 135°?

(b) Kevin turned anticlockwise through an angle of 270°. He is now facing South-East. In which direction was he facing?

3 Copy and complete this table. The first line has been done for you.

Start facing	Amount of turn	Finish facing
South	135° clockwise	North-West
North-East	90° clockwise	
West	135° anticlockwise	
	270° clockwise	East
	45° anticlockwise	West

4 A map of a cycle track is shown.

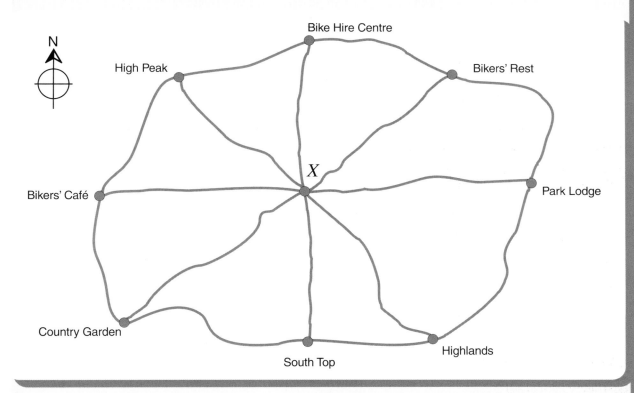

(a) (i) Which place is due North of South Top?
   (ii) Which place is due West of Park Lodge?
   (iii) Which place is North-East of Country Garden?
   (iv) Which place is North-West of Highlands?

(b) John is at the position marked *X* on the map.
   (i) Which place is South-East of John?
   (ii) In which direction does he need to cycle to reach Bikers' Rest?
   (iii) He cycles South-West. Which place will he reach?

Three-figure bearings

Bearings are used to describe the direction in which you must travel to get from one place to another.

A bearing is an angle measured from the North line in a clockwise direction.

The angle, which can be from 0° to 360°, is written as a three-figure number.

Bearings which are less than 100° include noughts to make up the three figures, e.g. 005°, 087°.

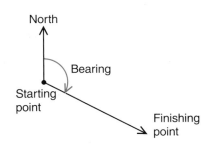

To show the direction given by a bearing

Example

The bearing of *C* from *D* is 153°. Draw a diagram to show this information.

The bearing of *C* **from** *D* tells you that *D* is the starting point.

1 Draw a North line. Mark and label point *D* on the North line.

2 Using your protractor, centred on point *D*, mark an angle of 153° measured in a clockwise direction from the North line.

3 Draw a line from *D* through the marked point.
An arrow is drawn on the line to show the direction in which you must travel to get to *C*.

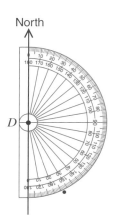
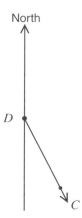

This diagram shows the position of Bath and Poole.

The bearing of Poole from Bath is 162°.

If you are at Bath, facing North and turn through 162° in a clockwise direction you will be facing in the direction of Poole.

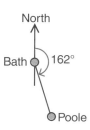

Back bearings

The return bearing of Bath from Poole is called a **back bearing**.
Back bearings can be found by using parallel lines and alternate angles.

The bearing of Poole from Bath is 162°.

a = 162° (alternate angles)

Required angle = 180° + 162° = 342°.
The bearing of Bath from Poole (the back bearing) is 342°.

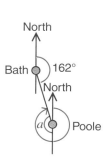

1 Use your protractor to find the three-figure bearings of A from B in each of the following.

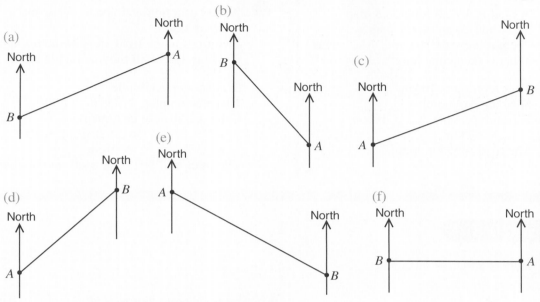

2 (a) Draw sketches to show the following information.
   (i)   The bearing of F from E is 050°.   (iv) The bearing of L from B is 260°.
   (ii) The bearing of C from H is 125°.   (v)   The bearing of A from J is 305°.
   (iii) The bearing of K from Q is 195°.   (vi) The bearing of X from T is 175°.

   (b) Use your sketches to give the back bearings for each of the directions in part (a).

3 The diagram shows the positions of
three oil rigs at A, B and C.

   (a) What is the bearing of A from B?
   (b) What is the bearing of B from A?
   (c) What is the bearing of C from B?
   (d) What is the bearing of B from C?
   (e) What is the bearing of C from A?
   (f) What is the bearing of A from C?

Scale drawing

Maps and plans are scaled down representations of real-life situations.
The **scale** used in drawing a map or plan determines the amount of detail that can be shown.

The distances between different points on a map are all drawn to the same scale.
There are two ways to describe a scale.

1 A scale of 1 cm to 10 km means that a distance of 1 cm on the map represents an actual distance
   of 10 km.

2 A scale of 1:10 000 means that all distances measured on the map have to be multiplied by 10 000
   to find the real distance.

1 A road is 3.7 cm long on a map.
The scale given on the map is
'1 cm represents 10 km'.
What is the actual length of the road?

1 cm represents 10 km.
Scale up, so multiply.
3.7 cm represents 3.7 × 10 km
        = 3.7 km
The road is 37 km long.

2 A plan of a field is to be drawn using a
scale of 1:500.
Two trees in the field are 350 metres apart.
How far apart will they be on the plan?

Scale down, so divide.
Distance on plan = 350 m ÷ 500
Change 350 m to centimetres.
        = 35 000 cm ÷ 500
        = 70 cm
The trees will be 70 cm apart on the plan.

Exercise 20.8

1 Here is a map of an island.

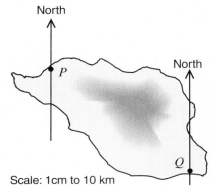

North

P

North

Q

Scale: 1cm to 10 km

(a) Use your protractor to find:
  (i) the bearing of P from Q,
  (ii) the bearing of Q from P.

(b) (i) Measure the distance between
      P and Q on the map.
  (ii) What is the actual distance
      between P and Q?

2 The diagram shows the flight path of a plane between two airports.

The diagram has been drawn to a scale of
1:250 000.
Use the diagram to find:
  (a) the actual distance between the airports,
  (b) the bearing of A from B,
  (c) the bearing of B from A.

North

B

North

A

3 A boat leaves port and sails on a bearing of 144° for 4 km. It then changes course and sails
due east for 5 km to reach an island.
Find by scale drawing:
  (a) the distance of the island from the port,
  (b) the bearing of the island from the port,
  (c) the bearing on which the boat must sail to return directly to the port.

4 A yacht sails on a bearing of 040° for 5000 m and then a further 3000 m on a bearing
of 120°.
Find by scale drawing:
  (a) the distance of the yacht from its starting position,
  (b) the bearing on which it must sail to return directly to its starting position.

5 An aircraft leaves an airport, at A, and flies on a bearing of 035° for 50 km and then on a bearing of 280° for a further 40 km before landing at an airport, at B.
Find by scale drawing:
   (a) the distance between the airports,
   (b) the bearing of B from A,
   (c) the bearing of A from B.

What you need to know

- An angle of 90° is called a **right angle**.
  An angle less than 90° is called an **acute angle**.
  An angle between 90° and 180° is called an **obtuse angle**.
  An angle greater than 180° is called a **reflex angle**.

- The sum of the angles at a point is 360°.

- Angles on a straight line add up to 180°.
  Angles which add up to 180° are called **supplementary angles**.
  Angles which add up to 90° are called **complementary angles**.

- When two lines cross, the opposite angles formed are equal and called **vertically opposite angles**.

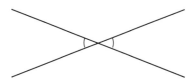

- When two parallel lines are crossed by a transversal the following pairs of equal angles are formed.

Corresponding angles	**Alternate angles**	**Allied angles**
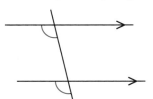	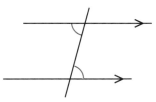	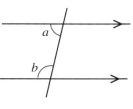
		$a + b = 180°$

- Compass points

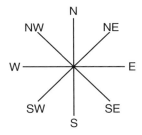

- **Bearings** are used to describe the direction in which you must travel to get from one place to another.
  A bearing is an angle measured from the North line in a clockwise direction.

- A bearing can be any angle from 0° to 360° and is written as a three-figure number.

1 The diagram shows a four-sided shape.

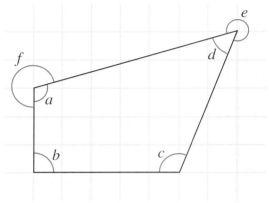

(a) Which of the marked angles are:
  (i) acute,
  (ii) obtuse,
  (iii) right-angled,
  (iv) reflex?
(b) Find by measurement the size of all the marked angles.

2 The diagram shows a picture drawn on grid paper.

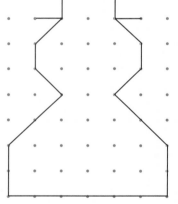

Copy the diagram.
(a) Mark on your diagram, with an X, an obtuse angle.
(b) Mark on your diagram, with a Y, a reflex angle.
(c) Mark on your diagram, with arrows, two lines which are parallel.

3 (a) This clock shows the time as 4 o'clock.

What is the angle between the two hands?

(b) A skater turns through 1.5 revolutions. What size angle does she turn through?

(c) Sanjit stands at O facing due North.
He turns clockwise through 135°.
Draw an accurate line to represent the direction he now faces.

SEG 1994

4 The lines AB and CD are parallel.

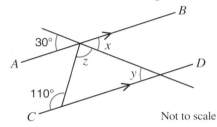

Not to scale

(a) Work out the size of angle x.
(b) Work out the size of angle y.
(c) Work out the size of angle z.

SEG 1996

5 In the diagram AOB and POQ are straight lines.
Angle $ROB = 90°$.
Angle $AOP = 27°$.

(a) (i) Work out the size of angle AOQ.
  (ii) Work out the size of angle POR.

(b) What angle is the same size as angle AOP?

6 The lines AB and CD are parallel.
XY is perpendicular to AB.
Angle $XZB = 127°$.

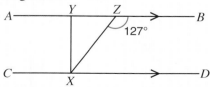

(a) Work out the size of angle ZXD.
(b) Work out the size of angle YXZ.

7 A map of part of the Mediterranean Sea is shown.

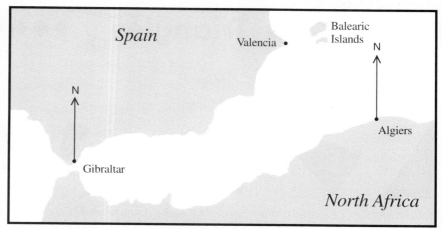

(a) A ship sails from Gibraltar to Algiers. The course is shown.
On what bearing does the ship sail?

(b) The ship then sails from Algiers to Valencia.
On what bearing does the ship sail?

8 The diagram shows the map of an island.

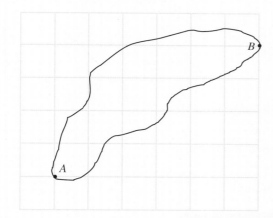

The map has been drawn to a scale of 1 cm to 5 km.

By measurement find:
(a) the bearing of *A* from *B*,
(b) the shortest distance between *A* and *B* in kilometres.

10 Axford is 70km from Moxley on a bearing of 065°. Parley is 55km from Moxley on a bearing of 125°.

(a) By using a scale of 1cm to 10km, draw an accurate diagram to show the positions of Axford, Parley and Moxley.

(b) What is the bearing of Moxley from Axford?

(c) By taking measurements from your diagram work out
   (i) the distance of Parley from Axford,
   (ii) the bearing of Parley from Axford.

9 Sam is looking at a map of villages *O*, *J*, and *K*.

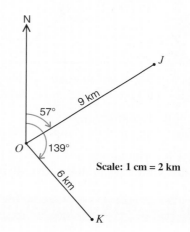

Scale: 1 cm = 2 km

She measures the distances and bearings of *J* and *K* from *O*.
J is 9 km from *O* on a bearing of 057°.
K is 6 km from *O* on a bearing of 139°.

(a) Find, by measuring, the bearing of *J* from *K*.

Another village, *L*, is 7 km from *O* on a bearing of 300°.
Copy the diagram above.

(b) Mark the position of *L* on your diagram.

SEG 1995

A **triangle** is a shape made by three straight lines.

The smallest number of straight lines needed to make a shape is 3. Can you explain why?

Types of triangle

Measure the angles in each of these triangles.

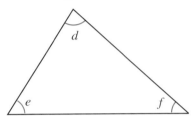
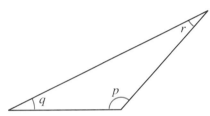
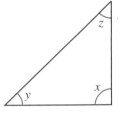

Angles *d*, *e* and *f* are all acute angles.
Triangles with three acute angles are called **acute-angled** triangles.

Angle *p* is an obtuse angle.
Triangles with an obtuse angle are called **obtuse-angled** triangles.

Angle *x* is a right angle.
Triangles with a right angle are called **right-angled** triangles.

The sum of the angles in a triangle

The sum of the three angles in a triangle is 180°.

Add up the three angles *d*, *e* and *f* in the triangle above.
Do the same for the other two triangles.
You may not always get 180°. Can you explain why?

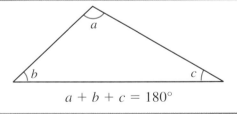

$$a + b + c = 180°$$

EXAMPLE

Without measuring, work out the size of the angle marked *a*.

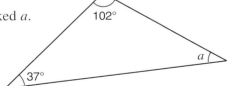

The sum of the angles in a triangle is 180°.
$$a + 102° + 37° = 180°$$
$$a + 139° = 180°$$
$$a = 180° - 139°$$
$$a = 41°$$

Exercise 21.1

1 Is it possible to draw triangles with the following types of angles?
Give a reason for each of your answers.

(a) three acute angles,
(b) one obtuse angle and two acute angles,
(c) two obtuse angles and one acute angle,
(d) three obtuse angles,
(e) one right angle and two acute angles,
(f) two right angles and one acute angle.

2 Is it possible to draw a triangle with these angles.
If a triangle can be drawn, what type of triangle is it?
Give a reason for each of your answers.

(a) 95°, 78°, 7°
(b) 48°, 62°, 90°
(c) 48°, 62°, 70°
(d) 90°, 38°, 52°
(e) 130°, 35°, 15°

3 Without measuring, work out the size of the third angle in each of these triangles.

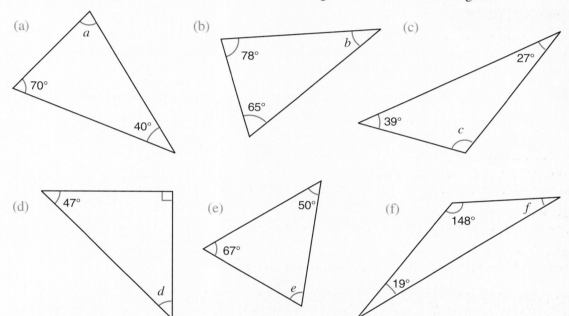

(a) *a*, 70°, 40°

(b) 78°, 65°, *b*

(c) 27°, 39°, *c*

(d) 47°, *d*

(e) 50°, 67°, *e*

(f) 148°, 19°, *f*

Exterior angle of a triangle

When one side of a triangle is extended, as shown, the angle formed is called an **exterior angle**.

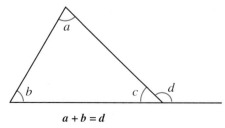

a + b = d

In any triangle the exterior angle is always equal to the sum of the two opposite interior angles.
Check this by measuring the angles *a*, *b* and *d* in the diagram.

This result can be easily proved.
$a + b + c = 180°$
(sum of angles in a triangle)
$c + d = 180°$
(supplementary angles)
$a + b + c = c + d$
$a + b = d$

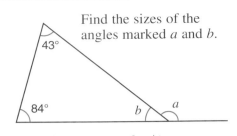

Find the sizes of the angles marked a and b.

Short but fully accurate

In Geometry we often abbreviate words and use symbols to provide the reader with full details using the minimum amount of writing.

Δ is short for triangle.
ext. $\angle$ of a Δ means exterior angle of a triangle.
supp. $\angle$'s means supplementary angles.

$a = 84° + 43°$ (ext. $\angle$ of a Δ)
$a = 127°$

$b + 127° = 180°$ (supp. $\angle$'s)
$b = 180° - 127°$
$b = 53°$

Exercise 21.2

You should be able to do this exercise without a calculator. Having completed the exercise you can use your calculator to check your working.

1   The following diagrams have not been drawn accurately, work out the size of the marked angles.

(a)
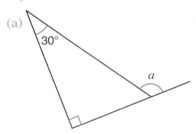

(b)
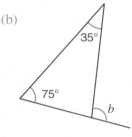

(c)
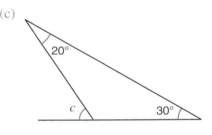

(d)
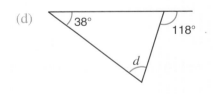

(e)
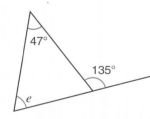

(f)
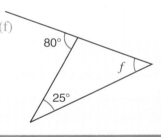

Naming parts of a triangle

Triangles are named by labelling each vertex with a capital letter.
Triangle ABC can be written as ΔABC.

Triangle ABC is formed by the sides AB, BC and AC.
Triangles and lines are often named in alphabetical order.
ΔABC is the same as ΔBCA.

The angles of a triangle are also described in terms of the vertices.
For example, the angle marked on the diagram is angle ACB or $\angle ACB$.
The middle letter is the vertex where the angle is made.

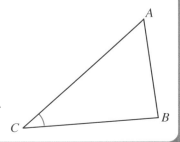

Special triangles

We have already seen that triangles can be described in terms of their angles but they can also be described in terms of their sides.
Measure the lengths of the sides of these triangles.
What do you notice?

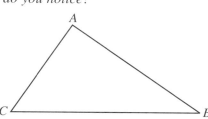 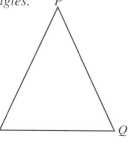 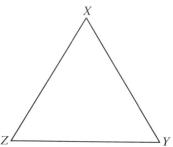

Triangle *ABC* has sides of different lengths.
A triangle with sides of different lengths is called **scalene**.

Triangle *PQR* has two equal sides. *PQ* = *PR*.
A triangle with two equal sides is called **isosceles**.

Triangle *XYZ* has three equal sides. *XY* = *YZ* = *XZ*.
A triangle with three equal sides is called **equilateral**.

Now measure the size of the angles of triangles *PQR* and *XYZ*.
What do you find?

In triangle *PQR*, angle *PQR* = angle *PRQ*.
An **isosceles** triangle has two equal sides and two equal angles.

In triangle XYZ, all the angles are equal to 60°.
An **equilateral** triangle has three equal sides and
three equal angles.

Notation used on sketch diagrams
A sketch is used when an accurate drawing is not required.
Dashes across lines show sides that are equal in length.
Equal angles are marked using arcs.

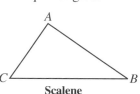 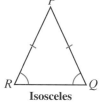 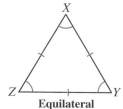

Scalene   **Isosceles**   **Equilateral**

Exercise **21.3**

1 Name three different triangles in the diagram.

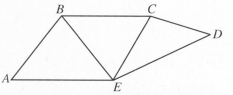

2 Give three-letter names to the marked angles in these diagrams.

(a)   (b)   (c)

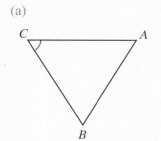 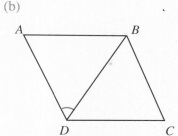 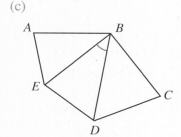

3 (a) On squared paper, draw triangles with the following coordinates
  (i)   (1,1),   (6,1),   (3,5),
  (ii) (1,1),   (5,1),   (1,4),
  (iii) (1,1),   (5,1),   (3,4),
  (iv) (1,1),   (6,1),   (9,5).

  (b) Which of the following words could be used to describe each of the triangles you have drawn?
    Acute-angled, Obtuse-angled or Right-angled.
    Scalene, Equilateral or Isosceles.

4 On squared paper, draw an isosceles triangle with coordinates:
A (3,3), B (9,3) and C (6,10).
Which two sides are equal?
Which two angles are equal?

5 Triangle ABC is isosceles with $AC = CB$.
A is at (3,0) and B is at (0,3).
Give the coordinates of the possible positions of C.

6 Triangle PQR is isosceles with angle RPQ = angle QRP.
P is the point (3,5) and R is the point (9,5).
Give the coordinates of the two possible positions of Q so that angle PQR is a right-angle.

7 The following diagrams have not been drawn accurately.
Work out the size of the angles marked with letters.

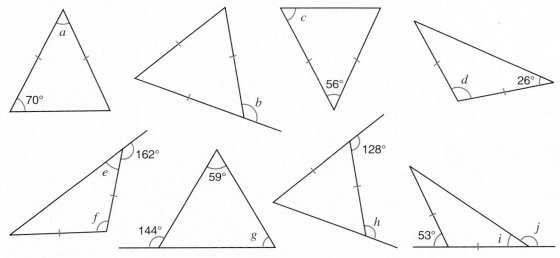

8 These diagrams have not been drawn accurately.
Work out the sizes of the required angles.

(a)

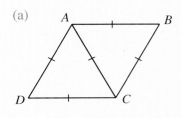

Find ∠BCD.

(b)

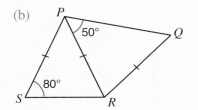

Find ∠PRQ and ∠QRS.

(c)

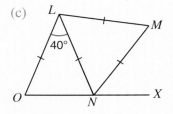

Find ∠MNX.

232

Your ruler, compasses and protractor can be used to draw triangles accurately.
Drawings can be made from written information or sketch diagrams.
Follow the instructions below to accurately draw two triangles.

Sketch diagram

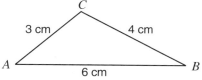

Information given:
Lengths of three sides of the triangle.

Step 1
Start by drawing the longest side, *AB*.
Draw a line 6 cm long.

Step 2
Set your compasses to a radius of 4 cm.
Draw an arc from *B*.

Step 3
Set your compasses to a radius of 3 cm.
Draw an arc from *A* to intersect (cross) the
arc drawn in step 2. Label the point.

Step 4
Draw the sides *AC* and *BC*.
Add labels.

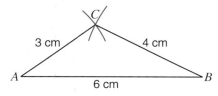

Sketch diagram

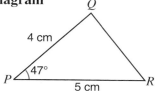

Information given:
Lengths of two sides of the triangle and the
size of the angle between the two sides.

Step 1
Start by drawing the longest side, *PR*.
Draw a line 5 cm long.

Step 2
∠*QPR* = 47° (acute angle)
Use your protractor to measure 47°.

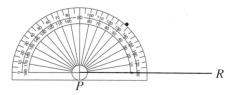

Step 3
Using the dot as guide, draw a line,
4 cm long, from *P*. Label point *Q*.

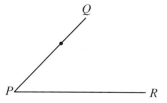

Step 4
Draw the line *QR* to complete the triangle.
Add labels.

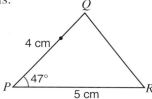

If you are given written information draw a sketch diagram first.

For example, information for triangle *ABC* could be given as:

Draw accurately triangle *ABC* with sides *AB* = 6 cm, *BC* = 4 cm and *AC* = 3 cm.

Activity

Write instructions which someone could follow to draw the following triangles accurately.

(a)

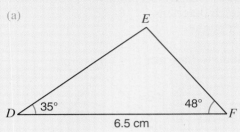

(b)

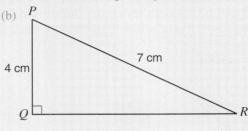

1 Use a ruler and compasses to draw accurately triangles with the following sides.
  (a)   4 cm, 5 cm, 6 cm.
  (b)   3.5 cm, 4.5 cm, 5 cm.
  (c) $AB = 4.8$ cm, $BC = 3.6$ cm, $AC = 6.2$ cm.
  (d) $PQ = 6$ cm, $QR = 6.5$ cm, $PR = 2.5$ cm.

2 Accurately draw the triangles using the information shown in the sketch diagrams below.

(a)

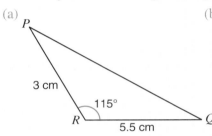

(b)   (c)

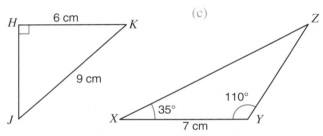

3 Use a ruler and protractor to draw the following triangles.
  (a) $AB = 4$ cm, $BC = 4$ cm, $\angle ABC = 40°$.
  (b) $PQ = 3.5$ cm, $PR = 5$ cm, $\angle QPR = 100°$.
  (c) $XY = YZ = ZX = 4$ cm
  (d) $FG = 5$ cm, $FH = 5$ cm, $\angle FGH = 40°$.

4 A sketch of triangle PQR is shown.
  (a)   Make an accurate drawing of triangle PQR.
  (b)   Measure and write down the length of PR.
  (c)   Measure and write down the size of angle QPR.

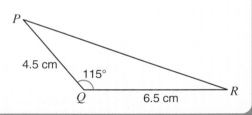

Triangles in semi-circles

In each diagram a triangle has been drawn in a semi-circle.
Measure the marked angles.
What do you notice?

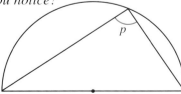
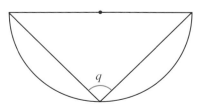
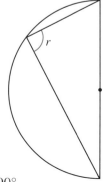

Angles p, q and r are all $90°$.

When a triangle is drawn in a semi-circle in this way, the angle formed is always $90°$.

Exercise 21.5

1 The following diagrams show triangles drawn in semi-circles.
Without measuring, work out the size of the marked angles.

(a)

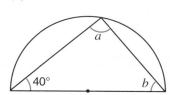

(b)

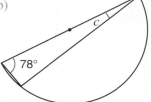

(c)

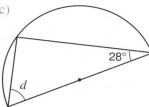

(d)

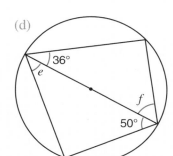

(e)

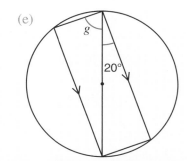

(f)

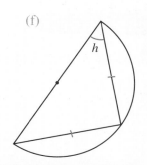

Perimeter of a triangle

The **perimeter** is the distance round the outside of a shape. The perimeter
of a triangle is the sum of the lengths of its three sides.

Measure the sides of this triangle.
What is the perimeter?

You should find:
$AB = 4$ cm, $BC = 5$ cm and $AC = 6$ cm.
Perimeter $= 4 + 5 + 6 = 15$ cm.

Area of a triangle

The area of a triangle is given by:

Area $= \frac{1}{2} \times$ base $\times$ perpendicular height.

The area, A, can be found using the formula:

$A = \frac{1}{2} \times b \times h$

In these triangles b is the base and h is the
perpendicular height.

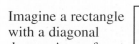
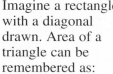

Imagine a rectangle
with a diagonal
drawn. Area of a
triangle can be
remembered as:

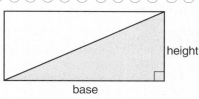

Area $= \dfrac{\text{base} \times \text{perpendicular height}}{2}$

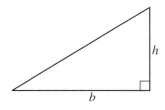
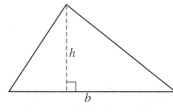
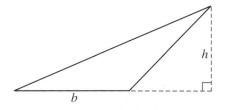

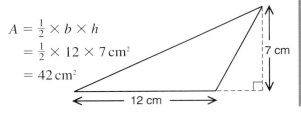

EXAMPLES

1 Calculate the area of this triangle.

$A = \frac{1}{2} \times b \times h$

$= \frac{1}{2} \times 12 \times 7 \, \text{cm}^2$

$= 42 \, \text{cm}^2$

2 This triangle has area $36 \, \text{cm}^2$. Find the height of the triangle.

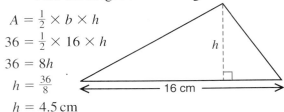

$A = \frac{1}{2} \times b \times h$

$36 = \frac{1}{2} \times 16 \times h$

$36 = 8h$

$h = \frac{36}{8}$

$h = 4.5 \, \text{cm}$

Exercise 21.6

1 Work out the lengths of the perimeters of these triangles.

(a)

(b)

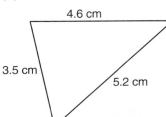

(c)

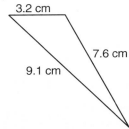

2 Which of the triangles *PQR*, *QRS* or *RST* has the largest perimeter?

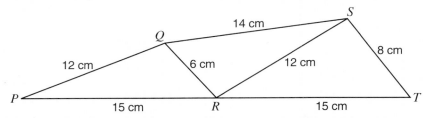

3 These triangles each have a perimeter of length 20 cm.
Work out the lengths of the marked sides.

(a)

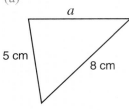

(b)

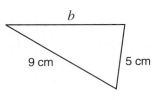

(c)

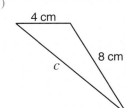

(d)

(e)

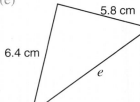

(f)

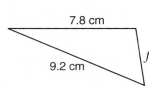

236

4 Calculate the areas of these triangles.

(a)

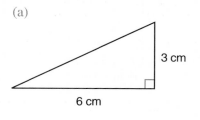

3 cm

6 cm

(b)

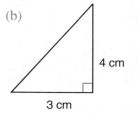

4 cm

3 cm

(c)

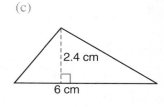

2.4 cm

6 cm

(d)

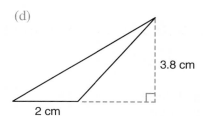

3.8 cm

2 cm

(e)

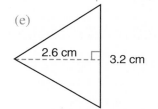

2.6 cm   3.2 cm

(f)

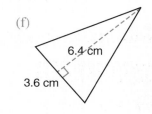

6.4 cm

3.6 cm

5 These triangles each have an area of 24 cm².
Calculate the height of each triangle.

(a)

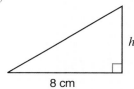

h

8 cm

(b)

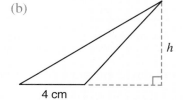

h

4 cm

(c)

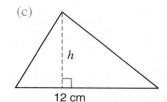

h

12 cm

6 These triangles each have an area of 32 cm².
Calculate the lengths of the marked sides.

(a)

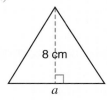

8 cm

a

(b)

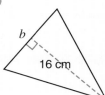

b

16 cm

(c)

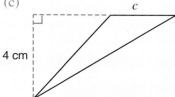

c

4 cm

7 This triangle has a perimeter of 45 cm.
Calculate the area of the triangle.

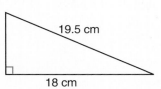

19.5 cm

18 cm

8 This triangle has an area of 37.5 cm².
Calculate the perimeter of the triangle.

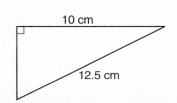

10 cm

12.5 cm

What you need to know

- Triangles can be:

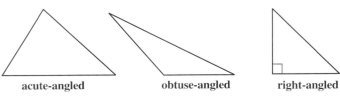

  acute-angled   obtuse-angled   right-angled

- The sum of the angles in a triangle is 180°.

  $a + b + c = 180°$

- The exterior angle is equal to the sum of the two opposite interior angles.

  $a + b = d$

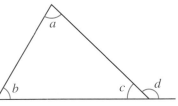

- Types of triangle:

  Scalene   **Isosceles**   **Equilateral**
  triangle   **triangle**   **triangle**

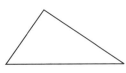

  All sides have   Two equal sides.   Three equal sides.
  different lengths.   Two equal angles.   Three equal angles, 60°.

- When a triangle is drawn in a semi-circle the angle formed is always 90°.

- Perimeter of a triangle is the sum of its three sides.

- Area of a triangle $= \dfrac{\text{base} \times \text{perpendicular height}}{2}$

  $A = \frac{1}{2} \times b \times h$

You should be able to:
- Draw triangles accurately using ruler, compasses, protractor.

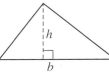   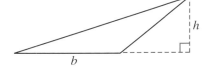

Review Exercise

1. Nicola has calculated the third angle of these triangles.

A

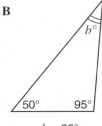

$a = 31°$

B

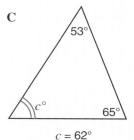

$b = 25°$

C

$c = 62°$

Not to scale

  She has made a mistake with one of them.
  (a) Which one?
  (b) Give a reason for your answer.

SEG 1994

238

2 In the diagram, triangle *ABC* is isosceles with *BA* = *AC*, and triangle *ACD* is right-angled with angle *CAD* = 90°.

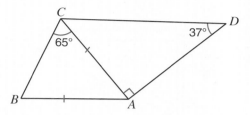

The diagram has not been drawn accurately.
(a) Angle *ADC* = 37°. Work out the size of angle *DCA*.
(b) Angle *ACB* = 65°. Work out the size of angle *BAC*.

3 In the diagram *AC* is parallel to *XY*.

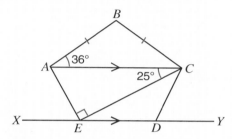

The diagram has not been drawn accurately.
(a) Angle *BAC* = 36°.
Work out the size of angle *BCA*, giving a reason for your answer.

(b) Angle *ACE* = 25°.
(i) Work out the size of angle *CAE*, giving a reason for your answer.
(ii) Work out the size of angle *AEX*.

4 *ABC* is an equilateral triangle.
ACD is an isosceles triangle.
Angle *BCD* = 40°.

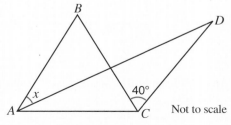

Work out the size of angle *x*, giving a reason for your answer.

SEG 1995

5 The side view of a workbench is shown.

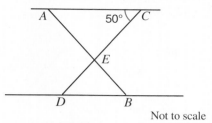

Not to scale

The sides *AC* and *DB* are parallel.
AE = *EC* and angle *ACD* = 50°.

(a) Work out the size of angle *BAC*, giving a reason for your answer.
(b) Work out the size of angle *AEC*, giving a reason for your answer.

SEG 1994

6 The diagram shows the end of a tent.
AP is perpendicular to *BC*.
BP = *PC*.

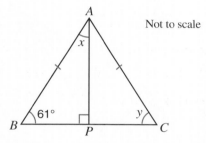

Not to scale

(a) Work out the size of angle *x*, giving a reason for your answer.
(b) Work out the size of angle *y*, giving a reason for your answer.

SEG 1994

7 The diagram below shows a prism.

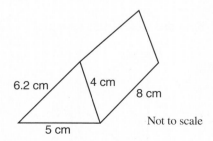

Not to scale

Make an accurate drawing of the triangular face of the prism.

SEG 1996

8 A sketch of triangle *LMN* is shown.
LM = 13.5 cm.   *LN* = 8 cm.
Angle *MLN* = 42°.

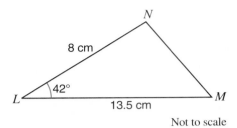

Not to scale

(a) Make an accurate drawing of triangle *LMN*.

(b) Measure and write down the size of angle *LNM*.

SEG 1996

9 In the diagram, *AB* equals *AC*.
BA and *CD* are parallel.
Angle *CAD* is 90° and angle *ADC* is 40°.

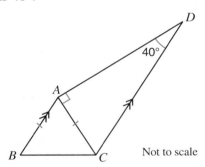

Not to scale

(a) Calculate angle *DCA*.

(b) (i) Write down another angle equal to *DCA*.

(ii) Give a reason for your answer.

(c) Calculate angle *ABC*.

SEG 1994

10 Find the area of this triangle.

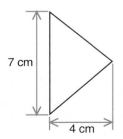

Not to scale

SEG 1995

11 (a) What is the area of this triangular flag?

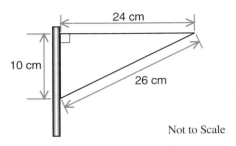

Not to Scale

(b) A triangular section on another flag has two angles of 54°.

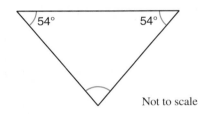

Not to scale

What is the size of the third angle?

SEG 1996

12 The diagram shows three triangles, *BAE*, *BED* and *BDC*.

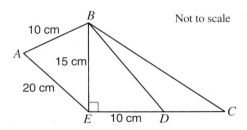

Not to scale

(a) Calculate the perimeter of triangle *BAE*.

(b) Calculate the area of triangle *BED*.

(c) The areas of triangles *BED* and *BDC* are equal.
Calculate the length of *DC*.

240

CHAPTER 22

Symmetry and Congruence

Lines of symmetry

These shapes are **symmetrical**.

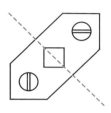

When each shape is folded along the dashed line the left-hand side will fit exactly over the right-hand side.

The dashed line is called a **line of symmetry**.

Some shapes have more than one line of symmetry.

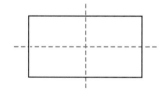
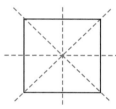

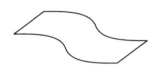

Rectangle
2 lines of symmetry.

Square
4 lines of symmetry.

Circle
Infinite number of lines of symmetry. Each diameter is a line of symmetry.

Shape with no lines of symmetry.

Exercise **22.1**

1 These shapes have **line symmetry**. Copy each shape and draw the line of symmetry.

(a)

(b)
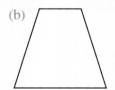

(c)
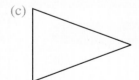

(d)
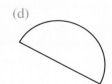

(e)
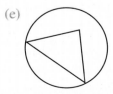

(f)

(g)

(h)

2 The following diagrams show half a shape.
The dashed line is the line of symmetry for the complete shape.
Copy the diagrams and complete each shape.

(a)

(b)

(c)

(d)

(e)

(f)

(g)

3 These shapes have been drawn accurately.
How many lines of symmetry has each shape?

(a)

(b)

(c)

(d)

(e)

(f)

4 How many lines of symmetry has each of these letters?

ACEHKNO

> **Rotational symmetry**

Is this shape symmetrical?

The shape does not have line symmetry.

Try placing a copy of the shape over the original and rotating it about the centre of the circle.

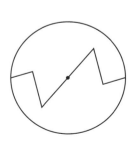

After 180° (a half-turn) the shape fits into its own outline.
The shape has **rotational symmetry**.
The point about which the shape is rotated is called the **centre of rotation**.
The **order of rotational symmetry** is 2. When rotating the shape through 360° it fits into its own outline twice (once after a half turn and again after a full-turn).

A shape can have both line symmetry and rotational symmetry.

Order of rotational symmetry 5.

Order of rotational symmetry 8.

Order of rotational symmetry 4.
4 lines of symmetry.

Exercise 22.2

1 What is the order of rotational symmetry for each of these shapes?

(a)

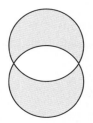

(b)

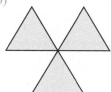

(c)

(d)

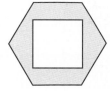

(e)

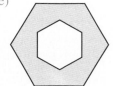

(f)

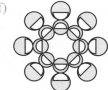

2 Look at these letters of the alphabet.

J M N O P X Y Z

(a) Which two letters have only line symmetry?
(b) Which two letters have only rotational symmetry?
(c) Which letters have rotational symmetry of order 2?
(d) Which letters have neither rotational nor line symmetry?

3 Make a copy of this shape.

(a) How many lines of symmetry does the
shape have?
(b) (i) Colour one square so that your shape
has rotational symmetry of order 2.
(ii) Mark the centre of rotational symmetry
on your shape.

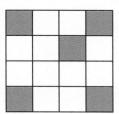

4 Make a copy of this shape.

(a) How many lines of symmetry does the shape have?

(b) (i) Colour one triangle so that your shape has rotational symmetry of order 3.

(ii) How many lines of symmetry does your shape have?

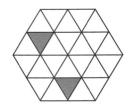

5 For each shape state

(i) the number of lines of symmetry,

(ii) the order of rotational symmetry.

(a)   (b)   (c)   (d)   (e)

Symmetry in three-dimensions

Planes of symmetry

So far we have looked at two-dimensional (flat) shapes.

Two-dimensional shapes can have line symmetry.

Three-dimensional objects can have **plane symmetry**.

A **plane of symmetry** slices through an object so that one half is the mirror image of the other half.

A cuboid has three planes of symmetry as shown.

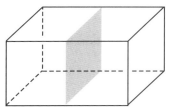 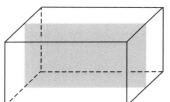 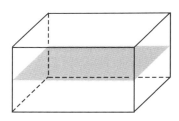

Axes of symmetry

A wall is built using cuboids.

In how many different ways can the next cuboid be placed in position?

If the cuboid can be placed in more than one way, it must have rotational symmetry about one or more **axes**.

A cuboid has three axes of symmetry.
The diagram shows one **axis of symmetry**.
The order of rotational symmetry about this axis is two.

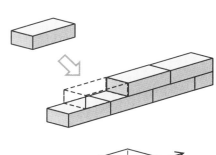

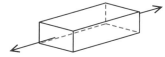

Exercise 22.3

1 How many planes of symmetry has a cube?

2 State the order of rotational symmetry about the axis shown in each of the following.

(a) Cube   (b) Square-based   (c) Cylinder   (d) Cone
                         pyramid

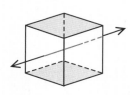 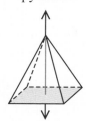 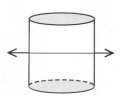 

3 Each end of this cuboid is a square.
The axes of symmetry are labelled *a*, *b* and *c*.
What is the order of rotational symmetry about
(a) axis *a*,
(b) axis *b*,
(c) axis *c*?

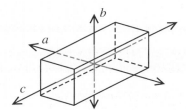

4 The diagram shows a cuboid, with a square base. On top of
the cuboid is a square-based pyramid with vertex *A* above
the centre of the top of the cuboid.

(a) How many planes of symmetry has the figure?
(b) How many axes of symmetry has the figure?
      Give the order of rotational symmetry about each axis.

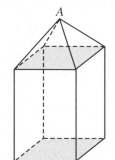

5 The diagram shows a triangular prism.
The ends of the prism are equilateral triangles.

(a) How many axes of symmetry has the prism?
(b) How many planes of symmetry has the prism?

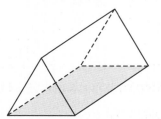

Congruent shapes

When two shapes are the same shape and size they are said to be **congruent**.
A copy of one shape would fit exactly over the second shape. Sometimes it is necessary to turn the copy
over to get an exact fit.
These shapes are all congruent.

1. Look at the shapes below. List five **pairs** of congruent shapes.

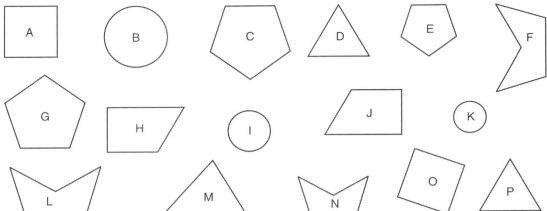

Congruent triangles

There are four ways to show that a pair of triangles are congruent.

1. Three sides. SSS

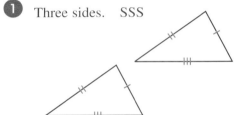

3. Two angles and a corresponding side.
ASA

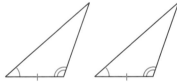

This can be written as AAS if the corresponding side is not between the angles.

2. Two sides and the included angle. SAS

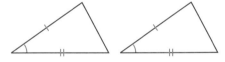

The included angle is the angle between the two sides.

4. Right angle, hypotenuse and one side.
RHS

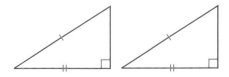

The hypotenuse is the side opposite the right angle and is the longest side in a right angled triangle.

EXAMPLE

Show that triangles *ABC* and *PQR* are congruent.

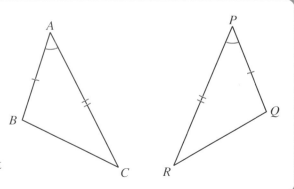

$AB = PQ$ (equal lengths, given)
$AC = PR$ (equal lengths, given)
$\angle BAC = \angle QPR$ (equal angles, given)

So triangles *ABC* and *PQR* are congruent.
Reason: SAS (Two sides and the included angle.)

Since the triangles are congruent we also know that
$BC = QR$, $\angle ABX = \angle PQR$ and $\angle ACB = \angle PRQ$.

① Triangle *ABC* has angles 90°, 50° and 40°.
Triangle *XYZ* also has angles 90°, 50° and 40°.
The triangles are not congruent.
Can you explain why?

② The following triangles have not been drawn accurately. State whether each pair of triangles is congruent or not. Where triangles are congruent give the reason.

(a)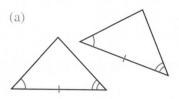

(b)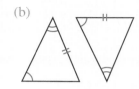

(c)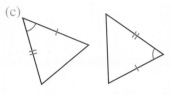

(d)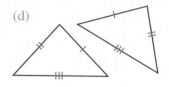

(e)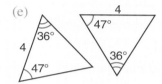

(f)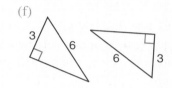

(g)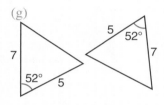

(h)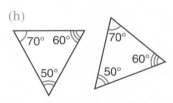

(i)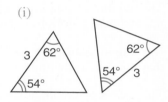

③ For each of the following, is it possible to draw a congruent triangle without taking any other measurements from the original triangle? If a triangle can be drawn give the reason for congruence which applies.

(a)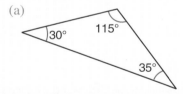

(b)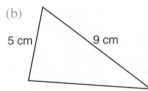

(c)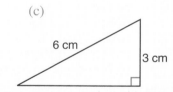

(d)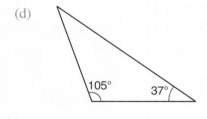

(e)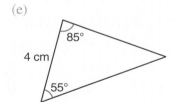

(f)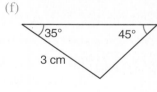

(g)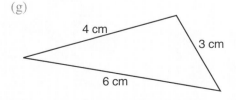

(h)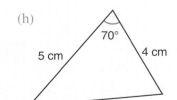

(i)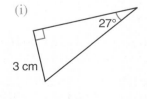

4 Show that triangles *DEF* and *PQR* are congruent.

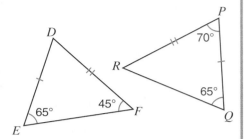

5 In the diagram *AB* is parallel to *CD*. *AB = CD* = 7 cm and ∠*ABD* = 25°.

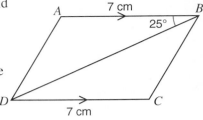

(a) What is the size of ∠*BDC* ?

(b) Show that triangles *ABD* and *BCD* are congruent.

(c) Name an angle which is the same size as ∠*CBD*.

What you need to know

- A two-dimensional shape has **line symmetry** if the line divides the shape so that one side fits exactly over the other.

- A two-dimensional shape has **rotational symmetry** if it fits into a copy of its outline as it is rotated through 360°.

- The number of times a shape fits into its outline in a single turn is the **order of rotational symmetry**.

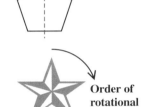

Order of rotational symmetry 5

- A **plane of symmetry** slices through a three-dimensional object so that one half is the mirror image of the other half.

- Three-dimensional objects can have **axes of symmetry**.

- When two shapes are the same shape and size they are said to be **congruent**.

- There are four ways to show that a pair of triangles are congruent:
  - SSS   Three equal sides.
  - SAS   Two sides and the included angle.
  - ASA   Two angles and a corresponding side.
  - RHS   Right angle, hypotenuse and one other side.

Review Exercise

1 All these patterns have five sides.

(a) Which pattern has more than one line of symmetry?

(b) Which pattern does not have rotational symmetry?

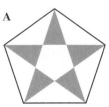

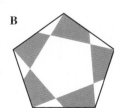
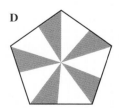

SEG 1997

248

2 Which of these diagrams has rotational symmetry?

A
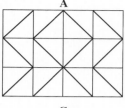

B
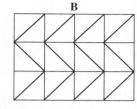

C
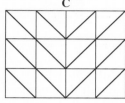

D
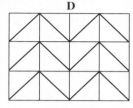

SEG 1996

3 These are the initials of the International Association of Whistlers.

I A W

Which of these letters has rotational symmetry?

SEG 1995

4 Half of a pattern is shown.
Complete the pattern so that it has rotational symmetry.

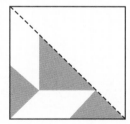

SEG 1995

5 (a) Draw the reflection of this shape in the mirror line *AB*.

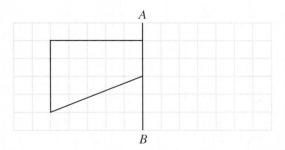

(b) Complete the diagram so that it has rotational symmetry.

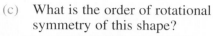

(c) What is the order of rotational symmetry of this shape?

SEG 1995

6 This pattern has one line of symmetry but no rotational symmetry.

(a) In the same way describe the symmetry of this pattern.

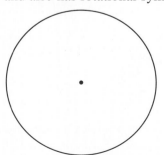

(b) Draw a circle like the one below. Use your circle to draw a pattern which has two lines of symmetry and also has rotational symmetry.

7 Write down the order of rotational symmetry for each diagram.

X

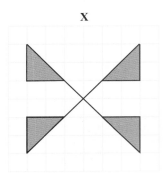

Y

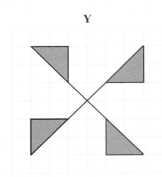

Z

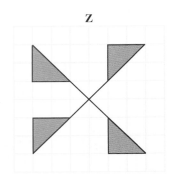

8 Draw a shape which has:

(a) exactly **one** line of symmetry,

(b) exactly **two** lines of symmetry,

(c) exactly **three** lines of symmetry,

(d) exactly **four** lines of symmetry,

(e) no lines of symmetry,

(f) an infinite number of lines of symmetry.

9 Make a copy of this regular pentagon. On your diagram draw in all the lines of symmetry.

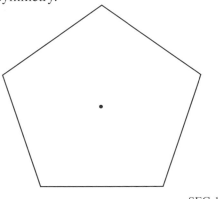

SEG 1996

10 This diagram has been drawn accurately.

(a) Which triangle is congruent to triangle *ABC*?

(b) Which triangle is congruent to triangle *ACF*?

(c) Which quadrilateral is congruent to quadrilateral *ABCF*?

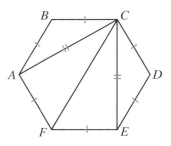

11 The diagram shows information about four triangles.

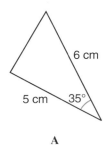

A

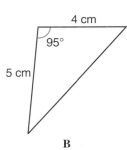

B

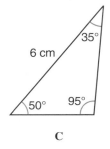

C

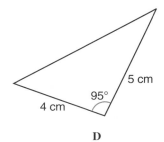

D

Which two triangles are congruent?
Give a reason for your answer.

CHAPTER 23

Quadrilaterals

A **quadrilateral** is a shape made by four straight lines.

Special quadrilaterals

Parallelogram

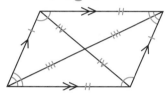

Opposite sides equal and parallel.
Opposite angles equal.
Diagonals bisect each other.

Rectangle

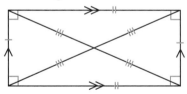

Opposite sides equal and parallel.
Angles of 90°.
Diagonals bisect each other.

Square

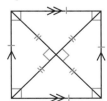

Four equal sides, opposite
sides parallel.
Angles of 90°.
Diagonals bisect each other at 90°.

Rhombus

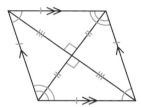

Four equal sides, opposite sides
parallel.
Opposite angles equal.
Diagonals bisect each other at 90°.

Kite

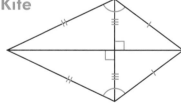

Two pairs of adjacent sides equal.
One pair of opposite angles equal.
One diagonal bisects the other at 90°.

Trapezium

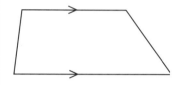

One pair of parallel sides.

Isosceles trapezium

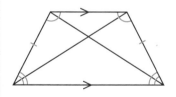

One pair of parallel sides.
Non-parallel sides equal.
Two pairs of equal angles.
Diagonals equal.

Remember:
Sides of equal length are marked with
the same number of **dashes**.
Lines which are parallel are marked
with the same number of **arrowheads**.
Angles of equal size are marked with
the same number of **arcs**.

Sum of the angles of a quadrilateral

The sum of the four angles of a quadrilateral is 360°.

Measure the angles of this quadrilateral.
Do the angles add up to 360°?

*You may not always get 360°.
Can you explain why?*

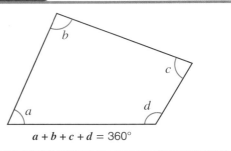

$$a + b + c + d = 360°$$

EXAMPLE   Without measuring, work out the size of the angle marked x.

PQ is parallel to *RS* and *PS* is parallel to *QR*.
PQRS could be either a parallelogram or a rhombus.
In both types of quadrilateral the opposite angles are equal.

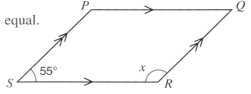

$$55° + 55° + x + x = 360°$$
$$110° + 2x = 360°$$
$$2x = 360° - 110°$$
$$2x = 250°$$
$$x = 125°$$

Symmetry of quadrilaterals

Remember:
A two-dimensional shape has line symmetry if the line divides the shape so that one side fits exactly over the other.
A two-dimensional shape has rotational symmetry if it fits into a copy of its own outline as it is rotated through 360°.

Parallelogram

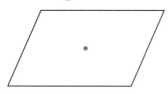

0 lines of symmetry.
Order of rotational symmetry 2.

Isosceles trapezium

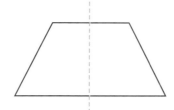

1 line of symmetry.

Rectangle

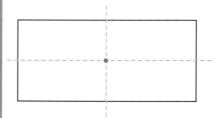

2 lines of symmetry.
Order of rotational symmetry 2.

Square

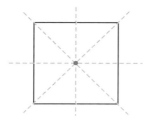

4 lines of symmetry.
Order of rotational symmetry 4.

Rhombus

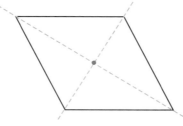

2 lines of symmetry.
Order of rotational symmetry 2.

Kite

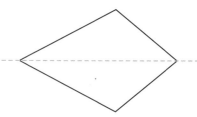

1 line of symmetry.

Exercise 23.1

You should be able to do this exercise without using your calculator. Having completed the exercise you can use a calculator to check your working.

1 (a) Draw quadrilaterals with the following coordinates.
   (i) A (3,1), B (1,3), C (2,6), D (6,2)
   (ii) E (1,0), F (6,2), G (8,9), H (3,7)
   (iii) J (3,0), K (0,4), L (3,8), M (6,4)
   (iv) P (1,1), Q (2,4), R (4,4), S (4,2)
   (v) W (3,1), X (1,3), Y (3,5), Z (5,3)

   (b) What special name is given to each of these quadrilaterals?

2 $PQRS$ is a rectangle. P is the point (1,4), Q (4,6), R (6,4).
Find the coordinates of S.

3 $ABCD$ is a rhombus. A is the point (3,0), B (0,4) and D (8,0).
Find the coordinates of C.

4 $WXYZ$ is a parallelogram. W is the point (1,0), X (4,1), Z (3,3).
Find the coordinates of Y.

5 $OABC$ is a kite. O is the point (0,0), B (5,5), C (3,1).
Find the coordinates of A.

6 $KLMN$ is an isosceles trapezium. K is the point (1,1), M (4,3), N (5,1).
Find the coordinates of L.

7 The following diagrams have not been drawn accurately. Work out the size of the angles marked with letters.

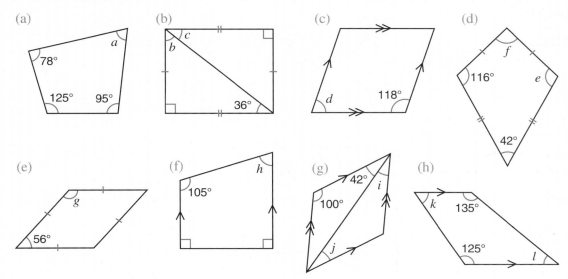

8 (a) Draw a rhombus of side 4 cm, with angles of 80° and 100°,
   (b) Mark on your diagram any lines of symmetry,
   (c) What order of rotational symmetry has the rhombus?

9 These quadrilaterals have been drawn on squared paper.

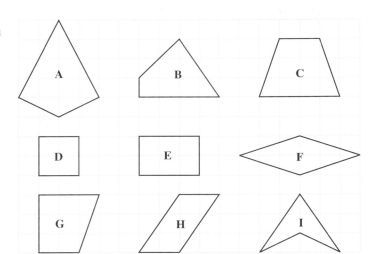

Copy and complete the table for each shape.

Shape	A	B	C	D	E	F	G	H	I
Number of lines of symmetry									
Order of rotational symmetry									

10 The flow chart is used to sort quadrilaterals.

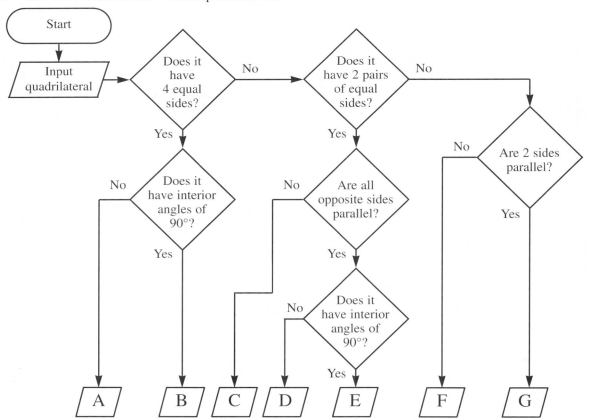

Use the flow chart to find which of the letters A to G applies to each of the following quadrilaterals.

(a) kite   (b) parallelogram   (c) rectangle
(d) rhombus   (e) square   (f) trapezium

Area of quadrilaterals

Area is the amount of surface covered by a shape.
The standard unit for measuring area is the square centimetre, cm^2.
Small areas are measured using square millimetres, mm^2.
Large areas are measured using square metres, m^2, or square kilometres, km^2.

1 cm
1 cm² 1 cm

Activity

Finding areas by counting squares

(a) A rectangle and a square have been drawn on centimetre-squared paper.

The rectangle covers 12 squares.
The area of each square of the paper is $1\,cm^2$.
The area of the rectangle is $12\,cm^2$.

What is the area of the square?

Is there a quicker way to find the areas of rectangles and squares without having to count squares?

If you can find a rule:
● Give it a test run on more shapes.
● Try to explain why the rule works.

(b) A parallelogram and a rhombus have been drawn on centimetre-squared paper.

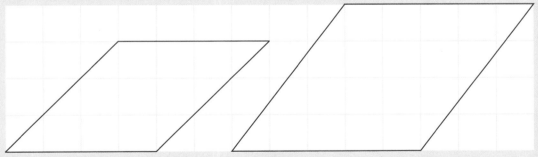

Find the area of each shape by counting squares.

Is there a quicker way to find the areas of parallelograms and rhombuses without having to count squares?

(c) A trapezium has been drawn on centimetre-squared paper.

Find the area of the trapezium by counting squares.

Is there a quicker way to find the areas of trapeziums without having to count squares?

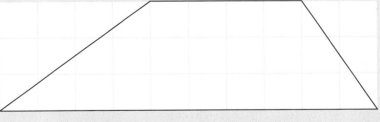

Area formulae

Rectangle

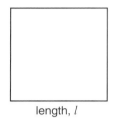

breadth, b

length, l

Area = length × breadth

$A = lb$

Square

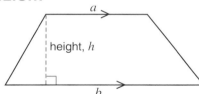

length, l

Area = length × breadth

In a square length = breadth

Area = (length)^2

$A = l^2$

Trapezium

a

height, h

b

Area = half the sum of the parallel sides × perpendicular height

$A = \frac{1}{2}(a + b)h$

Parallelogram

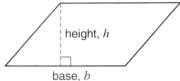

height, h

base, b

Area = base × height

$A = bh$

Rhombus

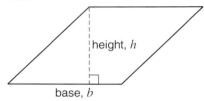

height, h

base, b

Area = base × height

$A = bh$

○○○○○○○○○○○○○○○○○○○○○○○

Base and perpendicular height

The **base** is the side of the shape from which the height is measured.

The base does not have to be at the bottom of the shape.

The height of a shape, measured at right angles to the base, is called the **perpendicular height**.

EXAMPLES

1 Find the area of this trapezium.

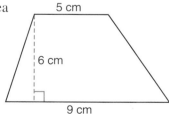

5 cm

6 cm

9 cm

$A = \frac{1}{2}(a + b)h$

$= \frac{1}{2}(5 + 9)\,6$

$= \frac{1}{2} \times 14 \times 6$

$= 42\,\text{cm}^2$

2 The area of a rectangular room is 17.5 m². The room is 5 m long. Find the width of the room.

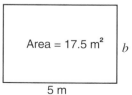

Area = 17.5 m²

b

5 m

$A = lb$

$17.5 = 5 \times b$

$b = \frac{17.5}{5}$

$b = 3.5\,\text{m}$

Exercise **23.2**

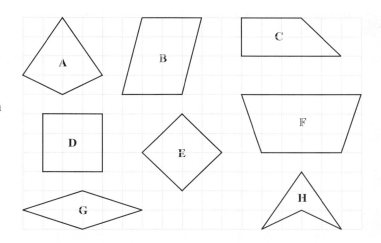

1 These shapes have been drawn on 1 cm squared paper.
Find the area of each shape.

2 Calculate the areas of these shapes.

(a)

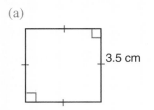

3.5 cm

(b)

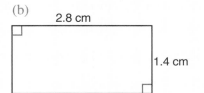

2.8 cm

1.4 cm

(c)

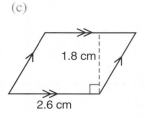

1.8 cm

2.6 cm

(d)

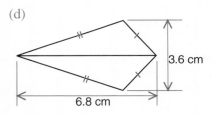

3.6 cm

6.8 cm

(e)

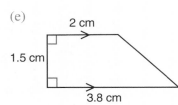

2 cm

1.5 cm

3.8 cm

(f)

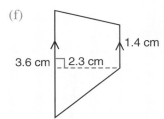

1.4 cm

3.6 cm   2.3 cm

3 A carpet measuring 4 m by 4 m is placed on a rectangular floor measuring 5 m by 6 m.
What area of floor is not carpeted?

4 The diagram shows a picture in a frame.
The outer dimensions of the frame are 18 cm by 10 cm. The frame is 2 cm wide.
What is the area of the picture?

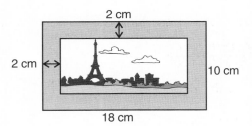

2 cm

2 cm

10 cm

18 cm

5 The diagram shows a bay window.
The parallel sides are 2.5 m and 3.5 m.
These sides are 2 m apart.
What is the area of the bay?

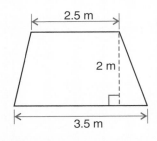

2.5 m

2 m

3.5 m

6 The diagram shows the dimensions of a kite.
What is the area of the kite?

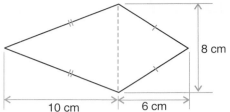

8 cm

10 cm   6 cm

7 A rectangle has an area of 36 cm².
The length of the rectangle is 9 cm. What is the breadth?

8 A rhombus of side 6 cm has an area of 48 cm².
What is the perpendicular height of the rhombus?

9 A trapezium has an area of 30 cm². The two parallel sides are 7 cm and 8 cm.
What is the perpendicular distance between the sides?

10 These shapes all have the same area. Calculate the values of *h* and *l*.

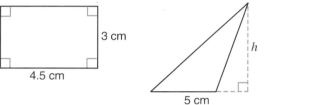

3 cm

4.5 cm

h

5 cm

3 cm

l

11 Each of these shapes has an area of 24 cm². Calculate the lengths marked with letters.

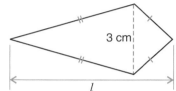

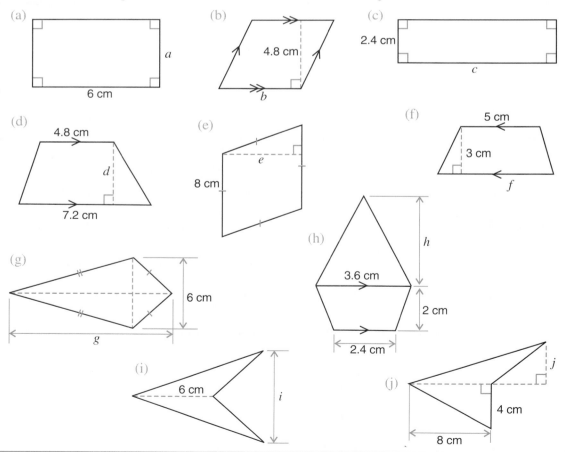

(a)

a

6 cm

(b)

4.8 cm

b

(c)

2.4 cm

c

(d)

4.8 cm

d

7.2 cm

(e)

e

8 cm

(f)

5 cm

3 cm

f

(g)

6 cm

g

(h)

3.6 cm

h

2 cm

2.4 cm

(i)

6 cm

i

(j)

j

4 cm

8 cm

- A **quadrilateral** is a shape made by four straight lines.
- The sum of the angles in a quadrilateral is 360°

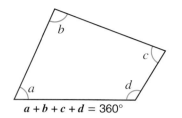

$$a + b + c + d = 360°$$

- Facts about these special quadrilaterals:

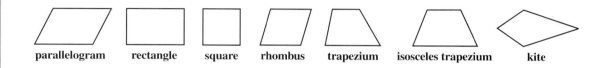

parallelogram   **rectangle**   **square**   **rhombus**   **trapezium**   **isosceles trapezium**   **kite**

Quadrilateral	Sides	Angles	Diagonals	Line symmetry	Order of rotational symmetry	Area formula
Parallelogram	Opposite sides equal and parallel	opposite angles equal	Bisect each other	0	2	$A = bh$
Rectangle	Opposite sides equal and parallel	All 90°	Bisect each other	2	2	$A = bh$
Rhombus	4 equal sides, opposite sides parallel	Opposite angles equal	Bisect each other at 90°	2	2	$A = bh$
Square	4 equal sides, opposite sides parallel	All 90°	Bisect each other at 90°	4	4	$A = l^2$
Trapezium	1 pair of parallel sides					$A = \frac{1}{2}(a + b)h$
Isosceles trapezium	1 pair of parallel sides, non-parallel sides equal	2 pairs of equal angles	Equal in length	1	1	$A = \frac{1}{2}(a + b)h$
Kite	2 pairs of adjacent sides equal	1 pair of opposite angles equal	One bisects the other at 90°	1	1	

The area of a quadrilateral in which the diagonals intersect at 90° can be worked out using, area = $\frac{1}{2}$ product of the diagonals.

Investigate.

1 The diagram shows a quadrilateral *PQRS*.
(a) What is the sum of the angles *p*, *q*, *r* and *s*?

Angle *p* = 85°, angle *q* = 148°, *PQ* = *QR* and *PS* = *SR*.
(b) (i) What type of quadrilateral is *PQRS*?
(ii) Calculate the size of angles *r* and *s*.

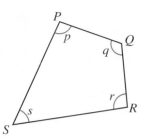

Not to scale

2 The diagram shows a quadrilateral with one side extended.
CB = *CD*, angle *BAD* = 50°, angle *BCD* = 40°
and angle *ADE* = 70°.

Calculate the size of angles *BDA* and *ABD*.

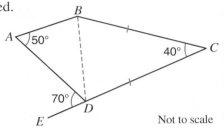

Not to scale

3 Three triangles are placed together to form a quadrilateral, as shown.

AB is parallel to *DC*.
BC = *AD* and *AE* = *EB*.
E is the mid-point of *DC*.

(a) What type of quadrilateral is *ABCD*?
(b) The diagram has one line of symmetry.
Copy the diagram and draw the line of symmetry.
(c) Name two angles which are the same size as angle
BAE, giving a reason for each of your answers.

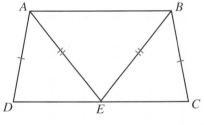

SEG 1996

4 In the diagram the triangles *PQR* and *SQR* are isosceles
with *PQ* = *QR* and *QS* = *SR*.

Angle *QPR* = 70°.

(a) (i) Work out the size of angle *SQR* giving a reason
for your answer.
(ii) Work out the size of angle *SQP*.

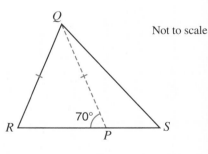

The triangle *SQR* is reflected in the line *SR* so that the
original and reflected figures form a quadrilateral *QSXR*,
as shown.

(b) Which of the following correctly describes the
quadrilateral *QSXR*?

square, rhombus, trapezium, rectangle, parallelogram, kite.

(c) (i) How many lines of symmetry has the
quadrilateral *QSXR*?
(ii) What name is given to the quadrilateral *QPXR*?
(iii) Work out the size of the angle *SXP*.

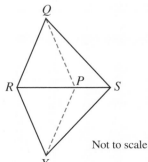

Not to scale

SEG 1995

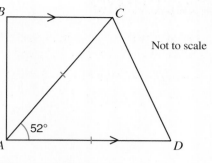

5 The diagram shows a quadrilateral *ABCD*.
BC is parallel to *AD*, *AC* = *AD*, angle *CAD* = 52°.

(a) (i) Write down the size of angle *BCA*.
    (ii) Give a reason for your answer.

(b) Work out the size of angle *BCD*.

SEG 1998 S

6 The shaded square has sides of length 1 cm.
It is enlarged a number of times as shown.

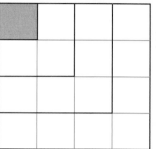

(a) Complete the table.

Length of side of square	1 cm	2 cm	3 cm	4 cm
Perimeter of square	4 cm	8 cm	12 cm	
Area of square	1 cm²	4 cm²		16 cm²

(b) Complete the following table.

Length of side of square	
Perimeter of square	
Area of square	64 cm²

The shaded square continues to be enlarged.

SEG 1994

7 This shape is formed from two overlapping squares with
AB = *BC* and angle *ABC* = 90°.

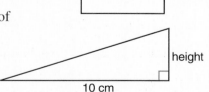

(a) The shape has line symmetry.
Copy the diagram and draw the lines of symmetry.
(b) The shape has rotational symmetry.
What is the order of rotational symmetry?

When drawn accurately, each square has an area of
16 cm² and *AB* = 1 cm.
(c) What is the area of the shape?

This triangle has an area of 16 cm².
(d) Calculate the height of the triangle.

SEG 1996

8 The diagram shows a quadrilateral *ABCD*.
Lengths *AB* and *AD* are each 5 m.
Lengths *CB* and *CD* are each 10 m.
Angle *DAB* = 60°. Angle *ADC* = 136°.

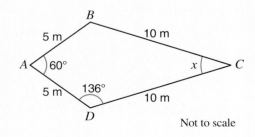

(a) Write down the length *BD*.
(b) What is the mathematical name of this
quadrilateral?
(c) Calculate the value of angle *x*.

SEG 1994

9 The diagram shows the cross-section of a prism. The cross-section is a trapezium with *PQ* parallel to *SR*.

Calculate the area of the cross-section.

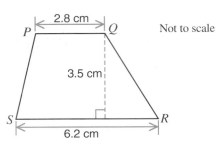

Not to scale

10 The diagram shows a kite *ABCD*.
AX = 2.4 cm, *DB* = 6.5 cm.
Calculate the area of the kite.

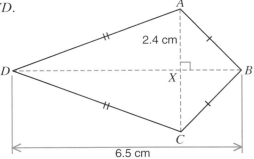

11 The diagram shows a square and a parallelogram. They both have the same area.
The square has an area of 24 cm².
Calculate the perpendicular height of the parallelogram.

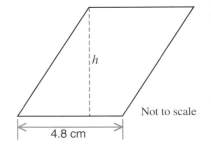

Not to scale

12 These shapes each have an area of 42 cm².
Calculate the lengths marked with letters.

(a)

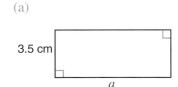

(b)

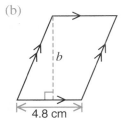

(c)

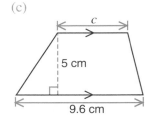

13 A trapezium *ABCD* is drawn inside a square of side 5 cm, as shown.
AB is parallel to *DC*. *AB* = 2.6 cm, *DC* = 4 cm and *AH* = 3.8 cm.

(a) What is the area of the square?
(b) What is the area of the shaded part of the square?
(c) What percentage of the square has been shaded?

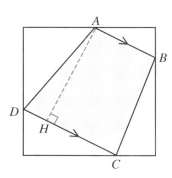

Not to scale

262

CHAPTER **24** **Polygons**

A **polygon** is a shape made by straight lines.
A three-sided polygon is a **triangle**.

A polygon is a many-sided shape.
Look at these polygons.

A four-sided polygon is
called a **quadrilateral**.

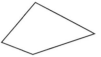

| **Pentagon** | **Hexagon** | **Heptagon** | **Octagon** |
| 5 sides | 6 sides | 7 sides | 8 sides |

Interior and exterior angles of a polygon

Angles formed by sides inside a polygon are called **interior angles**.

When a side of a polygon is extended, as shown, the angle formed
is called an **exterior angle**.

At each vertex of the polygon:
    interior angle + exterior angle = 180°

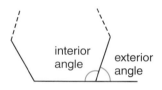

interior angle   exterior angle

Sum of the interior angles of a polygon

The diagram shows polygons with the diagonals from one vertex drawn.

P   Q   R   S

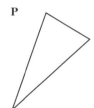 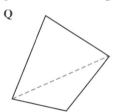 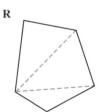 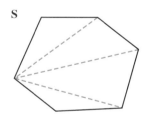

The diagonals divide the polygons into triangles.

Shape	Number of sides	Number of triangles	Sum of interior angles
P	3	1	$1 \times 180° = 180°$
Q	4	2	$2 \times 180° = 360°$
R	5	3	$3 \times 180° = 540°$
S	6	4	$4 \times 180° = 720°$

In general, for any n-sided polygon, the sum of the interior angles is $(n - 2) \times 180°$.

Sum of the exterior angles of a polygon

The sum of the exterior angles of **any** polygon is 360°.

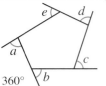

$a + b + c + d + e = 360°$

○○○○○○○○○○○○○○○○○○

To find the sum of the interior angles of a pentagon substitute $n = 5$ into $(n - 2) \times 180°$.

$(5 - 2) \times 180°$
$= 3 \times 180°$
$= 540°$

EXAMPLE

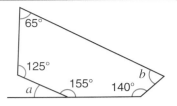

Find the sizes of the angles marked a and b.

$155° + a = 180°$ (int. angle + ext. angle = 180°)
$a = 180° - 155°$
$a = 25°$
The sum of the interior angles of a pentagon is 540°.
$b + 140° + 155° + 125° + 65° = 540°$
$b + 485° = 540°$
$b = 540° - 485°$
$b = 55°$

Exercise 24.1

You should be able to do this exercise without using a calculator. Having completed the exercise you can use a calculator to check your working.

1 Work out the sum of the interior angles of these polygons.

(a)
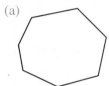

(b)
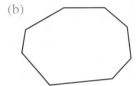

(c)
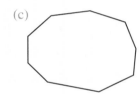

2 These diagrams have not been drawn accurately.
Work out the size of the angles marked with letters.

(a)
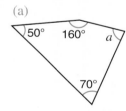

(b)
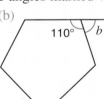

(c)
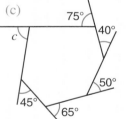

(d)
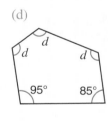

(e)
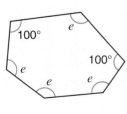

(f)
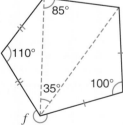

(g)
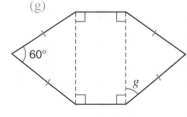

(h)
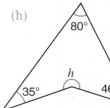

(i)
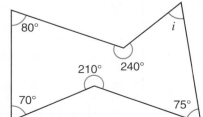

264

Regular polygons

A polygon with all sides equal and all angles equal is called a **regular polygon**.

A regular triangle is usually called an **equilateral triangle**.
A regular quadrilateral is usually called a **square**.

Regular hexagon   Regular octagon

Exterior angles of regular polygons

Measure the exterior angles of these regular polygons.
What do you find?

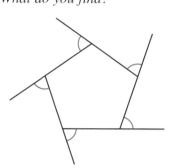

Regular pentagon

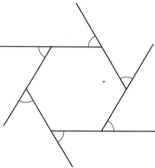

Regular hexagon

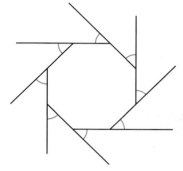

Regular octagon

You should find the exterior angles of a regular polygon are equal.

In general, for any regular *n*-sided polygon: exterior angle $= \frac{360°}{n}$

By rearranging the formula we can find the number of sides, *n*, of a regular polygon when we know the exterior angle. $n = \dfrac{360°}{\text{exterior angle}}$

EXAMPLE

A regular polygon has an exterior angle of 30°.
(a)   How many sides has the polygon?
(b)   What is the size of an interior angle of the polygon?

(a) $n = \dfrac{360°}{\text{exterior angle}}$

   $n = \dfrac{360°}{30°}$

   $n = 12$

Remember:
It is a good idea to write down the formula you are using.

(b)   interior angle + exterior angle $= 180°$
   int. $\angle + 30° = 180°$
   int. $\angle = 180° - 30°$
   interior angle $= 150°$

Exercise **24.2**

You should be able to do this exercise without using a calculator. Having completed the exercise you can use a calculator to check your working.

   (a)   Calculate the size of an exterior angle of a regular pentagon.
   (b)   What is the size of an interior angle of a regular pentagon?
   (c)   What is the sum of the interior angles of a pentagon?

2 Calculate (a) the exterior angle and (b) the interior angle of these regular polygons.

(i)  (ii) 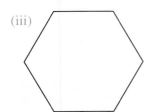 (iii) (iv)

3 A regular polygon has an exterior angle of 18°.
How many sides has the polygon?

4 Calculate the number of sides of regular polygons with an exterior angle of:–
(a) 9°   (b) 24°   (c) 40°   (d) 60°

5 A regular polygon has an interior angle of 135°.
How many sides has the polygon?

6 Calculate the number of sides of regular polygons with an interior angle of:–
(a) 108°   (b) 162°   (c) 171°   (d) 90°

7 The following diagrams are drawn using regular polygons.
Work out the values of the marked angles.

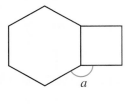 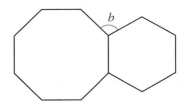 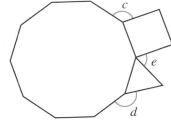

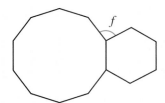 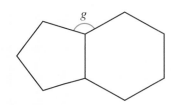 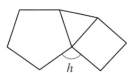

8 Find the sum of the interior angles of these regular polygons.
(a) A hexagon.
(b) An octagon.
(c) A decagon (10 sides).

9 A regular polygon has *x* sides. Each of its interior angle is *y*°.
Find a formula for *y* in terms of *x*.

10 A footpath is made in the shape of a regular pentagon *ABCDE*.
The point *B* is due east of point *A*.
(a) What is the bearing of *A* from *C*?
(b) What is the bearing of *E* from *B*?

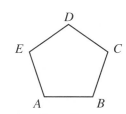

Tessellations

Covering a surface with identical shapes produces
a pattern called a **tessellation**.

To tessellate the shape must not overlap and there must be no gaps.

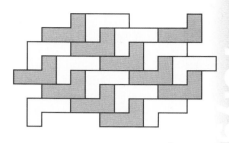

Regular tessellations

This pattern shows a tessellation of regular
hexagons.
This pattern is called a **regular tessellation** because
it is made by using a single regular polygon.

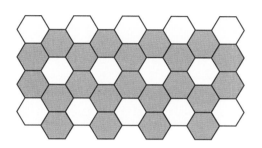

Semi-regular tessellations

Tessellations can be made using more than one
regular polygon.
Such patterns are called **semi-regular
tessellations**.

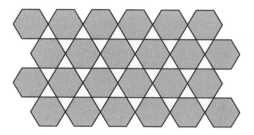

Exercise 24.3

1 Each of these diagrams shows a tessellation.
Continue the tessellation by drawing four more shapes.

(a)

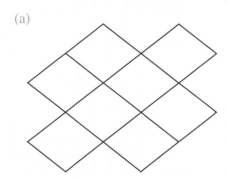

(b)

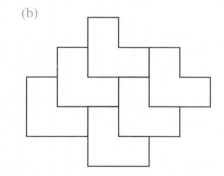

2 Draw diagrams to show tessellations of these shapes.

(a)

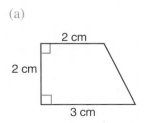

(b)

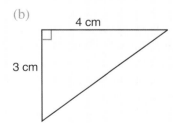

(c)

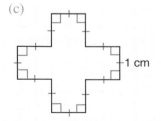

3 Draw a tessellation of (a) squares, (b) equilateral triangles.

4 Explain why regular pentagons will not tessellate.

5 (a) Draw a semi-regular tessellation using
    (i)   octagons and squares,
    (ii) squares and equilateral triangles,
    (iii) hexagons, squares and equilateral triangles.

   (b) What other shapes can be used to make semi-regular tessellations?
       Draw patterns to show these tessellations.

6 Any triangle can be used to make a tessellation.
Draw a triangle of your own, make copies, and show that it will tessellate.

7 (a) Do these quadrilaterals tessellate?

(i)

(ii)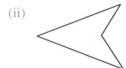

Can any quadrilateral be used to make a tessellation?
(b) Draw quadrilaterals of your own, make copies, and see if they will tessellate.

What you need to know

- A **polygon** is a many-sided shape made by straight lines.

- A polygon with all sides equal and all angles equal is called a **regular polygon**.

- Shapes you need to know:
  A 5-sided polygon is called a **pentagon**.
  A 6-sided polygon is called a **hexagon**.
  An 8-sided polygon is called an **octagon**.

- The sum of the exterior angles of any polygon is 360°.

- At each vertex of a polygon:
  interior angle + exterior angle = 180°

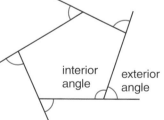
interior angle
exterior angle

- The sum of the interior angles of an n-sided polygon is given by:
  $(n - 2) \times 180°$

- For a regular n-sided polygon:
  exterior angle $= \frac{360°}{n}$

- A shape will **tessellate** if it covers a surface without overlapping and leaves no gaps.

- All triangles tessellate.

- All quadrilaterals tessellate.

- Equilateral triangles, squares and hexagons can be used to make **regular tessellations**.

- A regular pentagon cannot be used to make a tessellation.

IDEAS FOR INVESTIGATION

Copy these regular polygons.

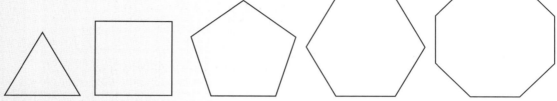

(a) Copy and complete the following table.

Polygon	Number of lines of symmetry	Order of rotational symmetry
Triangle		
Square		
Pentagon		
Hexagon		
Octagon		

(b) Using these results can you make a rule for finding the symmetries of regular polygons.

(c) What is the connection between the number of lines of symmetry and the angles between the sides of the polygon?

Review Exercise

① In the diagram $AB = BD = AF = DF$.
D is the mid-point of CE.
Angle BCD = Angle $DEF = 90°$.
Angle ADC = Angle $ADE = 90°$.
Angle $BAD = 50°$.

(a) What is the mathematical name of the shape $ABCEF$?

(b) Write down the size of
    (i) angle w,
    (ii) angle x,
    (iii) angle y,
    (iv) angle z.

Not to scale

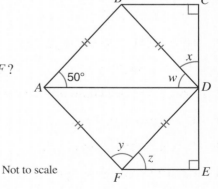

Polygons . . . . . Polygons . . . . Polygons . . . .

2 ABCDE represents a swimming pool. The shape of the pool is a regular pentagon.

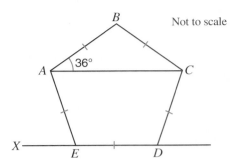

Not to scale

A rope joins A to C and is parallel to ED. Given that ∠BAC = 36°, calculate

(a) ∠ABC,
(b) ∠CAE,
(c) ∠AEX.

SEG 1988

3 A regular octagon, drawn below, has eight sides.
One side of the octagon has been extended to form angle p.

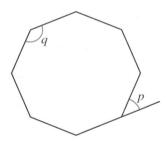

(a) Work out the size of angle p.
(b) Work out the size of angle q.

4 ABCDEF is a regular polygon.

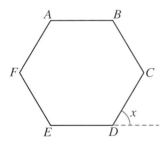

(a) What name is given to this polygon?
(b) What is the size of the exterior angle marked x?
(c) What is the sum of the interior angles?

5 The diagram below shows a pentagon with just one line of symmetry.

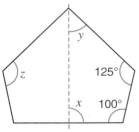

Not to scale

(a) Explain why angle x is 90°.
(b) Calculate the size of angle y.
(c) Write down the size of angle z.

SEG 1988

6 The diagram shows a regular octagon.

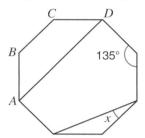

Not to scale

(a) Work out the size of angle x, giving a reason for your answer.
(b) What name is given to the quadrilateral ABCD?

SEG 1995

7 The diagram shows a regular octagon ABCDEFGH centre O.

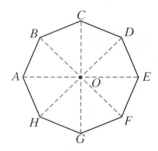

(a) Octagon ABCDEFGH is rotated clockwise about centre O, so that A moves to D, B moves to E and so on.
Through how many degrees has the octagon been rotated?
(b) The octagon is now rotated to return it to its original position. Through what angle and in what direction is it rotated?

SEG 1996

270

8 Kath investigates the maximum number of diagonals she can draw in these figures:

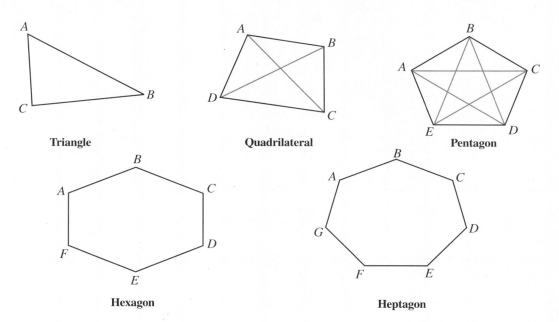

Triangle   Quadrilateral   Pentagon

Hexagon   Heptagon

She writes her results in a table.

Figure	Number of Vertices	Number of Diagonals
Triangle	3	0
Quadrilateral	4	2
Pentagon	5	5
Hexagon		
Heptagon		

(a) Copy Kath's table and fill in your results for the hexagon and heptagon.
(b) What is the maximum number of diagonals which could be drawn in a decagon (10 sided figure)?

SEG 1990

9 The diagram shows part of a garden path.
Each shape in the path is a regular polygon.

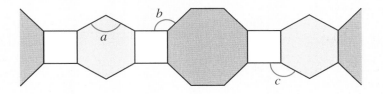

Work out the size of each lettered angle.

10 These tiling patterns have been drawn using regular polygons.

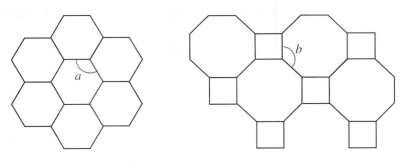

(a) Work out the size of angles a and b.
(b) Explain why a tiling pattern cannot be made with only regular pentagon's.

SEG 1996

11 Copy each of the following diagrams onto squared paper and draw six more shapes to continue the tessellations.

(a)

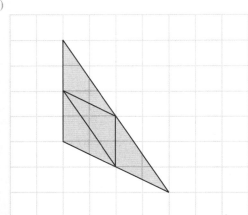

(b)

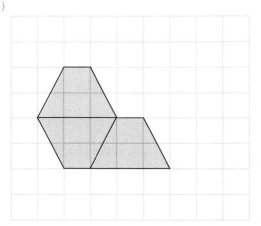

12 Copy the diagram and draw four more shapes to continue the tessellation.

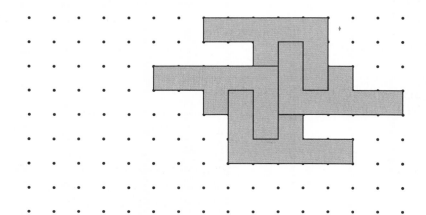

SEG 1995

CHAPTER 25

Circles and Combinations of Shapes

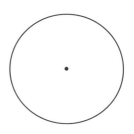

A **circle** is the shape drawn by keeping a pencil the same distance from a fixed point on a piece of paper.
Compasses can be used to draw circles accurately.

It is important that you understand the meaning of the following words:

Circumference – special name used for the perimeter of a circle.

Radius – distance from the centre of the circle to any point on the circumference.

Diameter – distance right across the circle, passing through the centre point. Notice that the diameter is twice as long as the radius.

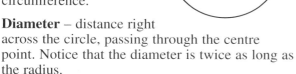

Chord – a line joining two points on the circumference. The longest chord of a circle is the diameter.

Tangent – a line which touches the circumference of a circle at one point only.

Arc – part of the circumference of a circle.

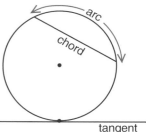

Activity

Draw a circle with radius 2 cm.
Use thread or the edge of a strip of paper to measure the circumference of your circle.
Draw circles with radii 3 cm, 4 cm and so on.
Measure the circumference of each circle and write your results in a table.
What do you notice?

Radius (cm)	2	3	4	5	6	7	8
Diameter (cm)							
Circumference (cm)							

The Greek letter π

The circumference of any circle is just a bit bigger than three times the diameter of the circle.
The Greek letter π is used to represent this number.
We use an approximate value for π, such as 3, $3\frac{1}{7}$, 3.14, or the π key on a calculator, depending on the accuracy we require.

The circumference of a circle

The circumference of a circle can be found using the formulae:

$$C = \pi \times d$$
or $\quad C = 2 \times \pi \times r$

Remember: $d = 2 \times r$

Short but accurate
We sometimes use letters in place of words.
C is short for circumference.
r is short for radius.
d is short for diameter.

EXAMPLES

1 Find the circumference of a circle with diameter 80 cm, giving your answer to the nearest centimetre. Take $\pi = 3.14$.

$C = \pi \times d$

$\quad = 3.14 \times 80$ cm

$\quad = 251.2$ cm

$\quad = 251$ cm, to the nearest centimetre.

2 A circle has circumference 37.2 cm. Find the radius of the circle, giving your answer to the nearest millimetre. Take $\pi = 3.14$.

$\quad C = 2 \times \pi \times r$

$37.2 = 2 \times 3.14 \times r$

$37.2 = 6.28 \times r$

$\quad r = \frac{37.2}{6.28}$

$\quad r = 5.923 \ldots$

$\quad r = 5.9$ cm, to the nearest millimetre.

3 Find the perimeter of this shape. Take $\pi = 3.14$.

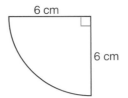

Find the circumference of a circle with radius 6 cm.

$\quad C = 2 \times \pi \times r$

$\quad = 2 \times 3.14 \times 6$ cm

$\quad = 37.68$ cm

Perimeter $= \frac{1}{4} \times$ circumference + two radii

$\quad = \frac{1}{4} \times 37.68 + (2 \times 6)$ cm

$\quad = 9.42 + 12$

$\quad = 21.42$ cm

Perimeter $= 21.4$ cm, correct to 3 sig. figs.

Exercise 25.1

1 **Do not use a calculator** for this question. Use the approximate rule
Circumference = 3 × diameter
to complete the table.

Radius (cm)	Diameter (cm)	Circumference (cm)
5	10	30
4	8	
10		60
15		
	24	72
	40	
		210

Questions 2 to 14.
Take π to be 3.14 or use the π key on your calculator.

2 Find the circumferences of these circles using the formula $C = \pi \times d$.

(a)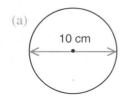
10 cm

(b)
7 cm

(c)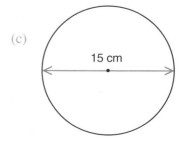
15 cm

3 Find the circumferences of these circles using the
formula $C = 2 \times \pi \times r$.

(a)

4 m

(b)

4.5 m

(c)

16 m

4 Find the perimeters
of these shapes.

(a)

8 cm

(b)

7.5 m

7.5 m

5 The lid of a circular biscuit tin has a
diameter of 24 cm.
How much tape is needed to go right
round the tin?

6 Stan marks the centre circle of a
football pitch. The radius of
the circle is 9.15 metres.
What is the
circumference
of the circle?

7 A scone-cutter is in the shape of a
semicircle.
The straight side of the semicircle is
12 cm long.
How long is the curved part?

8 The radius of a tractor wheel is
0.8 metres.
What is the circumference of the wheel?

9 A rail for the track of a toy train is a quarter circle of radius 15 cm.
Rails are put together to make different tracks.
Find the lengths of these tracks.

(a)

(b)

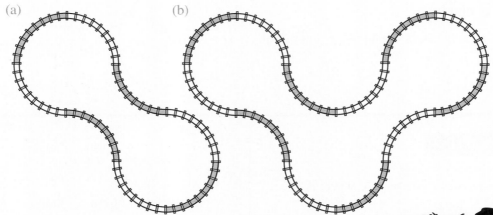

10 Two cyclists go once round a circular
track.
Eddy goes round the inside of the track
which has a radius of 20 m.
Jacques goes round the outside of the
track which has a radius of 25 m.
How much further does Jacques go?

11 The circumference of
a bicycle wheel is
190 cm.
Find the diameter
of the wheel, giving
your answer to the
nearest centimetre.

12 A circular mug has a circumference of 24 cm. Find the radius of the mug, giving your answer to the nearest millimetre.

13 The circumference of a copper pipe is 94 mm. Find, to the nearest millimetre, the diameter of the pipe.

14 The wheel of a wheelbarrow rotates 60 times when it is pushed a distance of 50 metres. Calculate the radius of the wheel, giving your answer to the nearest millimetre.

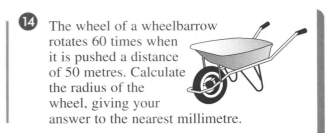

Area of a circle

Activity

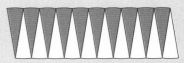

Cut out the 20 sectors.
Arrange them like this.

Draw a circle.
Divide it into 20 equal **sectors**.
Colour the sectors using two colours.

The circumference of a circle is given by $2 \times \pi \times r$.
Half of the circumference is $\pi \times r$.
So the length of the rectangle is $\pi \times r$.
The width of the rectangle is the same as the radius of the circle, r.

$\pi \times r$

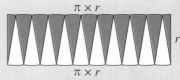

$\pi \times r$

Using area of a rectangle = length × breadth
  area of a circle = $\pi \times r \times r$
  area of a circle = $\pi \times r^2$

Take the end sector and cut it in half.
Place one piece at each end of the pattern

Area of a circle

The area of a circle can be found using the formula:

$A = \pi \times r^2$

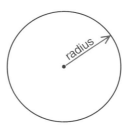

radius

EXAMPLE

1 The diameter of a bicycle wheel is 66 cm.
A plastic spoke cover is made to cover the wheel.
What is the area of the spoke cover?
Take $\pi = 3.14$.

$A = \pi \times r^2$
Diameter = 66 cm, so radius = 33 cm.

$A = 3.14 \times 33^2 \, cm^2$
 = 3419.46
 = 3420 cm² (correct to 3 significant figures)

(Notice that the answer given by the calculator has been rounded to a sensible degree of accuracy.)

276

EXAMPLE

2 The top of a tin of cat food has an area of 78.5 cm².
What is the radius of the tin?
Take $\pi = 3.14$.

$$A = \pi \times r^2$$
Substitute values for A and π.
$$78.5 = 3.14 \times r^2$$
Solve this equation to find r.
Divide both sides of the equation by 3.14.
$$\frac{78.5}{3.14} = r^2$$
$$r^2 = 25$$
Take the square root of both sides.
$$r = 5$$
The radius of the tin is 5 cm.

Mixed questions on area and circumference

Some questions will involve finding the area and some the circumference of a circle.
Remember: Choose the correct formula for area or circumference.
You need to think about whether to use the radius or the diameter.

Exercise 25.2

1 Do not use a calculator for this question.
Use the approximate rule:
Area = 3 × (radius)²
to complete this table.

Radius (cm)	Diameter (cm)	Area (cm²)
6	12	108
5	10	
	8	
3		
	16	
		300

Questions 2 to 7.
Take π to be 3.14 or use the π key on your calculator.

2 Find the areas of circles with:
  (a) radius 18 cm,
  (b) radius 2.4 cm,
  (c) diameter 50 cm,
  (d) diameter 8.4 km,
  (e) radius 0.4 cm,
  (f) diameter 365 m.

3 The base of a paddling pool is a circle with radius 84 cm. Find the area of the base.

4 A pattern on a quilt is a circle drawn inside a square of side 10 cm.
Find the area of the shaded region.

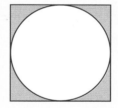

5 Find the areas of these shapes.

(a)   (b)

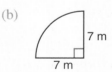

20 cm   7 m 7 m

6 The radius of a circular plate is 15 cm.
  (a) What is its area?
  (b) What is its circumference?

7 A circular flower bed has diameter 12 m.
  (a) How much edging is needed to go right round the bed?
  (b) The gardener needs one bag of fertiliser for each 7 m².
      How many bags of fertiliser are needed for this bed?

Finding areas by splitting shapes up

In earlier chapters you found the areas of various shapes using formulae.
Here is a reminder of those shapes.

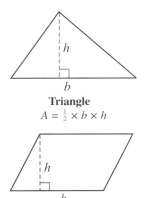

Triangle
$A = \frac{1}{2} \times b \times h$

Rectangle
$A = lb$

Square
$A = l^2$

Parallelogram
$A = bh$

Rhombus
$A = bh$

Trapezium
$A = \frac{1}{2}(a + b)h$

You can find the areas of lots of shapes by splitting them up into rectangles, triangles, circles, etc.
There are several ways to split up most shapes, but they should all give the same answer.

EXAMPLE

1

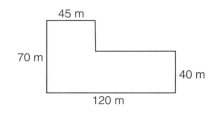

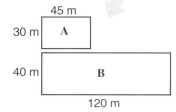

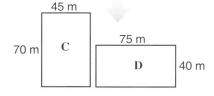

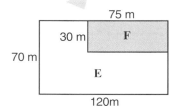

Area of shape is given by:
Area A + Area B
$= (45 \times 30) + (120 \times 40)$
$= 1350 + 4800$
$= 6150 \, \text{m}^2$

Area of shape is given by:
Area C + Area D
$= (45 \times 70) + (75 \times 40)$
$= 3150 + 3000$
$= 6150 \, \text{m}^2$

Area of shape is given by:
Area (E + F) − Area F
$= (120 \times 70) - (75 \times 30)$
$= 8400 - 2250$
$= 6150 \, \text{m}^2$

All the methods give the same answer so use the method you find easiest.

EXAMPLE

2 Find the area of this metal plate.

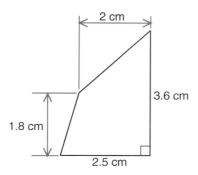

2 cm

3.6 cm

1.8 cm

2.5 cm

The plate can be split into a rectangle, A, and two triangles, B and C.

Area $A = 2 \times 1.8 = 3.6 \, \text{cm}^2$

Area $B = \frac{2 \times 1.8}{2} = 1.8 \, \text{cm}^2$

Area $C = \frac{0.5 \times 1.8}{2} = 0.45 \, \text{cm}^2$

Total area $= 3.6 + 1.8 + 0.45 = 5.85 \, \text{cm}^2$

Note: There are other methods. Try one!

Exercise 25.3

1 Find the areas of these shapes which are made up of rectangles.

(a)
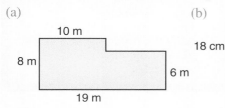
10 m
8 m
6 m
19 m

(b)
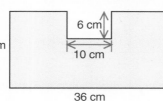
6 cm
18 cm
10 cm
36 cm

(c)
18 km
6 km
12 km
24 km
12 km
12 km
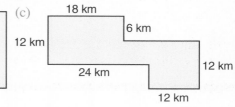

2 Find the areas of these flags.

(a)
20 cm
15 cm
28 cm

(b)
60 cm
32 cm
24 cm
32 cm

(c)
8 cm
20 cm
12 cm
30 cm

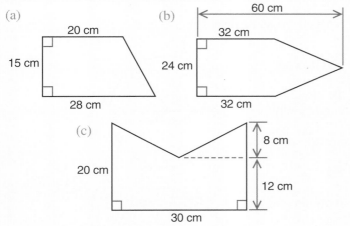

3 Find the area of the shaded square.

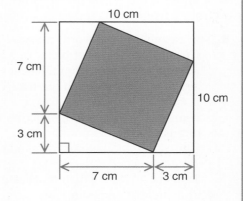
10 cm
7 cm
3 cm
10 cm
7 cm
3 cm

4 Find the areas of these shapes.

(a)
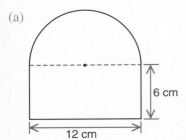
6 cm
12 cm

(b)
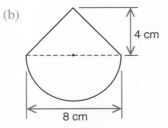
4 cm
8 cm

(c)
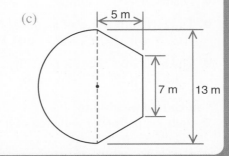
5 m
7 m
13 m

5 A window is made in the shape of a semicircle of radius 0.2 m on top of a rectangle of height 0.8 m.

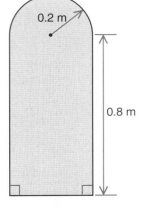

0.2 m

0.8 m

(a) What is the area of glass in the window?

(b) A plastic strip is made to go right round the edge of the window. How long is the strip?

6 Find the area and perimeter of the shaded shape.

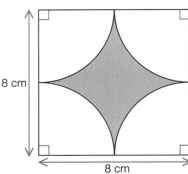

8 cm

8 cm

7 A right-angled triangle has sides 6 cm, 8 cm and 10 cm. Semicircles are drawn on each side.
Find the areas of A, B and C.

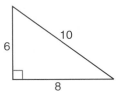

6   10

8

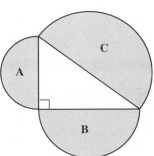

A   B   C

What do you notice about the areas of the three semicircles?

What you need to know

- A **circle** is the shape drawn by keeping a pencil the same distance from a fixed point on a piece of paper.

- The meaning of the words associated with circles:
  Circumference – perimeter of a circle.
  Radius – distance from the centre of the circle to any point on the circumference. The plural of radius is **radii**.
  Diameter – distance right across the circle, passing through the centre point.
  Chord – a line joining two points on the circumference.
  Tangent – a line which touches the circumference of a circle at one point only.
  Arc – part of the circumference of a circle.

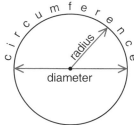

circumference
radius
diameter

- Diameter = 2 × radius

- The **circumference** of a circle is given by:
  $C = \pi \times d$ or $C = 2 \times \pi \times r$

- The **area** of a circle is given by:
  $A = \pi \times r^2$

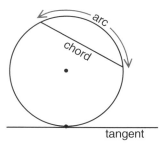

arc
chord
tangent

You should be able to:
- Find the perimeter and area of a variety of shapes by splitting them up into rectangles, triangles, circles, etc.

Take π to be 3.14 or use the π key on your calculator.

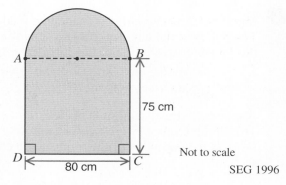
Not to scale
SEG 1996

1 The diagram shows a window.
The arc AB is a semicircle.
$BC = AD = 75$ cm, $DC = 80$ cm.

Calculate the area of the window.

2 Mr Digweed has a garden with a path one metre wide crossing it, as shown in the diagram below.

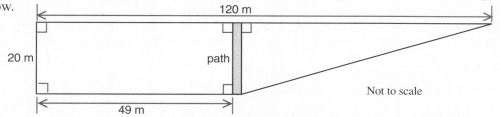
Not to scale

(a) Calculate the area of the rectangular section of the garden.
(b) Calculate the area of the triangular section of the garden.
(c) Calculate the total area of the garden **including** the path.

SEG 1994

3 Calculate the area of the following symmetrical shape.

Show all your working.

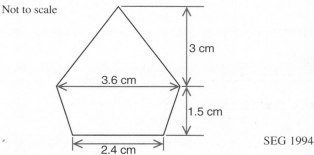
Not to scale
SEG 1994

4
14 cm

Not to scale

The diagram shows the front view of a cycle lamp.

(a) The circle has a radius of 4 cm.
Calculate the area of the circle.

(b) AB is the diameter of the circle and $ABCD$ is a rectangle.
Calculate the perimeter of the cycle lamp.

SEG 1997

5 This millstone is a circle of radius 24 inches.
A square of side length 12 inches is cut out of the centre of the circle as shown.

(a) Calculate the circumference of the millstone.

(b) Calculate the shaded area.

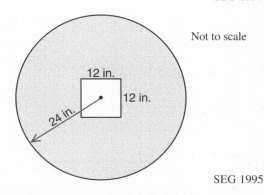
Not to scale

SEG 1995

6 Metal worktop supports are made in cylindrical and cuboidal shapes.
The radius of the circular cross-section of a cylindrical support is 3.5 cm and each edge of
the square cross-section of the cuboidal support is 6 cm.

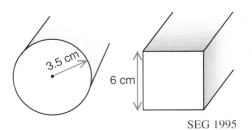

(a) Calculate the area of the circular cross-section
of a cylindrical support.

A new cylindrical support is made.
The circumference of its circular cross-section is the
same as the perimeter of the 6 cm square cross-
section.

(b) Calculate the radius of the circle.

SEG 1995

7 Suki rides to school on her bike. The distance is 2500 m.
The radius of a wheel on Suki's bike is 0.3 m.
Calculate the number of times that the wheel turns during Suki's journey.

SEG 1997

8 George takes part in an 80 metre bicycle race.
The rear wheel on his bicycle has a radius of 32 cm.

(a) How many times does his rear wheel rotate during the race?
(b) The front wheel on Sarah's bicycle has a circumference of 148 cm.
What is the diameter of the front wheel?

Javed is making a plastic cover for the rear wheel on his bicycle.
He cut out a circle of radius 32 cm.
(c) What is the area of this circle?
Give your answer to the nearest square centimetre.

SEG 1996

9 The Mario Brothers produce large
frozen pizzas of diameter 12 inches.
Paper discs are used in the packaging.
Each paper disc fits the base of the
pizza exactly.

(a) Calculate the area of one of these paper discs.
The discs are cut from sheets of paper 40 inches
wide and 1200 inches long.

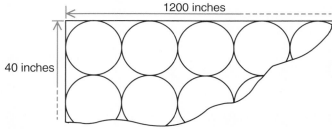

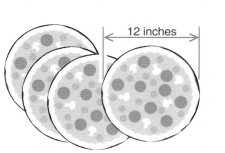

(b) (i) How many paper discs can be cut from the
sheet?
(ii) What area of the sheet is wasted?

SEG 1996

10 The Smith family has a circular dining table.
The circumference of the dining table is 320 centimetres.
(a) Calculate its radius.

The family uses circular table mats each of radius
11 centimetres.
(b) Work out the area covered by one of these mats.

SEG 1995

CHAPTER 26

Loci and Constructions

Following rules

Three students are given rules to follow.

John
Walk so that you are always 2 metres from the lamp post.

His path is a circle, radius 2 metres.

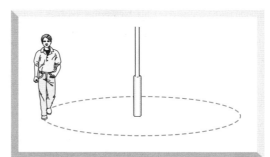

Hanif
Walk along a straight road.
You must keep 30 cm from the edge of the road and stay on the pavement.

His path is a straight line.

Sarah
Start from the corner of the lawn.
Walk across the lawn so that you are always the same distance from two sides.

Her path is a straight line.
The line cuts the angle in two.

Locus

The path of a point which moves according to a rule is called a **locus**.
If we talk about more than one locus we call them **loci**.

EXAMPLES   Draw sketches to show the loci of John, Hanif and Sarah.

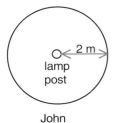

John

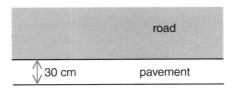

Hanif

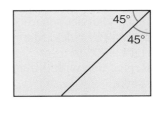

Sarah

1 Adam goes down this slide.
Make a sketch of the slide as viewed from the side and show the locus of his head.

2 A wire is stretched between two posts.
A ring slides along the wire and a dog is attached to the ring by a rope.
Make a sketch to show where the dog can go.

3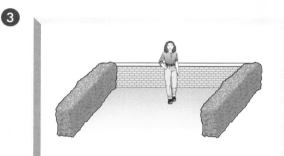

The diagram shows part of a rectangular lawn. Starting from the wall, Sally walks across the lawn so that she is always the same distance from the hedges.
Draw a sketch to show the locus of Sally.

4 *PQRS* is a square of side 8 cm.
A point *X* is inside the square.

X is less than 8 cm from *P*.
X is nearer to *PQ* than to *SR*.

Make a sketch showing where *X* could be.

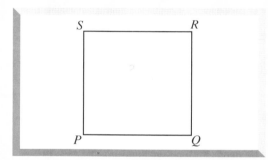

5 Sketch the locus of a point which is the same distance from *PQ* and *RS*.

[Hint: Take care to find all possible points.]

6 Mark two points 5 cm apart.
Label the points *X* and *Y*.

Place your set-square so that *X* and *Y* are on the shorter sides. Mark the point *P* where the right angle is.
Repeat this with different positions of the set-square.
What shape is the locus of *P*?

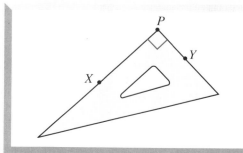

Sometimes it is necessary to construct loci accurately.

You are expected to use only a ruler and compasses.

Here are the methods for two constructions.

To draw the perpendicular bisector of a line

This means to draw a line at right angles to a given line dividing it into two equal parts.

1 Draw line *AB*.

2 Open your compasses to just over half the distance *AB*. Mark two arcs which cross at *C* and *D*.

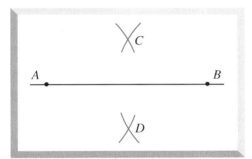

3 Draw a line which passes through the points *C* and *D*.

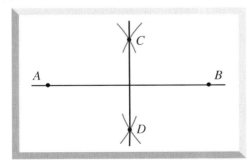

This line is the locus of a point which is the same distance from *A* and *B*.
Points on the line *CD* are **equidistant** (the same distance) from points *A* and *B*.
The line *CD* is at right angles to *AB*.
CD is sometimes called the **perpendicular bisector** of *AB*.

To draw the bisector of an angle

This means to draw a line which divides an angle into two equal parts.

1 Draw the angle *A*.
Use your compasses, centre *A*, to mark points *B* and *C* which are the same distance from *A*.

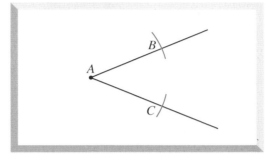

2 Use points *B* and *C* to draw equal arcs which cross at *D*.

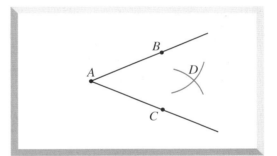

3 Draw a line which passes through the points *A* and *D*.

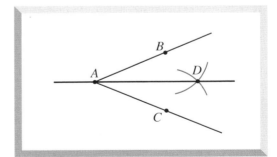

This line is the locus of a point which is the same distance from *AB* and *BC*.
Points on the line *AD* are **equidistant** from the lines through *AB* and *AC*.
The line *AD* cuts angle *BAC* in half.
AD is sometimes called the **bisector** of angle *BAC*.

1 Mark two points, A and B, 10 cm apart. Construct the perpendicular bisector of AB.

2 Use a protractor to draw an angle of 60°. Construct the bisector of the angle. Check that both angles are 30°.

3 Draw a triangle in the middle of a new page. Construct the perpendicular bisectors of all three sides. They should meet at a point, Y.

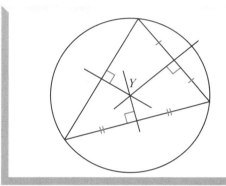

Put the point of your compasses on Y and draw the circle which goes through all three vertices of the triangle. This construction is sometimes called the **circumscribed circle of a triangle**.

4 Draw another triangle on a new page. Bisect each angle of the triangle. The bisectors should meet at a point, X.

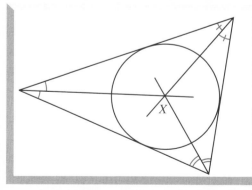

Put the point of your compasses on point X and draw the circle which just touches each side of the triangle. This construction is sometimes called the **inscribed circle of a triangle**.

5 Using a circle of radius 4 cm, copy the diagram above. Draw the perpendicular bisectors of the chords WX and YZ. What do you notice about the perpendicular bisectors?

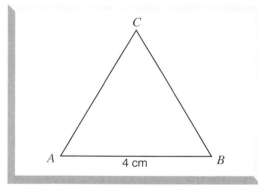

> The perpendicular bisector of a chord always passes through the centre of a circle.

6 Two trees are 6 metres apart. Alan walks so that he is always the same distance from each tree. Draw a scale diagram to show his path.

7 ABC is an equilateral triangle with sides 4 cm.

A point X is in the triangle. It is nearer to AB than to BC.
It is less than 3 cm from A.
It is less than 2 cm from BC.

Shade the region in which X could lie.

8 Draw a rectangle $ABCD$ with $AB = 6$ cm and $AD = 4$ cm.

(a) Mark, with a thin line, the locus of a point which is 1 cm from AB.

(b) Mark, with a dotted line, the locus of a point which is the same distance from A and B.

(c) Mark, with a dashed line, the locus of a point which is 3 cm from A.

9 Draw a right-angled triangle with sides of 6 cm, 8 cm and 10 cm.

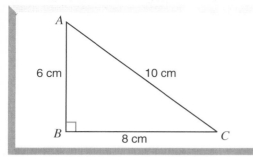

A point *X* is in the triangle.
It is 4 cm from *B*.
It is the same distance from *A* and *B*.

Mark accurately, the position of *X*.

10

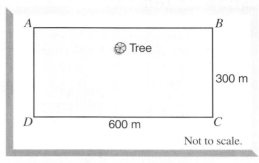

Not to scale.

(a) The diagram shows the sketch of a field.
Make a scale drawing of the field using 1 cm to represent 100 m.

(b) A tree is 400 m from corner *D* and 350 m from corner *C*. Mark the position of the tree on your drawing.

(c) John walks across the field from corner *D*, keeping the same distance from *AD* and *CD*.
Show his path on your diagram.

(d) Does John walk within 100 m of the tree in crossing the field?

What you need to know

- The path of a point which moves according to a rule is called a **locus**.

- The word **loci** is used when we talk about more than one locus.

Using a ruler and compasses you should be able to:
- Construct the **perpendicular bisector of a line**.

  Points on the line *CD* are **equidistant** from the points *A* and *B*.

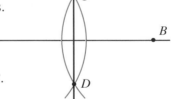

- Construct the **bisector of an angle**.

  Points on the line *AD* are **equidistant** from the lines *AB* and *AC*.

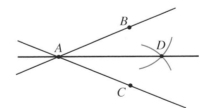

A coin is rolled along a line.
Sketch the locus of a point which starts off at the bottom.

What is the locus of the point if the coin rolls around another coin, or if the coins are not round, or … ?
Investigate.

1 The diagram shows a rectangular field *ABCD*.
The side *AB* is 80 m long. The side *BC* is 50 m long.
Draw the diagram using a scale of 1 cm to 10 m.

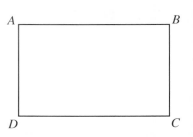

Treasure is hidden in the field.
(a) The treasure is equidistant from the sides *AB* and *AD*.
Construct the locus of points for which this is true.

(b) The treasure is 60 m from corner *C*.
Construct the locus of points for which this is true.

(c) Mark with an *X* the position of the treasure.

SEG 1994

2 Building Site

The diagram shows part of a building site.
The scale is 1 cm to 1 m.
People are not allowed to walk anywhere within 2 m of the site.

Copy the diagram.
Draw accurately the edge of the region where people may **not** walk.

SEG 1995

3 The diagram shows a penguin pool at a zoo.
It consists of a right-angled triangle and a semi-circle.
The scale is 1 cm to 1 m.
Copy the diagram.

A safety fence is put up around the pool.
The fence is always 2 m from the pool.
Draw accurately the position of your fence on your diagram.

SEG 1998

4 The diagram shows the points *X* and *Y*.

X •

• *Y*

Copy the diagram.

(a) On your diagram mark two possible points which are the same distance from *X* as they are from *Y*.
Label them *A* and *B*.

(b) Draw the locus of the points which are the same distance from *X* as they are from *Y*.

SEG 1995

5 A new radio telephone mast is to be erected to provide services for the three towns, Axon, Beaver and Caxton. The position of the three towns is shown. The diagram is drawn to a scale of 1 cm to 10 km.

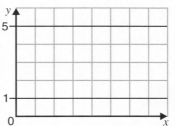

● Caxton

Axon ●

● Beaver

The mast is located in the triangle formed by Axon, Beaver and Caxton so that it is:

Equidistant from Axon and Beaver and 50 km from Caxton.

Construct the position of the mast on your diagram, and mark the position X.

6 A line is equidistant from $y = 1$ and $y = 5$. What is the equation of this line?

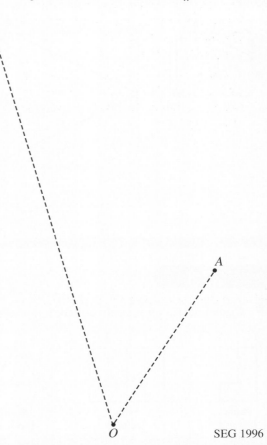

7 Beacons at O, A and B are on level ground. The beacons are used to guide aircraft landing at an airport.

The airport is equidistant from A and B.

To land at the airport an aircraft must fly directly above the line which is equidistant from OA and OB.

Copy the diagram. On your diagram, show the line above which an aircraft must fly when landing at the airport and mark with a cross the position of the airport.

SEG 1996

CHAPTER 27

Enlargements and Similar Figures

Activity

Designers often need the same diagram in different sizes.

Copy this diagram on squared paper.
Now draw the diagram again, exactly the same shape but twice the size.

Compare the lengths of sides and the sizes of angles.

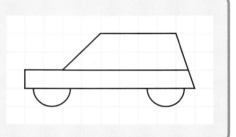

Enlargement

When a shape is enlarged:
    all **lengths** are multiplied by a **scale factor**,
    angles remain unchanged.

$$\text{Scale factor} = \frac{\text{new length}}{\text{original length}}$$

This can be rearranged to give
new length = original length × scale factor.

EXAMPLE

Enlarge this shape using a scale factor of 3.

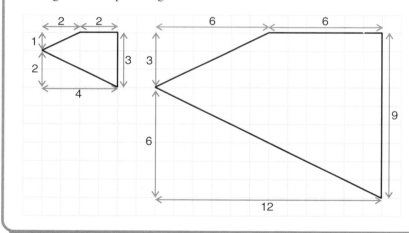

To draw an enlargement on a grid

Horizontal and vertical lines
Count the number of squares and multiply by the scale factor.

Slanting lines
Count across and up (or down) and multiply by the scale factor.

Exercise 27.1

1. Copy each diagram onto squared paper and draw an enlargement with the given scale factor.

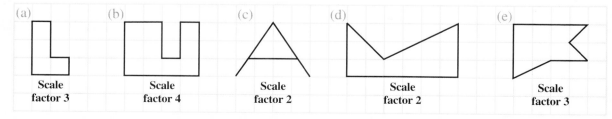

(a) Scale factor 3

(b) Scale factor 4

(c) Scale factor 2

(d) Scale factor 2

(e) Scale factor 3

2 Copy each diagram onto squared paper and draw an enlargement with the given scale factor.

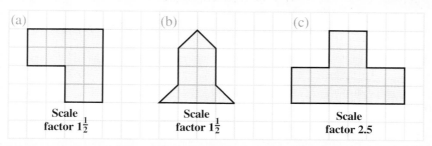

(a)

Scale
factor $1\frac{1}{2}$

(b)

Scale
factor $1\frac{1}{2}$

(c)

Scale
factor 2.5

Using a centre of enlargement

A slide projector makes an enlargement of a picture.
The light bulb is the **centre of enlargement.**

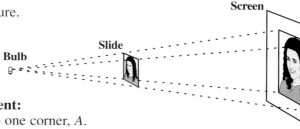

Screen

Slide

Bulb

To enlarge a shape using a centre of enlargement:
Draw a line from the centre of enlargement, P, to one corner, A.
Extend this line to A' so that the length of $PA' =$ the scale factor $\times$ the length of PA.
Do the same for other corners of the shape.
Join up the corners to make the enlarged shape.
Label the diagram.

EXAMPLES

1 Draw an enlargement of triangle ABC, centre P (0, 1) and scale factor 3.

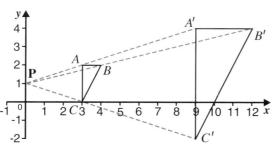

2 Use centre P (3, 2) and a scale factor of 2 to enlarge triangle ABC.

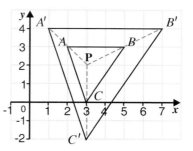

For each example:
Measure the lengths of PA and PA'.
Explain how the points A', B' and C' were found from the points A, B and C.
Check that the triangle has been enlarged by the correct scale factor.

To find the centre and scale factor of an enlargement:
Join pairs of corresponding points.
Extend the lines until they meet. This point is the centre of enlargement.
Measure a pair of corresponding lengths.

Scale factor $= \dfrac{\text{new length}}{\text{original length}}$

Enlargements and Similar Figures

EXAMPLE

Find the centre of enlargement and the scale factor when triangle XYZ becomes triangle $X'Y'Z'$.

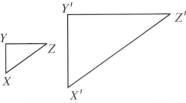

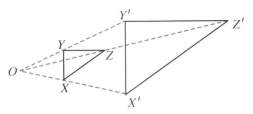

Scale factor $= \dfrac{X'Y'}{XY} = \dfrac{2.0}{0.8} = 2.5$

The centre of enlargement is the point O.

Exercise 27.2

1 Copy each diagram onto squared paper and enlarge it using the centre and scale factor given. You will need longer axes than those shown below.

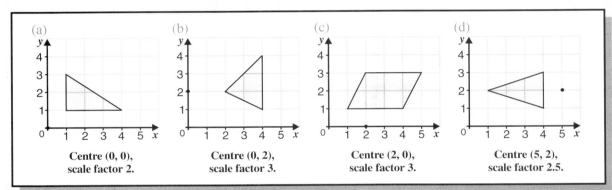

(a) **Centre (0, 0), scale factor 2.**

(b) **Centre (0, 2), scale factor 3.**

(c) **Centre (2, 0), scale factor 3.**

(d) **Centre (5, 2), scale factor 2.5.**

2 For each of the following diagrams find the scale factor and the coordinates of the centre of enlargement.

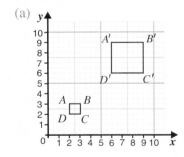

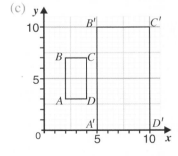

3 Copy these diagrams. For each diagram find the scale factor and mark the centre of enlargement.

(a)

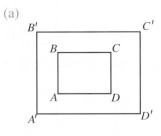

(b)

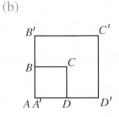

Using a scale factor which is a fraction

When the scale factor is a value between 0 and 1, such as 0.5 or $\frac{1}{3}$, the new shape is smaller than the original shape.

Even though the shape gets smaller it is still called an enlargement.

EXAMPLES

1 Draw an enlargement of this shape with centre (0, 1) and scale factor $\frac{1}{3}$.

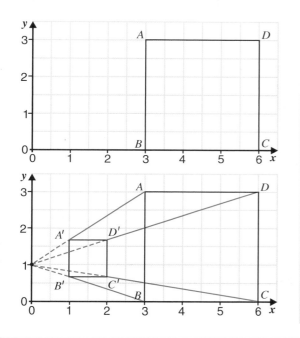

2 Draw an enlargement of this picture with scale factor $\frac{1}{2}$.

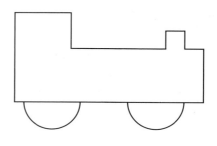

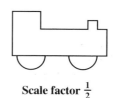

Scale factor $\frac{1}{2}$

Exercise 27.3

1 Copy each diagram onto squared paper and enlarge it with the centre and the scale factor given.

(a)
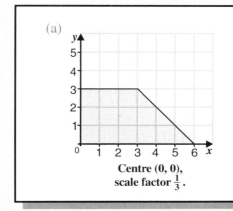

Centre (0, 0), scale factor $\frac{1}{3}$.

(b)
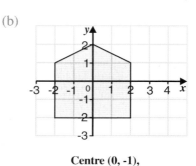

Centre (0, -1), scale factor $\frac{1}{2}$.

Enlargements and Similar Figures

2 Copy each diagram onto plain paper and enlarge it with the scale factor given.

(a)

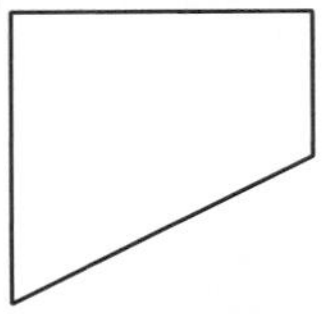

Scale factor $\frac{1}{2}$

(b)

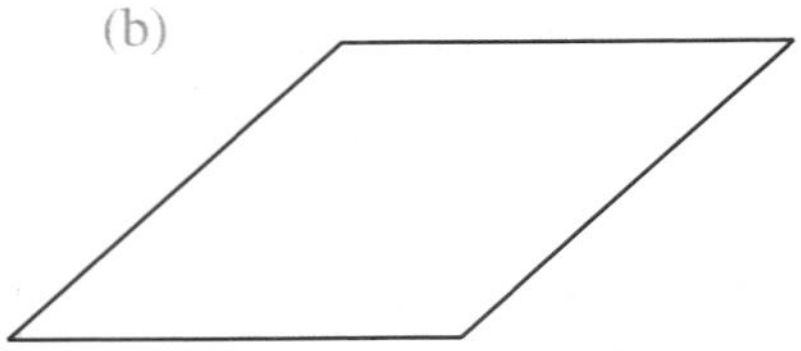

Scale factor $\frac{1}{3}$

(c)

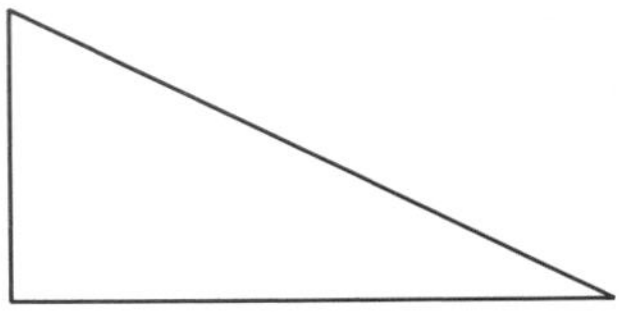

Scale factor 0.25

3 For each of the following diagrams give the centre of enlargement and the scale factor.

(a)

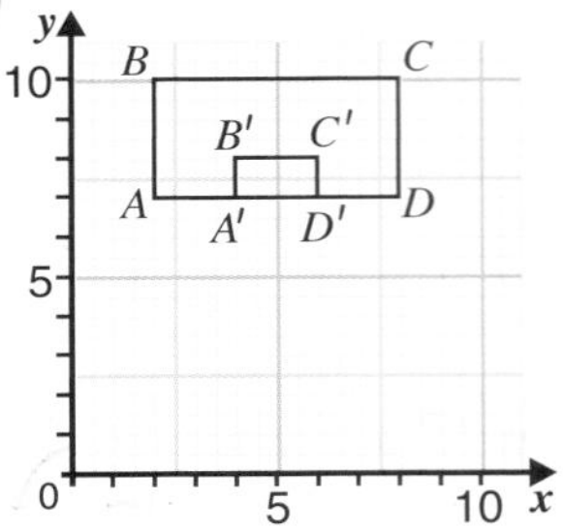

(b)

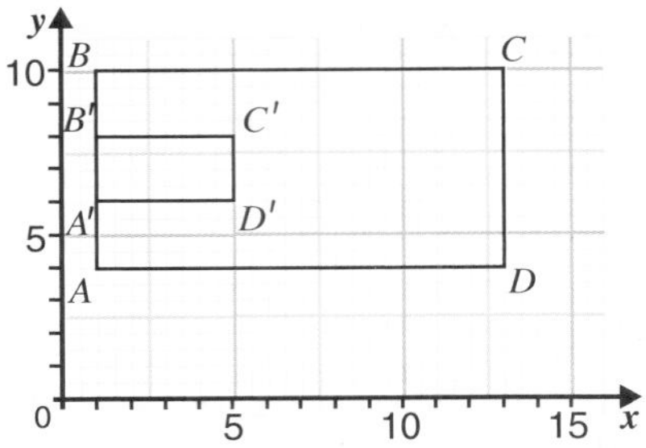

(c)

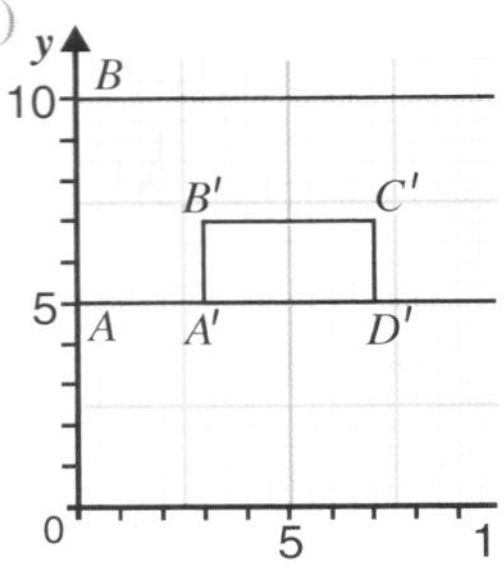

(d)

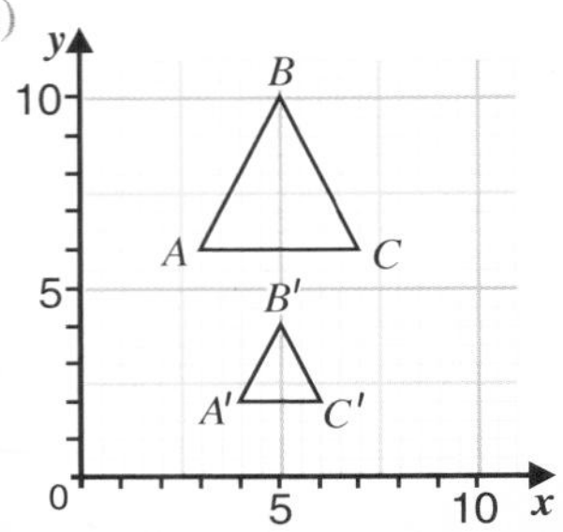

(e)

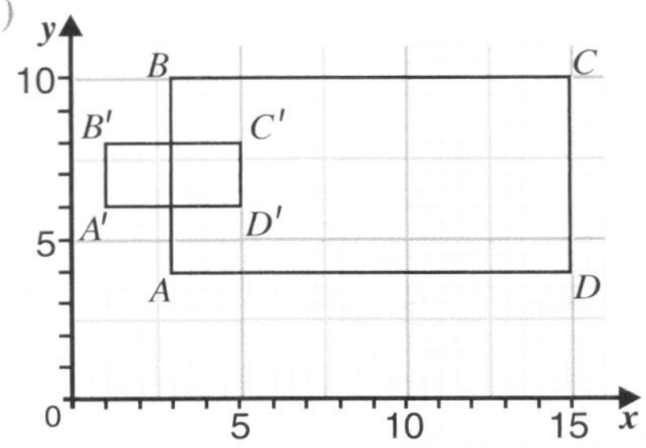

Similar figures

When one figure is an enlargement of another, the two figures are **similar**.

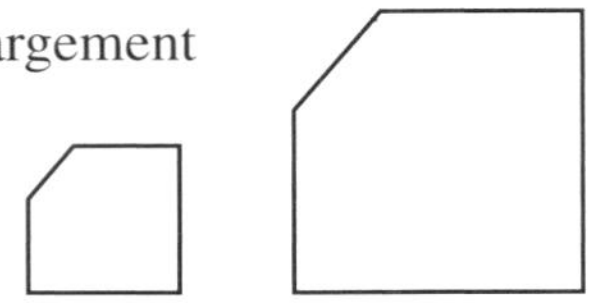

Sometimes one of the figures is rotated or reflected as well as enlarged. The two figures are still similar.

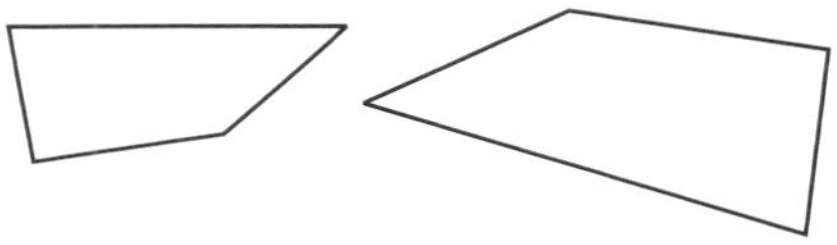

Three of these figures are similar. Which are they?

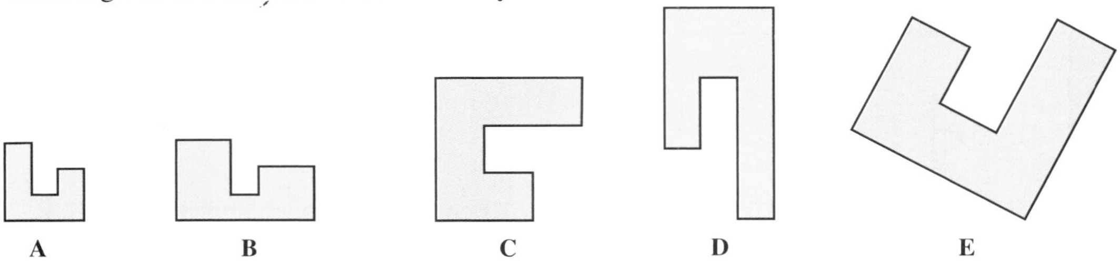

| A | B | C | D | E |

Figures C and E are enlargements of figure A.
Figures A, C and E are similar.

When two figures are **similar**:
their **shapes** are the same,
their **angles** are the same,
corresponding **lengths** are in the same ratio,
this ratio is the **scale factor** of the enlargement.

Activity

Figures X and Y are similar.
Y is an enlargement of X.
The ratio (or scale factor) is given

by $\dfrac{\text{new length}}{\text{original length}}$

Check that this ratio is the same for all four pairs
of corresponding sides.
Check that the angles are the same in the two figures.

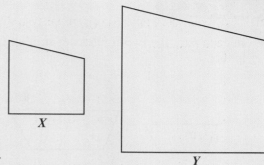

EXAMPLE

A photo has width 6 cm and height 10 cm.
An enlargement is made, which has width 8 cm.
Calculate the height of the enlargement.

There are two methods for working out questions like this.
Look at each method carefully and use the one you prefer.

Method 1
$\frac{h}{10} = \frac{8}{6}$
$h = \frac{8}{6} \times 10$
$h = 13.3$ cm, correct to 1 d.p.

Method 2
Scale factor $= \frac{8}{6}$
$h = 10 \times \frac{8}{6}$
$h = 13.3$ cm, correct to 1 d.p.

EXAMPLE

These two figures are similar.
Calculate the lengths of x and y.
Write down the size of the angle marked a.

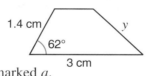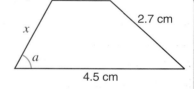

Method 1
Ratio of corresponding lengths
The corresponding sides are:

Small figure	Large figure
3	4.5
1.4	x
y	2.7

The corresponding sides are in the same
ratio, so:

$\frac{x}{1.4} = \frac{4.5}{3}$ $\frac{2.7}{y} = \frac{4.5}{3}$

$x = \frac{4.5}{3} \times 1.4$ $2.7 \times 3 = 4.5 \times y$

$x = 2.1$ cm $y = \frac{2.7 \times 3}{4.5}$

$\qquad\qquad\quad y = 1.8$ cm

Method 2
Scale factor method

The scale factor $= \frac{4.5}{3} = 1.5$

Lengths in the large figure are given by:
length in small figure $\times$ scale factor
$x = 1.4 \times 1.5$
$x = 2.1$ cm

Lengths in the small figure are given by:
length in large figure $\div$ scale factor
$y = 2.7 \div 1.5$
$y = 1.8$ cm

The size of the angle marked a.
The angles in similar figures are the same, so
$a = 62°$.

1 In each part, the two figures are similar. Calculate the lengths and angles marked with letters.

(a)

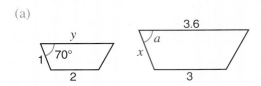

(b)

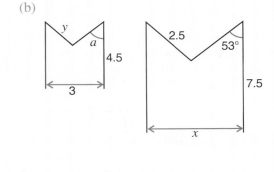

(c)

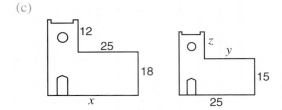

2 These two tubes are similar.

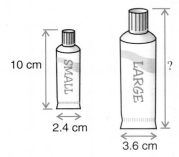

10 cm

2.4 cm

3.6 cm

The width of the small size is 2.4 cm and the height of the small size is 10 cm.
The width of the large size is 3.6 cm.
Calculate the height of the large size.

3 A shape has width 0.8 cm and length 2.4 cm. It is enlarged to give a new shape with width 1 cm. Calculate the length of the new shape.

4 A castle has height 30 m. The height of the castle wall is 6 m. A scale model of the castle has height 25 cm. Calculate the height of the castle wall in the scale model.

5 The dimensions of three sizes of paper are given.

Length (cm)	24	30	y
Width (cm)	x	20	32

All the sizes are similar.
Calculate the values of x and y.

Similar triangles

For any pair of similar triangles:
corresponding lengths are opposite equal angles,
the scale factor is the ratio of corresponding sides.

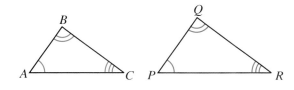

$$\frac{AB}{PQ} = \frac{BC}{QR} = \frac{CA}{RP} = \text{scale factor}$$

EXAMPLE

1 These two triangles are similar, with the equal angles marked.
Calculate the lengths x and y.

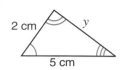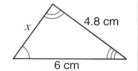

The corresponding sides are:

Small triangle	Large triangle
5	6
2	x
y	4.8

$\frac{x}{2} = \frac{6}{5}$
$x = \frac{6}{5} \times 2$
$x = 2.4 \text{ cm}$

$\frac{4.8}{y} = \frac{6}{5}$
$4.8 \times 5 = 6 \times y$
$y = 4.8 \times \frac{5}{6}$
$y = 4 \text{ cm}$

Alternative method
Scale factor $= \frac{6}{5} = 1.2$

$x = 2 \times 1.2$
$x = 2.4 \text{ cm}$

$y = 4.8 \div 1.2$
$y = 4 \text{ cm}$

EXAMPLE

2 Triangles ABC and PQR are similar. Calculate the lengths of AC and PQ.

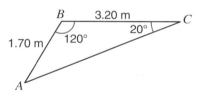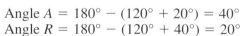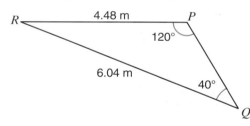

Angle $A = 180° - (120° + 20°) = 40°$
Angle $R = 180° - (120° + 40°) = 20°$

The corresponding sides are:

	Triangle ABC	Triangle PQR
Opposite 40°	3.20	4.48
Opposite 20°	1.70	PQ
Opposite 120°	AC	6.04

$\frac{6.04}{AC} = \frac{4.48}{3.20}$
$6.04 \times 3.20 = 4.48 \times AC$
$AC = \frac{6.04 \times 3.20}{4.48}$
$AC = 4.31 \text{ m}$, correct to 2 d.p.

$\frac{PQ}{1.70} = \frac{4.48}{3.20}$
$PQ = \frac{4.48}{3.20} \times 1.70$
$PQ = 2.38\text{m}$

Alternative method
Scale factor $= \frac{4.48}{3.20} = 1.4$

$AC = 6.04 \div 1.4$
$AC = 4.31 \text{ m}$, correct to 2 d.p.

$PQ = 1.70 \times 1.4$
$PQ = 2.38 \text{ m}$

Question 1 should be done without a calculator.

1 In each part, the triangles are similar, with equal angles marked. Calculate lengths x and y.

(a)

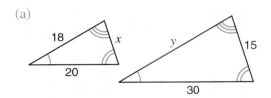

(b)

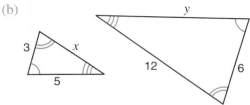

(c)

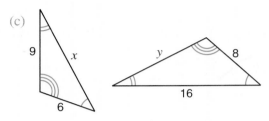

(d)

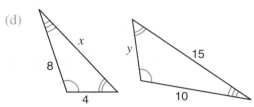

2 In each part the triangles are similar. Calculate the unknown lengths in both triangles.

(a)

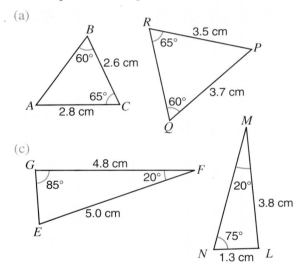

(b)

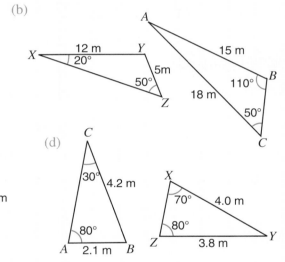

(c)

(d)

3 Triangles ABC and ADE are similar.
$\angle AED = \angle ACB$.

Calculate the lengths of AB and AE.

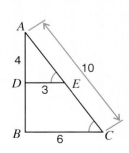

4 Triangles ABC and ADE are similar.
$\angle ADE = \angle ABC$.

(a) Write down the length of AB.
(b) Calculate the lengths BC and AC.
(c) What is the length of EC?

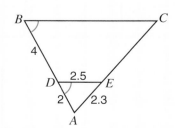

5 Triangles *PST* and *PQR* are similar.
∠*PTS* = ∠*PRQ*.

  (a) Write down the length of *PR*.
  (b) Calculate *QR*, *PQ* and *QS*.

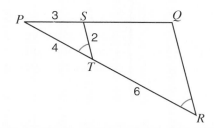

6 Triangles *DEF* and *DGH* are similar.
∠*DGH* = ∠*DEF*.

Calculate *GH* and *FH*.

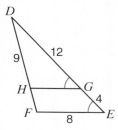

Showing that two triangles are similar

To show that two triangles are similar you have to show that:
    either   they have equal angles
    or   corresponding lengths are all in the same ratio.
If you can show that one of these conditions is true then the other one is also true.

EXAMPLE

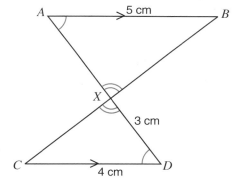

AB and *CD* are parallel lines. *AD* and *BC* meet at *X*.

(a) Prove that triangles *ABX* and *DCX* are similar.

(b) Which side in triangle *DCX* corresponds to *AX* in triangle *ABX*?

(c) Calculate the length of *AX*.

(a) ∠*BAX* = ∠*CDX* (alternate angles)
     ∠*AXB* = ∠*DXC* (vertically opposite angles)
     Triangles *ABX* and *DCX* contain two pairs of
     equal angles and so they are similar.

     *If two pairs of angles are equal then the third
     pair must be equal. Why?*

(b) ∠*ABX* = ∠*DCX*.
     Sides *AX* and *DX* are opposite these equal angles.
     So *DX* corresponds to *AX*.

(c) $\frac{AX}{3} = \frac{5}{4}$ (or scale factor $= \frac{5}{4}$)

     $AX = \frac{5}{4} \times 3$

     $AX = 3.75$ cm

> You **must** give reasons for any statements you make. Alternate angles, corresponding angles and vertically opposite angles were covered in Chapter 21.

EXAMPLE

Show that these two triangles are similar.

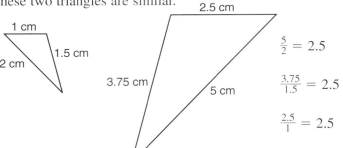

$\frac{5}{2} = 2.5$

$\frac{3.75}{1.5} = 2.5$

$\frac{2.5}{1} = 2.5$

All three pairs of corresponding sides are in the same ratio, so the triangles are similar.

Exercise 27.6

1 *BC* is parallel to *PQ*. Show that triangles *ABC* and *APQ* are similar and calculate the required lengths.

(a)

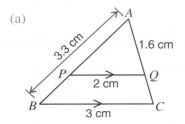

Calculate *AC* and *AP*.

(b)

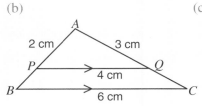

Calculate *AC* and *BP*.

(c)

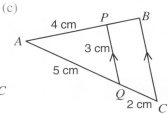

Calculate *BC* and *BP*.

(d)

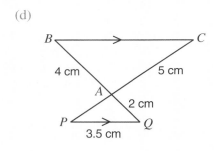

Calculate *AP* and *BC*.

(e)

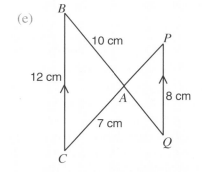

Calculate *AP* and *BQ*.

2 Show that these pairs of triangles are similar and find angle *x*.

(a)

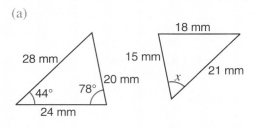

(b)

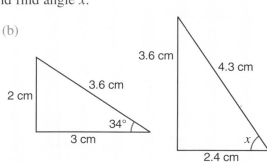

3 In each part show that triangles *ABC* and *APQ* are similar and find angle *x*.

(a)

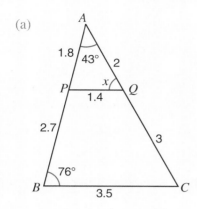

(b)

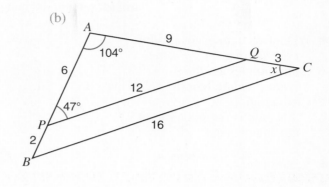

4 In each part explain why triangles *PQR* and *PYZ* are similar and calculate the required lengths.

(a)

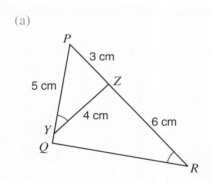

∠*PRQ* = ∠*PYZ*.
Calculate *QR* and *QY*.

(b)

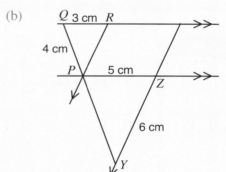

QR is parallel to *PZ* and
PR is parallel to *YZ*.
Calculate *PR* and *QY*.

(c)

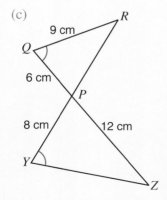

∠*PQR* = ∠*PYZ*.
Calculate *YZ* and *PR*.

(d)

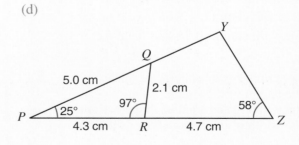

Calculate *YZ* and *QY*.

What you need to know

- When a shape is **enlarged**:   all **lengths** are multiplied by a **scale factor**,
                                    angles remain unchanged.

- When two figures are **similar**:
  their **shapes** are the same,
  their **angles** are the same,
  corresponding **lengths** are in the
  same ratio,
  this ratio is the **scale factor** of
  the enlargement.

- Scale factor $= \dfrac{\text{new length}}{\text{original length}}$

- For **similar triangles**:
  corresponding lengths are opposite
  equal angles,
  the scale factor is the ratio of the
  corresponding sides.

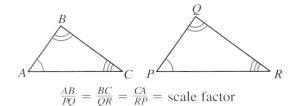

$\dfrac{AB}{PQ} = \dfrac{BC}{QR} = \dfrac{CA}{RP} =$ scale factor

Review Exercise

1 Draw and label an x axis from 0 to 12 and a y axis
from 0 to 6.
Enlarge the shape with scale factor 2 and centre $(0, 3)$.

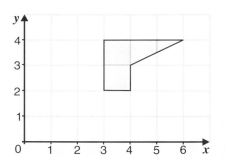

SEG 1997

2 Enlarge the shape in Question 1:
  (a) with centre $(2, 2)$ and scale factor 1.5,
  (b) with centre $(0, 0)$ and scale factor $\frac{1}{2}$.

3 Two similar solid shapes are made.
The height of the smaller shape is 7 cm.
The width of the smaller shape is 6 cm.
The width of the larger shape is 9.6 cm.

Calculate the height of the larger shape.

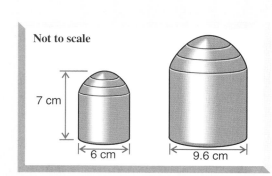

Not to scale

7 cm

6 cm

9.6 cm

SEG 2000 S

4 Two similar steam engines are cut out of a piece of card.

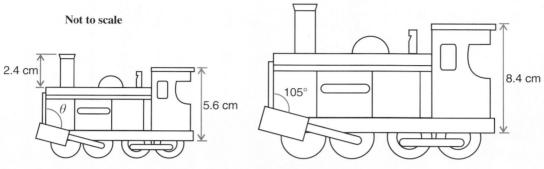

Not to scale

2.4 cm

5.6 cm

105°

8.4 cm

(a) Calculate the height of the funnel on the larger steam engine.
(b) The circumference of a wheel on the larger steam engine is 5.7 cm.
    Calculate the circumference of the same wheel on the smaller steam engine.
(c) What is the size of the angle marked θ on the smaller steam engine?

SEG 1994

5 These triangles are **similar**. They are **not** drawn accurately.
Angle A equals angle X.
Angle B equals angle Y.

Calculate the length of XY.

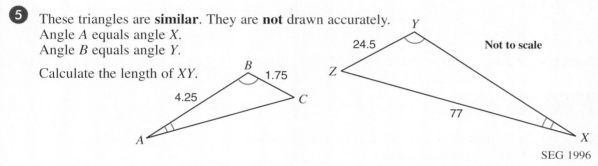

Not to scale

SEG 1996

6 All of these triangles are similar.

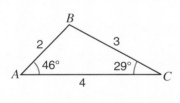

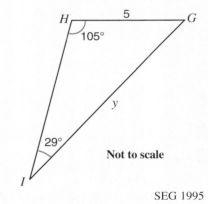

(a) Calculate the length x.
(b) Calculate the length y.
(c) What is the value of angle z?

Not to scale

SEG 1995

7 Duncan wants to measure the height of a tree.
He places a vertical stick of length 1.5 metres on level ground 100 metres from
the base of the tree.
The lengths of the shadows of the tree and the stick are 102.4 metres
and 2.4 metres respectively.

Calculate the height of the tree.

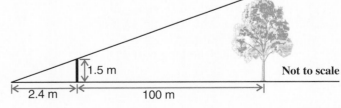

1.5 m

2.4 m

100 m

Not to scale

SEG 1994

8 The triangles *ABE* and *CDE* are **similar**.
Line *AB* is parallel to line *DC*.
Calculate the length of *AB*.

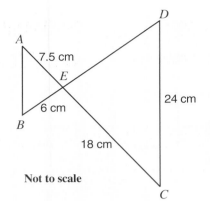

Not to scale

SEG 1995

9 The diagram shows a triangle *ABC*.
DE is parallel to *BC*.
Calculate the lengths
(a) *DE*,
(b) *AC*.

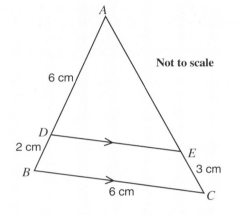

Not to scale

SEG 1997

10 State whether or not the triangles
ABC and *XYZ* below are similar.
Show working to support
your answer.

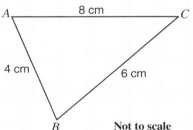
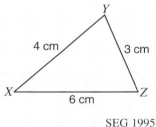

Not to scale

SEG 1995

11 (a) The logo shown is to be enlarged for a
new poster.
The distance *AB* is 3 cm on the original
shape.
On the enlarged shape *AB* is 13.5 cm
and *BC* is 7.8 cm.
What is the distance *BC* on the original
shape?

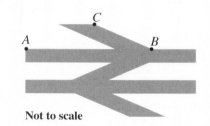

Not to scale

(b) In the diagram *AB* = 3 cm, *BC* = 2 cm
and *AE* = 2 cm.
Angles *AEB* and *ACD* are equal.
(i) Explain why triangle *ABE* is
similar to triangle *ADC*.
(ii) Calculate the length of *ED*.

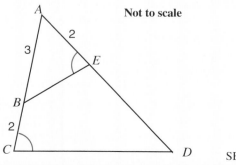

Not to scale

SEG 1996

3-dimensional shapes (or solids)

These are all examples of 3-dimensional shapes.

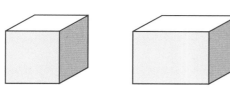

Cube   **Cuboid**

Cylinder

Sphere

Triangular prism

Pyramid with square base

Cone

What other 3-dimensional shapes do you know?

Making and drawing 3-dimensional shapes

Nets

3-dimensional shapes can be made using **nets**.

This is the net of a cube.

The net can be folded to make a cube.

 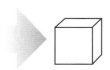

There are 12 different nets which can be used to make a cube. See how many of them you can draw.

This is a **cuboid**.

Draw an accurate net which can be used to make the cuboid.

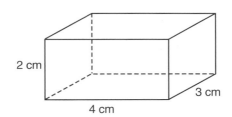

2 cm

3 cm

4 cm

2-dimensional drawings of 3-dimensional shapes

Isometric drawings are used to draw 3-dimensional shapes.
Here are two isometric drawings of a cube of side 2 cm.

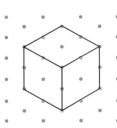

Exercise **28.1**

1 The diagram shows part of a net of a cube.

(a) In how many different ways can you complete the net?
Draw each of your nets.

(b) Explain why the diagram above is **not** the net of a cube.

2 Draw an accurate net for each of these 3-dimensional shapes.

(a)
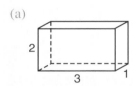

(b)
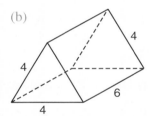

(c)
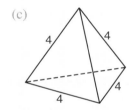

(d)
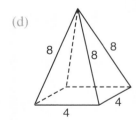

(e)
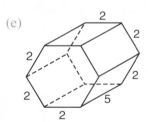

(f)
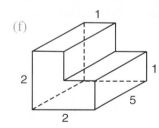

3 Draw these 3-dimensional shapes on isometric paper.
(a) (i) A cube of side 3 cm.
    (ii) A 3 cm by 2 cm by 1 cm cuboid.
    (iii) A 3 cm by 4 cm by 5 cm cuboid.
(b) Draw a net for each of the 3-dimensional shapes.

4 There are 8 different 3-dimensional shapes which can be made using 4 linking cubes.
One of them is shown.

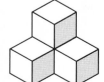

(a) Make all the 3-dimensional shapes using linking cubes.
(b) Draw the 3-dimensional shapes on isometric paper.
(c) Sketch a net for each of the 3-dimensional shapes.

Volume

Volume is the amount of space occupied by a three-dimensional shape.

This **cube** is 1 cm long, 1 cm wide and 1 cm high.
It has a volume of **1 cubic centimetre**.
The volume of this cube can be written as 1 cm³.

Volume = 1 cm³

Small volumes can be measured using cubic millimetres (mm³).
Large volumes can be measured using cubic metres (m³).

Activity

This **cuboid** is made using 24 one-centimetre cubes.

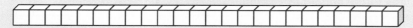

A cuboid made from 24 one-centimetre cubes has a volume of 24 cm³.

What other different cuboids can you make with 24 cubes? (There are 5 others.)
How many different cuboids can you make with 36 cubes?

How many one-centimetre cubes are used to make each of these cuboids?

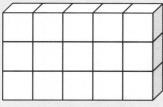

Cuboid A

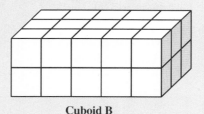

Cuboid B

15 cubes are used to make cuboid A.
Notice that there are 5 cubes on the bottom
layer. $5 \times 1 = 5$.
There are three layers. $5 \times 1 \times 3 = 15$.

24 cubes are used to make cuboid B.
Notice that there are 12 cubes on the bottom
layer. $4 \times 3 = 12$.
There are two layers. $4 \times 3 \times 2 = 24$.

Volume of a cuboid

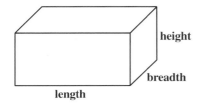

height
breadth
length

The formula for the volume of a cuboid is:
    Volume = length × breadth × height

This formula can be written using letters as:
    $V = l \times b \times h$

Volume of a cube
A cube is a special cuboid in which the
length, breadth and height all have the
same measurement.
Volume = length × length × length
$V = l^3$

EXAMPLE

Find the volume of a cuboid measuring 30 cm by 15 cm by 12 cm.
    Volume   = length × breadth × height
          = 30 cm × 15 cm × 12 cm
          = 5400 cm³

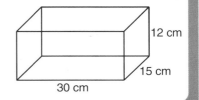

12 cm
15 cm
30 cm

Surface area of a cuboid

To find the surface area of a cuboid find the area of the
six rectangular faces and add the answers together.
Opposite faces of a cuboid are the same shape and size.

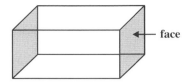

face

EXAMPLE

Find the surface area of the cuboid in Example 1.

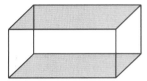

Top and bottom faces.
Each 30 cm × 15 cm.

Two side faces.
Each 15 cm × 12 cm.

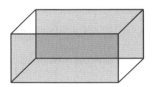

Front and back faces.
Each 30 cm × 12 cm.

Surface area = $(2 \times 30 \times 15) + (2 \times 15 \times 12) + (2 \times 30 \times 12)$
$= 900 + 360 + 720$
$= 1980 \text{ cm}^2$

Remember
The area of a rectangle is given by
the formula:
Area = length × breadth
$A = l \times b$

Exercise 28.2

You should be able to do questions 1 and 2 without using a calculator.
Having completed them you can use your calculator to check your answers.

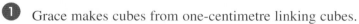

1 Grace makes cubes from one-centimetre linking cubes.
(a) How many small cubes are in each of the large cubes?
(b) What is the surface area of each large cube?

(iv)

(iii)

(ii)

(i)

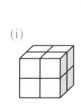 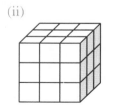 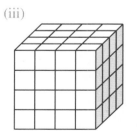 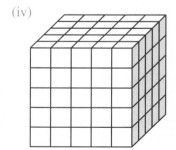

2 Calculate the volumes and surface areas of these cubes and cuboids.

(a)

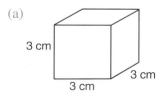

3 cm
3 cm
3 cm

(b)

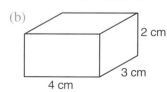

2 cm
3 cm
4 cm

(c)

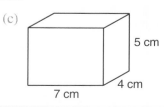

5 cm
4 cm
7 cm

308

3 Calculate the volumes and surface areas of these cuboids.
Where necessary give your answer to an appropriate degree of accuracy.
  (a) 3 cm by 5 cm by 10 cm.
  (b) 2.4 cm by 3.6 cm by 6 cm.
  (c) 18 cm by 24 cm by 45 cm.
  (d) 3.2 cm by 4.8 cm by 6.3 cm.
  (e) 5.8 cm by 10.6 cm by 14.9 cm.

Prisms

These shapes are all **prisms**.
What do these 3-dimensional shapes have in common?

 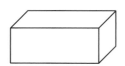  

You should have noticed that a **prism** has the same **cross-section** throughout its length.
If you make a cut at right angles to the length of a prism you will always get the same cross-section.

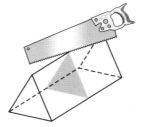

Explain why these shapes are not prisms.

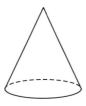  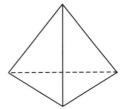

Volume of a prism

The formula for the volume of a prism is:
  Volume = area of cross-section × length.

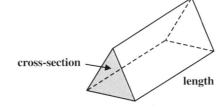

cross-section
length

Cylinder

A **cylinder** is a prism.
The **volume of a cylinder** can be written as:
Volume = area of cross-section × height
$$V = \pi r^2 \times h$$

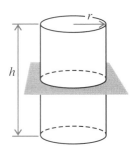

Remember
The area of a circle is given by the formula:
$$A = \pi r^2$$

Notice that length has been replaced by height.
Why is it more appropriate to use height instead of length?

EXAMPLES

Find the volumes of these prisms.

(a)

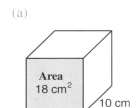

(b)

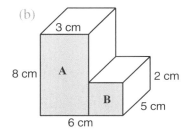

(c)

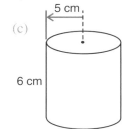

Volume = area of cross-
section × length
= 18 × 10
= 180 cm³

Area A = 8 × 3 = 24 cm²
Area B = 3 × 2 = 6 cm²
Total area = 30 cm²
Volume = 30 × 5 = 150 cm³

$V = \pi \times r^2 \times h$
= $\pi \times 5^2 \times 6$
= 471.238 …
= 471 cm³, correct to 3 s.f.

Exercise **28.3**

You should be able to do questions 1 and 2 without using a calculator.
Having completed these questions you can use your calculator to check your answers.

1 Find the volumes of these prisms.

(a)

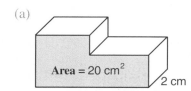
Area = 20 cm²
2 cm

(b)

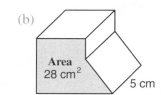
Area
28 cm²
5 cm

(c)

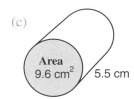
Area
9.6 cm²
5.5 cm

2 Calculate the shaded areas and the volumes of these prisms.

(a)

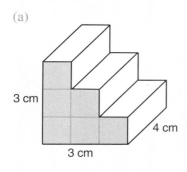

(b)

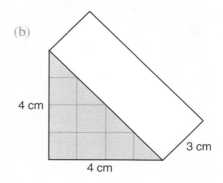

Questions 3 to 8.
Where necessary take π to be 3.14 or use the π key on your calculator.

3 Find the volumes of these prisms.

(a)
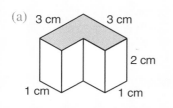

(b)
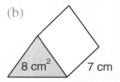

(c)
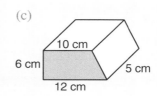

(d)
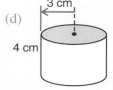

(e)
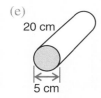

(f)
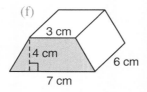

(g)
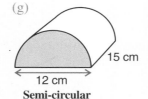

Semi-circular
cross-section

(h)
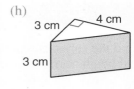

4 Which tin holds more cat food?

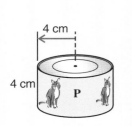

5 A cuboid has a volume of 76.8 cm³.
The length of the cuboid is 3.2 cm.
The breadth of the cuboid is 2.4 cm.
What is the height of the cuboid?

6 A cuboid has a square base of side
3.6 cm.
The volume of the cuboid is 58.32 cm³.
Calculate the height of the cuboid.

7 The radius of a cylinder is 5 cm.
It has a volume of 900 cm³.
Calculate the height of the cylinder,
giving your answer correct to
1 decimal place.

8 A cylinder is 8 cm high. It has a volume
of 183 cm³.
Calculate the radius of the cylinder
correct to 1 decimal place.

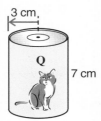

Surface area of a cylinder

The top and bottom of a cylinder are circles.
The curved surface of a cylinder is a rectangle.

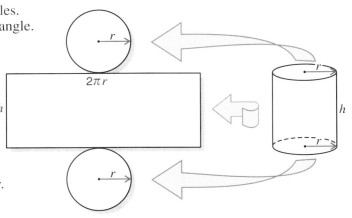

The rectangle has the same height, h, as the cylinder.
The length of the rectangle must be just long enough to "wrap around" the circle.
The lid of the cylinder has radius r and circumference $2\pi r$.
So the length of the rectangle is also $2\pi r$.

Area of lid $= \pi r^2$
Area of base $= \pi r^2$
Area of lid and base $= 2\pi r^2$

Area of rectangle $=$ length $\times$ breadth
$= 2\pi r \times h$
$= 2\pi rh$

If a cylinder has radius, r, and height, h, then the formula for the surface area is:

$$\text{Surface area} = 2\pi r^2 + 2\pi rh$$

Area of the top and bottom   Area of the rectangle

The formula for the surface area is sometimes given as:
Surface area $= 2\pi r(r + h)$

EXAMPLE

Find the surface area of a cylinder with radius 4 cm and height 6 cm. Take π to be 3.14.

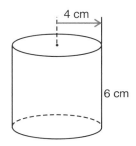

Area $= 2\pi rh + 2\pi r^2$
$= 2 \times 3.14 \times 4 \times 6 + 2 \times 3.14 \times 4^2$
$= 150.72 + 100.48$
$= 251.2 \text{ cm}^2$

Exercise 28.4

Take π to be 3.14 or use the π key on your calculator.

1 Find the surface areas of these cylinders.

(a)
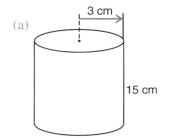

(b)
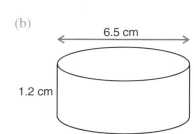

2 Show that the curved surface area of this can is approximately 75 cm².

3 A bucket is in the shape of a cylinder.

(a) Calculate the area of the bottom of the bucket.
(b) Calculate the curved surface area of the bucket.
(c) What is the volume of the bucket?

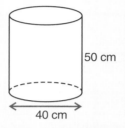

4 A concrete pipe is 150 cm long. It has an internal radius of 15 cm and an external radius of 20 cm.

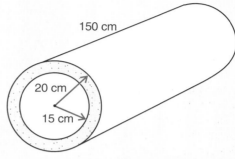

Calculate, giving your answers to 3 significant figures,
(a) the area of the curved surface inside of the pipe,
(b) the curved surface area of the outside of the pipe.

What you need to know

- **Faces**, **vertices** (corners) and **edges**.
  For example, a cube has 6 faces, 8 vertices and 12 edges.

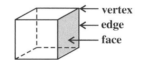

- A **net** can be used to make a solid shape.

- **Isometric paper** is used to make 2-dimensional drawings of 3-dimensional shapes.

- Volume is the amount of space occupied by a 3-dimensional shape.

- The formula for the volume of a **cuboid** is:
  Volume = length × breadth × height
  $$V = l \times b \times h$$

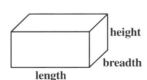

- Volume of a **cube** is:
  Volume = (length)³
  $$V = l^3$$

- To find the **surface area** of a cuboid find the area of the six rectangular faces and add the answers together.

- If you make a cut at right angles to the length of a **prism** you will always get the same cross-section.

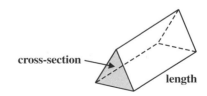

- Volume of a prism = area of cross-section × length

- A **cylinder** is a prism.
  Volume of a cylinder is:
  $$V = \pi \times r^2 \times h$$

  Surface area of a cylinder is:
  Surface area = $2\pi r^2 + 2\pi r h$

(a) Copy and complete the table below for these 3-dimensional shapes.

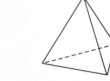

Triangular pyramid or tetrahedron

Triangular prism

Cube

Octahedron

Pyramid with square base

Name	Number of faces	Number of vertices	Number of edges
cube	6	8	12
tetrahedron	4		
triangular prism		6	
square based pyramid			8
octohedron	8		

(b) Investigate the relationship between the number of faces, vertices and edges of 3-dimensional shapes.

Review Exercise

In this exercise take π to be 3.14 or use the π key on your calculator.

1 The net of a triangular prism is shown.

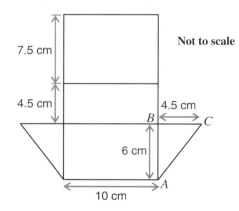

Not to scale

7.5 cm

4.5 cm

4.5 cm

B ↔ C

6 cm

10 cm

A

(a) Triangle ABC is right-angled. Calculate the area of the net.

(b) Use a ruler and protractor to make an accurate drawing of triangle ABC. Label your diagram.

SEG 1997

2 The diagram shows a square based pyramid.

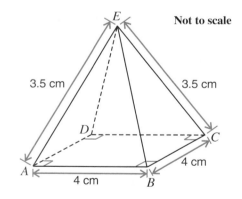

Not to scale

E

3.5 cm   3.5 cm

D C

A 4 cm B

4 cm

(a) Draw a **sketch** of a net for a square based pyramid.

(b) (i) Make an accurate drawing of triangle EBC.
(ii) Use your drawing to measure and write down the size of angle EBC.

SEG 1997

314

3 The diagram shows the blocks on which medal winners stand.

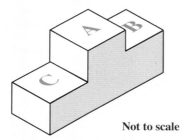

Not to scale

Each block is 1.2 m wide and 1.2 m deep. Block A is 1.4 m high, block B is 1.1 m high and block C is 0.8 m high. Work out the volume of all three blocks together.

SEG 1996

4 (a) Find the area of this rectangle.

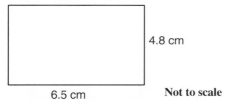

4.8 cm

6.5 cm   Not to scale

(b) Find the volume of this solid.

Not to scale

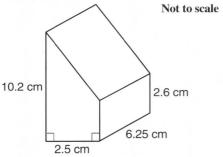

10.2 cm

2.6 cm

6.25 cm

2.5 cm

SEG 1996

5 A circular cable is 100 cm long with a radius of 2.5 cm.

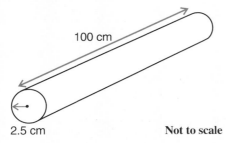

100 cm

2.5 cm   Not to scale

(a) What is the area of the circular end?
(b) What is the volume of the cable?

SEG 1994

6 The diagram shows triangle *ABC* with dimensions as shown.

Not to scale

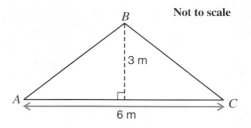

B

3 m

A   6 m   *C*

(a) Calculate the area of triangle *ABC*.

The roof of a warehouse is a triangular prism with dimensions as shown. The roof space is used for storage.

Not to scale

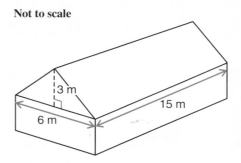

3 m

6 m

15 m

(b) Calculate the volume of storage space in the roof.

SEG 1994

7 To feed a lawn, one box of fertilizer is needed for every 9 m².
(a) How many boxes are needed to fertilize a circular lawn of radius 4 m?

The fertilizer is also sold in cylindrical drums.

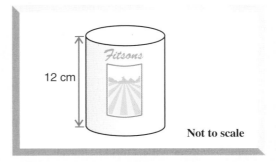

12 cm

Fitsons

Not to scale

The volume of a drum is 3060 cm³. The height of a drum is 12 cm.
(b) Calculate the radius of a drum.

SEG 2000 S

8 Tomato soup is sold in cylindrical tins. Each tin has a base radius of 3.5 cm and a height of 12 cm.

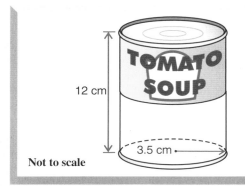

12 cm

3.5 cm

Not to scale

(a) Calculate the volume of soup in a full tin.

(b) Mark has a full tin of tomato soup for dinner. He pours the soup into a cylindrical bowl of radius 7 cm.

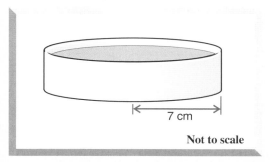

7 cm

Not to scale

What is the depth of the soup in the bowl?

SEG 1994

9 The diagram shows a cuboid which is just big enough to hold six tennis balls.

Not to scale

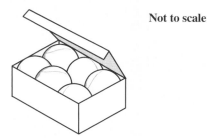

Each tennis ball has a diameter of 6.8 cm.

Calculate the volume of the cuboid.

SEG 1998

10 This loaf of bread is cut into 30 slices, as shown.

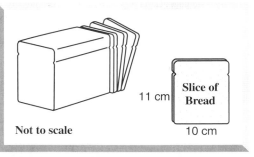

11 cm

Slice of Bread

10 cm

Not to scale

Each slice is approximately the shape of a cuboid of width 10 cm, length 11 cm and depth 8 mm.

(a) Calculate the volume of the loaf in cubic centimetres.

The same volume of bread is used to make a round loaf of length 24 cm.

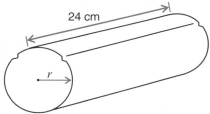

24 cm

r

Not to scale

(b) What is the radius of the round loaf?

SEG 1994

11 The diagram shows the uniform cross-section of a rubbish skip.

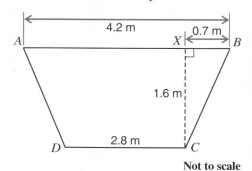

4.2 m

0.7 m

A   X   B

1.6 m

D   2.8 m   C

Not to scale

The cross-section is a trapezium. $AB = 4.2$ m, $CD = 2.8$ m, $XB = 0.7$ m and the height $CX = 1.6$ m.

(a) Calculate the size of angle XBC. The skip is 1.8 m wide.

(b) Calculate the volume of the skip, stating your units.

SEG 1998

CHAPTER 29

Pythagoras' Theorem

The longest side in a right-angled triangle is called the hypotenuse.

In any right-angled triangle it can be proved that:
   "The square on the hypotenuse is equal to the
   sum of the squares on the other two sides."

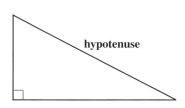

This is known as the **Theorem of Pythagoras**, or **Pythagoras' Theorem**.

Checking the Theorem of Pythagoras

Look at this triangle.

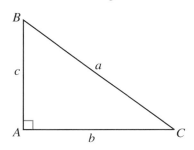

Notice that: the side opposite angle A is labelled a,
            the side opposite angle B is labelled b,
            the side opposite angle C is labelled c.

ABC is a right-angled triangle because $\angle BAC = 90°$.
   $a = 5\,\text{cm}$, so $a^2 = 25\,\text{cm}^2$.
   $b = 4\,\text{cm}$, so $b^2 = 16\,\text{cm}^2$.
   $c = 3\,\text{cm}$, so $c^2 = 9\,\text{cm}^2$.

$$a^2 = b^2 + c^2$$

Activity

Use a ruler and a pair of compasses to draw the following triangles accurately.

(a)
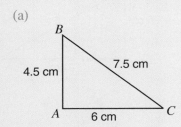

(b)
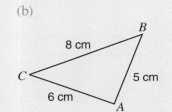

(c)
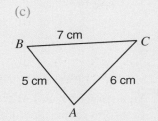

(d)
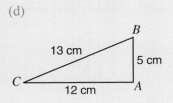

(e)
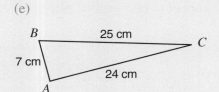

(f)
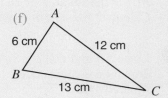

For each triangle: Measure angle BAC.
            Is angle $BAC = 90°$?
            Does $a^2 = b^2 + c^2$?
Explain your answers.

When we know the lengths of two sides of a right-angled triangle, we can use the Theorem of Pythagoras to find the length of the third side.

Finding the hypotenuse

EXAMPLE

The roof of a house is 12 m above the ground. What length of ladder is needed to reach the roof, if the foot of the ladder has to be placed 5 m away from the wall of the house?

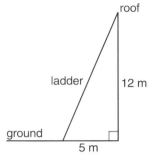

Using Pythagoras' Theorem.
$$l^2 = 5^2 + 12^2$$
$$l^2 = 25 + 144$$
$$l^2 = 169.$$

Take the square root of both sides.
$$l = \sqrt{169}$$
$$l = 13\,\text{m}$$

The ladder needs to be 13 m long.

Exercise 29.1

1 These triangles are right-angled.
Calculate the length of the hypotenuse.

(a)

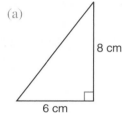

(b)

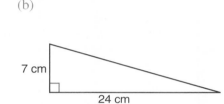

(c)

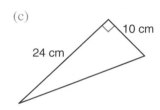

2 These triangles are right-angled.
Calculate the length of side a to one decimal place.

(a)

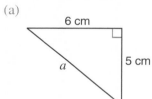

(b)

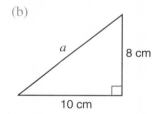

(c)

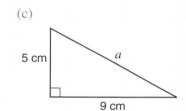

3 Squares $ABXY$ and $ACPQ$ are drawn on the sides AB and AC of a right-angled triangle ABC, as shown.
$ABXY$ has an area of 24.5 cm².
$ACPQ$ has an area of 28.8 cm².
Calculate the length of BC, correct to one decimal place.

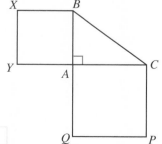

4 Lines AB and CD are drawn on a centimetre-squared grid.
Calculate the length of
(a) AB, and (b) CD.

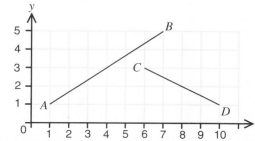

Finding one of the shorter sides

To find one of the shorter sides we can rearrange the Theorem of Pythagoras.

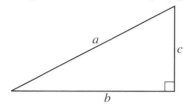

To find b we use: To find c we use:
$b^2 = a^2 - c^2$ $c^2 = a^2 - b^2$

To find the length of a shorter side of a right-angled triangle: Subtract the square of the known short side from the square on the hypotenuse. Take the square root of the result.

EXAMPLE

A wire used to keep a radio aerial steady is 9 metres long. The wire is fixed to the ground 4.6 metres from the base of the aerial. Find the height of the aerial, giving your answer correct to one decimal place.

Using Pythagoras' Theorem
$$9^2 = h^2 + 4.6^2$$
Rearranging this we get:
$$h^2 = 9^2 - 4.6^2$$
$$h^2 = 81 - 21.16$$
$$h^2 = 59.84$$
Take the square root of both sides.
$$h = \sqrt{59.84}$$
$$h = 7.735\ldots$$
$$h = 7.7\,\text{m, correct to 1 d.p.}$$

The height of the aerial is 7.7 m, correct to 1 d.p.

Exercise 29.2

1 Work out the length of side b.

(a)

(b)

(c)

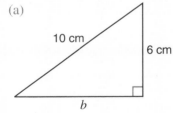
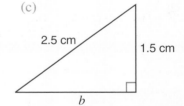

2 Work out the length of side c, correct to one decimal place.

(a)

(b)

(c)

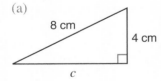
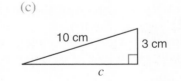

3 Two boats A and B are 360 m apart. Boat A is 120 m due east of a buoy. Boat B is due north of the buoy. How far is boat B from the buoy?

4 The diagram shows a right-angled triangle, *ABC*, and a square, *ACDE*.

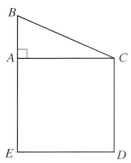

$AB = 2.5$ cm and $BC = 6.5$ cm.
Calculate the area of the square *ACDE*.

5 The diagram shows a right-angled triangle, *ABC*, and a square, *XYBA*.

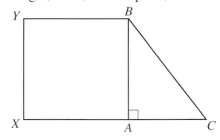

$BC = 6$ cm.
The square *XYBA* has an area of 23.04 cm².
Calculate the length of *AC*.

Problems involving the use of Pythagoras' Theorem

Questions leading to the use of Pythagoras' Theorem often involve:
Understanding the problem.
> What information is given?
> What are you required to find?

Drawing diagrams.
> In some questions a diagram is not given.
> Drawing a diagram may help you to understand the problem.

Selecting a suitable right-angled triangle.
> In more complex problems you will have to select a right-angled triangle which can be used to answer the question. It is good a idea to draw this triangle on its own, especially if it has been taken from a three-dimensional drawing.

EXAMPLE

The diagram shows the side view of a swimming pool.
It slopes steadily from a depth of 1 m to 3.6 m.
The pool is 20 m long.
Find the length of the sloping bottom of the pool,
giving the answer correct to three significant figures.

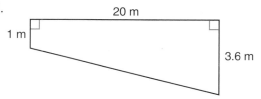

ΔCDE is a suitable right-angled triangle.
$CD = 3.6 - 1 = 2.6$ m

Using Pythagoras' Theorem in ΔFGH.
$DE^2 = CD^2 + CE^2$
$DE^2 = 2.6^2 + 20^2$
$DE^2 = 6.76 + 400$
$DE^2 = 406.76$
$DE = \sqrt{406.76}$ m
$DE = 20.1682 \ldots$ m
The length of the sloping bottom of the pool is 20.2 m, correct to 3 sig. figs.

Exercise 29.3

1 In each of the following, work out the length of the side marked x.

(a)

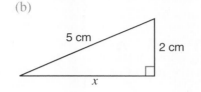

5 cm, x, 8 cm

(b)

5 cm, 2 cm, x

(c)

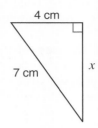

4 cm, 7 cm, x

(d)

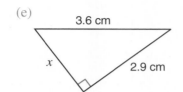

x, 2.4 cm, 1.7 cm

(e)

3.6 cm, x, 2.9 cm

(f)

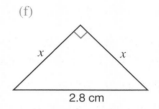

x, x, 2.8 cm

2 A rectangle is 8 cm wide and 15 cm long.
Work out the length of its diagonals.

3 The length of a rectangle is 24 cm. The diagonals of the rectangle are 26 cm.
Work out the width of the rectangle.

4 A square has sides of length 6 cm. Work out the length of its diagonals.

5 The diagonals of a square are 15 cm. Work out the length of its sides.

6 The height of an isosceles triangle is 12 cm. The base of the triangle is 18 cm.
Work out the length of the equal sides.

7 An equilateral triangle has sides of length 8 cm.
Work out the height of the triangle.

8 The diagram shows the side view of a car ramp.
The ramp is 110 cm long and 25 cm high.
The top part of the ramp is 40 cm long.
Calculate the length of the sloping part of the ramp.

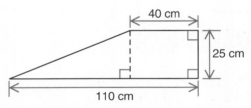

40 cm, 25 cm, 110 cm

9 The top of a lampshade has a diameter of 10 cm.
The bottom of the lampshade has a diameter of 20 cm.
The height of the lampshade is 12 cm.
Calculate the length, l, of the sloping sides.

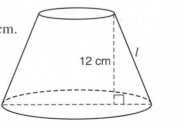

12 cm, l

10

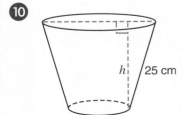

h, 25 cm

The top of a bucket has a diameter of 30 cm.
The bottom of the bucket has a diameter of 16 cm.
The sloping sides are 25 cm long.
How deep is the bucket?

What you need to know

- The longest side in a right-angled triangle is called the **hypotenuse**.

- The **Theorem of Pythagoras** states:
  "In any right-angled triangle the square on the hypotenuse is equal to the sum of the squares on the other two sides."

  $a^2 = b^2 + c^2$
  Rearranging gives:
  $b^2 = a^2 - c^2$
  $c^2 = a^2 - b^2$

- When we know the lengths of two sides of a right-angled triangle, we can use the Theorem of Pythagoras to find the length of the third side.

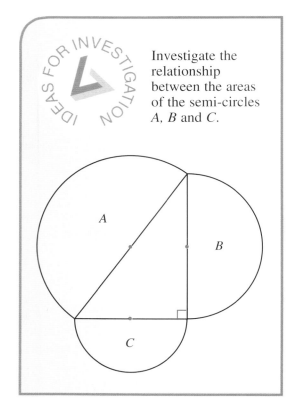

Investigate the relationship between the areas of the semi-circles A, B and C.

Review Exercise

1 Pauline is building a greenhouse.
The base, *PQRS* of the greenhouse should be a rectangle measuring 2.6 m by 1.4 m.

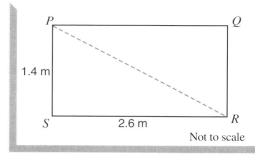

Not to scale

To check the base is rectangular Pauline has to measure the diagonal *PR*.

(a) Calculate the length of *PR* when the base is rectangular.

(b) When building the greenhouse Pauline finds angle *PSR* $>90°$.
She measures *PR*.
Which of the following statements is **true**?

X: *PR* is greater than it should be.
Y: *PR* is less than it should be.
Z: *PR* is the right length.

SEG 1995

2 The diagram shows the position of a ferry sailing between Folkestone and Calais.

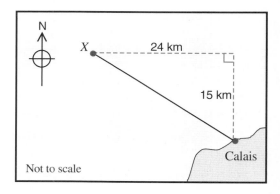

Not to scale

The ferry is at *X*.
The position of the ferry from Calais is given as:

North of Calais 15 km,
West of Calais 24 km.

Calculate the distance of the ferry from Calais.
Give your answer correct to **one** decimal place.

SEG 1997

322

3 James plans a game.
He hides objects at X, Y and Z and marks the positions on a plan.
The plan has been drawn using a scale of 1 cm to 100 m.

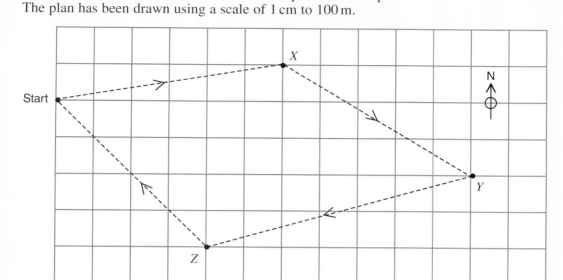

Calculate the distance a competitor must walk from Y to Z.
Give your answer to the nearest metre.

SEG 1996

4 Triangle PQR has dimensions as shown.

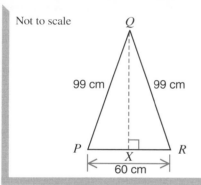

Calculate the height of QX.

5 This shape is a regular hexagon of side 12 cm.

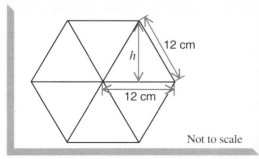

Calculate the height marked h.

6 The diagram shows a regular hexagon ABCDEF and a square DEGH.

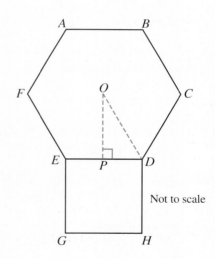

Not to scale

The hexagon has a perimeter of 48 cm.

(a) Calculate the area of the square.

(b) The centre of the hexagon is O and OD = 8 cm.
P is the midpoint of ED.
Calculate the distance OP.
You **must** show all your working.

SEG 1997

7 The coordinates of the points *A* and *B* are (6,8) and (1,1).

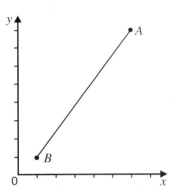

Work out the length of *AB*.

SEG 1996

8 A flagpole is held vertically by four wires as shown.

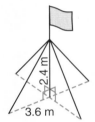

Each wire is fixed to the pole 2.4 m from the ground and to the ground 3.6 m from the foot of the pole.
Calculate the total length of wire needed.

9 The diagram consists of three right-angled triangles.
AB = 7 cm, *BC* = *DE* = 5 cm and *AE* = 12 cm.

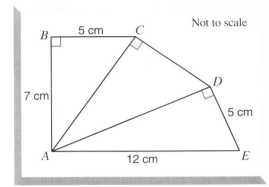

(a) Calculate the length *AC*.
(b) Calculate the length *AD*.

SEG 1996

10 The diagram shows a trapezium *ABCD*.

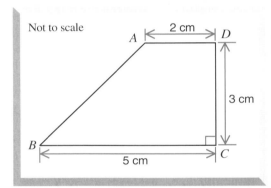

Calculate the length of the line *AB*.

11 John is standing 200 m due west of a power station and 300 m due north of a pylon. Calculate the distance of the power station from the pylon.

12 A helicopter flies from its base on a bearing of 045° for 20 km before landing. How far east of its base is the helicopter when it lands?

13 Helena is playing golf.

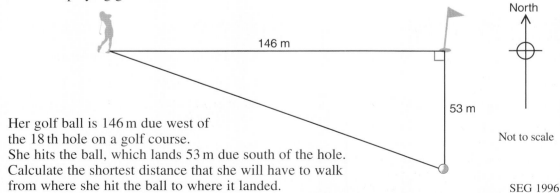

Her golf ball is 146 m due west of the 18 th hole on a golf course.
She hits the ball, which lands 53 m due south of the hole.
Calculate the shortest distance that she will have to walk from where she hit the ball to where it landed.

SEG 1996

CHAPTER 30

Trigonometry

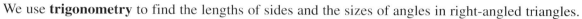

We use **trigonometry** to find the lengths of sides and the sizes of angles in right-angled triangles.

We already know that the longest side of a right-angled triangle is called the **hypotenuse**.

In order to understand the relationships between sides and angles the other sides of the triangle also need to be named.

The **opposite** side is the side directly opposite the angle being used and the **adjacent** is the side next to the angle.

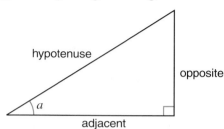

Look at this diagram.
It shows how the height of a kite changes as more and more string is let out.

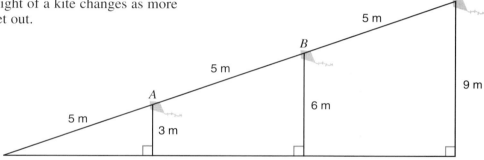

When the kite is at A, the string is 5 m long and the kite is 3 m high.

At A, the ratio $\frac{\text{height of kite}}{\text{length of string}}$, is therefore $\frac{3}{5} = 0.6$.

Calculate the value of the same ratio at B and C.

What do you notice?

When the kite is flying at angle a, the ratio $\frac{\text{height of kite}}{\text{length of string}}$ will always be the same whatever the length of the kite string and is called the **sine** of angle a.

Finding the length of the opposite side

The sine ratio

For any right-angled triangle:

$$\sin a = \frac{\text{opposite}}{\text{hypotenuse}}$$

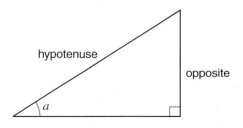

The sine ratio links three pieces of information:
  the size of an **angle**,
  the length of the side **opposite** the angle,
  the length of the **hypotenuse**.
If we are given the values for two of these we can find the value of the third.

325

Find the height of a kite when it is flying at an angle of 40° and the kite string is 12 m long.
Give the answer correct to 3 significant figures.

$$\sin a = \frac{\text{opp}}{\text{hyp}}$$

Substitute known values.

$$\sin 40° = \frac{h}{12}$$

Multiply both sides by 12.

$$h = 12 \times \sin 40°$$

Using your calculator, press:

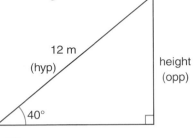

| 1 | 2 | × | sin | 4 | 0 | = |

Mathematical shorthand

Word	Abbreviation
sine	sin
opposite	opp
hypotenuse	hyp

$h = 7.713 \ldots$
$h = 7.71$ m, correct to 3 s.f.   The height of the kite is 7.71 m, correct to 3 s.f.

Exercise 30.1

1 Find the height, h, of these kites.
Give your answers correct to 3 significant figures.

(a)

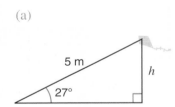

(b)

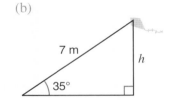

(c)

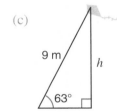

2 Calculate the lengths marked x.
Give your answers correct to 3 significant figures.

(a)

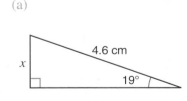

(b)

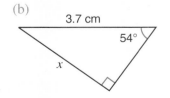

(c)

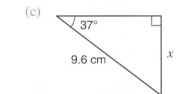

3 In $\triangle ABC$, angle $ACB = 90°$.
  (a) If $\angle BAC = 47.5°$ and $AB = 4.6$ m find BC.
  (b) If $\angle ABC = 67.4°$ and $AB = 12.4$ m find AC.
  (c) If $\angle BAC = 15.8°$ and $AB = 17.4$ cm find BC.
  (d) If $\angle BAC = 35°$ and $AB = 8.5$ cm find the size of
      $\angle ABC$ and then find AC.
Give your answers correct to 3 significant figures.

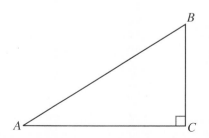

Finding an angle

If you are given the sine of an angle and asked to find the angle use the inverse sine function, sin⁻¹, on your calculator.

Using your calculator, press: [sin] [3] [0]
The display should read 0.5.
Clear the display and press: [sin⁻¹] [0] [.] [5] [=]
What do you notice?

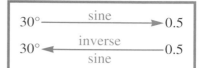

EXAMPLE

Find the size of angle a when the kite string is 12 m long and the kite is flying 7 m above the ground.
Give the answer correct to one decimal place.

$\sin a = \frac{\text{opp}}{\text{hyp}}$

Substitute known values.

$\sin a° = \frac{7}{12}$

$a = \sin^{-1} \frac{7}{12}$

Using your calculator, press: [sin⁻¹] [(] [7] [÷] [1] [2] [)] [=]

$a = 35.685 \ldots$

$a = 35.7°$, correct to 1 d.p.

Exercise 30.2

1 Find the size of angle a for each of these kites.
Give your answers correct to one decimal place.

(a)

(b)

(c)

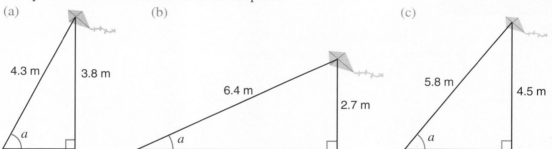

2 Find the size of angle x in each of these triangles.
Give your answers correct to one decimal place.

(a)

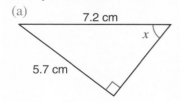

(b)

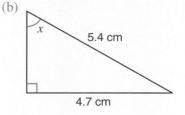

(c)

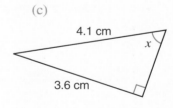

3 In $\triangle PQR$ angle $PQR = 90°$.
(a) If $QR = 4$ m and $PR = 10$ m find the size of $\angle QPR$.
(b) If $PQ = 4.7$ cm and $PR = 5.2$ cm find the size of $\angle PRQ$.
(c) If $QR = 7.2$ m and $PR = 19.4$ m find the size of $\angle QPR$.
(d) If $PQ = 3.7$ cm and $PR = 9.1$ cm find the size of $\angle QRP$ and then find the size of $\angle QPR$.
Give your answers correct to one decimal place.

Finding the hypotenuse

Find the length of the string, l, when a kite is 6 m high and the string makes an angle of 50° with the ground.
Give the answer correct to 3 significant figures.

$$\sin a = \frac{\text{opp}}{\text{hyp}}$$

Substitute known values.

$$\sin 50° = \frac{6}{l}$$

Multiply both sides by l.

$$l \times \sin 50° = 6$$

Divide both sides by sin 50°.

$$l = \frac{6}{\sin 50°}$$

Using your calculator, press:

$l = 7.832 \ldots$
$l = 7.83$ m, correct to 3 s.f.

The length of the string is 7.83 m, correct to 3 s.f.

Exercise 30.3

1 Find the lengths, l, of these kite strings.
Give your answers correct to 3 significant figures.

(a)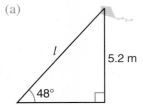

(b)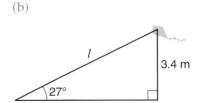

(c)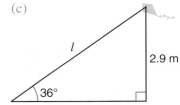

2 Calculate the length of side x in each of these triangles.
Give your answers correct to two decimal places.

(a)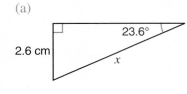

(b)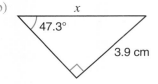

(c)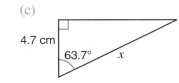

3 In $\triangle ABC$ angle $ACB = 90°$.
  (a) If $\angle BAC = 36.2°$ and $BC = 4.5$ m find AB.
  (b) If $\angle ABC = 64.7°$ and $AC = 15.8$ cm find AB.
  (c) If $\angle BAC = 12.7°$ and $BC = 14.7$ cm find AB.
  (d) If $\angle BAC = 72.8°$ and $AC = 7.6$ m find the size of $\angle ABC$ and then find AB.
  Give your answers correct to 3 significant figures.

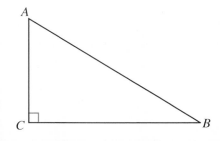

The cosine and tangent ratios

We have found that **sine** is the ratio $\frac{\text{opposite}}{\text{hypotenuse}}$.

In a similar way we can find two other ratios, the **cosine** of angle a and the **tangent** of angle a.

The cosine ratio

For any right-angled triangle:

$$\cos a = \frac{\text{adjacent}}{\text{hypotenuse}}$$

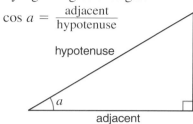

The cosine ratio links three pieces of information:
    the size of an **angle**,
    the length of the side **adjacent** to the angle,
    the length of the **hypotenuse**.
If we are given the values of two of these we can find the value of the third.

The tangent ratio

For any right-angled triangle:

$$\tan a = \frac{\text{opposite}}{\text{adjacent}}$$

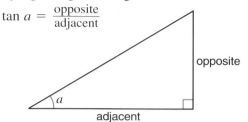

The tangent ratio links three pieces of information:
    the size of an **angle**,
    the length of the side **opposite** to the angle,
    the length of the side **adjacent** to the angle.
If we are given the values of two of these we can find the value of the third.

EXAMPLE

1

Write down the sin, cos and tan ratios for angle a in the triangle.

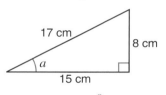

$\sin a = \frac{\text{opp}}{\text{hyp}} = \frac{8}{17}$

$\cos a = \frac{\text{adj}}{\text{hyp}} = \frac{15}{17}$

$\tan a = \frac{\text{opp}}{\text{adj}} = \frac{8}{15}$

Mathematical shorthand

Word	Abbreviation
adjacent	adj
opposite	opp
hypotenuse	hyp
sine	sin
cosine	cos
tangent	tan

How to select and use the correct ratio

There are only 3 different types of question for each of the ratios. Selecting the correct ratio is most important.
To do this:

1. Go to the angle you know (or want to find).
2. Name sides (opp, adj, hyp).
    If you are trying to find the length of a side, name that side first together with one other side of known length.
    If you are trying to find the size of an angle, name two sides of known length.
3. Select the correct ratio and write it down.

$\sin a = \frac{\text{opp}}{\text{hyp}}$ $\cos a = \frac{\text{adj}}{\text{hyp}}$ $\tan a = \frac{\text{opp}}{\text{adj}}$

    One way to remember the ratios is to use the initial letters, SOHCAHTOA.
    You may know another method.

4. Substitute known values from the question.
5. Rearrange to isolate the angle, or side, you are trying to find.
6. Use your calculator to find the size of the angle, or side, writing down more figures than you need for the final answer.
7. Correct to the required degree of accuracy.
8. Give the answer, stating the degree of approximation and giving the correct units. When giving the answer to a problem you should use a short sentence.

2 Find the length, h, giving the answer to 3 significant figures

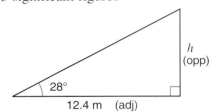

$$\tan a = \frac{\text{opp}}{\text{adj}}$$

Substitute known values.

$$\tan 28° = \frac{h}{12.4}$$

Multiply both sides by 12.4.

$$h = 12.4 \times \tan 28°$$

Using your calculator, press:

[1] [2] [.] [4] [×] [tan] [2] [8] [=]

$$h = 6.593 \ldots$$
$$h = 6.59 \, \text{m, correct to 3 s.f.}$$

3 Find the size of angle a, correct to one decimal place.

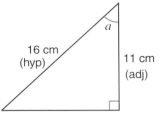

$$\cos a = \frac{\text{adj}}{\text{hyp}}$$

Substitute known values.

$$\cos a° = \frac{11}{16}$$

$$a = \cos^{-1} \frac{11}{16}$$

Using your calculator, press:

[cos⁻¹] [(] [1] [1] [÷] [1] [6] [)] [=]

$$a = 46.56 \ldots$$
$$a = 46.6°, \text{ correct to 1 d.p.}$$

Exercise 30.4

1 Write down the sin, cos and tan ratios for angle p in each of the following triangles.

(a)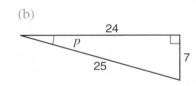

(b)

(c)

2 By choosing the correct ratio, calculate angle p in each of the following triangles. Give your answers correct to one decimal place.

(a)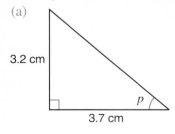

(b)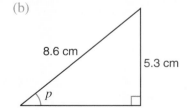

(c)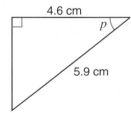

(d)

(e)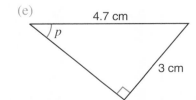

(f)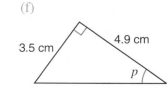

3 By choosing the correct ratio, calculate side a in each of the following triangles.

(a)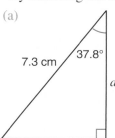

7.3 cm, 37.8°, a

(b)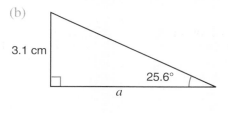

3.1 cm, 25.6°, a

(c)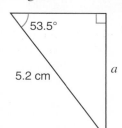

53.5°, 5.2 cm, a

(d)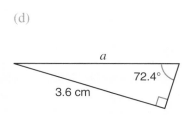

a, 72.4°, 3.6 cm

(e)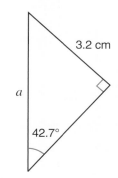

3.2 cm, a, 42.7°

(f)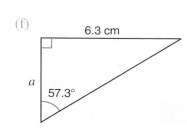

6.3 cm, a, 57.3°

4 An equilateral triangle has sides of length 5 cm. Calculate the height of the triangle.

5 An isosceles triangle has sides of length 10 cm, 10 cm and 6 cm. Calculate the angles of the triangle.

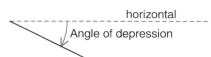

Angles of elevation and depression

When we look **up** from the horizontal the angle we turn through is called an **angle of elevation**.

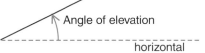

Angle of elevation

horizontal

horizontal

Angle of depression

When we look **down** from the horizontal the angle we turn through is called an **angle of depression**.

EXAMPLE

1 From a point on the ground, 30 m from the base of a pylon, the angle of elevation to the top of the pylon is 50°.

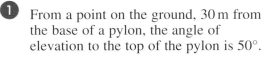
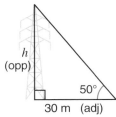

h (opp)

50°

30 m (adj)

Find the height of the pylon.

$\tan a = \frac{\text{opp}}{\text{adj}}$

$\tan 50° = \frac{h}{30}$

$h = 30 \times \tan 50°$

$h = 35.75 \ldots$

$h = 35.8$ m, correct to 3 s.f.

The height of the pylon is 35.8 m, correct to 3 s.f.

EXAMPLE

2 Staten Island Ferry is 270 m away from the base of the Statue of Liberty.
The ferry can be seen from a viewing point in the lantern, 85 m above the ground.
What is the angle of depression to the ferry from the viewing point?

$$\tan a = \frac{\text{opp}}{\text{adj}}$$
$$\tan d° = \frac{85}{270}$$
$$d = \tan^{-1} \frac{85}{270}$$
$$d = 17.47 \ldots$$
$$d = 17.5°, \text{ correct to 1 d.p.}$$

The angle of depression to the ferry from the viewing point is 17.5°, correct to 1 d.p.

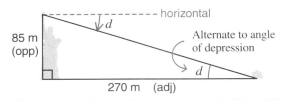

85 m (opp)

270 m (adj)

horizontal

Alternate to angle of depression

d

d

Exercise 30.5

1 From a point on the ground 20 m from the base of a tree, the angle of elevation of the top of the tree is 47°.
Calculate the height of the tree.

2 From a point on the ground 10 m from a block of flats, the angle of elevation of the top of the block is 76°.
Calculate the height of the block of flats.

3 A fishing boat is 200 m from the bottom of a vertical cliff. From the top of the cliff the angle of depression to the fishing boat is 34°.
(a) Calculate the height of the cliff.
(b) A buoy is 100 m from the bottom of the cliff. Calculate the angle of depression to the buoy from the top of the cliff.

47°

20 m

34°

200 m

4 A yacht is 200 m from the bottom of a lighthouse.
From the top of the lighthouse the angle of depression to the yacht is 48°.
Calculate the height of the lighthouse.

5 A cat is on the ground 25 m from the foot of a house. A bird is perched on the gutter of the house 15 m from the ground.
Calculate the angle of elevation from the cat to the bird.

Three-figure bearings

Remember:
Bearings are used to describe the direction in which you must travel to get from one place to another. They are measured from the North line in a clockwise direction. A bearing can be any angle from 0° to 360° and is written as a three-figure number.

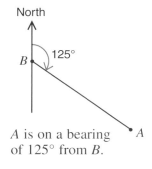

North

B

125°

A

A is on a bearing of 125° from *B*.

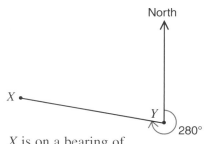

North

X

Y

280°

X is on a bearing of 280° from *Y*.

EXAMPLE

A plane flies 300 km on a bearing of 132° from an airport.
How far South and East is it from the airport?
Give the answers correct to 3 significant figures.

x is the distance South.
y is the distance East.
Using supplementary angles:
$\angle PAB = 180° - 132° = 48°$.

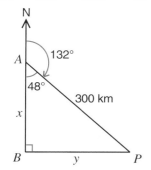

To find x

$\cos a = \frac{\text{adj}}{\text{hyp}}$

$\cos 48° = \frac{x}{300}$

$x = 300 \times \cos 48°$

$x = 200.73 \ldots$ km

$x = 201$ km, correct to 3 s.f.

To find y

$\sin a = \frac{\text{opp}}{\text{hyp}}$

$\sin 48° = \frac{y}{300}$

$y = 300 \times \sin 48°$

$y = 222.94 \ldots$ km

$y = 223$ km, correct to 3 s.f.

Sketch diagrams
Drawing a sketch diagram may help you to
understand the question.
More information can be added to the diagram as you
answer the question.

The plane is 201 km South and
223 km East of the airport,
correct to 3 s.f.

*How can you use Pythagoras'
Theorem to check the answer?*

Exercise 30.6

1. A plane flies 250 km on a bearing of 052.6°.
   (a) How far north is it from its original position?
   (b) How far east is it from its original position?

2. A helicopter leaves its base and flies 23 km on a bearing of 285°.
   How far west is it from its base?

3. A ship at A is 3.8 km due north of a lighthouse.
   A ship at B is 2.7 km due east of the same lighthouse.
   What is the bearing of the ship at B from the ship at A?

4. A helicopter has flown from its base on a bearing of 153°. Its distance east of base is 19 km.
   How far has the helicopter flown?

5. A fishing boat leaves port and sails on a straight course. After 2 hours its distance south of
   port is 24 km and its distance east of port is 7 km. On what bearing did it sail?

6. A yacht sails 15 km on a bearing of 053°, then 7 km on a bearing of 112°.
   How far north is the yacht from its starting position?

7. A plane flies 307 km on a bearing of 234°, then 23 km on a bearing of 286°.
   How far south is the plane from its starting position?

8. Jayne sails 1.5 km on a bearing of 050°. She then changes course and sails 2 km on a bearing
   of 140°. On what bearing must she sail to return to her starting position?

What you need to know

- **Trigonometry** is used to find the lengths of sides and the sizes of angles in right-angled triangles.

- You must learn the **sine**, **cosine** and **tangent** ratios.

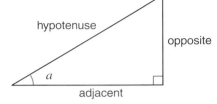

$$\sin a = \frac{\text{opposite}}{\text{hypotenuse}}$$

$$\cos a = \frac{\text{adjacent}}{\text{hypotenuse}}$$

$$\tan a = \frac{\text{opposite}}{\text{adjacent}}$$

- Each ratio links the size of an angle with the lengths of two sides. If we are given the values for two of these we can find the value of the third.

- When we look **up** from the horizontal the angle we turn through is called the **angle of elevation**.

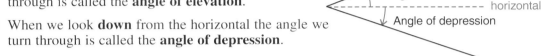

- When we look **down** from the horizontal the angle we turn through is called the **angle of depression**.

- **Three-figure bearings.**
  Bearings are used to describe the direction in which you must travel to get from one place to another. They are measured from the North line in a clockwise direction. A bearing can be any angle from 0° to 360° and is written as a three-figure number.

Review Exercise

1 When Jayne is 10 m from a haystack, the angle of elevation to the top of the haystack is 18°. Calculate *h*, the height of the haystack.

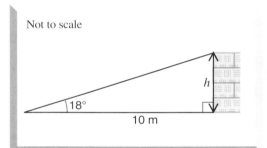

Not to scale

2 The design for a children's slide, *ABCD*, for a playground is shown.
The height of the slide, *BD*, is 136 cm.
The distance *DC* is 195 cm.

  (a)   Calculate the angle *BCD*.

  (b)   Angle *ABD* is 28°.
Calculate the distance of *AB*.

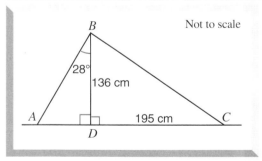

Not to scale

SEG 1997

3 Ajit stands 30 m from the base of a tree.
From ground level he measures the angle of elevation of the top of the tree.
He finds that this angle is 25°.
Calculate the height of the tree.

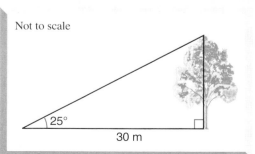

Not to scale

SEG 1994

4 A railway tunnel has a cross-section that is part of a circle of radius 2.1 metres.
The centre of the circle is at *O*.
Angle *AOC* = 50°.
Calculate *AB*.

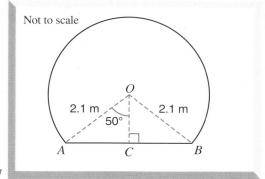

Not to scale

SEG 1997

5 This quadrilateral is made from two right-angled triangles.
(a) Calculate the length *x*.
(b) Calculate the angle *A*.

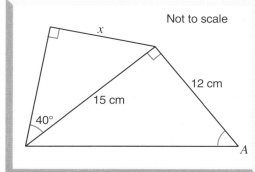

Not to scale

SEG 1995

6 The diagram shows a side view of two buildings.
The length *DE* = 15 m. Angle *FDE* = 20°.
(a) Calculate the height *EF*.

A telephone wire stretches from *C* to *F*.
The length *CF* = 20.9 m.
(b) Calculate the size of angle *CFD*.

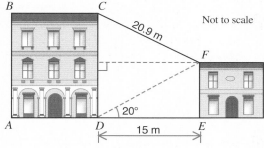

Not to scale

SEG 1998 S

7 An aircraft takes off from one end, A, of a runway and it passes over the other end of the runway, *B*, at a height of 317 m.
The angle of elevation of the aircraft from end *A* of the runway is 5°.
(a) Calculate the length of the runway *AB*.
Another aircraft, using the same runway, passes over point *B* at a height of 250 m.
(b) Calculate the angle of elevation of this aircraft from end *A* of the runway.

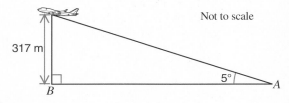

Not to scale

SEG 1995

8 Cos *PQR* = $\frac{12}{13}$

(a) Find (i) tan *PQR*,
(ii) sin *PQR*.

(b) *PQ* = 6 cm.
What are the lengths of *QR* and *PR*?

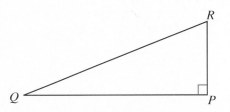

9 (a) Calculate the length, l, of this ladder

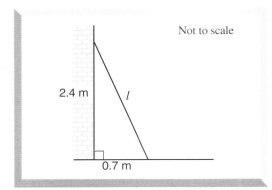

Not to scale

2.4 m

l

0.7 m

(b) A health and safety directive says:
'*A ladder must be placed at an angle of between 70° and 80° to the ground*'.
   (i) A ladder is required to reach a height of 4.7 metres. Calculate the length of the longest ladder that can be used safely.
   (ii) The same ladder is used to reach a height of 4.9 metres. Calculate whether or not the ladder is safe.

SEG 1996

10 A ship sails on a two stage journey from A to B to C.
The first stage of the journey from A to B is shown.
A to B is a journey of 90 km on a bearing of 032°.

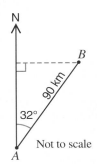

N

B

90 km

32°

Not to scale

A

(a) Calculate the distance travelled east during the first stage of this journey.

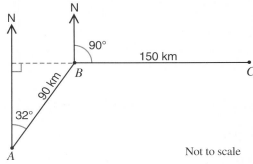

N   N
                90°
                        150 km
    B   C
90 km
32°
A   Not to scale

The second stage of the journey from B to C is a distance 150 km on a bearing of 090°.

(b) Find the total distance travelled east on the journey from A to C.
Hence calculate the bearing of C from A.

SEG 1996

11 A group of geography students need to calculate the width of a river.
They measure the angle of elevation of the top of an electricity pylon from opposite banks of the river, P and L.
The pylon is 70 metres high.

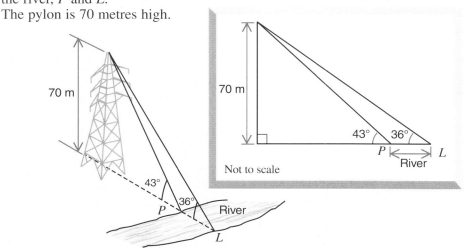

70 m

43°

P 36°

River

L

70 m

43° 36°

P   L
River

Not to scale

Calculate the width of the river PL.

SEG 1996

336

The movement of a shape from one position to another is called a **transformation**.
The change in position of the shape can be described in terms of a **reflection**, a **rotation** or a **translation**.

Reflection

Look at this diagram.
It shows a **reflection** of a shape in the line *AB*.
The line *AB* is sometimes called a **mirror line**.
Place a mirror on the line *AB* and look at
the reflection.
You should see that the image of the
shape is the same distance from the
mirror as the original.

Notation

The shape *P* is reflected in the line *AB*.
Shape P_1 is the **image** of *P*.
We also say that *P* is **mapped** onto P_1.

If the vertices of shape *P* are labelled *W*, *X*, *Y* and *Z*,
then:

    W is mapped onto W_1,
    X is mapped onto X_1,
    Y is mapped onto Y_1,
    Z is mapped onto Z_1.

If you join the points *W* and W_1:
The distance from *W* to the mirror line is the same
as the distance from the mirror line to W_1.
The line WW_1 is at right angles to the mirror line.

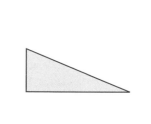

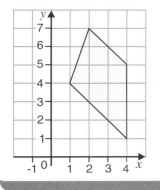

EXAMPLE   Copy the shape below onto squared paper.
Draw the reflection of the shape in the *y* axis.

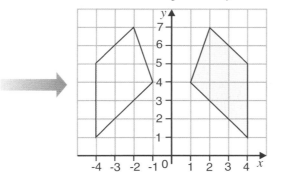

Notice that:
$(1, 4) \rightarrow (-1, 4)$
$(2, 7) \rightarrow (-2, 7)$
$(4, 5) \rightarrow (-4, 5)$
$(4, 1) \rightarrow (-4, 1)$
Can you see a pattern?

337

1 Copy each of the following shapes and draw the reflection of the shape in the line *AB*.

(a)

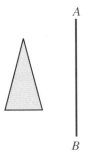

(b)

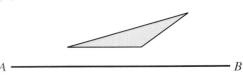

(c)

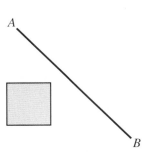

(d)

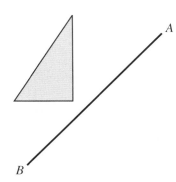

2 Copy each of the following shapes onto squared paper and draw the image of the shape after reflection in the line *AB*.

(a)

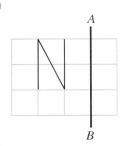

(b)

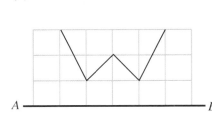

(c)

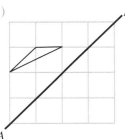

(d)

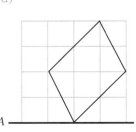

(e)

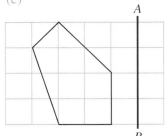

(f)

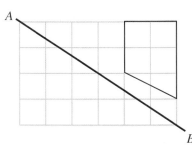

3 Copy each of the following shapes onto squared paper and then draw the reflection of each shape in the line given.

(a)

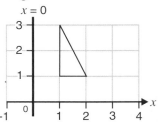

(b)

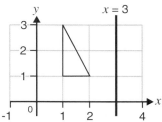

4 Copy each of the following shapes onto squared paper and then draw the reflection of each shape in the line given.

(a)

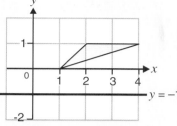

(b)

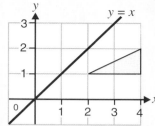

5

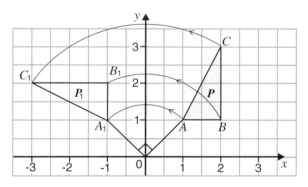

The diagram shows a quadrilateral *ABCD*.

Give the coordinates of *B* after:
(a) reflection in the *x* axis,
(b) reflection in the *y* axis,
(c) reflection in the line $x = 4$,
(d) reflection in the line $x = -1$,
(e) reflection in the line $y = x$.

Rotation

Look at this diagram.
It shows the **rotation** of a shape through 90° anticlockwise about *O* (the origin).

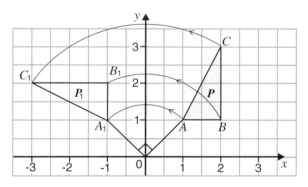

$$A \rightarrow A_1$$
$$AO = A_1O \text{ and } \angle AOA_1 = 90°.$$
What happens to points B and C?

The shape P_1 is the image of the shape *P*.
P is mapped onto P_1.

All points on the shape *P* are turned through the same angle about the same point.
This point is called the **centre of rotation**.

When a shape is rotated it stays the same shape and size but its **orientation** on the page changes.

For a rotation we need:
    a centre of rotation,
    an amount of turn,
    a direction of turn.

Copy the shape below onto squared paper. Draw the image of the shape after it has been rotated through 90° clockwise about the point *C* (1, 1).

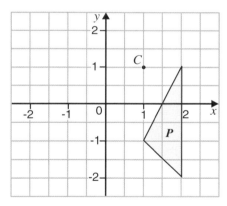

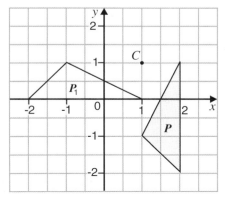

1 Copy each of the following shapes onto squared paper and draw the new position of the shape after it has been rotated through 90°, clockwise about the origin (0, 0).

(a)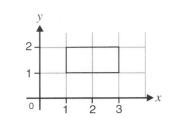

(b)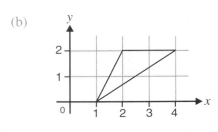

(c)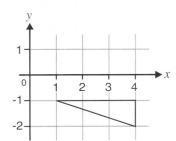

(d)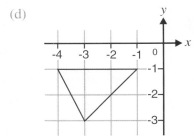

2 Copy each of the following shapes onto squared paper and then draw the new position of the shape after it has been rotated through 180°, about the point *X*.

(a)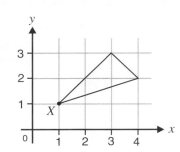

(b)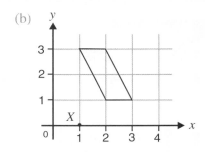

(c)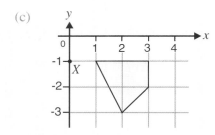

(d)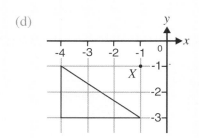

3 The diagram shows a quadrilateral *ABCD*.

Give the coordinates of *B* after:
(a) a rotation through 90°, clockwise about (0, 0),
(b) a rotation through 90°, anticlockwise about (0, 0),
(c) a rotation through 180°, about (0, 0),
(d) a rotation through 90°, clockwise about (3, 1),
(e) a rotation through 90°, anticlockwise about (3, 1),
(f) a rotation through 180°, about (3, 1).

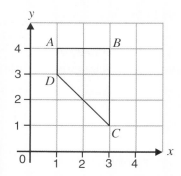

Look at this diagram.
It shows a **translation** of a shape with vector $\begin{pmatrix} 2 \\ -1 \end{pmatrix}$.

The shape P_1 is the image of the shape P.
P is mapped onto P_1.

All points on the shape P are moved the same distance in the same direction without twisting or turning.

A **vector** can be used to describe a translation.
The top number describes the **horizontal** part of the movement:

$+$ = to the right, $\quad -$ = to the left

The bottom number describes the **vertical** part of the movement:

$+$ = upwards $\qquad -$ = downwards

When a shape is translated it stays the same shape and size and has the same orientation.

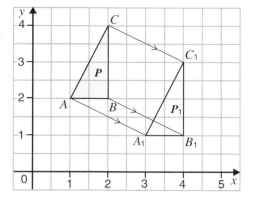

$A\ (1, 2) \rightarrow A_1\ (3, 1)$
$B\ (2, 2) \rightarrow B_1\ (4, 1)$
$C\ (2, 4) \rightarrow C_1\ (4, 3)$
Can you see a pattern?

EXAMPLE

Write down the translation which maps L onto L_1.
$A\ (5, -2) \rightarrow A_1\ (1, 1)$

To translate from A to A_1 move:
4 units to the left, and
3 units upwards.

This can be written as $\begin{pmatrix} -4 \\ 3 \end{pmatrix}$.

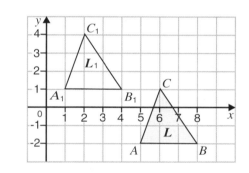

Exercise **31.3**

 Copy the shape onto squared paper.

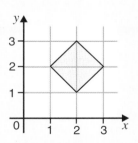

Draw the new position of the shape after each of the following translations.

(a) $\begin{pmatrix} 3 \\ 2 \end{pmatrix}$ (b) $\begin{pmatrix} 2 \\ -3 \end{pmatrix}$

(c) $\begin{pmatrix} -2 \\ 3 \end{pmatrix}$ (d) $\begin{pmatrix} -2 \\ -3 \end{pmatrix}$

2 The diagram shows a quadrilateral $ABCD$.

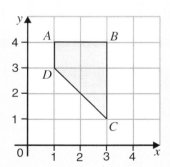

Give the coordinates of B after the shape has been translated with vector:

(a) $\begin{pmatrix} 2 \\ 1 \end{pmatrix}$ (b) $\begin{pmatrix} -2 \\ 2 \end{pmatrix}$

(c) $\begin{pmatrix} 1 \\ -3 \end{pmatrix}$ (d) $\begin{pmatrix} -2 \\ -3 \end{pmatrix}$

3 The translation $\begin{pmatrix} 2 \\ -1 \end{pmatrix}$ maps S (5, 3) onto T.

What are the coordinates of T?

4 Write down the translation which maps:
(a) X (1, 1) onto P (3, 2),
(b) X (1, 1) onto Q (2, −1),
(c) X (1, 1) onto R (−2, 2),
(d) X (1, 1) onto S (−2, −1).

5 The diagram shows quadrilateral S.
Copy S onto squared paper.

(a) The translation $\begin{pmatrix} 3 \\ 2 \end{pmatrix}$ maps S onto T.

Draw and label T.

(b) Write down the translation which maps T onto S.

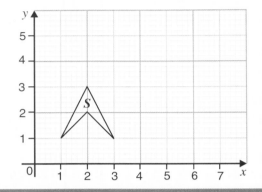

Enlargement

This diagram shows another transformation, called an **enlargement**.
It shows an enlargement with scale factor 2 and centre O.

The shape P_1 is the image of shape P.
P is mapped onto P_1.

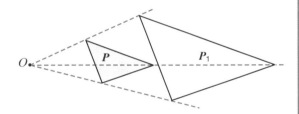

When a shape is enlarged:
  angles remain unchanged,
  all **lengths** are multiplied by a **scale factor**.

Scale factor $= \dfrac{\text{new length}}{\text{original length}}$

For an enlargement we need:
  a centre of enlargement,
  a scale factor.

Enlargement was covered in Chapter 27, as an introduction to similar figures. You may wish to look at pages 290 to 294 before doing Exercise 31.4.

Exercise **31.4**

1 Copy the following shapes and draw the enlargement, with scale factor 2, centre O.

(a)

(b)

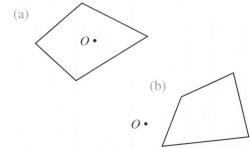

2 Copy the following shapes and draw the enlargement, with scale factor $\frac{1}{2}$, centre O.

(a)

(b)

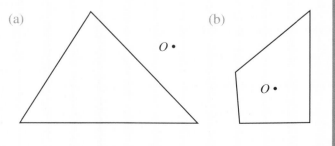

3 Copy the following shapes onto squared paper and draw the enlargements given.

(a) Scale factor 2, centre (1, 2).

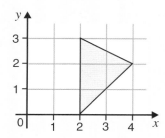

(b) Scale factor $1\frac{1}{2}$, centre (2, 1).

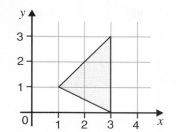

4 The diagram shows a quadrilateral *ABCD*.

Give the coordinates of *B* after an enlargement:
(a) scale factor 2, centre (0, 0),
(b) scale factor 3, centre (0, 0),
(c) scale factor 2, centre (0, 2),
(d) scale factor 3, centre *C* (3, 1),
(e) scale factor 2, centre *D* (1, 3),
(f) scale factor 2, centre *A* (1, 4).

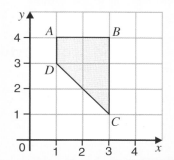

Describing transformations

Look at the shapes in this diagram.

We can describe the single transformation which maps *A* onto *B* as a **reflection** in the line $x = 3$.

We can describe the single transformation which maps *A* onto *C* as a **rotation** of 180° about (2, 1).

We can describe the single transformation which maps *A* onto *D* as a **translation** with vector $\begin{pmatrix} 2 \\ -3 \end{pmatrix}$.

The flow chart below can be used to decide what type of transformation has taken place.
The details required to fully describe each type of transformation are also given.

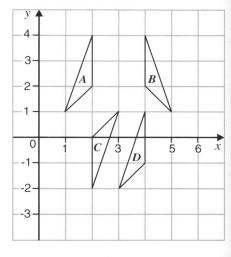

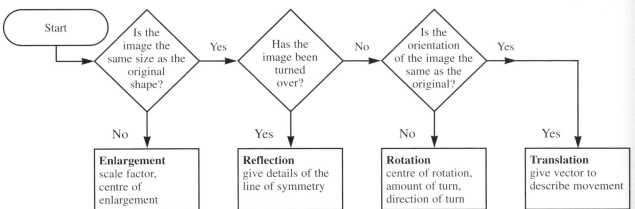

Try following the flow chart for the diagram above.

To find a line of reflection

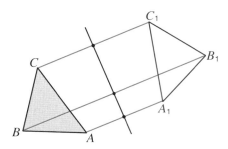

1. Join each point to its image point.
2. Put a mark halfway along each line.
3. Use a ruler to join the marks.

To find the centre and scale factor of an enlargement

This was covered in Chapter 27.
You may wish to look at this work before doing the next exercise.

To find the centre and angle of rotation

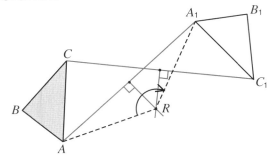

1. Join each point with its image point.
2. Put a mark halfway along each line.
3. Use a set-square to draw a line at right angles to each line. The point where the lines cross is the centre of rotation, R.
4. Join one point and its image to the centre of rotation.
5. The angle of rotation is given by the size of the angle ARA_1.

Exercise 31.5

1. Describe fully the single transformations which map L onto L_1, L_2, L_3, L_4, L_5 and L_6.

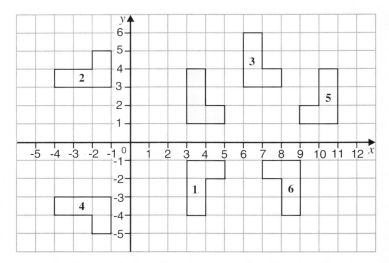

2. Describe fully the single transformation which maps
   (a) T onto U,
   (b) T onto V,
   (c) T onto W.

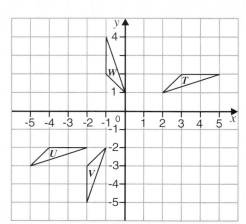

3 Describe fully the single transformation which maps
  (a) A onto B,
  (b) A onto C,
  (c) A onto D.

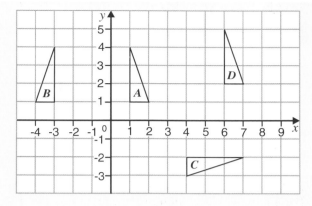

4 Describe the single transformation which maps ABCD onto PQRS.

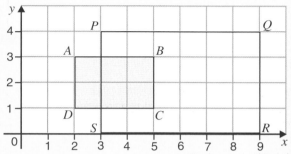

5 Describe fully the single transformation which maps ABC onto XYZ.

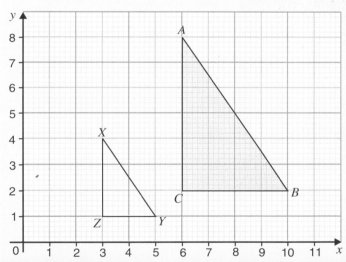

Combinations of transformations

Look at this diagram.

P has been mapped onto P₁ by a reflection in the x axis.

Then P₁ has been mapped onto P₂ by a reflection in the y axis.

Describe the single transformation which maps P onto P₂.

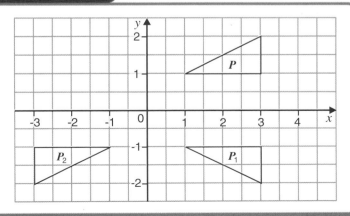

EXAMPLE

Copy triangle Q onto squared paper.

(a) Q is mapped onto Q_1 by a rotation through 90°, clockwise about (0, 0). Draw and label Q_1.

(b) Q_1 is mapped onto Q_2 by a reflection in the line $y = 0$. Draw and label Q_2.

(c) Describe the single transformation which maps Q onto Q_2.

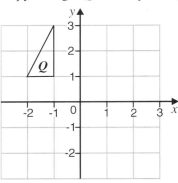

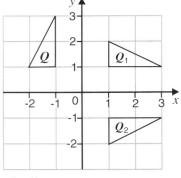

(c) Reflection in the line $y = x$.

Exercise 31.6

1 The diagram shows a quadrilateral labelled A.
Copy the diagram onto squared paper.

(a) A is mapped onto A_1 by a reflection in the line $x = 0$. Draw and label A_1.

(b) A_1 is mapped onto A_2 by a reflection in the line $x = 4$. Draw and label A_2.

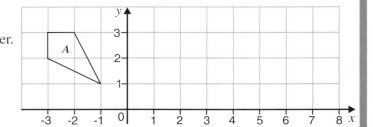

(c) Describe fully the single transformation which maps A onto A_2.

2 The diagram shows a triangle labelled P.
Copy the diagram onto squared paper.

(a) P is mapped onto P_1 by a reflection in the line $y = x$. Draw and label P_1.

(b) P_1 is mapped onto P_2 by a reflection in the line $x = 5$. Draw and label P_2.

(c) Describe fully the single transformation which maps P onto P_2.

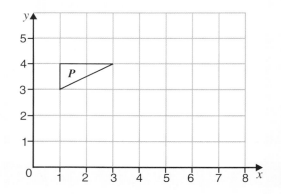

3 The diagram shows a triangle labelled T.
Copy the diagram onto squared paper.

(a) Rotate T through 90° clockwise about (0, 0) to T_1. Draw and label T_1.

(b) Reflect T_1 in the line $y = 0$ to T_2. Draw and label T_2.

(c) Reflect T_2 in the line $x = 0$ to T_3. Draw and label T_3.

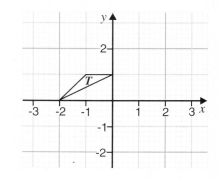

(d) Describe fully the single transformation which maps T onto T_3.

4 The diagram shows a quadrilateral labelled Q.
Copy the diagram onto squared paper.

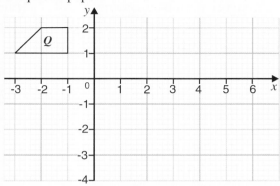

(a) Q is mapped onto Q_1 by a rotation through $90°$, anticlockwise about $(0, 0)$.
Draw and label Q_1.

(b) Q_1 is mapped onto Q_2 by a rotation through $90°$, anticlockwise about $(2, 0)$.
Draw and label Q_2.

(c) Describe fully the single transformation which maps Q onto Q_2.

5 The diagram shows a shape labelled S.
Copy the diagram onto squared paper.

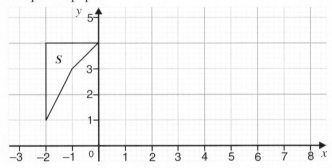

(a) The translation $\begin{pmatrix} 4 \\ 2 \end{pmatrix}$ maps S onto S_1. Draw and label S_1.

(b) The translation $\begin{pmatrix} -8 \\ 1 \end{pmatrix}$ maps S_1 onto S_2. Draw and label S_2.

(c) Describe fully the single transformation which maps S onto S_2.

6 The diagram shows a triangle labelled R.
Copy the diagram onto squared paper.

(a) R is mapped onto R_1 by a rotation through $90°$, anticlockwise about $(0, 0)$. Draw and label R_1.

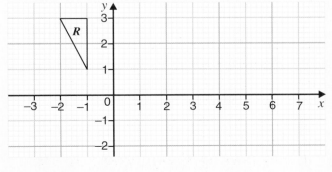

(b) R_1 is mapped onto R_2 by a reflection in the line $y = -x$. Draw and label R_2.

(c) R_2 is mapped onto R_3 by a reflection in the line $x = 3$. Draw and label R_3.

(d) Describe fully the single transformation which maps R onto R_3.

What you need to know

- The movement of a shape from one position to another is called a **transformation**.

- **Single transformations** can be described in terms of a reflection, a rotation, a translation or an enlargement.

- **Reflection**: The image of the shape is the same distance from the mirror line as the original.

- **Rotation**: All points are turned through the same angle about the same point, called a centre of rotation.

- **Translation**: All points are moved the same distance in the same direction without twisting or turning.

- **Enlargement**: This topic was first covered in Chapter 27 as an introduction to similar figures.

- How to fully describe a transformation.

Transformation	Image has equal angles?	Image same shape and size?	Details needed to describe the transformation
Reflection	Yes	Yes	Mirror line, sometimes given as an equation.
Rotation	Yes	Yes	Centre of rotation, amount of turn, direction of turn.
Translation	Yes	Yes	Vector: Top number = horizontal movement, bottom number = vertical movement.
Enlargement	Yes	No	Centre of enlargement, scale factor.

Review Exercise

1. The diagram shows triangle *T*.
   Copy the diagram onto squared paper.

   (a) Triangle *A* is obtained by rotating triangle *T* through 90°, clockwise about *O*.
   Draw and label triangle *A* on the diagram.

   (b) Triangle *B* is obtained by reflecting triangle *T* in the *y* axis.
   Draw and label triangle *B* on the diagram.

   (c) Describe fully the single transformation which maps triangle *A* onto triangle *B*.

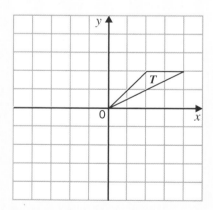

348

2 *ABEO* is a board with three black shapes painted on it. Immediately next to it is a white card, *BCDE*, which has three holes cut out of it.

Describe fully the single transformation which will move the card and place it on top of the board in such a way that all three black shapes show through the holes.

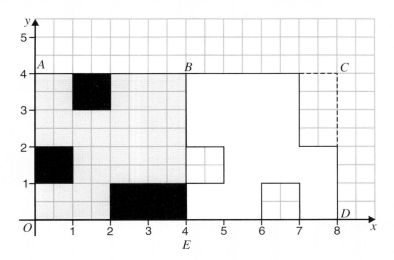

SEG 1990

3 Copy the following diagram.
Draw an enlargement of rectangle *A* using scale factor 3 and centre of enlargement *P*.

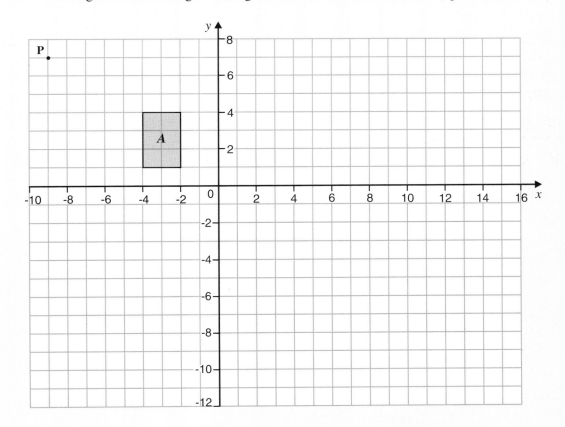

SEG 1995

4 The diagram shows two transformations of the shaded rectangle *PQRS*.

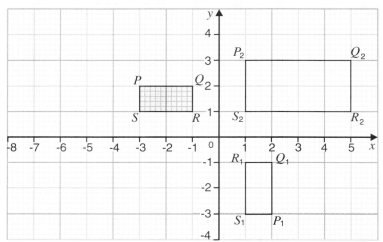

Describe fully the single transformation which takes:
. (a) *PQRS* onto $P_1Q_1R_1S_1$.
  (b) *PQRS* onto $P_2Q_2R_2S_2$.

SEG 1998 S

5 The diagram shows a rectangle *ABCD*.

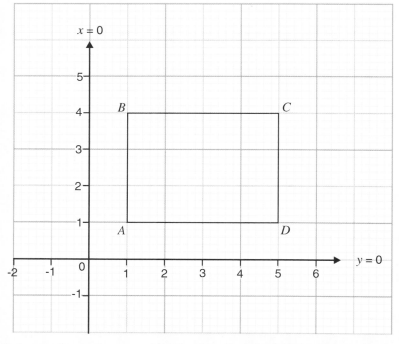

(a) The rectangle *ABCD* is rotated about the vertex *A* to a new position $AB_1C_1D_1$.
     The coordinates of B_1 are (–2, 1).
     What are the coordinates of C_1?
(b) The rectangle *ABCD* is reflected in the line $x = 2$ onto $A_2B_2C_2D_2$.
     What are the coordinates of C_2?
(c) The rectangle *ABCD* is enlarged with scale factor 2 from the centre *A* (1, 1) onto $AB_3C_3D_3$.
     What are the coordinates of C_3?

SEG 1991

6 Copy the diagram onto squared paper.

(a) Describe fully the single transformation which will map P onto P_1.

(b) Draw the reflection of P_1 in the line $y = x$ and label it P_2.

(c) Describe fully the single transformation which will map P onto P_2.

(d) Enlarge P by a scale factor of 2, centre (2, 1).

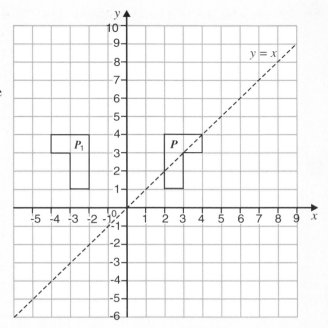

SEG 1996

7 The diagram shows the positions of two parallelograms, $ABCD$ and $A_1 B_1 C_1 D_1$.

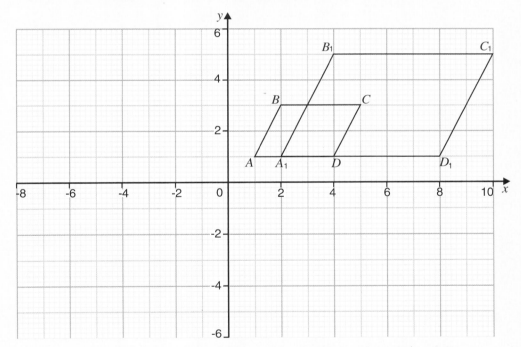

(a) Describe fully the single transformation which takes $A_1B_1C_1D_1$ onto $ABCD$.

Copy the diagram onto squared paper.

(b) Rotate $ABCD$ through $180°$ about (1, 0) to $A_2B_2C_2D_2$. Draw and label $A_2B_2C_2D_2$.

(c) Rotate $ABCD$ through $180°$ about (–1, 0) to $A_3B_3C_3D_3$. Draw and label $A_3B_3C_3D_3$.

(d) Describe fully a single transformation which will take $A_3B_3C_3D_3$ onto $A_2B_2C_2D_2$.

8 The diagram shows a kite labelled K.
Copy the diagram onto squared paper.

(a) The translation $\begin{pmatrix} 3 \\ -1 \end{pmatrix}$ maps K onto K_1.
Draw and label K_1.

(b) Describe the single transformation which maps K_1 onto K.

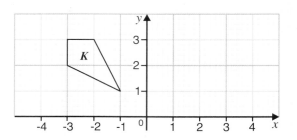

9 The diagram shows a triangle labelled A. Copy the diagram onto squared paper.

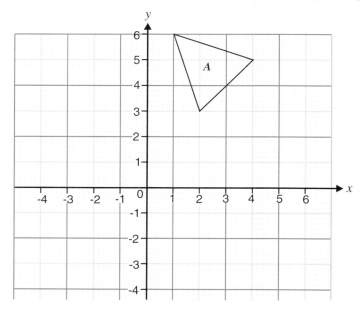

(a) A is mapped onto A_1 by a reflection in the line $x = 0$.
Draw and label A_1.

(b) A_1 is mapped onto A_2 by a reflection in the line $y = x$.
Draw and label A_2.

(c) Describe fully the single transformation which maps A onto A_2.

10 The diagram shows a trapezium labelled Q.
Copy the diagram onto squared paper.

(a) Q is mapped onto Q_1 by a reflection in the x axis.
Draw and label Q_1.

(b) Q_1 is mapped onto Q_2 by a translation with vector $\begin{pmatrix} 2 \\ 4 \end{pmatrix}$.
Draw and label Q_2.

(c) Q_2 is mapped onto Q_3 by a reflection in the line $y = x$.
Draw and label Q_3.

(d) Describe fully the single transformation which maps Q onto Q_3.

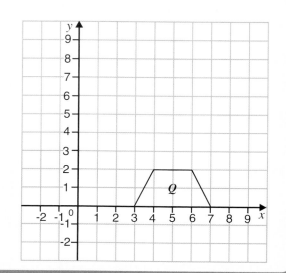

CHAPTER **32**

Understanding and Using Measures

Units of measurement

Different units can be used to measure the same quantity. For example:

The same **length** can be measured using centimetres, kilometres, inches, miles, ...
The same **mass** can be measured using grams, kilograms, pounds, ounces, ...
The same **capacity** can be measured using litres, millilitres, gallons pints, ...

There are two sorts of units in common use — **metric** units and **imperial** units.

Metric Units	Imperial Units	Conversions
Length 1 kilometre (km) = 1000 metres (m) 1 m = 100 centimetres (cm) 1 m = 1000 millimetres (mm) 1 cm = 10 mm	**Length** 1 foot = 12 inches 1 yard = 3 feet 1 mile = 1760 yards	**Length** 5 miles is about 8 km 1 inch is about 2.5 cm 1 foot is about 30.5 cm 1 m is about 39 inches
Mass 1 tonne (t) = 1000 kilograms (kg) 1 kg = 1000 grams (g)	**Mass** 1 pound = 16 ounces 14 pounds = 1 stone 2240 pounds = 1 ton	**Mass** 1 kg is about 2.2 pounds
Capacity and volume 1 litre = 1000 millilitres (ml) 1 cm³ = 1 ml 1 m³ = 1000 litres	**Capacity and volume** 1 gallon = 8 pints	**Capacity and volume** 1 litre is about 1.75 pints 1 litre is about 0.2 gallons

Note: metric values use $1\,cm^3 = 1\,ml$ and $1\,m^3 = 1000\,litres$.

Activity Which of the units mentioned in these statements are metric and which are imperial?

This sheet is 8 foot by 4 foot and 6 millimetres thick.

I did about 300 miles last week so I'll need about 8 gallons to fill the tank. How many litres is that?

The olympic champion runs 100 metres at an average speed of nearly 25 miles per hour.

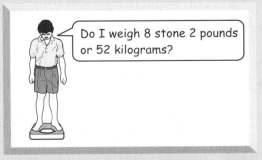

Do I weigh 8 stone 2 pounds or 52 kilograms?

353

1 (a) How many millimetres are there in 4.32 m?
(b) How many metres are there in 423 cm?
(c) How many metres are there in 52.4 km?

(a) 1 m = 1000 mm.
4.32 m = 4.32 × 1000 mm
= 4320 mm

(b) 1 m = 100 cm.
423 cm = 423 ÷ 100 m
= 4.23 m

(c) 1 km = 1000 m.
52.4 km = 52.4 × 1000 m
= 52400 m

2 (a) Convert 40 cm to inches.
(b) How many pints are there in a 4 litre carton of milk.
(c) How long is 400 km in miles?

(a) 1 inch is about 2.5 cm.
40 cm is about 40 ÷ 2.5 inches.
40 cm is about 16 inches.

(b) 1 litre is about 1.75 pints.
4 litres is about 4 × 1.75 pints
4 litres is about 7 pints.

(c) 8 km is about 5 miles.
400 ÷ 8 = 50
50 × 5 = 250
400 km is about 250 miles.

Exercise 32.1

Do not use your calculator in questions 1 to 8.

1 (a) How many metres are there in 3123 mm?
(b) How many centimetres are there in 4.5 m?
(c) How many metres are there in 3.24 km?
(d) How many grams are there in 1 tonne?
(e) How many litres are there in 400 ml?

2 A can of coke contains 330 ml. How many litres of coke are there in 6 cans?

3 One lap of a running track is 400 m. How many laps are run in an 8 km race?

4 Ben takes two 5 ml doses of medicine four times a day. Ben stops taking the medicine after 5 days. Originally, there was $\frac{1}{4}$ of a litre of medicine. How much medicine is left?

5 Twenty children at a party share equally 1 kg of fruit pastilles and 600 g of wine gums. What weight of sweets does each child receive?

6 A recipe for a dozen biscuits uses 240 g of flour. James has 1.2 kg of flour. How many biscuits can he make?

7 Convert each quantity to the units given.
(a) 10 kg to pounds.
(b) 20 litres to pints.
(c) 5 metres to inches.
(d) 6 inches to millimetres.
(e) 50 cm to inches.

8 A box contains 200 balls. Each ball weighs 50 g. Estimate the total weight in pounds.

9 James is 5 feet 8 inches tall. Estimate James' height in centimetres.

10 James weighs 10 stone 6 pounds. Estimate James' weight in kilograms.

11 Estimate:
(a) the number of metres in 2000 feet,
(b) the number of kilometres in 3 miles,
(c) the number of feet in 170 centimetres,
(d) the number of pounds in 1250 grams.

12 A sheet of card measures 12 inches by 20 inches. What is the area of the card in square centimetres?

EXAMPLES

1 The Great Wall of China, the longest man-made structure in the world, is about 2350 km long.
Degree of accuracy: nearest 50 km.

2 Earthquake shock waves travel through rock at a speed of approximately 25 000 km/hour.
Degree of accuracy: nearest 1000 km/hour.

3 The smallest mammal is the Kitti's hog-nosed bat.
It weighs about 1.5 g.
Degree of accuracy: nearest 0.1 g.

4 The current Olympic record for the men's 100 m is 9.92 seconds.
Degree of accuracy: nearest 0.01 seconds.

Exercise 32.2

1 Give a sensible estimate and an appropriate unit for the following measures:
(a) the length of a matchstick,
(b) the length of a football pitch,
(c) the weight of a ruler,
(d) the weight of a double decker bus,
(e) the volume of drink in a glass,
(f) the volume of water in a fish tank.
In each case state the degree of accuracy you have chosen for your estimate.

2 The diagram, which is drawn to scale, shows a man standing next to a tree. Using an appropriate metric unit estimate the height of the tree. State the degree of accuracy that you have used in making your estimate.

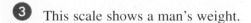

3 This scale shows a man's weight.

What is the man's weight?
Give your answer in an appropriate unit and state the degree of accuracy you have used.

4 How much milk is in this jug?

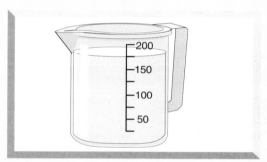

Give your answer in an appropriate unit and state the degree of accuracy you have used.

5 "My teacher's height is about 1.7 mm",
This statement is incorrect.

It can be corrected by changing the unit:
"My teacher's height is about 1.7 m",
or it can be corrected by changing the quantity.
"My teacher's height is about 1700 mm".

Each of these statements is also incorrect.
"Tyrannosaurus, a large meat eating dinosaur, is estimated to have been about 12 cm long".
"The tallest mammal is the giraffe which grows up to about 5.9 mm tall".
"My car used 5 ml of petrol on a journey of 35 miles".
"The area of the school hall is about 500 mm²".

Correct each statement:
(a) by changing the unit,
(b) by changing the quantity.
For each statement give the degree of accuracy that is used.

Harder conversions

Some units of measurement are more difficult to convert.

EXAMPLES

1 Convert 22.5 m² to square yards.

1 yard = 3 × 30.5 = 91.5 cm
91.5 cm = 91.5 ÷ 100 = 0.915 m.
An area of 1 square yard
= 0.915 × 0.915 m².
22.5 ÷ 0.915² = 26.9 (to 3 significant figures).
22.5 m² is equivalent to 26.9 square yards.

2 Convert a speed of 60 miles per hour to km per hour.

5 miles = 8 km.
60 ÷ 5 = 12,   12 × 8 = 96
60 miles = 96 km.
60 miles per hour = 96 km per hour.

3 Convert a speed of 60 miles per hour to metres per second.

60 miles per hour = 96 km per hour.
96 km per hour = 96 000 m per hour
In 1 hour there are 60 × 60 = 3600 seconds.
96 000 ÷ 3600 = 26.7 (to 3 significant figures).
60 miles per hour = 26.7 metres per second.

4 Convert a density of 66 pounds/ft³ to kg/m³.

66 pounds = 66 ÷ 2.2 = 30 kg.
66 pounds/ft³ = 30 kg/ft³.
1 foot = 0.305 m.
1 ft³ = 0.305³ m³ = 0.0284 m³.
30 kg/ft³ = 30 ÷ 0.0284 = 1056.3 kg/m³.
66 pounds/ft³ = 1056.3 kg/m³.

Exercise 32.3

You may use a calculator in this exercise. Give your answers to a suitable degree of accuracy.

1 30 g of grass seed is needed to sow 1 m² of lawn.
What weight of grass seed is needed to sow a rectangular lawn measuring 40 foot by 30 foot?

2 (a) Convert a volume of 10 cubic inches to cubic centimetres.
(b) How many cubic feet are there in 20 m³?

3 Concrete is sold by the cubic metre.
A path, 31 feet long, 5 feet wide and 1 foot 6 inches deep, is to be made of concrete. How many cubic metres of concrete are needed?

4 Rashid needs 40 square yards of carpet. Carpet is sold using square metres. Calculate the area of carpet that Rashid needs in square metres.

5 Convert the following speeds to km per hour.
(a) 30 miles per hour,
(b) 50 miles per hour,
(c) 30 metres per second.

6 Convert the following speeds to miles per hour.
(a) 60 km per hour,
(b) 40 metres per second.

7 Convert the density 50 g/mm³ to kg/m³.

8 (a) A car does 40 miles to the gallon. How many kilometres does it do per litre?
(b) A car does 9.6 kilometres to the litre. How many miles does it do per gallon?

9 A train leaves King's Cross at 6.15 a.m. It arrives in Newcastle at 9.34 a.m. The train travels a distance of 262 miles.
(a) Calculate its average speed in miles per hour.
(b) Calculate its average speed in kilometres per hour.

10 Billy drives 24 miles at an average speed of 64 km/hour.
He sets out on his journey at 0810. At what time does his journey end?

Discrete and continuous measures

Discrete measures

Discrete measures can only take particular values.

For example:
  The number of people on a bus is 42.
  Two ice skating judges give scores of 5.1 and 5.2.
The number of people on a bus must be a whole number.
The ice skating scores show that a discrete measure does not need to be a whole number. They are discrete because scores are not given between numbers like 5.1 and 5.2.

Other examples of discrete measures

1. The number of pupils in a school is 630. This is a discrete measure because the number of pupils can only be a particular whole number.
2. The size of a pair of shoes. This is a discrete measure because the size can only take particular values like 5, $5\frac{1}{2}$, 6 …

Continuous measures

James was 14 on the day of his 14th birthday. He will still be called 14 years old right up to the day before his 15th birthday.
So, although James is 14, his actual age is any age within a range of 1 year.

I am 14.

I am 14 years and 3 months.

Jenny is **not** exactly 14 years and 3 months old.
However, Jenny's age is given to a greater degree of accuracy than James' age because the range of possible ages in her case is smaller.
What is the range of possible ages in Jenny's measurement of her age?

Measures which can lie within a range of possible values are called **continuous measures**.
The value of a continuous measure depends on the accuracy of whatever is making the measurement.

Other examples of continuous measures

1 Billy and Chandni stand against a scale on the classroom wall.

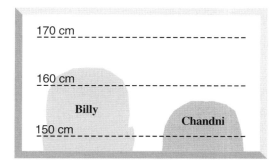

Billy is taller than Chandni but both of their heights are recorded as 160 cm because the scale only measures to the nearest 10 cm.
Make a copy of the scale.
Mark on it some more heights that would be recorded as 160 cm to the nearest 10 cm.

2 This diagram shows the first two runners in a 400 metre race as they cross the winning line.

Both runners were timed at 63 seconds. However, the winner has run faster than the runner who was second. So 63 seconds must represent different times.
What degree of accuracy do you think has been used to measure the time in the race?
Give some possible times for these runners if the time had been measured to the nearest one tenth of a second.

A closer look at continuous quantities

1 Jane is 160 cm tall to the nearest 10 cm. What are the limits between which her true height lies?

When rounding to the nearest 10:
The smallest value that rounds to 160 is 155.
155 cm is the smallest height that Jane can be.
The largest value that rounds to 160 is 164.$\dot{9}$.
164.$\dot{9}$ cm is the largest height that Jane can be.
For ease the value 164.$\dot{9}$ is normally called 165 (even though 165 rounds to 170).

So Jane's actual height is any height from 155 cm to 165 cm.
This can be written as the inequality:
$155 \leqslant$ Jane's height < 165

2 Jane is 162 cm tall to the nearest 1 cm. What are the limits between which her true height lies?

When rounding to the nearest 1:
The smallest value that rounds to 162 is 161.5.
161.5 cm is the smallest height that Jane can be.
The largest value that rounds to 162 is 162.4$\dot{9}$.
162.4$\dot{9}$ cm is the largest height that Jane can be.
For ease the value 162.4$\dot{9}$ is normally called 162.5 (even though 162.5 rounds to 163).

So Jane's actual height is any height from 161.5 cm to 162.5 cm.
This can be written as the inequality:
$161.5 \leqslant$ Jane's height < 162.5

Exercise 32.4

1 State whether each of the following are discrete or continuous measures.
  (a) The volume of wine in a wine glass.
  (b) The votes cast for the Independent Party candidate in a Local election.
  (c) The number of pages in a newspaper.
  (d) The time it takes to walk to school.
  (e) The number of beds in a hospital.
  (f) The weight of your best friend.

2 For each of the following measures state whether the value given is an exact value or give the limits within which it could lie.
  (a) A book has 224 pages.
  (b) A bus was 5 minutes late.
  (c) Tom has two brothers.
  (d) I weigh 63 kg.
  (e) Judy is 153 cm tall.

3 What are the slowest and fastest possible times:
  (a) of Derek who runs exactly 100 metres in 13 seconds measured to the nearest second,
  (b) of Jan who swims exactly 100 metres in 82.6 seconds measured to the nearest tenth of a second?

4 Tina is 1.53 m tall.
  (a) To what degree of accuracy is Tina's height given?
  (b) What are the limits between which her true height lies?

5 (a) What is the minimum weight of a 62 kg parcel measured to the nearest kilogram?
  (b) What is the minimum length of a 2.3 m shelf measured to the nearest 0.1 m?
  (c) What is the minimum time for a race timed at 12.63 seconds measured to the nearest one hundredth of a second?

6 What degree of accuracy has been used to make these estimates of the length of a corridor:
  (a) About 120 m.
      The smallest possible length is 115 m.
  (b) About 100 m.
      The smallest possible length is 75 m.
  (c) About 200 m.
      The smallest possible length is 150 m.

Dimensions and formulae

Formulae can be used to calculate perimeters, areas and volumes of various shapes.
By analysing the **dimensions** involved it is possible to decide whether a given formula represents a perimeter, an area or a volume.

Length (L) has **dimension 1.**
Length (L) × Length (L) = **Area** (L^2) has **dimension 2.**
Length (L) × Length (L) × Length (L) = **Volume** (L^3) has **dimension 3.**

The size of this square based cuboid depends on:
 x, the length of the side of the square base,
 y, the height of the cuboid.

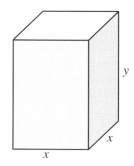

The total **length** of the edges of the cuboid is given by the formula:
 $E = 8x + 4y$
This formula involves:
Numbers: 8 and 4
Lengths(L): x and y
The formula has **dimension 1**.

The total **surface area** of the cuboid is given by the formula:
 $S = 2x^2 + 4xy$
This formula involves:
Numbers: 2 and 4
Areas (L^2): $x \times x$ and $x \times y$
The formula has **dimension 2**.

The **volume** of the cuboid is given by the formula:
 $V = x^2y$
This formula Involves:
Volume (L^3): $x \times x \times y$
This formula has **dimension 3**.

EXAMPLE

In each of these expressions the letters a, b and c represent lengths.
Use dimensions to check whether the expressions could represent a perimeter, an area or a volume.

(a) $2a + 3b + 4c$ (b) $3a^2 + 2b(a + c)$
(c) $2a^2b + abc$ (d) $3a + 2ab + c^3$

> **Note**
> When checking formulae and expressions numbers can be ignored because they have no dimension.
> ≡ means 'is equivalent to'.

(a) $2a + 3b + 4c$
  Write this using dimensions.
  L + L + L ≡ 3L ≡ L
  $2a + 3b + 4c$ has dimension 1 and could represent a perimeter.

(b) $3a^2 + 2b(a + c)$
  Write this using dimensions.
  L^2 + L(L + L)
  ≡ L^2 + L(2L)
  ≡ L^2 + 2L^2
  ≡ 3L^2
  ≡ L^2
  $3a^2 + 2b(a + c)$ has dimension 2 and could represent an area.

(c) $2a^2b + abc$
  Write this using dimensions.
  L^2 × L + L × L × L
  ≡ L^3 + L^3
  ≡ 2L^3
  ≡ L^3
  $2a^2b + abc$ has dimension 3 and could represent a volume.

(d) $3a + 2ab + c^3$
  Write this using dimensions.
  L + L × L + L^3
  ≡ L + L^2 + L^3
  The dimensions are **inconsistent**.
  $3a + 2ab + c^3$ represents neither a perimeter, an area or a volume.

Exercise **32.5**

1 p, q, r and x, y, z represent lengths.
For each formula state whether it represents
a length, an area or a volume.

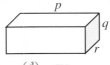
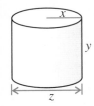

(a) pq (b) $2\pi x$ (c) $p + q + r$ (d) πz
(e) pqr (f) $2(pq + qr + pr)$ (g) $\pi x^2 y$ (h) $2\pi x(x + y)$

2 In each of the expressions below x, y and z represent lengths.
By using dimensions decide whether each expression could represent a perimeter, an area, a
volume or none of these.
Explain your answer in each case.

(a) $x + y + z$ (b) $xy + xz$ (c) xyz (d) $x^2(y^2 + z^2)$
(e) $x(y + z)$ (f) $\dfrac{x^2}{y}$ (g) $\dfrac{xz}{y}$ (h) $x + y^2 + z^3$
(i) $xy(y + z)$ (j) $x^3 + x^2(y + z)$ (k) $xy(y^2 + z)$ (l) $x(y + z) + z^2$

3 The diagram shows a discus.
x and y are the lengths shown on the diagram.
These expressions could represent certain quantities
relating to the discus.

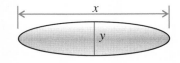

$\pi(x^2 + y^2)$ $\pi x^2 y^2$ πxy $2\pi(x + y)$

(a) Which of them could be an expression for:
    (i) the longest possible distance around the discus,
    (ii) the surface area of the discus.
(b) Use dimensions to explain your answers to part (a).

4 x, y and z represent lengths.
(a) $A = xyz + z(x - y) + 2y$
This is not a formula for either
perimeter, area or volume.
Use dimensions to explain why.
(b) $P = 3z(x + y)$
This could be a formula for area.
Use dimensions to explain why.
(c) $V = x^2 y + z^2(2x - y) + 2y^3$
This could be a formula for volume.
Use dimensions to explain why.

5 p, q, r and s represent the lengths of the
edges of this triangular prism.

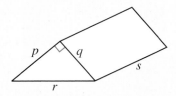

Match the formulas to the measurements.

Formulas
$\frac{1}{2}pqs$ $2(p + q + r + \frac{3s}{2})$ $s(p + q + r) + pq$

Measurements
Edge length   Surface area   Volume

6 These arrows are similar.

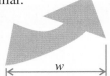

w represents the width of any arrow.
k and c are numbers.
H represents the height of the arrow and
A its area.
Which of the following statements could
be correct and which **must** be wrong.
(a) $H = kw$ (b) $H = ckw$
(c) $H = kw + c$ (d) $A = cw$
(e) $A = kw^2$ (f) $A = kw^3$

Give a reason for each of your answers
and where you think the formula **must**
be wrong suggest what it might be for.

7 In these formulae a, b and c represent
lengths and A represents an area.
(a) $a = b + c$ (b) $a^2 = bc$
(c) $A = a^2 + bc$ (d) $c = A + ab$
(e) $Ab = a^3$ (f) $A = \dfrac{a^2}{c} + b^2$
Which of the formulas have consistent
dimensions?

You need to know:

- the common units — both **metric** and **imperial** — used to measure **length**, **mass** and **capacity**.

- how to convert from one unit to another. This includes knowing the connection between one metric unit and another and the approximate equivalents between metric and imperial units.

- how to convert measures such as areas or volumes and speed or density from one unit to another.

- how to estimate measurements using sensible units and a suitable degree of accuracy.

- that a **discrete measure** can only take a particular value and a **continuous measure** lies within a range of possible values which depends upon the degree of accuracy of the measurement.

- that a continuous measure is more accurate when the range of possible values is smaller.

- how to distinguish between formulas for length, area and volume by considering **dimensions**.

IDEAS FOR INVESTIGATION

Shoe size is a discrete measure. Foot size is a continuous measure.
Investigate the connection between foot size and shoe size.

Review Exercise

Do not use your calculator in Questions 1 to 6.

1 (a) Anna measures her hand span to be 18 cm.

18 cm

Not to scale

What is this in metres?

(b) An exercise book is 0.3 cm thick. What is this in millimetres?

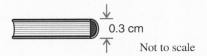

0.3 cm

Not to scale

SEG 1995

2 How many 40 gram bags of sweets can Billy make with 3 kg of sweets?

3 One cake contains 0.2 pounds of butter. How many cakes can be made with 5 kg of butter?

4

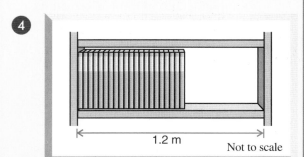

1.2 m

Not to scale

How many magazines, each 0.6 cm thick, will fit on a bookcase shelf which is exactly 1.2 m wide?

5 One glass of lemonade contains 300 ml. How many glasses of lemonade can be poured from three jugs each of which contain 2.5 litres?

6 Add 0.0021 tonnes, 640 grams and 0.023 kilogrammes.
Give your answer in kilogrammes.

7 Show that a metric tonne of coal and an imperial ton of coal are approximately the same weight.

8 (a) Which is longer 10 000 metres or 6 miles?
(b) Which is shorter $\frac{3}{8}$ of an inch or 10 mm?

9 One litre of water weighs 1 kg.
One litre of water is approximately 0.22 of a gallon.
(a) Estimate the weight of one gallon of water in pounds.
(b) Calculate how many litres are equivalent to one gallon.
Give your answer correct to one decimal place.

SEG 1996

10 Tim is 5 feet 10 inches tall and weighs 72 kg.
Sam is 165 cm tall and weighs 11 stone 7 pounds.
Who is taller? Who is heavier?

11 Ben buys 4 lb 4 oz of apples which cost £1.24 per kg.
453 grams is equal to 1 lb.
(a) Calculate the weight of the apples in kilograms, writing down all the figures shown on your calculator display.
(b) (i) For the purpose of calculating the cost, write this weight to an appropriate degree of accuracy.
(ii) Explain why you used this degree of accuracy.

SEG 1996

12 Convert an area of 25 m² to:
(a) cm² (b) square feet.

13 Convert a speed of 30 miles per hour into feet per second.
1 mile = 5280 feet.

SEG 1995

14 James runs at an average speed of 12 miles/hour.
Tim runs at an average speed of 320 m/minute.
Who runs the fastest?

15 According to the instructions Vinyl Matt paint covers about 13 m²/litre.
(a) Estimate the area covered with 2 gallons of paint?
(b) Estimate how many litres of paint is needed to cover a wall which measures 18 feet by 10 feet.

16 The total surface area of the Earth's oceans is 362 million square kilometres.
To what degree of accuracy is this measurement given?

17 Write down three examples of:
(a) a discrete quantity,
(b) a continuous quantity.

18 Which of these measurements is discrete and which is continuous?
(a) Two pints of milk.
(b) Two 1 pint bottles of milk.
Explain your answer.

19 A blue whale weighs 140 tonnes to the nearest 10 tonnes.
What is the smallest possible weight of a blue whale?

20 (a) What is the greatest possible difference between the times of two runners who both run a race in 12.2 seconds timed to the nearest tenth of a second?
(b) What is the smallest possible length of a piece of string which measures 25 cm to the nearest centimetre.

SEG 1995

21 When measured to the nearest 100 ml the volume of a container was found to be 600 ml.
When measured to the nearest 10 ml the volume of the same container was found to be 650 ml.
Give an example of a volume that agrees with **both** of these measurements.

22 Write down the smallest and largest possible values of each of the following measures.

(a) 1 km measured to:
    (i) the nearest 100 m,
    (ii) the nearest 10 m,
    (iii) the nearest 1 m,
    (iv) the nearest 10 cm.

(b) 5000 gallons measured to:
    (i) the nearest 1000 gallons,
    (ii) the nearest 100 gallons,
    (iii) the nearest 10 gallons,
    (iv) the nearest gallon.

(c) 20 seconds measured to:
    (i) the nearest second,
    (ii) the nearest tenth of a second,
    (iii) the nearest hundredth of a second.

(d) 1000 kg measured to:
    (i) the nearest 500 kg,
    (ii) the nearest 50 kg,
    (iii) the nearest 5 kg,
    (iv) the nearest 20 kg,
    (v) the nearest 200 kg.

23 Which formula represents the total surface area of this hexagonal prism.

$11.2r^3$, $2\pi r^2 + 6r^2$, $11.2r$, $11.2r^2$.

Explain your answer.

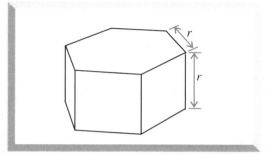

24 A solid has height h and length d.

(a) Explain why this could be a formula for the surface area of the solid:
$$A = \frac{d(5d + 4h)}{4}$$

(b) Explain why the dimensions of this formula are not consistent:
$$V = \frac{d^2(d + 3h^2)}{12}$$

(c) Make one change to the formula for V to make it dimensionally consistent with a volume formula.

25 In these expressions x and y are lengths.
$2(x + 3y)$, $3x^2y + 2y^2x$, $2x^2 + 2y(x + y)$
The expressions are for a length, an area and a volume. Which is which?

26 The letters a, b, h, l and r represent lengths.
Consider the following formulae.

ab, $\frac{2}{3}\pi r^3$, πr, $4\pi rl$, $\frac{\pi r^2 h}{3}$, $\sqrt{a^2 + b^2}$

(a) Which of these formulae represent areas?
(b) Use dimensions to explain how you can tell which formulae represent areas.

SEG 1994

27 This table shows formulae for lengths, areas and volumes of various shapes.

a, b, h, l, r and s are lengths.
Copy the table and complete the boxes beneath the formulae.
Put **L** in the box if the formula is for length.
Put **A** in the box if the formula is for area.
Put **V** in the box if the formula is for volume.

Formula	
$\pi r^2 h + \frac{2}{3}\pi r^3$	
$2\pi r + 2s$	
$2\pi r^2 + \pi rl$	
$\frac{h^2}{2}(a + b)$	

Section Review - Shape, Space and Measures

1 Margaret is making a model. One triangular face of the model is shown.

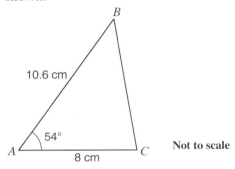

B

10.6 cm

54°

A 8 cm C

Not to scale

(a) Make an accurate drawing of this triangle.

(b) Measure angle *ACB*, on your drawing, correct to the nearest degree.

SEG 1995

2 The diagram shows the side elevation of the roof of a house. Lines *AB* and *CD* are horizontal and *DE* is vertical.

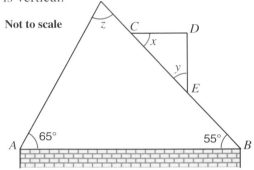

Not to scale

z C D

x

y

E

A 65° 55° B

(a) Explain why angle z = 60°.

(b) (i) Write down the size of angle *x*.

(ii) Give a reason for your answer.

(c) Calculate the size of angle *y*.

SEG 1996

3 A pair of garden shears is shown closed and in two positions when open.

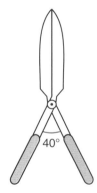

40°

40°

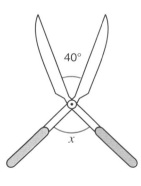

40°

x

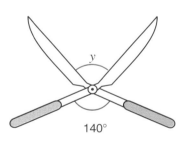

y

140°

Not to scale

(a) Calculate the size of angle *x*.

(b) Calculate the size of angle *y*.

SEG 1993

4 (a) Which of these shapes has not got rotational symmetry?

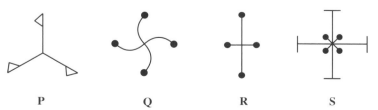

P Q R S

(b) Draw a shape which has exactly two lines of symmetry **and** rotational symmetry.

SEG 1995

364

5 This is the net of a square based pyramid.

The length of each side of the square is 3.5 cm.

The height of each triangle is 4 cm.

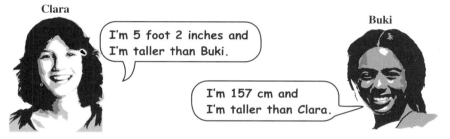

4 cm

3.5 cm

(a) Calculate the area of the square base.
(b) Calculate the area of **one** triangular face.
(c) What is the **total** area of the net?

Not to scale

SEG 1994

6 Two girls are talking about their heights.

Clara

I'm 5 foot 2 inches and I'm taller than Buki.

Buki

I'm 157 cm and I'm taller than Clara.

They cannot both be right.
Calculate who is taller.
You **must** show all your working.

> 0.394 inches = 1 cm.
> 12 inches = 1 foot.

SEG 1995

7 (a) Megan is 5 feet 3 inches tall.
   1 cm = 0.394 inches.
   12 inches = 1 foot.
   Calculate Megan's height in centimetres.
   Give your answer to an appropriate degree of accuracy.
(b) An electronic weighing scale gives Megan's weight as 63.4792 kg.
   Give her weight correct to an appropriate degree of accuracy.

SEG 1995

8 The diagram shows a solid drawn on isometric paper.
On isometric paper, draw an enlargement of the solid so that each edge of the enlargement is twice as long as the edge of the original solid.

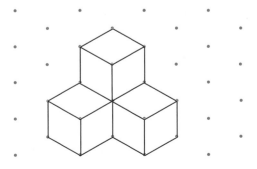

SEG 1997

9 The diagram shows a triangular prism.

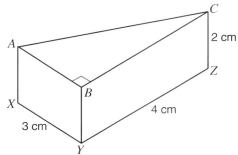

Angle $ABC = 90°$
$XY = 3$ cm, $YZ = 4$ cm and $CZ = 2$ cm.
(a) Calculate the volume of the prism, stating your units.
(b) Draw an accurate net of the prism.

SEG 1998

10 Andre is rolling a hoop along the ground.

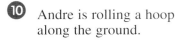

The hoop has a diameter of 60 cm.
(a) What is the circumference of the hoop?
Take π to be 3.14 or use the π key on your calculator.
(b) What is the minimum number of times the hoop must rotate to cover a distance of 5 m?

SEG 1994

11 In the diagram, the arcs AM and BM are each a quarter of a circle.

(a) Enlarge the given shape so that it fits exactly inside the rectangle $PQRS$.

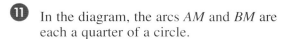

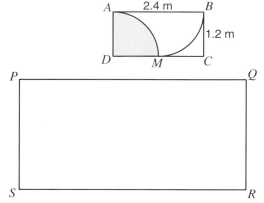

(b) Calculate the area of the rectangle $ABCD$.
(c) Calculate the shaded area AMD.

SEG 1997

12 (a) This is part of a tessellation of regular hexagons.

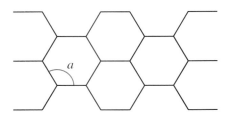

Calculate the interior angle of a hexagon, marked a.

(b) This is part of a tessellation of squares an regular octagons.

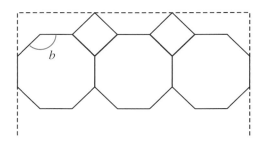

(i) Calculate the interior angle of the octagon, marked b.
(ii) Continue the tessellation above by drawing one more square and one more regular octagon inside the dotted lines.

SEG 1994

13 The diagram shows a regular octagon with centre O.

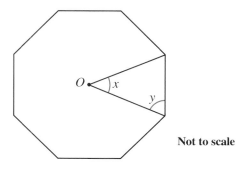

Not to scale

(a) Work out the size of angle x.
(b) Work out the size of angle y.

SEG 1998

14 The pentagon shown has four equal angles each labelled a.
Angle EDC is $100°$

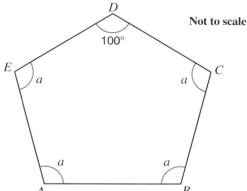

Not to scale

(a) Calculate the value of a.
(b) Calculate the size of angle CEA.
(c) Draw two lines on the pentagon to form two congruent triangles.
Name these triangles.

SEG 1991

15 The sketch shows the vertical cross-section of a feeding trough.
All measurements are in millimetres.
AB and DE are horizontal. AF and BC are vertical.

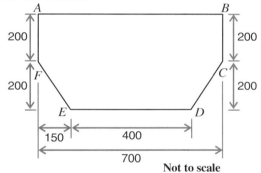

Calculate the area of cross-section
$ABCDEF$, in mm^2.

Not to scale

SEG 1988

16 The diagram shows the dimensions of a box of
lawn fertilizer.
(a) Calculate the volume of the box.

One box of fertilizer is needed for every $9\,m^2$
of lawn.
(b) How many boxes are needed to fertilize a
circular lawn of radius $4\,m$?

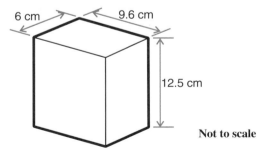

Not to scale

The fertilizer is also sold in cylindrical drums.
The volume of a drum is $3060\,cm^3$.
The height of a drum is $12\,cm$.
(c) Calculate the radius of a drum, stating
your units.

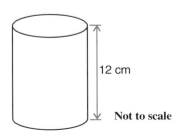

Not to scale

SEG 1997

17 A cylindrical paddling pool has a radius of 2.5 m and a depth of 0.28 m.

(a) Calculate the volume of the pool.

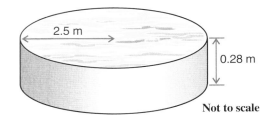

2.5 m

0.28 m

Not to scale

The pool is surrounded by a concrete path of width 50 cm.

(b) Calculate the surface area of the concrete path.

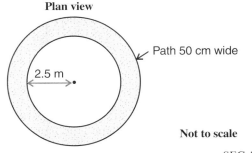

Plan view

2.5 m

Path 50 cm wide

Not to scale

SEG 1996

18 John has a piece of string to measure the perimeter of shapes. It fits exactly round a rectangle 10 cm by 8 cm.

(a) He uses the same length of string to form a circle.
Calculate the radius of the circle.
Take π to be 3.14 or use the π key on your calculator.

(b) Use your answer to (a) to find the area of the circle.

SEG 1994

19 Colin ran along a track for ten seconds.
He measured the distance he had run as 83 m, to the nearest metre.
What are the upper and lower limits for this distance?

SEG 1996

20 Two straight roads are shown on the diagram.
A new gas pipe is to be laid from Bere equidistant from the two roads.
The diagram is drawn to a scale of 1 cm to 1 km.

(a) Copy the diagram and construct the path of the gas pipe.

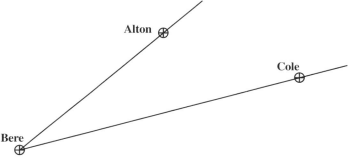

Alton

Cole

Bere

(b) The gas board needs a construction site depot.
The depot must be equidistant from Bere and Cole.
The depot must be less than 4 km from Alton.
Draw loci on the diagram to represent this information.

(c) The depot must be nearer the road through Cole than the road through Alton.
Mark on your diagram, with a cross, a possible position for the site depot which satisfies all these conditions.

21 (a) Triangle *D* is an enlargement of triangle *C*, scale factor 3, centre *W*.
Copy the diagram onto squared paper and draw triangle *D*.

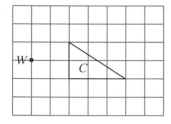

(b) Triangle *F* is an enlargement of triangle *E*, scale factor $\frac{1}{2}$, centre *X*.
Copy the diagram onto squared paper and draw triangle *F*.

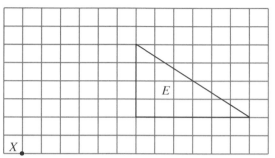

SEG 1994

22 (a) What type of transformation will move
  (i) triangle *T* onto triangle *A*,
  (ii) triangle *T* onto triangle *B*?

(b) Describe fully the single transformation which will move triangle *T* onto triangle *C*.

(c) Write down two triangles which are similar but not congruent.

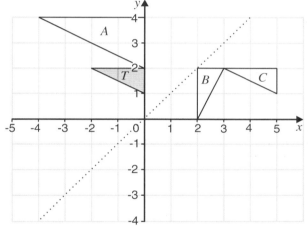

SEG 1993

23 The movement from *ABCD* to $A_1B_1C_1D_1$ is a rotation.
Find (a) the centre of rotation,
    (b) the angle of rotation.

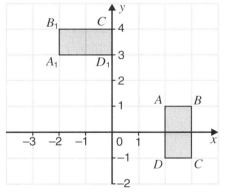

SEG 1988

24 (a) On squared paper draw triangle ABC with coordinates *A*(2, 1), *B*(4, 1) and *C*(4, 2).
(b) Reflect triangle *ABC* in the line *y* = *x*. Label the image $A_1B_1C_1$.
(c) The triangle $A_1B_1C_1$ is reflected in the *x* axis to give triangle $A_2B_2C_2$.
Draw triangle $A_2B_2C_2$.
(d) Describe fully the single transformation which will take triangle *ABC* onto triangle $A_2B_2C_2$.

SEG 1993

25 The diagrams show a car jack. *ABCD* is a rhombus.

(a) When diagonal *AC* = 48 cm, diagonal *BD* = 20 cm.
  (i) Calculate the length *AB*.
  (ii) Calculate the size of angle *BAC*.

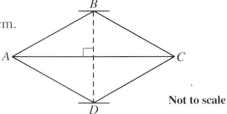

Not to scale

Mr Jenning wants to take a wheel off his car.
He needs to raise the car jack to a vertical
height of 36 cm.

(b) Calculate the length *AC*.

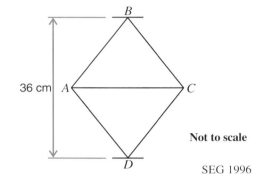

36 cm

Not to scale

SEG 1996

26 A frog sits on one side of a road. Directly opposite the frog is a vertical lamp post of height 15 feet. The angle of elevation of the top of the lamp post from the frog is 31°.

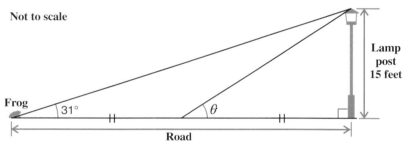

Not to scale

Lamp
post
15 feet

Frog

31°

θ

Road

(a) Calculate the width of the road.
(b) Calculate the angle of elevation, θ, of the top of the lamp post when the frog is exactly half way across the road.

SEG 1994

27 The diagram shows the design for a wooden ramp. Face *ABED* is perpendicular to the base *OABC*.

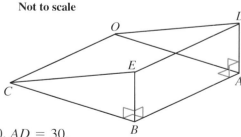

Not to scale

O

D

E

C

A

B

OA = 100, *AB* = 80, *AD* = 30.

(a) Calculate the length of *EC*.

The ramp is to be used for wheelchair access to a building. The maximum recommended slope is 15 degrees to the horizontal.

(b) Is the ramp design suitable?
  You must show **all** your working.

SEG 1995

370

28 In the diagram PQ is parallel to BC. Angle QAP is common to both triangles.

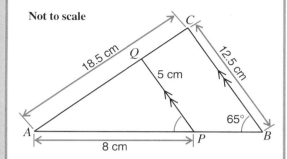

Not to scale

(a) Calculate the length AB.
(b) Write down the size of angle QPA.

SEG 1994

29 Pentagons $ABCDE$ and $PQRST$ are similar. All measurements are given in centimetres.
(a) Calculate the length of AB.
(b) Calculate the size of angle QRS.

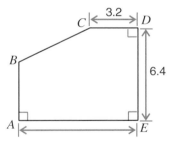

Not to scale

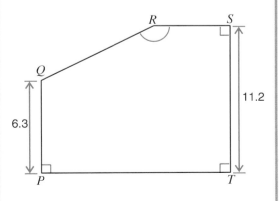

SEG 1995

30 The diagram shows the course sailed by a yacht from O to A and then from A to B.

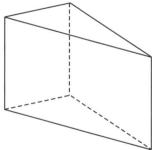

North

Not to scale

A is 3 km from O
B is 5 km from A on a bearing of 150°.
Angle OAB is 90°
Calculate the bearing on which the yacht must sail to return directly from B to O.
No marks will be given for a scale drawing.

SEG 1998

31 The letters a, b, c and d are all lengths, measured in cm, connected with this triangular prism.

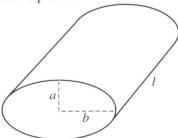

From the following list choose the correct formula for each measurement below.
$\frac{1}{2}abd$, $2(a + b + c) + 3d$, $ad + bd + cd + ab$.
(a) Total edge length (cm).
(b) Total surface area (cm²).
(c) Volume (cm³).

SEG 1994

32 The diagram shows a child's play brick in the shape of a prism.

The following formulae represent certain quantities connected with this prism.
πab, $\pi(a + b)$, πabl, $\pi(a + b)l$
Which of these formulae represent areas?

SEG 1995

Collection and Organisation of Data

To answer questions such as:

Which is the most popular colour of car?

Is it going to rain tomorrow?

Which team won the World Cup in 1998?

we need to collect data.

Data is continually being collected.
Governments collect data to assist in the planning of roads, schools, hospitals, housing, etc.
Manufacturers collect data to plan future production.
Organisations collect data about sporting achievements, investments and spending.
People collect data to plan DIY projects, holidays and diets.

Types of data

Data is made up of a collection of **variables**.
Each variable can be described, numbered or measured.

Data which can only be **described** in words is **qualitative**. Such data is often organised into categories, such as make of car, colour of hair, etc.

Data which is given **numerical** values, such as shoe size or height, is **quantitative**.
Quantitative data is either **discrete** or **continuous**.

> **Discrete** data can only take certain values, usually whole numbers, but may include fractions (e.g. shoe sizes).

> **Continuous** data can take any value within a range and is measurable (e.g. height, weight, temperature, etc.).

EXAMPLES

The taste of an orange is a qualitative variable.

The number of pips in an orange is a discrete quantitative variable.

The surface area of an orange is a continuous quantitative variable.

Exercise 33.1

State whether the following data is qualitative or quantitative.
If the data is quantitative state whether it is discrete or continuous.

1 The colours of cars in a car park.

2 The weights of eggs in a carton.

3 The numbers of desks in classrooms.

4 The names of students in a class.

5 The sizes of spanners in a toolbox.

6 The depths that fish swim in the sea.

7 The number of goals scored by football teams on a Saturday.

8 The brands of toothpaste on sale in supermarkets.

9 The sizes of ladies dresses in a store.

10 The heights of trees in a wood.

Collection of data

Data can be collected in a variety of ways; by observation, by interviewing people and by using questionnaires. The method of collection will often depend on the type of data to be collected.

Data collection sheets

Data collection sheets are used to record data.
To answer the question, "Which is the most popular colour of car?", we could draw up a simple data collection sheet and record the colours of passing cars by observation.

EXAMPLE

A **data collection sheet** for colour of car is shown, with some cars recorded.

Colour of car	Tally	Frequency
Black	||	2
Blue	ⅢⅢ Ⅲ	13
Green	||||	4
Red	ⅢⅢ |	
Silver	Ⅲ ||	
White	ⅢⅢ ||||	
	Total	

The colour of each car is recorded in the **tally** column by a single stroke.

To make counting easier, groups of 5 are recorded as Ⅲ.

How many red cars are recorded?
How many cars are recorded altogether?

Colour is a discrete variable. The total number of times each colour appears is called its **frequency**. A table for discrete data with the totals included is called a **frequency distribution**.

For large amounts of discrete data, or for continuous data, we organise the data into **groups** or **classes**. When data is collected in groups it is called a **grouped frequency distribution** and the groups you put the data into are called **class intervals**.

EXAMPLE

The weights of 20 boys are recorded in the grouped frequency table shown below.

Weight w kg	Tally	Frequency
$50 \leqslant w < 55$	|	1
$55 \leqslant w < 60$	|||	3
$60 \leqslant w < 65$	Ⅲ ||||	9
$65 \leqslant w < 70$	Ⅲ |	6
$70 \leqslant w < 75$	|	1
	Total	20

Weights are grouped into class intervals of equal width.

$55 \leqslant w < 60$ means 55 kg, or more, but less than 60 kg.

John weighs 54.9 kg. *In which class interval is he recorded?*
David weighs 55.0 kg. *In which class interval is he recorded?*

What is the width of each class interval?

1 The colours of 40 cars in a car park are shown.

red	red	blue	green	white	grey
blue	red	red	grey	white	green
red	white	white	blue	red	white
blue	blue	green	black	white	blue
red	silver	silver	blue	red	red
silver	white	white	red	blue	green
red	blue	silver	white		

(a) Make a frequency table for the data.
(b) Which colour of car is most popular?

2 The days of the week on which some students were born are recorded.

Monday	Monday	Sunday	Wednesday	Thursday
Friday	Saturday	Tuesday	Monday	Friday
Thursday	Sunday	Monday	Friday	Tuesday
Thursday	Wednesday	Tuesday	Monday	Wednesday
Friday	Monday	Saturday	Friday	Thursday
Tuesday	Thursday	Monday	Sunday	Tuesday
Saturday	Wednesday	Friday	Thursday	Tuesday
Monday	Wednesday	Friday	Sunday	Thursday
Tuesday	Wednesday	Sunday		

(a) Make a frequency table for the data.
(b) How many students are included?
(c) On which day of the week did most births occur?

3 The ages of 40 people are shown below.

27	34	54	57	3	12
15	19	29	30	33	47
35	20	39	28	9	11
26	42	50	26	10	7
33	49	21	18	1	25
24	34	19	20	27	37
43	56	37	34		

(a) Copy and complete the grouped frequency table for the data given.

Age	Tally	Frequency
0 - 9		
10 - 19		
20 - 29		

(b) What is the width of each class interval?
(c) How many people are in the class interval 30–39?
(d) How many people are less than 20 years old?
(e) How many people are 40 or older?

4 The heights, in centimetres, of 36 girls are recorded as follows.

148	161	175	156	155	160	178	159	170
163	147	150	173	169	170	174	166	163
162	158	155	165	168	154	156	163	167
172	170	165	160	164	172	157	173	161

(a) Copy and complete the grouped frequency table for the data.

Height h cm	Tally	Frequency
$145 \leqslant h < 150$		
$150 \leqslant h < 155$		

(b) What is the width of each class interval?
(c) How many girls are in the class interval $155 \leqslant h < 160$?
(d) How many girls are less than 160 cm?
(e) How many girls are 155 cm or taller?

5 Draw up a data collection sheet to record the month in which people were born.
Collect data from 50 people.
(a) Make a frequency table for the data.
(b) In which month did most births occur?

Databases

If we need to collect data for more than one type of information, for example; the make, colour, registration letter and mileage of cars; we will need to collect data in a different way.

We could create a **data collection card** for each car.

Car	1
Make	Vauxhall
Colour	Grey
Registration letter	P
Mileage	18 604

Alternatively, we could use a data collection sheet and record all the information about each car on a separate line.

This is an example of a simple **database**.

Car	Make	Colour	Registration letter	Mileage
1	Vauxhall	Grey	P	18 604
2	Ford	Blue	M	33 216
3	Ford	White	N	27 435
4	Nissan	Red	L	32 006

When all the data has been collected, separate frequency or grouped frequency tables can be drawn up.

1 The following database gives information about a group of 16 year old students.

Student	Gender	Height (cm)	Shoe size	Pulse rate (beats/min)
Mary	F	162	6	72
Alan	M	170	8	64
Jim	M	186	10	72
Tony	M	180	10	68
Laura	F	172	8	70
Jane	F	168	7	82
Wendy	F	155	5	72
Mark	M	180	9	68
Peter	M	168	8	62
Beryl	F	166	7	72

(a) Which student has the smallest shoe size?
(b) What is the gender of the student with the highest pulse rate?
(c) Which students are the same height?
(d) How many students are taller than Jane?
(e) Which students have a pulse rate of 72?
(f) What is the difference between the highest pulse rate and the lowest pulse rate?

2 A database of cars is shown.

Car	Make	Colour	Registration letter	Mileage
1	Vauxhall	Grey	P	18 604
2	Ford	Blue	M	33 216
3	Ford	White	N	27 435
4	Nissan	Red	L	32 006
5	Vauxhall	Blue	M	31 598
6	Ford	Green	L	37 685
7	Vauxhall	Red	P	21 640
8	Nissan	White	M	28 763
9	Ford	White	N	30 498
10	Vauxhall	White	P	9 865
11	Nissan	Red	R	7 520
12	Vauxhall	Grey	p	16 482

(a) (i) Draw up separate frequency tables for make, colour and registration letter.
   (ii) Draw up a grouped frequency table for mileage.
       Use class intervals of 5000 miles, starting at $0 \leqslant m < 5000$, $5000 \leqslant m < 10\,000$, . . .

(b) (i) Which make of car is the most popular?
   (ii) How many Ford cars are white?
   (iii) How many cars have a mileage of 30 000 or more?
   (iv) How many cars have a P registration letter?

3 (a) By using copies of the data collection card for cars or by using a copy of the data collection sheet, record information about the cars in your school car park.

(b) Draw up frequency tables for make, colour and registration letter and a grouped frequency table for mileage.

(c) (i) Which make of car is the most popular?
(ii) Which colour of car is the most popular?
(iii) How many cars have a mileage of 30 000 or more?
(iv) How many cars have a P registration letter?

4 Use data collection cards to collect information about students in your class. Include gender, height, shoe size and pulse rate.
Compare your data with the data in question 1.
What differences do you find?

5 (a) Design a data collection card to collect information on the leisure time activities of students.

(b) Draw up frequency or grouped frequency tables for the data.

(c) Which leisure time activity is the most popular?

(d) What differences are there in the leisure time activities of male and female students?

Questionnaires

Questionnaires are frequently used to collect data. In business they are used to get information about products or services and in politics they are frequently used to test opinion on a range of issues and personalities.

When constructing questions for a questionnaire you should:

(1) use simple language, so that everyone can understand the question;

(2) ask short questions which can be answered precisely, with a "yes" or "no" answer, a number; or a response from a choice of answers;

(3) provide tick boxes, so that questions can be answered easily;

(4) avoid open-ended questions, like: "What do you think of education?" which might produce long rambling answers which would be difficult to collate or process;

(5) avoid leading questions, like: "Don't you agree that there is too much bad language on television?" and ask instead:
"Do you think that there is too much bad language on television?"

Yes ☐   No ☐

(6) ask questions in a logical order.

Multiple-response questions

In many instances a choice of responses should be provided.

Instead of asking "How old are you?" which does not indicate the degree of accuracy required and many people might consider personal, we could ask instead:

Which is your age group?

under 18 ☐

18 to 40 ☐

41 to 65 ☐

over 65 ☐

Notice there are no gaps and only **one** response applies to each person.

Sometimes we invite **multiple responses** by asking questions, such as:

Which soaps do you watch?

Coronation Street ☐

Eastenders ☐

Emmerdale ☐

Brookside ☐

Hollyoaks ☐

Tick as many as you wish.

1 In preparing the questions for a questionnaire on radio listening habits the following questions were rejected.

   (a)   When do you listen to the radio?
   (b)   What do you like about radio programmes?
   (c)   Don't you agree that the radio gives the best news reports.

Explain why each question is unsuitable and rewrite the question so that it could be included in the questionnaire.

2 In preparing questions for a survey on the use of a library the following questions were considered. Explain why each question in its present form is unsuitable and rewrite the question.

   (a)   How old are you?
   (b)   How many times have you used the library?
   (c)   Which books do you read?
   (d)   How could the library be improved?

3 A school is to conduct a homework survey.
Suggest five questions which could be included.

4 A survey of reading habits is to be conducted.
Suggest five questions which could be included.

5 A survey of eating habits is to be conducted.
Suggest five questions which could be included.

Hypothesis

A **hypothesis** is a statement that may or may not be true.
To test a hypothesis we can construct a questionnaire, carry out a survey and analyse the results.

EXAMPLE   A questionnaire to test the hypothesis, "People think it is better to give than to receive." could include questions like these.

1.   **Gender:** male ☐   female ☐

2.   **Age:**   11 - 16 ☐   17 - 21 ☐   22 - 59 ☐   60 & over ☐

3.   **Do you think it is better to give than to receive?**
              Yes ☐   No ☐

4.   **To which of the following have you given in the last year?**
         School ☐   Charities ☐   Church ☐
         Hospital ☐   Special appeals ☐   Homeless ☐

Other (please list) _____

Suggest another question which could be included.

33

Sampling

When you carry out a survey, the **sample** of people you ask should be large enough to make the results meaningful and representative of the whole group or the results may be **biased**.
For example; to test the hypothesis "Girls are more intelligent than boys", you would need to ask equal numbers of boys and girls from various age groups.

Exercise **33.5**

1 Design a questionnaire to test the hypothesis:
"Children watch more television than adults".
Consider: (a)   does gender affect people's opinions?
               (b)   do people's opinions change with age?

2 Design a questionnaire to test the hypothesis:
"Boys are better at estimating than girls".
Consider: (a)   suitable tests,
               (b)   does the ability to estimate change with age?

3 Design a questionnaire to test the hypothesis:
"People think that everyone should take part in sport".
Describe the sample you could use to test this hypothesis.

4 Design a questionnaire to test the hypothesis:
"People think that animals should not be used to test drugs".
Describe the sample you could use to test this hypothesis.

5 Design a questionnaire to test the hypothesis:
"Children have too much homework".
Describe the sample you could use to test this hypothesis.

Two-way tables

We have already seen that the results of a survey can be recorded on data collection sheets and then collated using frequency or grouped frequency tables. We can also illustrate data using **two-way tables**.

A two-way table is used to illustrate the data for two different features (variables) in a survey.

EXAMPLE

The following two-way table shows the results of a survey.

	Wear Glasses	
	Yes	No
Boys	4	14
Girls	3	9

How many boys wear glasses?
How many children wear glasses?
How many children were surveyed?

Do the results of the survey prove or disprove the hypothesis,
"More boys wear glasses than girls"?
Explain your answer.

1 The two-way table shows the results of a survey to test the hypothesis: "More girls are left-handed than boys".
Do the results prove or disprove the hypothesis?
Explain your answer.

	Left-handed	
	Yes	No
Boys	3	18
Girls	2	12

2 The two-way table shows the results of a survey.

		E	D	C	B	A
Grade in Mathematics	A			1	2	2
	B		1	2	5	2
	C		1	8	3	
	D		3	3	2	
	E	2	1	2		

Grade in English

(a) How many students achieved the same grade in both subjects?
(b) How many students got a grade A, B or C in Mathematics?
(c) Do the results prove or disprove the hypothesis: "Students get better grades in English than Mathematics"? Explain your answer.

3 The two-way table shows the number of boys and girls in families taking part in a survey.

		0	1	2	3	4
Number of girls	4					
	3	1		2		
	2	1	2	3		
	1	5	9		1	1
	0		3		2	

Number of boys

(a) (i) How many families have two children?
(ii) Does the data support the hypothesis: "More families have less than 2 children than more than 2 children"? Explain your answer.

(b) (i) How many girls are included in the survey?
(ii) Does the data support the hypothesis: "More boys are born than girls"? Explain your answer.

4 The two-way table shows the age and gender of people taking part in a survey.

	Age				
	Under 18	18 to 25	26 to 40	41 to 64	65 and over
Female	0	2	7	9	7
Male	0	4	17	19	10

Give a reason why the data collected may not be representative of the whole population.

5 Suggest a hypothesis of your own.
(a) Design a suitable questionnaire to test your hypothesis.
(b) Choose a suitable sample and collect data.
(c) Does the data prove your hypothesis?

- **Qualitative** data – Data which can only be described in words.

- **Quantitative** data – Data that has a numerical value.
  Quantitative data is either **discrete** or **continuous**.
  Discrete data can only take certain values.
  Continuous data has no exact value and is measurable.

- **Data Collection Sheets** – Used to record data during a survey.

- **Tally** – A way of recording each item of data on a data collection sheet.
  A group of five is recorded as ⊬⊦⊦.

- **Frequency Table** – A way of collating the information recorded on a data collection sheet.

- **Grouped Frequency Table** – Used for continuous data or for discrete data when a lot of data has to be recorded.

- **Database** – A collection of data.

- **Class Interval** – The width of the groups used in a grouped frequency distribution.

- **Questionnaire** – A set of questions used to collect data for a survey.
  Questionnaires should:
  (1) use simple language,
  (2) ask short questions which can be answered precisely,
  (3) provide tick boxes,
  (4) avoid open-ended questions,
  (5) avoid leading questions,
  (6) ask questions in a logical order.

- **Hypothesis** – A hypothesis is a statement which may or may not be true.

- **Two-way Tables** – A way of illustrating two features of a survey.

Review Exercise

1 This is the printout from a computer database.

Group A	Won	Drawn	Lost	Goals scored	Goals against
Romania	2	0	1	5	5
Switzerland	1	1	1	5	4
USA	1	1	1	3	3
Colombia	1	0	2	4	5

Group C	Won	Drawn	Lost	Goals scored	Goals against
Germany	2	1	0	5	3
Spain	1	2	0	6	4
South Korea	0	2	1	4	5
Bolivia	0	1	2	1	4

Group B	Won	Drawn	Lost	Goals scored	Goals against
Brazil	2	1	0	6	1
Sweden	1	2	0	6	4
Russia	1	0	2	7	6
Cameroon	0	1	2	3	11

Group D	Won	Drawn	Lost	Goals scored	Goals against
Nigeria	2	0	1	6	2
Bulgaria	2	0	1	6	3
Argentina	2	0	1	6	3
Greece	0	0	3	0	10

Use the information above to answer these questions.
  (a) How many games were won by Nigeria?
  (b) Which country scored the most goals?

SEG 1996

2 The weights, in grams, of 24 bananas are shown.

128	120	184	113	170	206	179	99
92	156	234	192	106	163	180	100
119	150	173	232	115	200	166	196

Copy and complete the grouped frequency table for these bananas.

Weight (g)	Tally	Frequency
$80 \leqslant g < 120$		
$120 \leqslant g < 180$		
$180 \leqslant g < 250$		

3 Kathryn is conducting a survey on television viewing habits.
She thinks of two questions for the questionnaire.

Question 1. How old are you?
Question 2. When do you watch television?

(a) Explain why each of these questions is unsuitable.
(b) Rewrite each of these questions so that she could include them in her questionnaire.

SEG 1996

4 The following questionnaires were designed to find out how pupils travelled to school.

A
Please complete.

All answers should be put in the space provided.

Name .... Age ....

1. How do you come to school?

....

2. When do you leave home?

....

3. How long is your journey?

....

Thank you.

B
This questionnaire is part of a GCSE project.

1. How do you travel to school?

Walk	Bus	Car	Bicycle

2. How far do you travel to school?

0 - 1	1 - 2	2 - 3	Over 3 km

3. How long does your journey take?

....

(a) Write down one strength of questionnaire A and one weakness of questionnaire B.

(b) The following question was written to replace question 3 in both questionnaires.

How long is your journey to school?

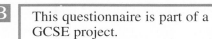

Under 5	5 - 10	10 - 15	15 - 20

Rewrite this question in a more suitable form.

SEG 1996

5 The table shows the age and gender of people taking part in a survey to test the hypothesis "Children have too much homework".

	Age				
	Under 11	11 to 16	17 to 25	26 to 50	Over 50
Male	0	4	6	5	5
Female	0	0	0	0	0

Give three reasons why the sample is biased.

6 In a survey of community life on a new housing estate the following question is suggested.

(a) "What do you most like about living here?"

An alternative is proposed.

(b) "Tick the box which describes why you most like living here."

Design of houses ☐

Friendliness of neighbours ☐

More open space ☐

Give one advantage of each form of question.

SEG 1995

7 Rosemary wants to know how people in her neighbourhood spend their leisure time.
She has produced a questionnaire to help her gather the information she needs.
Two of the questions that Rosemary used on her questionnaire are shown.

Question 1. How old are you?

Question 2. What is your favourite sport?

Rewrite each question so that there are 3 possible responses.

Each question must be in a more appropriate form for a questionnaire.

SEG 1996

8 Lorraine is writing a questionnaire for a survey about her local Superstore.

She thinks that the local people visit the store more often than people from further away.
She also thinks that local people spend less money per visit.

Write three questions which would help her to test these ideas.

Each question should include three responses from which people choose one.

SEG 1994

9 A bus company wants to carry out a survey.

It wants to find out the distribution of the age of its passengers and the frequency with which they use buses.

The bus company intends to use a questionnaire.

Write **two** questions and responses that will enable the bus company to carry out the survey.

SEG 1995

10 Each student in Year 10 and 11 was asked to select one sport.
The choices made are shown in the table.

		Outdoor Sports		Indoor Sports	
		Hockey	Tennis	Badminton	Squash
Year 11	Girls	12	10	15	5
	Boys	10	15	7	19
Year 10	Girls	14	9	17	3
	Boys	15	12	11	13

(a) How many students chose hockey?
(b) How many more girls chose tennis than squash?
(c) One girl says that boys usually prefer outdoor sports.

Do the figures in the table support this view? Explain your answer.   SEG 1994

11 The table shows the number of people working different shifts at a factory.

Sex	Age (years)	Shift		
		Morning	Afternoon	Evening
Men	Under 30	6	8	9
	30 and over	7	12	17
Women	Under 30	8	11	18
	30 and over	6	15	23

John thinks that the proportion of people aged 30 years and over who work the evening shift
is greater than the proportion of people who are under 30 years of age who work the evening
shift.
Is he correct? You must show all your working.

          SEG 1996

12 In a survey about children, Valerie asked a
number of women how many boys and girls
they each have.
Her findings are shown in the table.

(a) How many of these women have
no children?
(b) How many women were included in
the survey?
(c) How many boys did these women
have altogether?

Number of girls						
5						
4	1	1				
3	3	4				
2	3		1			1
1	4	7	1		1	
0	8	3	1		1	
	0	1	2	3	4	5

Number of boys

          SEG 1994

384

Most people find numerical data easier to understand if it is presented in a pictorial or diagrammatical form. For this reason television reports, newspapers and advertisements frequently use graphs and diagrams to present data.

There are many ways of presenting data. Data which can be counted can be presented using a pictogram, bar chart or pie chart.

Pictograms

A **pictogram** uses symbols to represent information.
Each symbol can represent one or more items of data.

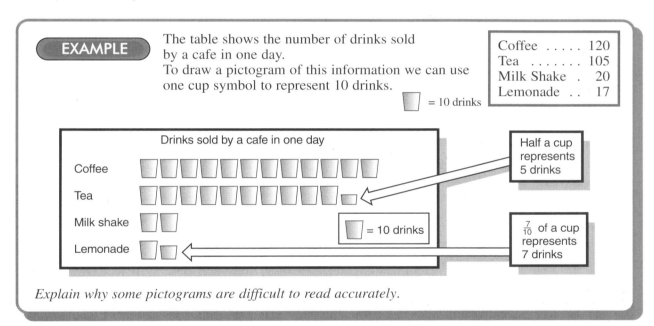

Explain why some pictograms are difficult to read accurately.

Exercise 34.1

1 The pictogram shows the number of first class and second class stamps sold by a post office in one hour.

(a) How many first class stamps were sold?
(b) Estimate how many second class stamps were sold.

2 The pictogram shows the results of a survey of how students travel to college.

(a) Fifteen students cycle to college. How many students walk?

(b) How many students were included in the survey?

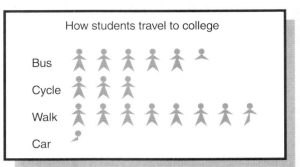

3 One hundred boys were asked which sport they preferred. The table shows the results.

Draw a pictogram to represent this information.

Use 🚶 = 5 boys

Sport	Football	Cricket	Rugby	Hockey	Basketball
Number of boys	45	3	15	10	27

Bar charts

Bar charts are a simple but effective way of displaying data.
Bars can be drawn either horizontally or vertically.

EXAMPLE

The table shows how a class of children travelled to school one day.

Method of travel	Bus	Cycle	Car	Walk
Boys	2	7	1	5
Girls	3	1	5	6

The bar charts below show this information.

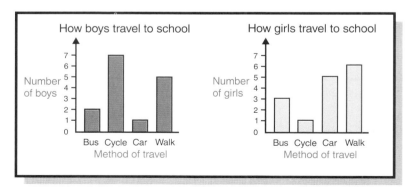

Notice that:
Bars are the same width.

There are gaps between the bars because data that can be counted is discrete.

The height of each bar gives the **frequency**.

The tallest bar represents the most frequent variable (category).

The most frequently occurring variable is called the **mode** or **modal** category.
Sometimes there may not be a mode, because no one value appears more than any other value.
Cycle is the modal category for the boys.
Which method of travel is the mode for the girls?

Bar charts are also used to compare data. To make it easier to compare information for boys and girls we can draw both bars on the same diagram, as shown.

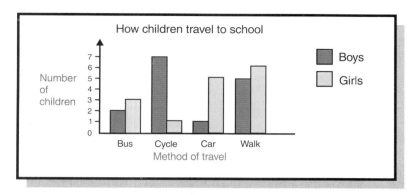

How many children travel to school by car?

Which method of travel is the least popular?

What percentage of girls walk to school?

Compare and comment on the methods of travel used by the boys and girls.

Bar-line graphs

Instead of drawing bars to show frequency we could draw vertical lines.
Such graphs are called **bar-line graphs** or **vertical line graphs**.
The lines can be drawn horizontally or vertically.

EXAMPLE

The graph shows the number of goals scored by a football team in 10 matches.

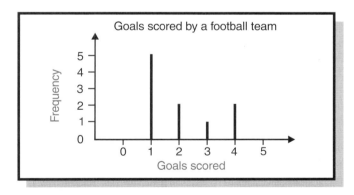

The frequency represents the number of matches played.

In how many matches was only one goal scored?

What is the difference between the largest number of goals scored in a match and the smallest number of goals scored?

The difference between the largest and smallest variable is called the **range**.
The range for the number of goals scored is $4 - 1 = 3$.

1 The bar chart shows the time Jim spent watching television each day last week.

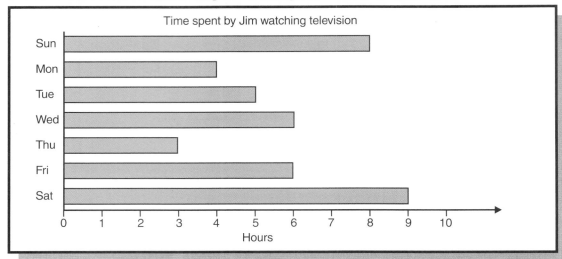

(a) On which day did Jim watch the most television?
(b) How many hours did Jim spend watching television on Tuesday?
(c) How many hours did Jim spend watching television last week?
(d) On which day did Jim spend a third of the day watching television?
(e) What fraction of the day did Jim spend watching television on Wednesday?
(f) What is the range of the number of hours per day Jim spent watching television?

2 The table shows the amount of pocket money given each week to a number of Year 11 girls.

Amount (£)	1	2	3	4	5	6	7	8	9	10
Number of girls	0	0	1	5	10	4	0	3	0	7

(a) Draw a bar-line graph of the data.
(b) What is the modal amount of pocket money?
(c) What is the range of the amount of pocket money given each week?
(d) What percentage of the girls got less that £5?

3 The bar-line graph illustrates the number of goals scored per match by a hockey team.

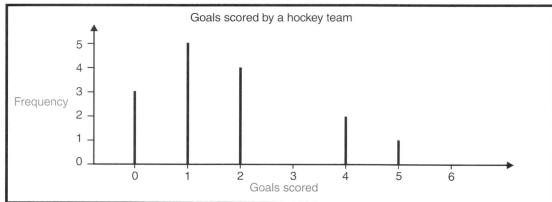

(a) How many matches have the team played?
(b) Which number of goals scored is the mode?
(c) What is the range of the number of goals scored?
(d) In what percentage of games were no goals scored?

4 The bar chart shows the results of a survey of the shoe sizes of pupils in a Year 9 class.

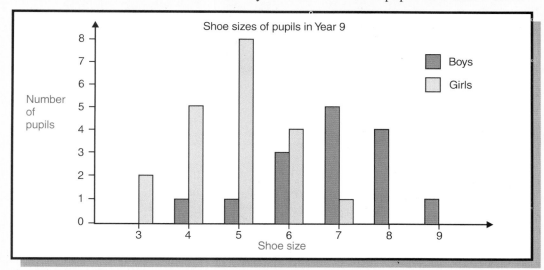

(a) Which size of shoe is the mode for the girls?
(b) Which size of shoe is the mode for the boys?
(c) How many pupils have shoe size 6?
(d) What percentage of boys have shoe size 8 or 9?
(e) What percentage of girls have shoe size 3 or 4?
(f) What is the range of shoe size for girls?
(g) What is the range of shoe size for boys?
(h) Compare and comment on the shoe sizes of boys and girls.

5 The bar chart shows the day of birth for a group of children.

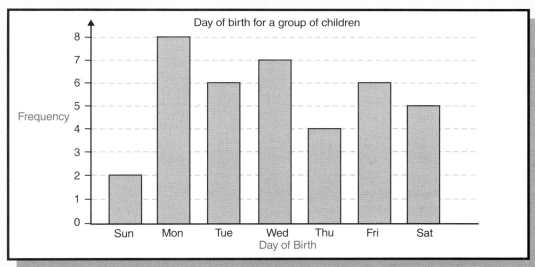

(a) How many children are in the group?
(b) Which day of birth is the mode?
The table shows the day of birth for the girls.

Day of birth	Sun	Mon	Tue	Wed	Thu	Fri	Sat
Number of girls	1	5	2	3	3	1	4

(c) Draw up a table to show the day of birth for the boys.

Bar charts are useful for comparing the various types of data (categories) with each other.
To compare each category with **all** the data collected we use a **pie chart**.

A pie chart is a circle which is divided up into sectors.
The whole circle represents the total frequency and each sector represents the frequency of one part (category) of the data.

Drawing pie charts

The table shows the ways in which some children like to eat eggs.

Method of cooking	Poached	Boiled	Scrambled	Fried
Number of children	5	8	6	11

To show this information in a pie chart we must find the angles of the sectors which represent each category.

First calculate the angle which represents each child.
30 children are represented by 360°.
1 child is represented by 360° ÷ 30 = 12°.
Sector angle = Number of children in category × 12°

Method of cooking	Poached	Boiled	Scrambled	Fried	**Total**
Number of children	5	8	6	11	**30**
Sector angle	60°	96°	72°	132°	**360°**

Using a table allows you to keep your work tidy and to make checks.

Method of Cooking Eggs

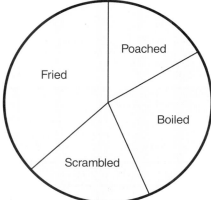

The whole circle represents the total frequency of 30.

Each sector represents the frequency of one category (method of cooking).

390

Exercise 34.3

1 The table shows the colour of cars in a car park.

Colour of car	Blue	Green	Red	Silver	White
Number of cars	10	3	8	6	9

Draw a pie chart to show this information.

2 The table shows information about the trees in a wood.

Type of tree	Ash	Beech	Maple	Rowan	Silver Birch
Number of trees	15	20	5	19	31

Draw a pie chart for this data.

3 The table shows the results of a survey to find the most popular takeaway food.

Type of takeaway	Fish & Chips	Chicken & Chips	Chinese	Pizza
Number of people	165	204	78	93

Draw a pie chart for this data.

4 The results of a survey to find the most popular terrestrial television channel is shown.

Television channel	BBC1	BBC2	ITV	Ch4	Ch5
Percentage of people	33	14	32	13	8

Show the information in a pie chart.

5 The breakfast cereal preferred by some adults is shown.

Breakfast cereal	Cornflakes	Muesli	Porridge	Branflakes
Number of adults	25	20	12	15

Show the information in a pie chart.

Interpreting pie charts

Pie charts are useful for showing and comparing proportions of data. However, they do not show frequencies. Such information can be found by interpreting the pie chart.

To interpret a pie chart we need to know:
● the sector angles (can be measured from an accurately drawn pie chart), **and**
● the total frequency represented by the pie chart, **or**
  the frequency represented by one of the sectors.

EXAMPLE

The pie chart shows the makes of 120 cars.
(a) Which make of car is the mode?
(b) How many of the cars are Ford?

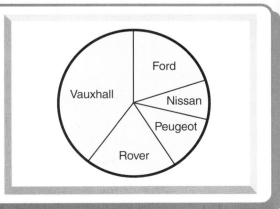

(a) The sector representing Vauxhall is the largest. Therefore, Vauxhall is the mode.

(b) The angle of the sector representing Ford is 72°.
The number of Ford cars = $\frac{72}{360} \times 120 = 24$

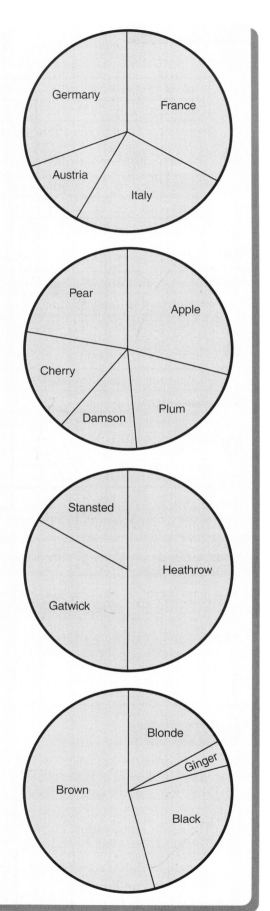

1 The pie chart shows the holiday destinations of 180 people.

   (a) Which holiday destination is the mode?

   (b) How many people went to Italy?

   (c) How many people went to Germany?

   (d) How many people went to Austria?

2 The pie chart shows the five types of fruit tree sold by a garden centre.

   21 apple trees were sold.

   (a) How many plum trees were sold?

   (b) How many fruit trees were sold altogether?

3 The pie chart shows the departure airports of some travellers.

   (a) Which airport is the mode?

   (b) 360 travellers departed from Gatwick.
        How many travellers departed from Heathrow?

   (c) How many travellers are there altogether?

4 The pie chart illustrates the results of a survey of the colour of hair of 48 boys.

   (a) Which colour of hair is the mode?

   (b) How many boys have brown hair?

   (c) What percentage of boys have black hair?

34

5 The pie chart shows the different types of tree in a forest.

There are 54 oak trees and these are represented by a sector of 27°.

(a) The pine trees are represented by an angle of 144°.
How many pine trees are there?

(b) There are 348 silver beech trees.
Calculate the angle of the sector representing silver birch trees.

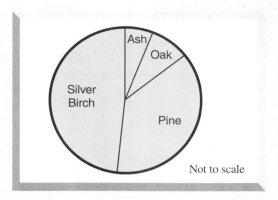

Not to scale

Line graphs

In monitoring progress and in business it is often necessary to show the trend (increases and decreases) over a period of time so that future performance can be predicted. The type of graph used in this situation is called a **line graph.**

EXAMPLE

The table shows the temperature of a patient taken every half-hour.

Time	0930	1000	1030	1100	1130	1200
Temperature °C	36.9	37.1	37.6	37.2	36.5	37.0

To draw a line graph of this information, the given values are plotted and then joined to show the trend.

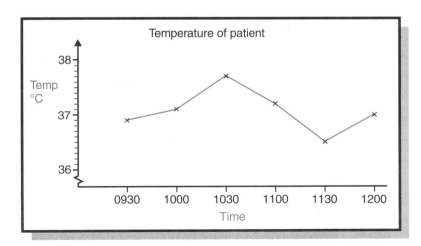

Only the plotted points show **known values**.

Lines are drawn to show the **trend**.

What is the highest temperature recorded?

*Explain why the graph can only be used to give an **estimate** of the patient's temperature at 1115.*

1 The midday temperature at a seaside resort was recorded each day for one week. The line graph shows the results.

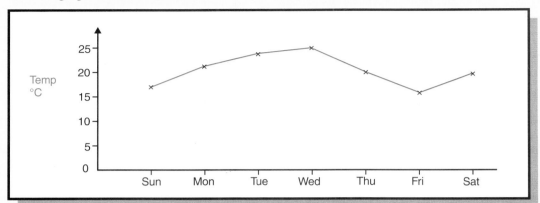

(a) What was the midday temperature on Thursday?
(b) Explain why you cannot use this line graph to estimate the temperature at midnight on Monday.

2 Each year, on his birthday, a teenager records his height. The table shows the results.

Age (yrs)	13	14	15	16	17	18	19
Height (cm)	145	151	157	165	174	179	180

(a) Draw a line graph to represent this information.
(b) Use your graph to estimate:
    (i) the height of the teenager when he was $14\frac{1}{2}$ years of age,
    (ii) the age of the teenager when he reached 160 cm in height.

3 The table shows the amount of money in Jayne's savings account at the end of each month, for six months.

Month	January	February	March	April	May	June
Amount (£)	106	131	155	95	119	132

(a) Draw a line graph to represent this information.
(b) Use your graph to estimate the amount in her account in the middle of February.
(c) Explain what happened to the account between March and April.

Grouped frequency distributions

We use bar charts when data can be counted and there are only a few different items of data. If there is a lot of data or if the data is continuous, we draw a **histogram** or a **frequency polygon**.

Histograms

Histograms are used to present data contained in grouped frequency distributions. In this section we will only be drawing histograms for grouped frequency distributions which have equal class width intervals. Histograms with equal class width intervals look like bar charts with no gaps.

Frequency polygons

A **frequency polygon** is drawn by plotting the frequencies at the midpoint of each class interval and then joining successive points with straight lines.

Frequency polygons are often used to compare two, or more, grouped frequency distributions on the same diagram.

EXAMPLE

The frequency distribution of the heights of some boys is shown.

Height (cm)	130−	140−	150−	160−	170−	180−
Frequency	1	7	12	9	3	0

Note:
130− means 130 or
more but less than 140.

Draw a histogram and a frequency polygon to illustrate the data.

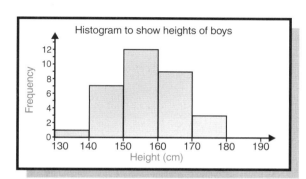

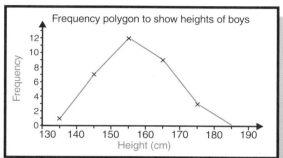

Individual bars are not labelled because the horizontal axis represents a **continuous** variable.

Exercise 34.6

1 A frequency distribution of the heights of some girls is shown.

Height (cm)	130−	140−	150−	160−	170−	180−	190−
Frequency	3	5	12	4	1	0	0

Draw a histogram to illustrate the data.

2 The table shows the distances travelled to school by 100 children.

Distance (km)	0−	2−	4−	6−	8−	10−	12−	14−16
Frequency	26	32	22	10	6	3	1	0

Draw a frequency polygon to illustrate this information.

3 The frequency distribution of the weights of some students is shown.

Weight (kg)	40−	50−	60−	70−	80−	90−100
Number of males	0	6	11	5	2	1
Number of females	3	14	8	0	0	0

(a) On the same diagram draw a frequency polygon for the males and a frequency polygon for the females.

(b) Compare and comment on the weights of male and female students.

4 The table shows the results for competitors in the 1997 and 1998 Schools' Javelin Championship.
Only the best distance thrown by each competitor is shown.

Distance thrown (m)	Number of competitors 1997	Number of competitors 1998
$10 \leqslant m < 20$	0	1
$20 \leqslant m < 30$	3	4
$30 \leqslant m < 40$	14	19
$40 \leqslant m < 50$	21	13
$50 \leqslant m < 60$	7	11
$60 \leqslant m < 70$	0	2

(a) On the same diagram draw a frequency polygon for the 1997 results and then a frequency polygon for the 1998 results.

(b) Compare and comment on the results.

What you need to know

- **Pictogram**. Used for data which can be counted.
  Symbols are used to represent either single items or groups of data.

- **Bar chart**. Used for data which can be counted.
  Often used to compare quantities of data in a distribution.
  Bars can be drawn horizontally or vertically.
  Bars are the same width and there are gaps between bars.
  The length of each bar represents frequency.
  The longest bar represents the **mode**.
  The difference between the largest and smallest variable is called the **range**.

- **Pie chart**. Used for data which can be counted.
  Often used to compare proportions of data, usually with the total.
  The whole circle represents all the data.
  The size of each sector represents the frequency of data in that sector.
  The largest sector represents the **mode**.

- **Line graph**. Used to show **trend**.
  Only the plotted points represent actual values.
  Points are joined by lines to show the trend.

- **Histogram**. Used to illustrate **grouped frequency distributions.**
  The horizontal axis is a continuous scale.

- **Frequency polygon**. Used to illustrate grouped frequency distributions.
  Often used to compare two or more distributions on the same diagram.
  Frequencies are plotted at the midpoints of the class intervals and joined with straight lines.
  The horizontal axis is a continuous scale.

Review Exercise

1 The pictogram shows the number of new houses built in different years by a builder.

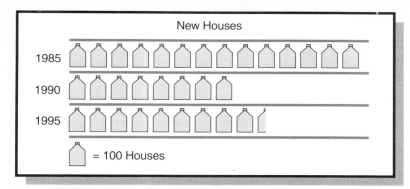

New Houses

1985

1990

1995

⌂ = 100 Houses

(a) How many houses were built in 1985?
(b) Estimate the number of houses built in 1995.

2 The bar chart shows the number of ice-cream cones sold at an ice-cream kiosk on a weekday in April.

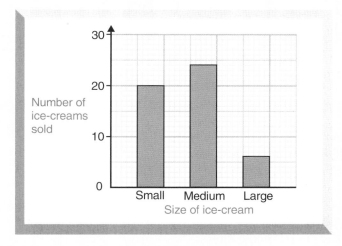

(a) Which size of ice-cream is the mode?
(b) How many large ice-creams were sold?
(c) How many ice-creams were sold altogether?
(d) What percentage of the ice-creams sold were large?
(e) Had the survey been carried out in August suggest two differences you would expect to see in the data.

3 Some families on holiday at a seaside resort were questioned about their holiday accommodation.

Type of accommodation	Hotel	Bed & Breakfast	Self-catering	Caravan	Camping	Other
Number of families	9	17	11	8	2	3

(a) Draw a bar chart to show this information.
(b) What is the most popular type of accommodation?
(c) How many families were questioned?
(d) What percentage of these families had Bed and Breakfast?

4 Kay delivers the following newspapers to houses on her paper round.

Paper	Express	Guardian	Mail	Mirror	Sun	Times
Number of copies	8	4	12	13	11	2

(a) Draw a horizontal bar-line graph of the data.
(b) Which newspaper is the mode?
(c) What percentage of houses take the Express?

5 In a school survey a record was made of all the reasons given by pupils for being absent. The results for one day are shown in the frequency diagram.

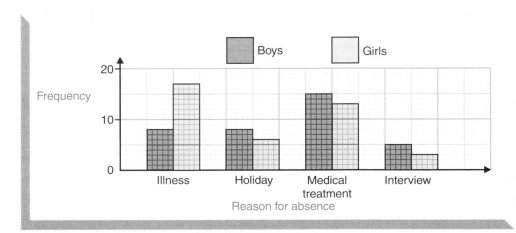

(a) Taking boys and girls together which reason for absence is the mode?
(b) How many pupils were absent that day?
(c) What proportion of those absent for an interview were girls?

SEG 1997

6 Toni sells Strawberry, Vanilla and Chocolate ice-creams. Each day he keeps a tally of the number of ice-creams sold.
One Sunday he makes the following tally.

Strawberry	ℍℍ ℍℍ ℍℍ ℍℍ ℍℍ ‖
Vanilla	ℍℍ ℍℍ ℍℍ ℍℍ ℍℍ ℍℍ ‖‖
Chocolate	ℍℍ ℍℍ ‖

He sold seventy-two ice-creams in total.
This information is to be illustrated in a pie chart.

(a) Copy and complete this table to show the angles of the three sectors in the pie chart.

Flavour of ice-cream	Angle of sector
Strawberry	
Vanilla	
Chocolate	

(b) Draw the pie chart to represent his ice-cream sales that day.

SEG 1995

7 You have been asked to illustrate the following information on a pie chart.

TYPICAL SPORT DIET		
Food type	**%**	**Angle**
Carbohydrate	60	216°
Fat	25	
Protein	15	

(a) (i) Calculate the angle of the sector which represents fat.
   (ii) Draw the pie chart.

(b) These pie charts show two other types of diet.

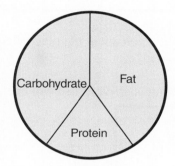

Average "Western diet"   Healthy diet

Comment on the differences between the two types of diet shown on these pie charts.

SEG 1994

8 Kathryn asked people,
"Which television channel do you prefer to watch?"

The pie chart represents their replies.

(a) Which television channel is the mode?
(b) BBC1 was preferred by 45 of these people.
   How many people did she ask altogether?

SEG Winter 1996 2410/3

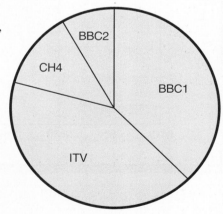

9 Jim bought his house in 1980.
The table shows the value of Jim's house on January 1st at 5 yearly intervals.

Year	1980	1985	1990	1995
Value of house (£)	60 000	95 000	68 000	84 000

(a) Draw a line graph to show this information.
(b) Estimate the value of Jim's house on July 1st 1983.
(c) Jim uses the graph to estimate the value of his house on January 1st 2000.
   Give a reason why his estimate may not be very accurate.

10 The table shows the time, to the nearest minute, it took for the first point to be scored in 40 rugby matches.

6	26	43	40	10
16	24	41	15	23
8	32	7	19	8
28	6	17	5	11
28	13	16	16	18
36	13	38	17	18
10	16	10	24	9
21	4	25	34	8

(a) Copy and complete the tally and frequency table for the given data.

Time (minutes)	Tally	Frequency
0 and less than 10		
10 and less than 20		
20 and less than 30		
30 and less than 40		
40 and less than 50		

(b) Draw a histogram to illustrate the data.

(c) What does the histogram tell you about the time taken for the first point to be scored?

SEG 1995

11 The graph shows the results of a survey of the times at which pupils arrived at school one day.

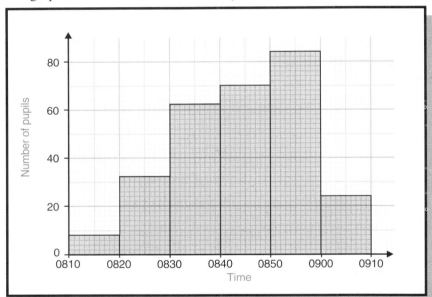

(a) (i) How many pupils arrived for school between 0830 and 0850?

(ii) How many pupils attended school that day?

There were 24 pupils who were late for school.
The reasons given for being late are shown in the pie chart.

(b) (i) Which reason for lateness is the mode?

(ii) Use the pie chart to work out how many of these pupils overslept.

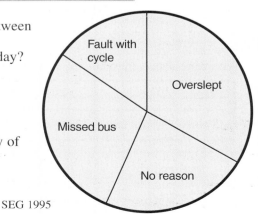

SEG 1995

12 The pie chart shows how **Mr McKenzie** spent his weekly income in 1992.
He spent £40 per week on housing.

(a) How much was his weekly income in 1992?

(b) He spent 10% of his weekly income on fuel and light.
How much did he spend on fuel and light each week?

(c) What percentage of his weekly income was spent on food?

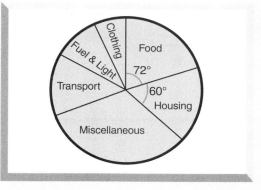

SEG 1993

13 The grouped frequency table shows the results of a survey about the distance travelled to work by people each day.

Distance (km)	0−	4−	8−	12−	16−	20−24
Number of people	10	24	30	8	7	1

(a) Draw a histogram to illustrate this information.
(b) How many people travelled less than 8 kilometres?

14 The table shows the length of time taken by some children to complete a puzzle.

(a) Draw a frequency polygon to show the data.

(b) How many children took 30 minutes or more to complete the puzzle?

Time (minutes)	Number of children
0−	0
10−	10
20−	25
30−	18
40−	7
50−60	0

15 The table gives information about the weight of the potato crop produced by 100 potato plants of two different types.

Weight of potatoes per plant w kg	Number of plants Type X	Number of plants Type Y
$0 \leqslant w < 0.5$	0	0
$0.5 \leqslant w < 1.0$	3	0
$1.0 \leqslant w < 1.5$	12	6
$1.5 \leqslant w < 2.0$	55	39
$2.0 \leqslant w < 2.5$	23	32
$2.5 \leqslant w < 3.0$	7	23
$3.0 \leqslant w < 3.5$	0	0

(a) On the same diagram draw a frequency polygon for each type of potato.

(b) Which type of potato produces the heavier crop?

(c) (i) Which type of potato has more variation in the weight of the crop?
(ii) Give a reason for your answer.

SEG 1994

Activity

Some friends went on a school trip. They each brought different amounts of spending money, as follows:

Penny £15	Keith £35	Nishpal £40	Jayne £10	Stephen £50	Ben £60
Charlotte £35	Suzie £50	Dan £55	Vicki £35	Jack £55	

Which was the most common amount of money?
Who brought the middle amount of money? How much was this?
If the friends shared out their money equally, how much would each person get?
Ben brought the most and Jayne the least. What was the difference in the amounts of spending money Ben and Jayne brought?

Range

The difference between the highest and lowest amounts is called the **range**.

> The range was introduced in Chapter 34.

Types of average

The most common amount is called the **mode**.
When the amounts are arranged in order of size, the middle one is called the **median**.
When the money is shared out equally, the amount each person gets is called the **mean**.

Finding the average

To find the mode:
The mode is the most common amount.

EXAMPLE

Find the mode of these distances, which are in miles:
5, 5, 7, 5, 4, 7, 8, 5.

There are three 5's, two 7's and one each of the other distances. The mode of the distances is 5 miles.
Sometimes we say that the modal distance is 5 miles.

> Some groups of numbers have two modes.
> For example: 1, 1, 3, 2, 5, 1, 2, 4, 2.
> There are three 1's and three 2's.
> There are two modes, 1 and 2.

To find the median:

First arrange the amounts in order of size.
The **median** is the middle amount.

Sometimes there is not just one middle amount, but two.
In such cases the median is the mean of the two middle amounts.

1 Here is a list of the heights of some people, in metres:
1.25, 1.28, 1.26, 1.34, 1.22, 1.25, 1.26
Find the median height.

Arrange the heights in order of size.
1.22, 1.25, 1.25, **1.26**, 1.26, 1.28, 1.34

The median height is 1.26m.

2 Find the median of these prices of cans of drink, in pence:
32, 34, 31, 33, 30, 31, 31, 34.

Arrange the prices in order.
30, 31, 31, **31**, **32**, 33, 34, 34

Median = $\frac{31 + 32}{2}$ = 31.5

The median price is 31.5p.

To find the mean:

Find the total of the amounts.
Divide the total by the number of amounts.

This can be written as: Mean = $\frac{\text{Total of all amounts}}{\text{Number of amounts}}$

This formula can be arranged as:

Total of amounts =
Mean × Number of amounts

Find the mean of these distances, in miles: 5.2, 6.8, 4.7, 7.6, 5.7, 4.8, 5.3.

$$\frac{5.2 + 6.8 + 4.7 + 7.6 + 5.7 + 4.8 + 5.3}{7}$$

$$= \frac{40.1}{7} = 5.7285\ldots$$

The mean distance is 5.7 miles, correct to one decimal place.

Exercise 35.1

Questions 1 to 6.
Do not use a calculator. Show your working clearly.

1 Find the mode, median and mean for each set of data.
  (a) 7, 1, 5, 5, 3, 8, 6
  (b) 110, 115, 112, 110, 103
  (c) 4 m, 5 m, 3 m, 6 m, 6 m, 6 m, 3 m, 7 m
  (d) 2 kg, 8 kg, 4 kg, 3 kg, 5 kg, 2 kg, 3 kg, 4 kg, 6 kg, 2 kg
  (e) £3.50, £3.00, £1.00, £3.50, £4.00, £3.50, £6.00

2 7 people have an average of 9 computer games each.
How many computer games do they have altogether?

3 The mean of six numbers is 5. Five of the numbers are 2, 3, 7, 8 and 6. What is the other number?

4 The mean of seven numbers is 6. Six of the numbers are 2, 5, 7, 3, 7 and 10. What is the other number?

5 The mean length of 8 rods is 75 cm.
An extra rod is added.
The mean length of the 9 rods is 81 cm.
What is the length of the extra rod?

6 The median of eight numbers is 30.5.
Seven of the numbers are 25, 24, 32, 36, 30, 29 and 33.
What is the other number?

Question 7.
You may use a calculator to answer this question.

7 Find the median and mean of these lists.
  (a) 2.3 kg, 8.0 kg, 4.5 kg, 3.7 kg, 5.2 kg, 2.3 kg, 3.1 kg.
  (b) 4.23 m, 5.45 m, 6.53 m, 2.76 m, 4.96 m, 5.06 m, 3.50 m, 7.99 m.
  (c) £3.52, £3.34, £1.56, £3.58, £0.67, £3.53.
  (d) 20.4, 22.1, 19.8, 14.3.
  (e) 113, 125, 132, 120, 131.

A **frequency distribution table** is used to present data.

EXAMPLE

Johti was interested in the number of books carried by students in their bags. This table shows the results of the survey:

Find the mode, median and mean number of books carried.

Number of books	2	3	4	5	6
Frequency	7	5	1	3	5

To find the mode:
The **mode** is the **amount** with the greatest frequency.
7 students each carry 2 books.
This is more than any other number of books.
The mode number of books carried is 2.

To find the median:
The median is the **middle amount**.

We could list the numbers of books carried by the 21 students in order and split them up like this:

| 10 students with the smallest number of books | middle student | 10 students with the greatest number of books |

This shows that the median number of books is carried by the 11th student in the list.
From the table we can see that 7 students carry 2 books each, and the next 5 students each carry 3 books.
So the 11th student carries 3 books.

The median number of books carried is 3.

To find the mean:

$$\text{Mean} = \frac{\text{Total of all amounts}}{\text{Number of amounts}}$$

The best way to do this is to use a table.

Mathematical shorthand
Σ is the Greek letter 'sigma'.

Σf means the sum of frequencies.

Σfx means the sum of the values of fx

$$\text{Mean} = \frac{\Sigma fx}{\Sigma f}$$

Number of books x	Number of students (frequency) f	Frequency × Number of students $f \times x$
2	7	14
3	5	15
4	1	4
5	3	15
6	5	30
Totals	$\Sigma f = 21$	$\Sigma fx = 78$

$$\text{Mean} = \frac{\text{Total of all amounts}}{\text{Number of amounts}} = \frac{\Sigma fx}{\Sigma f}$$

$\text{Mean} = \frac{78}{21} = 3.714\ldots$

Mean number of books carried by the students = 3.7, correct to 1 decimal place.

EXAMPLE

Calculate the mode, median and mean of the ages for the data shown in the bar chart.

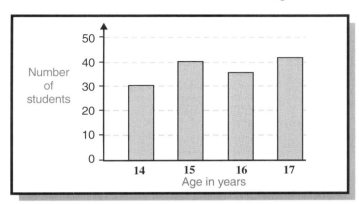

The most common age is shown by the tallest bar.
So the modal age is 17 years.

Use a table to find the median and the mean.

Age x	Frequency f	Frequency × Age $f \times x$
14	30	420
15	40	600
16	36	576
17	41	697
Totals	$\Sigma f = 147$	$\Sigma fx = 2293$

The middle student is given by:

$$\frac{147 + 1}{2} = 74$$

The 74th student in the list has the median age.
Median age is 16 years.

$$\text{Mean} = \frac{\text{Total of all ages}}{\text{Number of students}} = \frac{\Sigma fx}{\Sigma f}$$

$$\text{Mean} = \frac{2293}{147} = 15.598\ldots$$

Mean age is 15.6 years, correct to 1 d.p.

Exercise 35.2

1. During a certain week, a saleswoman sold the following numbers of various sizes of a particular style of shoe.

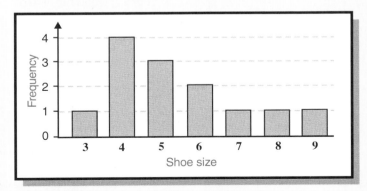

(a) Show the data in a frequency distribution table.
(b) She decides to display the median size in the window. Which size is this?
(c) Her assistant says it would be better to display the modal size. Which size is this?
(d) Calculate the mean size. Comment on your answer.

2 Pat recorded the weekly earnings of a group of students. Her results were as follows:

£15	£30	£20	£35	£15	£15	£20
£25	£35	£15	£25	£20	£25	£25
£25	£20	£25	£15	£35		

(a) Show the data in a frequency distribution table.
(b) What was the modal amount?
(c) How many people were in the group?
(d) What was the median weekly earnings?
(e) Calculate the total weekly earnings of the group.
(f) Calculate the mean weekly earnings.

3 Find the mode, median and mean for the following data.

(a)

Number of letters delivered	1	2	3	4	5	6
Number of days	6	9	6	6	2	1

(b)

Number of siblings	0	1	2	3	4	5
Frequency	1	4	10	4	1	1

(c)

Number of days absent in a year	0	1	2	3	4	5	6	7	8	9	10	11
Number of students	56	0	0	4	14	10	24	11	21	15	8	2

4 Calculate the mode, median and mean price of a bottle of milk for the data shown in the bar chart.

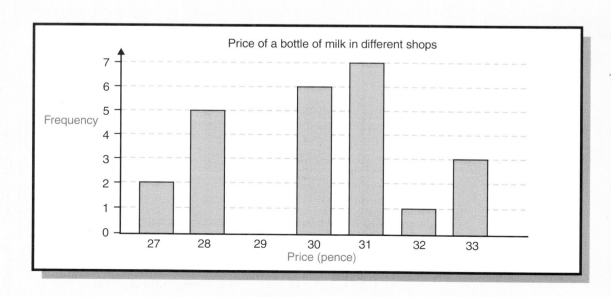

406

Grouped frequency distributions

When there is a lot of data, or the data is continuous, **grouped frequency distributions** are used. Data is collected in **groups** or **classes**.

Grouped frequency distributions were introduced in Chapter 34.

For example:

P

Diameter (cm)	Frequency
$80 \leq x < 85$	4
$85 \leq x < 90$	7
$90 \leq x < 95$	15
$95 \leq x < 100$	10

Q

Mass (kg)	Frequency
40 -	3
50 -	10
60 -	16
70 - 80	12

R

Number of marks	Frequency
0 - 9	5
10 - 14	9
15 - 20	12
21 - 30	8

Tables P and Q have **equal** class intervals. Table R has **unequal** class intervals.

For grouped frequency distributions the true values of the mode, median and mean cannot be found as the actual values of the data are not known.

To find the modal class:
The **modal class** is the class (or group) with the highest frequency.

What is the modal class for each of the distributions above?

To find the mean:
First find the **midpoint** of each class.
Midpoint = average of highest and lowest values.
Then assume that all values in the class are equal to the value of the midpoint.

Estimated mean $= \dfrac{\text{Total of all amounts}}{\text{Number of amounts}} = \dfrac{\Sigma fx}{\Sigma f}$

The answer will only be an **estimate** of the mean.
Explain why.

To find the class which contains the median:
Find the total number of values, n.
Find the middle value, given by $\frac{n+1}{2}$.
Find which class contains this value.

For example.
In table Q above, there are 41 values.
The median is the $\frac{41+1}{2} = 21$st value.
The 21st value is in the class 60-70.
The median lies in the class 60-70.

For each of the tables P and R, find the class which contains the median.

EXAMPLE

Calculate an estimate of the mean mass of the children in this table.

Mass (kg)	Frequency
40 -	3
50 -	10
60 -	6
70 - 80	12

Mass (kg)	Midpoint x	Frequency f	Frequency $\times$ Midpoint $f \times x$
40 - 50	45	3	135
50 - 60	55	10	550
60 - 70	65	6	390
70 - 80	75	12	900
Totals		$\Sigma f = 31$	$\Sigma fx = 1975$

Midpoint of $40-50$ kg class is given by:
$\dfrac{40+50}{2} = \dfrac{90}{2} = 45$

Estimate of mean $= \dfrac{\Sigma fx}{\Sigma f} = \dfrac{1975}{31} = 63.709\ldots$

Estimate of mean mass $= 63.7$ kg, correct to 3 sig. figs.

1 Give the modal class and calculate an estimate of the mean for each of the following.
Find also which class contains the median.

(a)

Time spent watching TV per week (hours)	0 -	10 -	20 -	30 -	40 - 50
Number of students	2	8	5	14	7

(b)

Diameter of stone (cm)	$0 \leqslant d < 1$	$1 \leqslant d < 2$	$2 \leqslant d < 3$	$3 \leqslant d < 4$
Number of stones	20	30	17	22

(c)

Salary (£000's)	$10 \leqslant s < 15$	$15 \leqslant s < 20$	$20 \leqslant s < 25$	$25 \leqslant s < 30$	$30 \leqslant s < 35$
Number of employees	79	32	14	0	2

2 Calculate an estimate of the mean for each of the following tables.

Number of fish caught in an hour	Number of anglers
0 - 2	4
3 - 5	12
6 - 8	8
9 - 11	2

Height in metres (to nearest 0.1 m)	Number of trees
3.0 - 3.4	12
3.5 - 3.9	10
4.0 - 4.4	23
4.5 - 4.9	18
5.0 - 5.4	13

3 (a) Calculate an estimate of the mean mark.
Notice that the class intervals are not all equal.
(b) Which class interval contains the median?

Mark	Number of students
0 - 19	12
20 - 29	23
30 - 34	25
35 - 39	14
40 - 50	3

4 Some women walked one mile. The time taken by each was recorded.
The results are as follows.

Time t minutes	$12 \leqslant t < 16$	$16 \leqslant t < 20$	$20 \leqslant t < 24$	$24 \leqslant t < 28$	$28 \leqslant t < 32$
Number of women	1	9	43	22	5

(a) What is the modal class for the time taken?
(b) Calculate an estimate of the mean time taken.

SEG 1998

Comparing distributions

By answering the following questions, compare the marks obtained by boys and girls in a test.

Mark (out of 10)	7	8	9	10
Number of boys	2	5	3	0
Number of girls	4	0	2	1

(a) What was the highest mark?

A girl got the highest mark of 10.

(b) Which set of marks was more spread out?

Range = highest mark - lowest mark
Boys: Range = $9 - 7 = 2$
Girls: Range = $10 - 7 = 3$
The girls' marks were more spread out.

(c) Were the marks for the boys or the girls better overall?

Calculate the mean for each set of marks.
Boys:
Mean = $\frac{2 \times 7 + 5 \times 8 + 3 \times 9 + 0 \times 10}{10}$

$= \frac{81}{10} = 8.1$

Girls:
Mean = $\frac{4 \times 7 + 0 \times 8 + 2 \times 9 + 1 \times 10}{7}$

$= \frac{56}{7} = 8$

The boys did better overall.

Note:
To compare the overall standard, the median could be used instead of the mean.

Exercise 35.4

1 Use means and ranges to compare the following distributions.

(a)

Jays

Number of goals scored per hockey match	Number of matches
0	3
1	5
2	2
3	2
4	1
5	2

Wasps

Number of goals scored per hockey match	Number of matches
0	0
1	2
2	3
3	1
4	2
5	0

(b)

Number of visits to the cinema last month	0	1	2	3	4	5	6	More than 6
Number of women	8	9	7	3	2	1	1	0
Number of men	0	12	7	1	0	0	0	0

2 For each of the following, calculate the medians and the ranges. Use your results to compare 'Before' with 'After'.

(a)   Monthly sales of bicycles, before and after a marketing campaign.

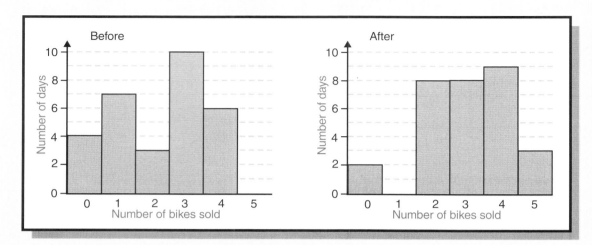

(b)   Numbers of faults per machine, before and after servicing.

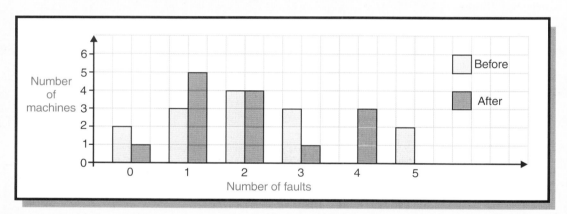

3 Compare the ages of the customers in these two restaurants.
Explain why it is only possible to find an approximate value for the range.

Age range	0 - 9	10 - 19	20 - 29	30 - 39	40 - 59	60 - 89
MacQuick	8	9	10	7	2	4
Pizza Pit	2	4	15	15	8	6

4 The number of words typed per minute by a group of students is shown below.
45   51   58   59   63   87   64   59   58   63   63

(a)   What is the range of their typing speeds?
(b)   Calculate the mean typing speed for these students.

For another group of students the mean of their typing speeds is 42 words per minute and the range is 67.

(c)   Comment on the typing speeds of these two groups of students.

410

5 The frequency polygon shows the lengths of 50 randomly chosen telephone calls made by a firm during March. The table below shows similar information for April.

(a) Draw a frequency polygon using the figures for April.
(b) During which month were the calls longer on average?
(c) During which month were the calls more varied in length?

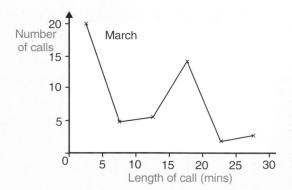

April

Length of call (minutes)	0 -	5 -	10 -	15 -	20 -	25 - 30
Number of calls	9	18	3	12	8	0

6 Deepak thought that the girls in his class wore smaller shoes than the boys on average, but that the boys' shoe sizes were less varied than the girls'.
He did a survey to test his ideas. The table shows his results. Was he correct?

Shoe size	$4\frac{1}{2}$	5	$5\frac{1}{2}$	6	$6\frac{1}{2}$	7	$7\frac{1}{2}$	8	$8\frac{1}{2}$	9	$9\frac{1}{2}$
Number of boys	1	0	5	4	4	2	1	0	1	0	0
Number of girls	0	2	0	2	3	0	2	0	3	1	1

Which is the best average to use?

Many questions in mathematics have definite answers. This one does not.
Sometimes the mean is best, sometimes the median and sometimes the mode. It all depends on the situation and what you want to use the average for.

EXAMPLE

1 A youth club leader gets a discount on cans of drinks if she buys all one size. She took a vote on which size people wanted. The results were as follows:

Size of can (ml)	100	200	330	500
Number of votes	9	12	19	1

Mode = 330ml
Median = 200ml
Mean = 245.6ml, correct to one decimal place.

Which size should she buy?

The mean is no use at all because she can't buy cans of size 245.6ml. Even if the answer is rounded to the nearest whole number (246ml), it's still no use.
The median is possible because there is an actual 200ml can. However, only 12 out of 41 people want this size.
In this case the **mode** is the best average to use, as it is the most popular size.

2 A lecturer sets a unit test. He wants to choose a minimum mark for a distinction so that 50% of his students get this result. Should he use the modal mark, the median mark or the mean mark?

The median mark is the middle mark, so half the students will get the median mark or higher. The lecturer must use the median mark.
Explain why the modal mark and the mean mark are not suitable.
The median mark cannot be decided until after the test.
Explain why.

Exercise 35.5

In questions 1 to 3 find all the averages possible.
State which is the most sensible and why.

1 On a bus: 23 people are wearing trainers,
          10 people are wearing boots,
           8 people are wearing lace-up shoes.

2 20 people complete a simple jigsaw. Their times, in seconds, are recorded.
5, 6, 8, 8, 9, 10, 11, 11, 12, 12, 12, 15, 15, 15, 15, 18, 19, 20, 22, 200.

3 Here are the marks obtained by a group of 11 students in a mock exam. The exam was marked out of 100.
5, 6, 81, 81, 82, 83, 84, 85, 86, 87, 88.

4 The times for two swimmers to complete each of ten 25m lengths are shown below.

| Swimmer A | 30.1 | 30.1 | 30.1 | 30.6 | 30.7 | 31.1 | 31.1 | 31.5 | 31.7 | 31.8 |
| Swimmer B | 29.6 | 29.7 | 29.7 | 29.9 | 30.0 | 30.0 | 30.1 | 30.1 | 30.1 | 44.6 |

Which is the better swimmer? Explain why.

5 The table shows the number of runs scored by two batsmen in several innings.

| Batsman A | 0 | 0 | 10 | 12 | 20 | 22 | 50 | 51 | 81 | 104 | | |
| Batsman B | 0 | 24 | 25 | 27 | 28 | 30 | 33 | 34 | 44 | 45 | 46 | 96 |

Which is the better batsman? Explain why.

6 The table shows the sales of a particular type of boot in a shop during May. The manager wishes to display the average size of the boot in the window. Which size should be displayed? Explain why.

| Boot size | 4 | 5 | 6 | 7 | 8 | 9 |
| Number of pairs sold | 5 | 1 | 10 | 10 | 15 | 4 |

- There are three types of **average**: the **mode**, the **median** and the **mean**.

- The **mode** is the most common amount.

- To find the **median**, first arrange the amounts in order of size.
  The median is the middle amount (or the mean of the two middle amounts).

- To find the **mean**, find the total of the amounts. Divide the total by the number of amounts.

  $$\text{Mean} = \frac{\text{Total of all amounts}}{\text{Number of amounts}}$$

- The **range** is the difference between the highest and lowest amounts.

- To find the mean of a **frequency distribution** use:

  $$\text{Mean} = \frac{\text{Total of all amounts}}{\text{Number of amounts}} = \frac{\Sigma fx}{\Sigma f}$$

- To find the mean of a **grouped frequency distribution**, first find the value of the midpoint of each class. Then use:

  $$\text{Estimated mean} = \frac{\text{Total of all amounts}}{\text{Number of amounts}} = \frac{\Sigma fx}{\Sigma f}$$

- Choosing the best average to use:

  When the most **popular** value is wanted use the **mode**.

  When **half** of the values have to be above the average use the **median**.

  When a **typical** value is wanted use either the **mode** or the **median**.

  When all the **actual** values have to be taken into account use the **mean**.

  When the average should not be distorted by a few very small or very large values do **not** use the mean.

Review Exercise

1 Find the range, mode, median and mean for the following sets of data.
   (a) 8.7 m, 8.3 m, 4.0 m, 3.0 m, 2.5 m, 4.5 m, 3.5 m, 4.5 m, 6.0 m.
   (b) £13.50, £14.00, £8.00, £8.50, £13.00, £8.00, £10.80, £3.25.

2 (a) Pauline measures the length of some English cucumbers.
       The lengths in centimetres are:
       27, 28, 29, 30, 31, 31, 32, 33, 35, 37, 39.

       (i)   What is the range of the lengths of these cucumbers?
       (ii) What is the mean length of these cucumbers?

   (b) Pauline measures the lengths of some Spanish cucumbers. The range of the lengths of these cucumbers is 6 cm and the mean is 30 cm.
       Comment on the differences on these two varieties of cucumber.

                                                                    SEG 1998

3 The table shows the percentage silver content of twenty ancient coins.

(a) Calculate the mean percentage silver content for
(i) the Roman coins,
(ii) the Greek coins.

(b) Use your answers to part (a) to compare the percentage silver content of the Greek coins with the percentage silver content of the Roman coins.

	Percentage silver content				
Roman coins	5.6	6.7	6.6	7.2	6.3
Chinese coins	6.8	6.7	6.2	5.4	7.3
Egyptian coins	5.1	7.0	5.8	6.9	7.6
Greek coins	5.6	7.2	6.6	6.8	5.7

SEG 1997

4 The weekly wages of employees are recorded.

Wage (£)	100 -	200 -	300 -	400 -	500 -	600 - 1000
Frequency	2	13	4	0	2	12

(a) Which is the modal group?
(b) In which group is the median value?
(c) Without calculating, state which of the mean, mode or median is the largest. Explain your answer.

SEG 1997

5 In an experiment 50 people were asked to estimate the length of a rod to the nearest centimetre.
The results were recorded.

Length (cm)	20	21	22	23	24	25	26	27	28	29
Frequency	0	4	6	7	9	10	7	5	2	0

(a) Find the value of the median.
(b) Calculate the mean length.
(c) In a second experiment another 50 people were asked to estimate the length of the same rod.
The most common estimate was 23 cm.
The range of the estimates was 13 cm.
Make **two** comparisons between the results of the two experiments.

SEG 1995

6 David is playing cricket.
The table shows the number of runs he has scored off each ball so far.

Number of runs	0	1	2	3	4	5	6
Number of balls	3	8	4	3	5	0	2

(a) (i) What is the median number of runs per ball?
(ii) Calculate the mean number of runs per ball.

Off the next five balls, David scores the following runs:
4, 4, 5, 3 and 6.
(b) (i) Calculate the new median.
(ii) Calculate the new mean.

(c) Give a reason why the mean is used, rather than the median, to give the average number of runs scored per ball.

SEG 1998

7 There are 14 women in a nursing home. The graph shows the distribution of their ages.

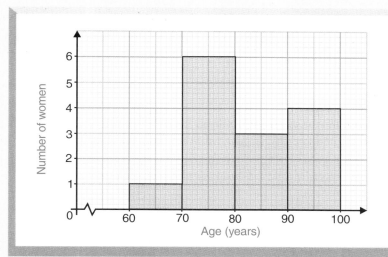

(a) Copy and complete the table for these data.

(b) Calculate an estimate of the mean age of these women.

Age y years	Number of women
$60 \leqslant y < 70$	
$70 \leqslant y < 80$	
$80 \leqslant y < 90$	
$90 \leqslant y < 100$	

SEG 1996

8 Mrs Wright marks the English essays of a large number of boys and girls. She finds that she has the following grouped frequency distribution of marks.

Mark	1 - 5	6 - 10	11 - 15	16 - 20	21 - 25
Number of essays	0	27	52	29	7

(a) Calculate an estimate of the mean mark.

The frequency polygon shows the distribution of marks for the boys. Copy the graph.

(b) (i) On the same axes, draw the frequency polygon for the distribution of marks for the girls.

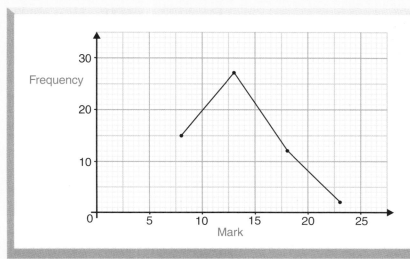

(ii) Use the frequency polygons to compare the means and ranges of the two distributions.

CHAPTER 36

Scatter Graphs

When we investigate statistical information we often find there are connections between sets of data, for example height and weight. In general taller people weigh more than shorter people.

To see if there is a connection between two sets of data we can plot a **scatter graph**.
The scatter graph below shows information about the heights and weights of ten boys.

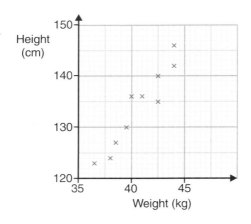

Each cross plotted on the graph represents the weight and height of one boy.

The diagram shows that taller boys generally weigh more than shorter boys.

Exercise **36.1**

1 The scatter graph shows the shoe sizes and heights of a group of girls.

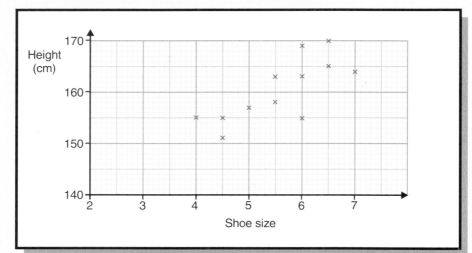

(a) How many girls wear size $6\frac{1}{2}$ shoes?
(b) How tall is the girl with the largest shoe size?
(c) Does the shortest girl wear the smallest shoes?
(d) What do you notice about the shoe sizes of taller girls compared to shorter girls?

2 The scatter graph shows the marks obtained by a group of students in a test in English and a test in French.

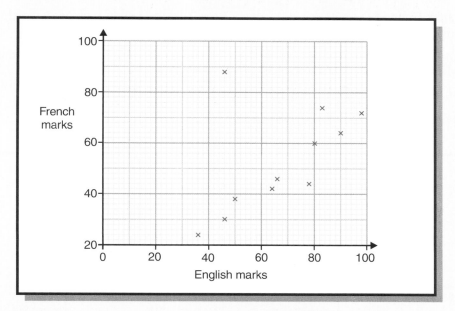

(a) Janice got the top mark in English. What mark did she get in French?
(b) The results of one student look out of place.
   (i) What marks did the student get in English and in French?
   (ii) Give a possible reason why this student has different results from the rest of the group.

3 The scatter graph shows the pulse rates of a group of women after doing aerobics for one minute and their weight.

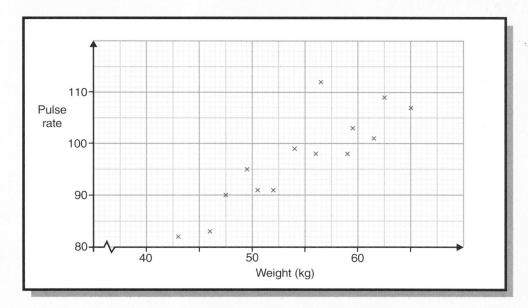

(a) How many of these women weigh less than 50 kg?
(b) What is the weight of the woman with the lowest pulse rate?
(c) What do you notice about the pulse rates of heavier women compared to lighter women?

Correlation

The relationship between two sets of data is called **correlation**.

In general the scatter graph of the heights and weights, shows that as height increases, weight increases. This type of relationship shows there is a **positive correlation** between height and weight.

But if as the value of one variable increases the value of the other variable decreases, then there is a **negative correlation** between the variables.

When no relationship exists between two variables there is **zero correlation**.

The following graphs show types of correlation.

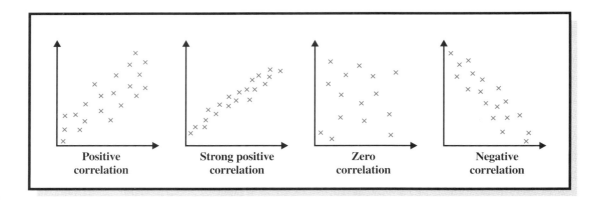

As points get closer to a straight line the stronger the correlation.
Perfect correlation is when all the points lie on a straight line.

 (a) Which of these graphs shows the strongest positive correlation?
(b) Which of these graphs shows perfect negative correlation?
(c) Which of these graphs shows the weakest correlation?

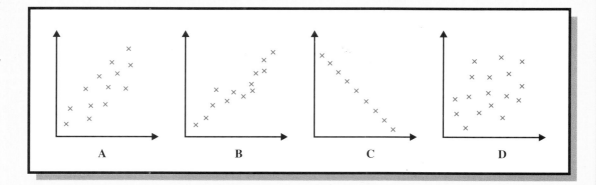

2 Describe the type of correlation you would expect between:
(a) the age of a car and its secondhand selling price,
(b) the heights of children and their ages,
(c) the shoe sizes of children and the distance they travel to school,
(d) the number of cars on the road and the number of road accidents,
(e) the engine size of a car and the number of kilometres it can travel on one litre of fuel.

418

3 The table shows the distance travelled and time taken by motorists on different journeys.

Distance travelled (km)	30	45	48	80	90	100	125
Time taken (hours)	0.6	0.9	1.2	1.2	1.3	2.0	1.5

(a) Draw a scatter graph for the data.
(b) What do you notice about distance travelled and time taken?
(c) Give one reason why the distance travelled and the time taken are not perfectly correlated.

4 Tyres were collected from a number of different cars. The table shows the distance travelled and depth of tread for each tyre.

Distance travelled (1000 km)	4	5	9	10	12	15	18	25	30
Depth of tread (mm)	9.2	8.4	7.6	8	6.5	7.4	7	6.2	5

(a) Draw a scatter graph for the data.
(b) What do you notice about the distance travelled and the depth of tread?
(c) Give one reason why the distance travelled and the depth of tread are not perfectly correlated.

Line of best fit

We have seen that **scatter graphs** can be used to illustrate two sets of data and from the distribution of points plotted an indication of the relationship which exists between the data can be seen.

The scatter graph of heights and weights has been redrawn below and a **line of best fit** has been drawn, by eye, to show the relationship between height and weight.

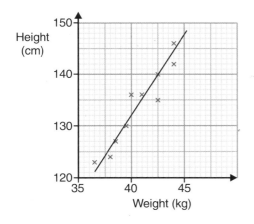

Lines of best fit
- The slope of the line shows the trend of the points.
- A line is only drawn if the correlation (positive or negative) is strong.
- The line does not have to go through the origin of the graph.

Where there is a relationship between the two sets of data the line of best fit can be used to estimate other values.

A boy is 132 cm tall.
Using the line of best fit an estimate of his weight is 40 kg.

In a similar way we can use the line to estimate the height of a boy when we know his weight.
A boy weighs 43 kg. Estimate his height.

1 The table shows the ages and weights of ten babies.

Age (weeks)	2	4	9	7	13	5	6	1	10	12
Weight (kg)	3.5	3.3	4.2	4.7	5	3.8	4	3	5	5.5

(a) (i) Use this information to draw a scatter graph.
    (ii) Draw a line of best fit by eye.

(b) Mrs Wilson's baby is 11 weeks old.
    Use the graph to estimate the weight of her baby.

2 The table shows the sales and profits for eight shops.

Sales (£)	400	570	340	530	500	290	370	560
Profit (£)	80	110	72	100	106	55	65	116

(a) (i) Use this information to draw a scatter graph.
    (ii) Draw a line of best fit by eye.

(b) Use the graph to estimate:
    (i) the profit for a shop whose sales were £480,
    (ii) the sales for a shop whose profit was £60.

3 The table shows the weights and fitness factors for a number of women.
The higher the fitness factor the fitter a person is.

Weight (kg)	45	48	50	54	56	60	64	72	99	112
Fitness Factor	41	48	40	40	35	40	34	30	17	15

(a) (i) Use this information to draw a scatter graph.
    (ii) Draw the line of best fit by eye.

(b) Use the graph to estimate:
    (i) the fitness factor for a woman whose weight is 80 kg,
    (ii) the weight of a woman whose fitness factor is 22.

4 The table shows the marks obtained by students in examinations in statistics at Easter and in the summer.

Mark at Easter	30	19	59	39	67	15	70	11	56	44
Mark in the summer	41	29	77	50	84	24	89	16	71	59

(a) (i) Use this information to draw a scatter graph.
    (ii) Draw the line of best fit by eye.

(b) Another student scored 35 marks in the Easter examination but did not sit the summer examination. What mark would you predict for this student in the summer examination?

- A **scatter graph** can be used to show the relationship between two sets of data.

- The relationship between two sets of data is referred to as **correlation**.

- You should be able to recognise **positive** and **negative** correlation.

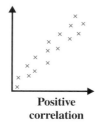
Positive correlation

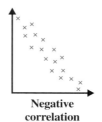
Negative correlation

- When there is a relationship between two sets of data a **line of best fit** can be drawn on the scatter graph.
  The correlation is stronger as points get closer to a straight line.
  Perfect correlation is when all the points lie on a straight line.

 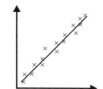 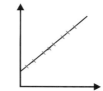 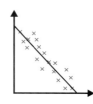

- The line of best fit can be used to **estimate** the value from one set of the data when the corresponding value of the other set is known.

IDEAS FOR INVESTIGATION

1 Record the resting pulse rates for 10 members of your class.

Ask them to run on the spot for one minute and then take their pulse rate again, call this the exercise rate.

Plot a scatter graph of "resting" pulse rate against "exercise" pulse rate and draw a line of best fit.

What type of correlation exists between the resting pulse rates and the exercise pulse rates for these pupils?

Take the resting pulse rate of someone else.

Can you use your graph to estimate their exercise pulse rate?

Ask them to run on the spot and comment on the results.

2 Investigate the statement: "Taller people have bigger feet".
You might like to consider age and gender separately.

1 The data from a survey of teachers, was used to plot several scatter graphs.

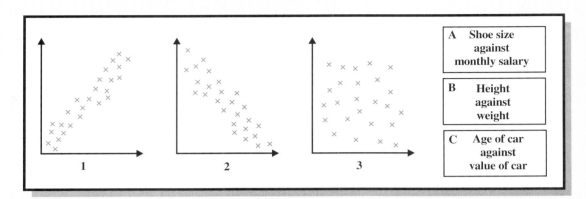

A	**Shoe size against monthly salary**
B	**Height against weight**
C	**Age of car against value of car**

Match each scatter graph to the correct description.

SEG 1994

2 Copy the axes given below.
Sketch a scatter graph to show the correlation between age and value of a television set.

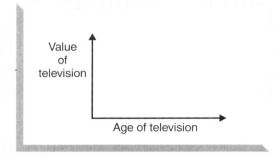

SEG 1996

3 The table shows a record of the temperature at midday and the number of ice creams sold each Sunday between 1 pm and 2 pm.

Temperature (°C)	5	10	25	26	20	18	15
Number of ice creams	23	25	45	44	40	35	35

(a) Draw a scatter diagram of this information.
Label the horizontal axis **Temperature (°C)**, from 0 to 30.
Label the vertical axis **Number of ice creams**, from 0 to 50.

(b) What type of correlation is shown on the scatter diagram?

(c) Draw a line of best fit and use it to predict the number of ice creams sold on a Sunday when the temperature is 30°C.

SEG 1997

4 The scatter diagram shows the heights of some plants, d days after germinating.

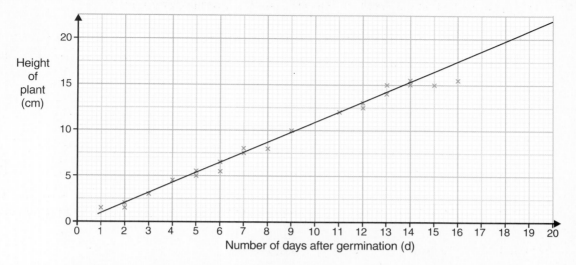

A line of best fit has been drawn on the diagram.
(a) Use the line of best fit to estimate the height of a plant:
   (i)   10 days after germination,
   (ii) 20 days after germination.

(b) Which of your two answers in (a) is likely to be more reliable?
    Give a reason for your answer.

SEG 1998

5 The scatter graph shows the height and shoe size of seven adults.

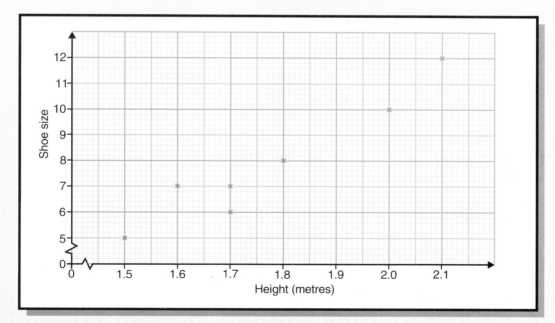

(a) Describe the relationship suggested by the scatter graph.

(b) Copy the scatter graph.
    Draw a line of best fit on your scatter graph.

(c) Use your line to estimate the shoe size of a person whose height is 1.9 metres.

SEG 1998

6 (a) Sketch a scatter graph to show the most likely result of plotting:

(i) "weight" against "height",

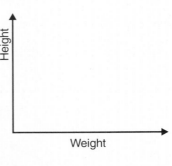

(ii) "age" against "fitness".

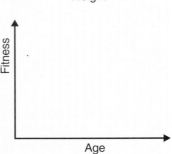

(b) Part of a fitness test included running on the spot for one minute and then recording the pulse rate.

The scatter graph shows the results.

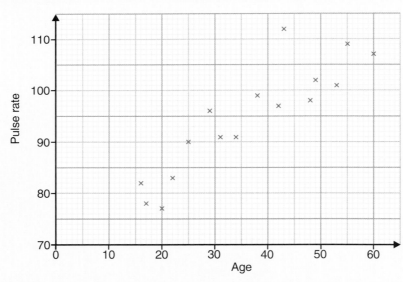

Copy the scatter graph.

(i) Draw a line of best fit on the scatter graph.

(ii) Donna is aged 50. She did not take part in the fitness test.
She runs on the spot for one minute. Estimate her pulse rate.

(iii) Give one reason why her actual pulse rate may be different from your answer in part (ii).

SEG 1995

7 The table gives information about the age and value of a number of cars of the same type.

Age (years)	1	3	$4\frac{1}{2}$	6	3	5	2	$5\frac{1}{2}$	4	7
Value (£)	8200	5900	4900	3800	6200	4500	7600	2200	5200	3200

(a) Use the information to draw a scatter graph.
Label the horizontal axis **Age (years)**, from 0 to 7.
Label the vertical axis **Value (£)**, 0 to 9000.

(b) What does the graph tell you about the value of these cars as they get older?

(c) The information is correct but the age and value of one of these cars looks out of place.
Give a possible reason for this.

(d) Draw a line of best fit.

(e) John has a car of this type which is $3\frac{1}{2}$ years old and is in average condition.
Use the graph to estimate its value.

8 Dr Malik wants to buy a car. She collects information about engine capacity and fuel economy.
She draws a scatter graph as shown.

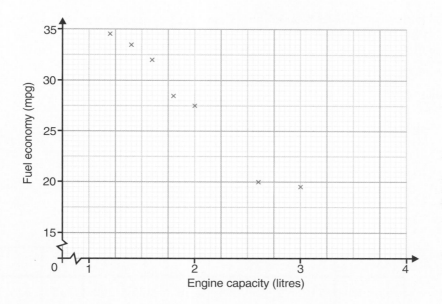

(a) Copy the scatter graph.
Draw a line of best fit on your scatter graph.

(b) Use your graph to estimate the fuel economy of a car with an engine capacity of:
(i) 2.3 litres,
(ii) 3.5 litres.

(c) Which of the two estimates in (b) is more reliable?
Give a reason for your answer.

Dr Malik decides to buy a car with a fuel economy of at least 30 mpg.
(d) Use your graph to estimate the largest engine capacity that she should consider.

SEG 1998 S

9 The gestation period and life expectancy for various mammals are given in the following table.

Mammal	Gestation period (days)	Life expectancy (years)
Mouse	18	1.5
Fox	60	14
Rat	22	2
Mole	30	6
Jack rabbit	44	7
Rabbit	28	3
Arctic wolf	64	8
Otter	65	13

(a) Plot this information as a scatter graph.

(b) One of the points does not fit very well.
  (i) Circle this point on your graph.
  (ii) Write down the name of the mammal represented by this point.

(c) Draw the line of best fit on the scatter graph.

(d) Use the line of best fit to estimate
  (i) the life expectancy of a mammal that has a gestation period of 35 days,
  (ii) the gestation period of a mammal whose life expectancy is 4.5 years.

SEG 1994

10 In September, a travel company asked customers about their holidays.
Eight customers were asked to give a score for their holiday.
They were asked to rate the holiday on a scale of 1 to 10.
The table shows their replies and the cost of each holiday.

1 = very bad
10 = perfect

Rating	2	5	6	7	7	8	8	9
Cost (£)	210	250	265	270	300	290	315	329

(a) (i) Plot a scatter graph for these data.
      Label the horizontal axis **Rating**, from 0 to 10.
      Label the vertical axis **Cost (£)**, from 210 to 340.
  (ii) What does this graph tell you about the connection between the rating and the cost?

(b) On the graph, draw the line of best fit.

Another customer gave a score of 4 for her holiday.
(c) (i) Use the scatter graph to estimate the cost of her holiday.
  (ii) Give one reason why your answer may not be a very good estimate.

SEG 1995

426

CHAPTER 37

Cumulative Frequency

Cumulative frequency tables

This **frequency table** shows the masses of some stones recorded during an experiment.

Mass (kg)	20 -	30 -	40 -	50 -	60 - 70
Number of stones	3	5	10	8	4

The first class is $20 - 30$ kg.
The **upper class boundary** of this class is 30 kg.
What are the upper class boundaries of the other groups?

The information given in a frequency table can be used to make a **cumulative frequency table**.

Mass (kg), less than	20	30	40	50	60	70
Cumulative frequency	0	3	8	18	26	30

Mass of stone (less than)	Number of stones
20 kg	0
30 kg	0 + 3 = 3
40 kg	0 + 3 + 5 = 8
50 kg	0 + 3 + 5 + 8 + 10 = 18

Cumulative frequency graph

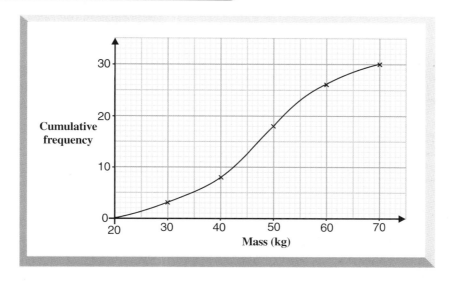

To draw a **cumulative frequency graph**:

1. Draw and label:
   the **variable** on the horizontal axis,
   cumulative frequency on the vertical axis.

2. Plot the cumulative frequency against the upper class boundary of each class.

3. Join the points with a smooth curve.

Median

The median of 13 numbers is the 7th number.
The median of 14 numbers is between the 7th and
8th numbers.
We could call this the "$7\frac{1}{2}$th" number.
For n numbers, the rule for finding the median is:

$\qquad$ Median = $\frac{1}{2}(n + 1)$th number

> The median of a frequency distribution is
> the value of the middle number.
> On a cumulative frequency graph this
> value is read from the horizontal axis.

Interquartile range

The **range** of a set of data was covered in Chapter 34 and again in Chapter 35.
It measures how spread out the data is.
Range = highest value − lowest value.
The range is influenced by extreme high or low values of data and can be misleading.

A better way to measure spread is to find the range of the
middle 50% of the data.
This is called the **interquartile range**.
Interquartile range = Upper Quartile − Lower Quartile

For n numbers the rules for finding the quartiles are:

Lower Quartile = $\frac{1}{4}(n + 1)$th number

Upper Quartile = $\frac{3}{4}(n + 1)$th number

> On a cumulative frequency
> graph the values of the
> Upper Quartile and the
> Lower Quartile are read
> from the horizontal axis.

EXAMPLE

Using the cumulative frequency graph from the previous
page, estimate:
(a) the median mass of the stones,
(b) the interquartile range of the masses of the stones.

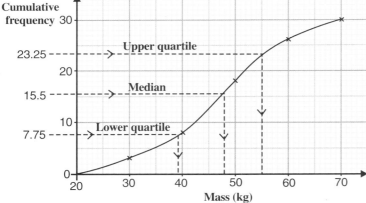

> **When n is large**
> When the total frequency, n,
> is 'large' you need not bother
> with '+1' in the rules for the
> median, lower quartile and upper
> quartile.
>
> Instead use:
> $\qquad$ median = $\frac{1}{2}n$th number
> $\qquad$ lower quartile = $\frac{1}{4}n$th number
> $\qquad$ upper quartile = $\frac{3}{4}n$th number
> 'Large' means greater than 50.
> *Explain why.*

(a) There are 30 stones.
$\frac{1}{2}(30 + 1) = 15.5$, so the median is the
mass of the 15.5th stone.
Read along from 15.5 on the vertical axis
and down to the horizontal axis.
This is shown on the graph.
Median = 48 g.

*Why are the values for the median and
interquartile range only estimates?*

(b) $\frac{1}{4}(30 + 1) = 7.75$, so the lower quartile
is the mass of the 7.75th stone.
$\frac{3}{4}(30 + 1) = 23.25$, so the upper quartile
is the mass of the 23.25th stone.
Read these values from the graph.

IQR = Upper Quartile − Lower Quartile
$\qquad$ = 55 − 39
$\qquad$ = 16 g
The interquartile range is 16 g.

1. Silvia made a record of the times students took to walk to school in the morning.

Time (minutes)	0 -	5 -	10 -	15 -	20 -	25 - 30
Number of students	3	8	12	10	5	2

(a) Copy and complete this cumulative frequency table.

Time (minutes), less than	0	5	10	15	20	25	30
Cumulative frequency							

(b) Draw a cumulative frequency graph for the data.
(c) Use your graph to find:
   (i) the median time,
   (ii) the upper quartile time,
   (iii) the lower quartile time.
(d) Calculate the interquartile range of the times.

2. A secretary weighed a sample of letters to be posted.

Mass (g)	20 -	30 -	40 -	50 -	60 -	70 -	80 − 90
Number of students	2	4	12	7	8	17	3

(a) How many letters were in the sample?
(b) Copy and complete the cumulative frequency table.

Mass (g)	< 30	< 40	< 50	< 60	< 70	< 80	< 90
Cumulative frequency							

(c) Draw a cumulative frequency graph for the data.
(d) Use your graph to find:
   (i) the median weight of a letter,
   (ii) the interquartile range of the weights.

3. This frequency table shows the length of time a group of students spend watching television in one week.

Time (t hours)	$0 \leqslant t < 5$	$5 \leqslant t < 10$	$10 \leqslant t < 15$	$15 \leqslant t < 20$	$20 \leqslant t < 25$	$25 \leqslant t < 30$
Number of students	2	8	5	14	7	4

(a) Make a cumulative frequency table for the data using the upper class boundaries 5, 10, 15, …
(b) Draw a cumulative frequency graph to illustrate the data.
(c) Use your graph to find:
   (i) the median length of time,
   (ii) the interquartile range of the times.

4 This table shows the annual salaries of people employed by a firm.

Annual salary (£000's)	Number of employees
$10 \leqslant x < 15$	79
$15 \leqslant x < 20$	32
$20 \leqslant x < 25$	14
$25 \leqslant x < 30$	0
$30 \leqslant x < 35$	1
$35 \leqslant x < 40$	1

(a) Make a cumulative frequency table for the data.
(b) Draw a cumulative frequency graph for the data.
(c) Use your graph to find:
    (i) the median salary,
    (ii) the interquartile range of salaries.

Another look at cumulative frequency graphs

In some frequency distributions there are gaps between the classes.

Some variables are discrete and can only take certain values.
In many cases these are whole numbers.

For example, this frequency distribution table shows the number of spelling mistakes found in some essays.

Number of mistakes	0 - 5	6 - 10	11 - 15	16 - 20
Number of essays	9	17	8	3

The first class ends at 5. The highest number of spelling mistakes in the class 0 - 5 is 5.
The second class starts at 6.
We take the upper class boundary for the class 0 - 5 to be halfway between 5 and 6, at 5.5.
What are the upper class boundaries for the other classes?

In the following example there are gaps between the classes, because the lengths are measured to the nearest centimetre.

EXAMPLE

In an experiment Sophie measured and recorded the longest roots of plants.

Length (to nearest cm)	0 - 2	3 - 5	6 - 8	9 - 11	12 - 14
Number of plants	0	14	35	23	10

(a) Make a cumulative frequency table for the data Sophie collected.
(b) Draw a cumulative frequency graph for the data.
(c) Use your graph to find:
    (i) the median length,
    (ii) the interquartile range of lengths.
(d) How many plants had roots at least 11.2 cm long?

The class 3 - 5 includes measurements from 2.5 cm to 5.5 cm. The upper class boundary is 5.5.

(a)

Length (cm) less than	2.5	5.5	8.5	11.5	14.5
Cumulative frequency	0	14	47	70	80

(b)

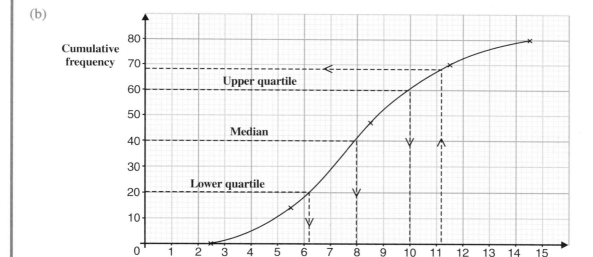

Remember Cumulative frequency is plotted against the upper class boundary for each class.

(c) (i) There are 80 plants.
$\frac{1}{2}$ of 80 = 40, so the median is the length of the roots of the 40th plant.
Median = 8.0 cm.

(ii) For the lower quartile use $\frac{1}{4}$ of 80 = 20.
Lower quartile = 6.2 cm
For the upper quartile use $\frac{3}{4}$ of 80 = 60.
Upper quartile = 10.0 cm
IQR = Upper Quartile − Lower Quartile
= 10.0 − 6.2
= 3.8 cm

(d) From 11.2 on the horizontal axis read upwards to the graph and across to the vertical axis. There are 68 plants of length less than 11.2 cm.
So the number of plants with roots at least 11.2 cm long is 80 − 68 = 12 plants.

1 The times taken by competitors to complete the crossword in an annual competition were recorded to the nearest minute.

Time (minutes)	10 - 14	15 - 19	20 - 24	25 - 29	30 - 34
Frequency	7	21	37	12	3

(a) Copy and complete the cumulative frequency table.

Time (minutes)	< 9.5	< 14.5	< 19.5	< 24.5	< 29.5	< 34.5
Cumulative frequency						

(b) Draw a cumulative frequency graph for the data.
(c) Use your graph to find:
   (i)   the interquartile range of times,
   (ii) the number of competitors who took less than last year's winning time of 16 minutes to complete the crossword.

2 Draw a cumulative frequency graph for the results shown in this table.

Number of marks	0 - 20	21 - 25	26 - 30	31 - 40
Number of students	5	9	12	8

(a) Find the median mark.
(b) Find the interquartile range of marks.
(c) The minimum mark for a Grade A is 33. What percentage of students gained Grade A?
(d) 10% of students failed. What was the minimum mark for a pass?

3 Carlo weighed some sweets to the nearest 10 g.

Weight (to nearest 10 g)	0 - 10	20 - 30	40 - 50	60 - 70	80 - 90
Number of sweets	15	36	54	12	3

(a) Copy and complete this cumulative frequency table.

Weight (g), less than	0	15	35	55	75	95
Cumulative frequency						

(b) Draw a cumulative frequency graph for Carlo's data.
(c) Use your graph to find:
   (i)   the median weight of a sweet,
   (ii) the interquartile range of weights.
(d) How many sweets had a weight greater than 65 g?

4 A survey was made of the heights of plants produced by a batch of seed.

Height (cm)	80 -	85 -	90 -	95 -	100 - 105
Frequency	20	35	15	11	14

(a) How many plants were measured in the survey?
(b) Make a cumulative frequency table for the data.
(c) Draw a cumulative frequency graph for the data.
    Label the horizontal axis from 70 cm to 110 cm.
(d) Use your graph to estimate:
    (i) the median height,
    (ii) the interquartile range of heights,
    (iii) the number of plants taller than 97.5 cm.
(e) The shortest 10 plants are used for testing. Estimate the height of the tallest of these 10 plants.

5 The times spent listening to the radio last week by some students is shown.

Time (t hours)	$0 \leqslant t < 5$	$5 \leqslant t < 10$	$10 \leqslant t < 15$	$15 \leqslant t < 20$	$20 \leqslant t < 30$	$30 \leqslant t < 40$
Number of students	7	15	18	24	12	4

(a) Make a cumulative frequency table for the data.
(b) Draw a cumulative frequency graph for the data.
(c) Use your graph to find the interquartile range of times.
(d) What percentage of the students spent more than 25 hours per week listening to the radio?

6 The heights of a number of men are shown in this table.

Height (cm)	Number of men
140 -	1
150 -	6
160 -	8
170 -	21
180 - 190	14

Draw a cumulative frequency graph for the data.
Use your graph to find:
(a) the median and interquartile range of heights,
(b) the number of men whose heights were less than 155 cm,
(c) the number of men whose heights were at least 163 cm,
(d) the maximum height of the shortest 20 men,
(e) the minimum height of the tallest 10% of men.

Comparing distributions

EXAMPLE

A firm tested a sample of electric motors produced by an assembly line. They kept a running total of the numbers of motors which had failed at any time. This cumulative frequency graph was plotted using the data collected.

(a) Find the median lifetime of a motor.

(b) Find the interquartile range of lifetimes.

(c) A sample of motors, produced by another assembly line, was tested and found to have:
Median lifetime = 1900 hours
Upper quartile = 2000 hours
Lower quartile = 1700 hours
Compare the two samples of motors.

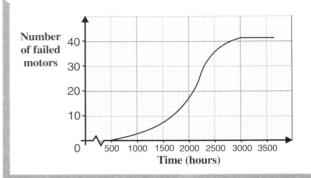

(a) Median lifetime = 2100 hours

(b) IQR = Upper Quartile − Lower Quartile
= 2300 − 1700
= 600 hours

(c) For the second sample:
Median = 1900 hours
IQR = 2000 − 1700 = 300 hours
The first sample has a greater median time. On average, they lasted 200 hours longer than motors in the second sample.

The spread of the second sample (given by the IQR) is much smaller. It is 300 hours, compared with 600 hours for the first sample.

Exercise 37.3

1 The heights of a group of boys and a group of girls were recorded separately.
The results are shown by the cumulative frequency graphs.

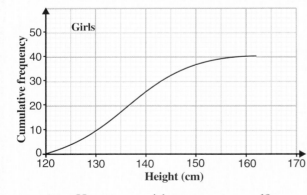

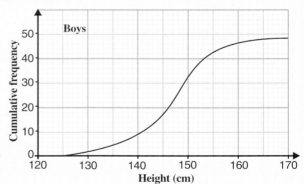

(a) How many girls were measured?
(b) Find the interquartile range of heights of the girls.
(c) Find the interquartile range of heights of the boys.

(d) Use your answers to parts (b) and (c) to comment on the heights of the girls compared with the boys.
(e) How many boys are taller than the tallest girl?

2 The milk yields of a herd of cows is shown in the table below.

Milk yield (litres)	$5 \leqslant x < 10$	$10 \leqslant x < 15$	$15 \leqslant x < 20$	$20 \leqslant x < 25$	$25 \leqslant x < 30$
Number of cows	15	28	37	26	25

(a) Use the data to draw a cumulative frequency graph.
(b) Use your graph to estimate:
    (i) the median milk yield,
    (ii) the interquartile range of milk yields.
(c) A neighbouring farmer calculated the following results for his herd of cows.
    Median yield = 22 litres, Lower quartile = 9 litres, Upper quartile = 28 litres.
    Compare and comment on the data for the two herds.

3 A record is kept of the number of people arriving at a meeting, measured from the time the doors are opened.

Time (minutes)	0 -	10 -	20 -	30 -	40 -	50 -	60 - 70
Frequency	2	5	6	7	8	4	4

(a) Copy and complete the cumulative frequency table and draw the cumulative frequency graph.

Time (minutes)	$\leqslant 10$	$\leqslant 20$	$\leqslant 30$	$\leqslant 40$	$\leqslant 50$	$\leqslant 60$	$\leqslant 70$
Cumulative frequency							

(b) People are late for the meeting if they arrive more than 35 minutes after the doors are opened.
    How many people were late for the meeting?
(c) The same number of people attended a second meeting.
    The following results were recorded.
        Median time of arrival   31 minutes
        Interquartile range   11 minutes
    Make **two** comparisons between the times of arrival at the first meeting and the second meeting.

                                                                                          SEG 1997

4 The length of life of 100 batteries of a certain make was recorded.
The table shows the results.

Length of life (hours)	< 10	< 15	< 20	< 25	< 30	< 35	< 40
Cumulative frequency	0	2	9	50	86	96	100

(a) Draw a cumulative frequency graph to illustrate these data.
(b) How many batteries had a life of more than 32 hours?
(c) Use your graph to estimate:
    (i) the median,
    (ii) the interquartile range.
(d) Another make of battery has a median length of life of 25 hours and an interquartile range of 7 hours.
    Is this make of battery likely to be more reliable than the first?
    Give a reason for your answer.

                                                                                        SEG 1998

What you need to know

- The information given in a frequency table can be used to make a **cumulative frequency table**.

- To draw a **cumulative frequency graph**:
  1. Draw and label:
     the variable on the horizontal axis,
     cumulative frequency on the vertical axis.
  2. Plot the cumulative frequency against the
     upper class boundary of each class.
  3. Join the points with a smooth curve.

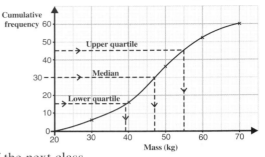

- If the question does not give the upper class
  boundaries, then the upper class boundary of
  each class is equal to the lower class boundary of the next class.

- When the classes have gaps between them then the upper class boundary is halfway between the
  end of one class and the beginning of the next.

- The **median** is the value of the middle number.
  The **lower quartile** is the value located at $\frac{1}{4}$ of the total frequency.
  The **upper quartile** is the value located at $\frac{3}{4}$ of the total frequency.
  The **interquartile range** measures the spread of the middle 50% of the data.
  Interquartile range = Upper Quartile − Lower Quartile

Review Exercise

1. This cumulative frequency diagram shows information about the distances travelled to work
   each day by a group of adults.

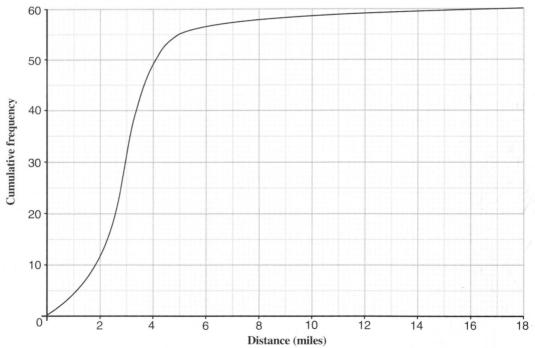

   (a) What is the median distance travelled?
   (b) Find the interquartile range.
       Explain how you obtain your answer.
   (c) Give a reason why the interquartile range is a better measure of spread than the range
       for this data.

SEG 2000 S

2 There were 360 people who took part in an 8 mile sponsored run.
The range of finishing time is shown on the following cumulative frequency curve.

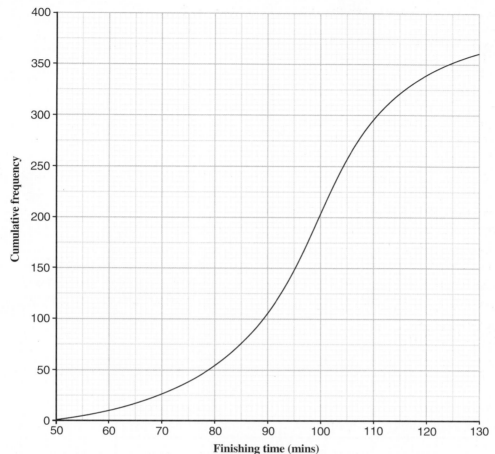

(a) Use the curve to estimate the median finishing time.
(b) Estimate the interquartile range.
(c) How many runners beat last year's winning time of 75 minutes?

SEG 1995

3 A sample of 40 trout is taken at a fish farm.

Mass (g)	40 -	50 -	60 -	70 -	80 -	90 - 100
Frequency	2	3	8	9	13	5

(a) Copy and complete the cumulative frequency table.

Mass (g)	< 50	< 60	< 70	< 80	< 90	< 100
Cumulative frequency						

(b) Draw the cumulative frequency graph.
(c) Find the median mass of the trout.
(d) Find the interquartile range of the mass of the trout.
(e) A second sample of trout has a median mass of 75 g, an upper quartile of 93 g and a lower quartile of 55 g.
Compare and comment on the spread of the data in these two samples.

SEG 1997

4 A researcher has timed how long it took each of 140 children to complete a puzzle.
  (a) Copy and complete the table below and use it to draw a cumulative frequency curve.

Time (in minutes)	Frequency	Cumulative frequency
0 and less than 9.5	12	
9.5 and less than 19.5	25	
19.5 and less than 29.5	42	
29.5 and less than 39.5	35	
39.5 and less than 49.5	18	
49.5 and less than 59.5	8	

  (b) Use your graph to find the median time taken by the children.
  (c) Use your graph to calculate the interquartile range of the times of the children.
  (d) The interquartile range of the times for a second group of children was 13 minutes.
      What can you conclude from this about the times of the two groups of children?

SEG 1995

5 The lengths of the middle finger of 105 female students are given in the table.
The measurements are to the nearest millimetre.

Finger length (mm)	Frequency	Cumulative frequency
60 - 74	9	
75 - 79	9	
80 - 84	14	
85 - 89	15	
90 - 94	18	
95 - 99	17	
100 - 104	15	
105 - 114	8	

  (a) Copy and complete the cumulative frequency table.
  (b) (i) What is the upper class boundary of the class interval that has a frequency of 14?
      (ii) Draw the cumulative frequency curve for the data.
  (c) Use your graph to find:
      (i) the median finger length,
      (ii) the interquartile range.

SEG 1994

6 Claire did a survey on students' part time weekly earnings. Some of her results are shown in the table.

(a) Use this information to draw a possible cumulative frequency curve.

(b) Find the interquartile range.

(c) How many students' weekly earnings were more than £20?

Number of students	59
Lowest earnings	£5
Highest earnings	£37
Median	£15
Lower quartile	£12
Upper quartile	£21

SEG 1996

7 The numbers of journeys made by a group of people using public transport in one month is summarised in the table.

Number of journeys	0 - 10	11 - 20	21 - 30	31 - 40	41 - 50	51 - 60	61 - 70
Number of people	4	7	8	6	3	4	0

(a) Copy and complete the cumulative frequency table.

Number of journeys	⩽ 10	⩽ 20	⩽ 30	⩽ 40	⩽ 50	⩽ 60	⩽ 70
Cumulative frequency							

(b) (i) Draw the cumulative frequency graph.
   (ii) Use your graph to estimate the median number of journeys.
   (iii) Use your graph to estimate the number of people who made more than 44 journeys in the month.

(c) The numbers of journeys made using public transport in one month, by another group of people, are shown in the graph.

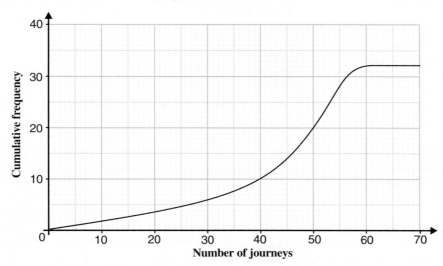

(i) Find the interquartile range for this group of people.
   Explain how you found your answer.
(ii) Make one comparison between the numbers of journeys made by these two groups.

SEG 1995

8 Two types of leaves were collected and their lengths measured.
The results are shown by the cumulative frequency curves.

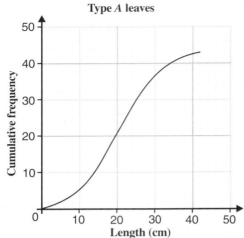

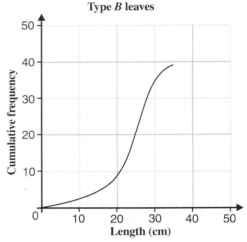

(a) How many type A leaves were collected?

(b) (i) Find the interquartile range for the type B leaves.

(ii) The interquartile range for the type A leaves was 12 cm.
What does this show about the length of the type A leaves compared with the type B leaves?

(c) How many type A leaves were longer than the longest type B leaf?

SEG 1995

9 The times for 160 adults to complete an exercise schedule are shown on the frequency diagram.

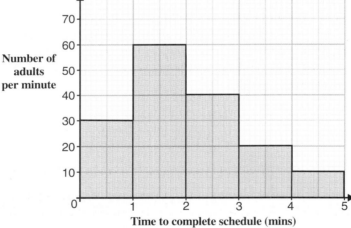

(a) Construct a cumulative frequency table for the data.

(b) Draw the cumulative frequency curve.

(c) Use your graph to estimate the time it would take 40% of the adults to complete the exercises.

(d) Use your graph to find the number of adults who took more than 3.5 minutes to complete the exercises.

Time in minutes	Cumulative frequency
⩽ 1	
⩽ 2	
⩽ 3	
⩽ 4	
⩽ 5	

SEG 1995

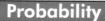
Probability

How likely or unlikely it is that an event will occur can be calculated or estimated using the idea of **probability**.

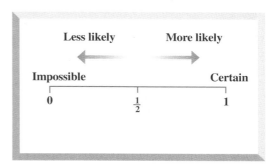

Probability words
In any situation involving uncertainty there are a number of possibilities or **outcomes** that may occur. Outcomes which are of particular interest are called **events**.

Probabilities have numerical values between 0 and 1.
A **probability of 0** means that an event is **impossible**.
A **probability of 1** means that an event is **certain**.
Probabilities are written either as a fraction, a decimal or a percentage.

Describe the likelihood that an event will occur if it has a probability of $\frac{1}{2}$.

Exercise 38.1

1. Describe each of the following events as:
   Impossible   Unlikely   Likely   Certain

   (a) A 6 is scored at least 500 times when a normal dice is rolled 600 times.
   (b) A 6 is scored at least 80 times when a normal dice is rolled 600 times.
   (c) An even number is scored at least once when a normal dice is rolled 600 times.
   (d) It will rain on three days running in April.
   (e) It will rain on three days running in August.
   (f) A coin is tossed five times and lands on its edge each time.
   (g) A coin is tossed five times and lands heads up on each occasion.
   (h) A coin is tossed five times and lands heads up at least once.

Calculating probabilities using equally likely outcomes

Probabilities can be **calculated** in situations where each outcome is equally likely to occur.

In such situations, the probability of an event, X, occurring is given by:

$$P(X) = \frac{\text{Number of possible outcomes in the event}}{\text{Total number of possible outcomes}}$$

> In this book P(X) stands for the probability of X.

Remember
Probabilities can only be calculated using this method in situations where there are **equally likely outcomes**.

Probability words
In many probability situations things are taken or picked at **random**. For example:

A card is taken at random from a pack of cards. This means that each card has an equal chance of being taken.

A boy is picked at random from a group. This means that any boy in the group is equally likely to be picked.

1 A card is taken at random from a full pack of playing cards with no jokers. What is the probability that the card:
(a) is red?
(b) is a heart?
(c) has an odd number on it?

A card is taken at **random** from the pack so there are 52 possible **equally likely** outcomes.

(a) There are 26 red cards in the pack so there are 26 possible outcomes in the event 'taking a red card'.
$P(\text{red}) = \frac{26}{52} = \frac{1}{2}$

(b) There are 13 hearts in the pack so there are 13 possible outcomes in the event 'taking a heart'.
$P(\text{heart}) = \frac{13}{52} = \frac{1}{4}$

(c) There are 20 cards with odd numbers in a pack so there are 20 possible outcomes in the event 'taking a card with an odd number on it'.
$P(\text{odd}) = \frac{20}{52} = \frac{5}{13}$

2 This table shows how 100 counters are coloured red or blue and numbered 1 or 2.

	Red	Blue
1	23	19
2	32	26

The 100 counters are put in a bag and a counter is taken from the bag at random.
(a) Calculate the probability that the counter is red.
(b) Calculate the probability that the counter is blue and numbered 1.

A counter is taken at **random** from the bag so there are 100 possible **equally likely** outcomes.

(a) There are 55 (23 + 32) red counters in the bag so there are 55 possible outcomes in the event 'taking a red counter'.
$P(\text{red}) = \frac{55}{100} = \frac{11}{20}$

(b) There are 19 blue counters numbered 1 in the bag so there are 19 possible outcomes in the event 'taking a counter that is blue and numbered 1'.
$P(\text{blue and 1}) = \frac{19}{100}$

Exercise 38.2

1 The eleven letters of the word MISSISSIPPI are written on separate tiles.
The tiles are placed in a bag and mixed up. One tile is selected at random.
What is the probability that the tile selected shows:
(a) the letter S,
(b) the letter I,
(c) the letter P?

2 The letters of the word TRIGONOMETRY are written on separate cards. The cards are shuffled and dealt, face down, onto a table. A card is selected at random. What is the probability that the card selected shows:
(a) the letter T,
(b) the letter R,
(c) a vowel?
Write your answers in their simplest form.

3 A card is taken at random from a full pack of playing cards with no jokers.
(a) What is the probability that the card is an ace?
(b) What is the probability that the card is a club?
(c) What is the probability that the card has a prime number on it?

4 A fair dice is rolled.
(a) What is the probability of obtaining a six?
(b) What is the probability of obtaining a number greater than 4?
(c) What is the probability of obtaining a square number?

5 A bag contains 4 red counters, 3 white counters and 3 blue counters.
A counter is taken from the bag at random. What is the probability that the counter is:
(a) red,
(b) not red,
(c) white or blue,
(d) red, white or blue,
(e) green?

6 500 tickets are sold in a raffle.
Elaine buys one ticket.
(a) What is the probability that Elaine wins first prize?

Sam says that the probability that a girl wins first prize is 50%.
(b) Explain why Sam might be wrong.

7 There are 6 red counters and 4 green counters in a box.
Counters are taken from the box at random and are not put back.
(a) What is the probability that the first counter taken out is red?
(b) If the first counter taken out is red, what is the probability that the second counter taken out is red?
(c) If the first counter taken out is green, what is the probability that the second counter taken out is red?

8 In a hat there are twelve discs numbered from 43 to 54.
Nina takes a number from the hat at random. What is the probability that Nina takes a disc:
(a) with at least one 4 on it,
(b) that has not got a 4 on it,
(c) that has a 3 or a 4 on it?

9 This table shows the way that fifty red and blue counters are numbered either 1 or 2.

	Red	Blue
1	12	8
2	8	22

One of the counters is chosen at random.
What is the probability that the counter is:
(a) a 1,   (b) blue,   (c) blue and a 1?

A blue counter is chosen at random.
(d) What is the probability that it is a 1?

A counter numbered 1 is chosen at random.
(e) What is the probability that it is blue?

10 The table shows the way that 120 pupils from year 7 travel to Linfield School.

	Boys	Girls
Walk	23	17
Bus	15	20
Car	12	8
Bike	20	5

A pupil from year 7 is chosen at random.
What is the probability that the pupil:
(a) walks to school,
(b) is a girl who travels by car,
(c) is a boy who does not travel by bus?

A girl from year 7 is chosen at random.
What is the probability that:
(d) she walks to school,
(e) she does not travel by car?

A year 7 pupil who travels by bike is chosen at random.
(f) What is the probability that the pupil is a boy?

11 The table shows the number of boys and girls in a class of 30 pupils who wear glasses.

	Boy	Girl
Wears Glasses	3	1
Does not wear glasses	11	15

A pupil from the class is picked at random.
(a) What is the probability that it is a boy?
(b) What is the probability that it is a girl who does not wear glasses?
A girl from the class is picked at random.
(c) What is the probability that she wears glasses?
A pupil who wears glasses is picked at random.
(d) What is the probability that it is a boy?

12 Tim plays a friend at Noughts and Crosses.
He says: 'I can either win, draw or lose, so the probability that I will win must be $\frac{1}{3}$'.
Explain why Tim is wrong.

Estimating probabilities using relative frequency

In question 12 in Exercise 38.2, probabilities **cannot** be calculated using equally likely outcomes.
In such situations probabilities can be estimated using the idea of **relative frequency**.

The relative frequency of an event, X, occurring is given by:

$$R(X) = \frac{\text{Number of times the event occurs in an experiment (or is observed)}}{\text{Total number of trials in the experiment (or total number of observations)}}$$

In this book R(X) stands for the relative frequency of X.

It is not always necessary to perform an experiment or make observations.
Sometimes the information required can be found in past records.

Probability words
Probability experiments are made up of a lot of repeated parts called **trials**.
For example, in Example 1 each trial is carried out by dropping the drawing pin once.

Relative frequency is the frequency of an event occurring related to the total number of trials (or observations).

EXAMPLES

1 In an experiment a drawing pin is dropped for 100 trials. The drawing pin lands point side up 37 times. What is the relative frequency of the drawing pin landing point side up?

$$R(\text{lands point side up}) = \frac{37}{100}$$
$$= 0.37$$

2 50 cars are observed passing the school gate. 14 red cars are observed. What is the relative frequency of a red car passing the school gate?

$$R(\text{a red car passes}) = \frac{14}{50}$$
$$= 28\%$$

3 Rainfall records show that in April it rained in Newcastle on 24 days in 1998.
Estimate the probability of rain in Newcastle on a day in April.

The number of times the event is observed is 24.
There are 30 days in April.
So the total number of observations = 30.

$$R(\text{rain on a day in April}) = \frac{24}{30} = 0.8$$

An estimate of the probability of rain in Newcastle on a day in April is 0.8.

4 Jamie does the following experiment with a bag containing 2 red and 8 blue counters.

This is the sort of graph that Jamie might get.

Take a counter from the bag at random. Record the colour then put the counter back in the bag. Repeat this for 100 trials.

Jamie calculates the relative frequency of getting a red counter every 10 trials and shows his results on a graph.
Draw a graph showing the results that Jamie might get.

$P(\text{Red}) = \frac{2}{10} = 0.2$
This is shown on the graph by the dotted line.

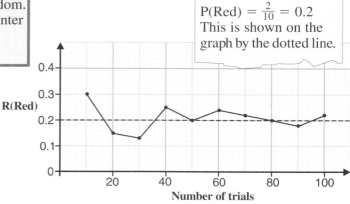

Jamie's graph illustrates: As the number of trials increases R(Red) gets closer to P(Red). Relative frequency gives a better estimate of probability the larger the number of trials.

Try Jamie's experiment yourself and see what sort of results you get.

EXAMPLE

5 Three faces of a dice are red, two faces are green and one face is blue.
Sadiq and Helen do an experiment with the dice to test how fair it is when it is rolled.
Their results are shown in the table.
Sadiq says "My results show that the dice is fair".

(a) Explain why Sadiq might be wrong.

(b) Is the dice fair? Explain your answer.

Student	Number of trials	R(Red)	R(Green)	R(Blue)
Sadiq	20	0.5	0.3	0.2
Helen	300	0.46	0.29	0.25

Using equally likely outcomes:
P(Red) = 0.5, P(Green) = 0.33 and P(Blue) = 0.17
to an accuracy of two decimal places.
The dice is **fair** if the relative frequencies are close
to the probabilities after a large number of trials.

(a) Sadiq might be wrong because he uses too few
trials in his experiment.

(b) Although Sadiq's results suggest that the dice
might be fair, Helen's results are more reliable
because of the larger number of trials.
Her results suggest that it is more likely that
the dice is **unfair**.

Probability words
Situations where all the possible
outcomes are equally likely are said
to be **fair**.
Another word for this is **unbiased**.
When all the possible outcomes are
not equally likely the situation is
said to be **unfair** or **biased**.

Exercise 38.3

1 A gardener plants 40 daffodil bulbs of which 36 grow into daffodil plants.
What is the relative frequency that a daffodil plant grows from a bulb?

2 A bag of counters contains red (R), green (G), white (W) and blue (B) counters.
In an experiment James takes a counter from the bag at random and then replaces it.
He repeats this trial 30 times and gets these results.

W R R W G R B G W R B W W G G

R R W B G B B W G R R W B R W

(a) Calculate the relative frequency of James taking a white counter from the bag.
James continues the experiment for **another** 270 trials. He gets **another** 111 white counters.
(b) Estimate the probability of James taking a white counter from the bag.

3 Gemma keeps a result of her chess games with Helen.
Out of the first 10 games, Gemma wins 6. Out of the first 30 games Gemma wins 21.
Estimate the probability that Gemma will win her next game of chess with Helen.

4 The results of games of chess played by four children at a chess club is shown in this table.
(a) Calculate the relative frequency of a win for each player.
(b) Which of these relative frequencies is most likely to give the best estimate of the
probability that the child will
win their next game.
Explain your answer.
(c) If Tom plays Pam, who do
think is the most likely to win?
Explain your answer.

Player	Games won	Games drawn	Games lost
Tom	4	2	6
Sam	8	1	7
Kim	3	0	1
Pam	9	2	9

5 Sally stood at her school gate and recorded the colour of 50 passing cars.

This table shows her results.

Colour	Frequency
Red	14
White	19
Blue	6
Green	5
Other	6

What is the relative frequency of a white car passing?
How likely is this to be a good estimate of the probability of a white car passing?
Explain your answer.

7 A counter is taken from a bag at random.
Its colour is recorded and the counter is then put back in the bag.
This is repeated 300 times.
The number of red counters taken from the bag after every 100 trials is shown in the table.

Number of trials	Number of red counters
100	52
200	102
300	141

(a) Calculate the relative frequency after each 100 trials.
(b) Estimate the probability of taking a red counter from the bag.

6 Five students do an experiment to test the fairness of this spinner.

This table shows the data the students collect.

Student	Number of trials	Faces landed on			
		1	2	3	4
Peter	20	6	5	4	5
Sam	60	22	21	8	9
Daron	250	90	85	35	40
Tracy	40	15	15	6	4
Peter	150	48	54	22	26

(a) Peter looks at his data and decides that the spinner is likely to be fair.
Why could he be wrong?
(b) Which student's data gives the best test of fairness of the spinner?
Explain your answer.
(c) Use the data from **all** the experiments to estimate the probability of the spinner landing on each number.

8 The diagram shows a spinner which is spun a number of times.
The graph shows the relative frequency of the spinner landing on the number 1 plotted against the number of times the spinner is spun.

(a) The spinner is a fair spinner.
How can you tell from the graph?

(b) How might the relative frequency of the spinner landing on the number 3 change with the number of trials?
Show your answer on a graph with relative frequency plotted after every 20 trials.

[Graph: R(1) on vertical axis from 0 to 0.3, Number of trials on horizontal axis from 0 to 200]

Estimating outcomes

This connection between relative frequency and probability can be used to estimate outcomes from an experiment, observations or past records.

EXAMPLES

1 Estimate the number of Heads you would get if you tossed a fair coin 1000 times?

For a large number of trials R(Head) is a good estimate of P(Head).
So ... after a large number of trials R(Head) = 0.5.

$$R(Head) = \frac{\text{Number of Heads}}{\text{Total number of trials}} \quad so \quad 0.5 = \frac{\text{Number of Heads}}{1000}$$

So, estimate of number of Heads = $1000 \times 0.5 = 500$.

2 A counter was taken at random from a bag of counters and then replaced.
This was repeated 1000 times.
The relative frequency of getting a red counter was found to be 0.147.
There are 20 counters in the bag. Estimate the number of red counters.

Because of the large number of trials it can be assumed that a good estimate of P(red) is 0.147.

$0.147 = \frac{\text{Number of red counters}}{20}$ which gives an estimate of 0.147×20 red counters = 2.94

There must be a whole number of red counters, so the most likely number in the bag is 3.

Exercise 38.4

1 A fair octahedral dice has its eight faces numbered 1, 2, 3, 4, 5, 6, 7 and 8.
The dice is rolled 400 times.
Estimate the number of times it lands on: (a) 1,   (b) 5,   (c) 8,   (d) an even number?

2 During the manufacture of switches for electrical circuits, some of the switches are tested.
This testing shows that the relative frequency of a switch being faulty is 0.02.
James buys 300 switches.
(a)   Estimate the number of faulty switches that James buys.
(b)   Explain why this is only an approximation.

3 (a)   Lilin tossed a coin a large number of times and got 550 tails.
How many times do you think she tossed the coin?
(b)   Tony rolled a dice a large number of times and got 150 ones.
How many times do you think he rolled the dice?

4 A bag containing 50 coloured balls is used in an experiment.
In the experiment a ball is taken at random from the bag and its colour is recorded.
The ball is then put back in the bag. This is repeated 300 times.
The number of times each colour is taken from the bag is:
     Red 77,   Blue 91,   White 132.
Estimate the number of each coloured ball in the bag.

5 The manager of a restaurant analyses all the meals ordered from the lunchtime menu.
He works out that the relative frequency of a customer ordering soup as a starter is 0.63.
800 customers order from the lunchtime menu each month.
Estimate how many of them are likely to order soup.

When a coin is tossed the event 'heads' cannot occur at the same time as the event 'tails'.
When a person is picked at random the event 'girl' cannot occur at the same time as the event 'boy'.
When a card is taken at random from a pack of cards the event 'the Ace of Hearts' cannot occur at the same time as the event 'a black card'.

Events which **cannot occur at the same time** are called **mutually exclusive events**.

*Why are the events pick a red card from a pack of cards and pick the Ace of Hearts from the same pack of cards **not** mutually exclusive?*

When a dice is rolled you must either get a six (6) or not get a six (not 6).
This pair of events are **mutually exclusive**.
The event rolling a dice and either getting a six **or** not getting a six is **certain** to occur.

So ...   P(6 or not 6) = 1

Now ... $P(6) = \frac{1}{6}$ and $P(\text{not } 6) = \frac{5}{6}$ so ... $P(6) + P(\text{not } 6) = 1$

So ...   P(6 or not 6) = P(6) + P(not 6)

This example illustrates the following rules.

When A and B are mutually exclusive events:
    P(A or B) = P(A) + P(B)

Because the events A and not A are certain to occur and must be mutually exclusive:
    P(not A) = 1 − P(A)

The spinner has a ring of numbers inside a ring of colours.
These tables show some of the probabilities of the arrow stopping
on each colour and number when the spinner is spun.

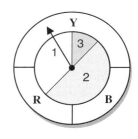

Red(R)	Yellow(Y)	Blue(B)
0.25	0.5	

1	2	3
0.375	0.5	

Safia spins the spinner once.
(a)   What is the probability of the arrow stopping on blue?
(b)   What is the probability of the arrow stopping on blue or 1?

(a)   The arrow stopping on R, Y or B is
      certain to occur.
      P(R) + P(Y) + P(B) = 1
      0.25 + 0.5 + P(B) = 1
          0.75 + P(B) = 1
                  P(B) = 1 − 0.75
                  P(B) = 0.25

(b)   The arrow stopping on B and the arrow
      stopping on 1 are mutually exclusive.
      P(B or 1) = P(B) + P(1)
                = 0.25 + 0.375
                = 0.625

Show that the probability of the arrow stopping on red or blue or 3 is 0.625.
*Can you explain why P(B or 2) = 0.5 and **not** P(B) + P(2)?*

1 State whether or not each of the following pairs of events are mutually exclusive.
   (a) Winning a football match.
       Losing a football match.
   (b) Meeting a person with blue eyes.
       Meeting a person with brown hair.
   (c) Picking a King from a pack of cards.
       Picking an Ace from a pack of cards.
   (d) It snows tomorrow.
       It doesn't snow tomorrow.
   (e) It snows tomorrow.
       It rains tomorrow.
   (f) Getting a six with a dice.
       Getting an even number with a dice.

2 A fish is taken at random from a tank containing only red fish and black fish. The probability that the fish is black is $\frac{2}{5}$. What is the probability that the fish is red?

3 Tina has a bag of black and white beads. She takes a bead from the bag at random. The probability that the bead is white is $\frac{8}{15}$. What is the probability that the bead is black?

4 The probability of a switch working is 0.96. What is the probability of a switch not working?

5 Six out of every 100 men are taller than 1.85 m.
A man is picked at random.
What is the probability that he is not taller than 1.85 m?

6 A bag contains red, white and blue balls. A ball is taken from the bag at random. The probability of taking a red ball is 0.4. The probability of taking a white ball is 0.35.
What is the probability of taking a white ball or a blue ball?

7 A spinner can land on red, white or blue. The probability of the spinner landing on red is 0.2.
The probability of the spinner landing on red or on blue is 0.7.
The spinner is spun once.
What is the probability that the spinner lands:
   (a) on blue, (b) on white?

8 A bag contains red, green, blue, yellow and white counters.
The table shows the probabilities of obtaining each colour when a counter is taken from the bag at random.

Red	Green	Blue	Yellow	White
30%	25%	20%	20%	10%

   (a) (i) How can you tell that there is a mistake in the table?
       (ii) The probability of getting a white counter is wrong. What should it be?

A counter is taken from the bag at random.
   (b) (i) What is the probability that it is either green or blue?
       (ii) What is the probability that it is either red, green or blue?
       (iii) What is the probability that it is not yellow?

9 Some red, white and blue cubes are numbered 1 and 2.
The table shows the probabilities of obtaining each colour and number when a cube is taken at random.

	Red	White	Blue
1	0.1	0.3	0
2	0.3	0.1	0.2

A cube is taken at random.
   (a) What is the probability of taking a red cube?
   (b) What is the probability of taking a cube numbered 2?
   (c) State whether or not the following pairs of events are mutually exclusive.
       Give a reason for each answer.
       (i) Taking a cube numbered 1 and taking a blue cube.
       (ii) Taking a cube numbered 2 and taking a blue cube.
   (d) (i) What is the probability of taking either a blue cube or a cube numbered 1 (or both)?
       (ii) What is the probability of taking either a blue cube or a cube numbered 2 (or both)?

EXAMPLES

1 A fair coin is thrown twice.
Identify all of the possible outcomes and
write down their probabilities.

Method 1
List the outcomes systematically.

1st throw	2nd throw
Head (H)	Head (H)
Head (H)	Tail (T)
Tail (T)	Head (H)
Tail (T)	Tail (T)

Method 2
Use a **possibility space diagram**.

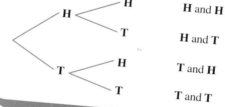

2nd throw	T	H & T	T & T
	H	H & H	T & H
		H	T
		1st throw	

When a fair coin is tossed
twice, there are four
possible outcomes.
Because the coin is fair all
the possible outcomes are
equally likely.
Because all the outcomes
are equally likely their
probabilities can be
worked out.

Method 3
Use a **tree diagram**.

1st throw	2nd throw	Outcome
H	H	H and H
	T	H and T
T	H	T and H
	T	T and T

The lines are called
the **branches** of the
tree diagram.

P(H and H) = P(H and T) = P(T and H) = P(T and T) = $\frac{1}{4}$.

2 A fair dice is rolled twice.
Use a possibility space diagram to show all the possible outcomes.
What is the probability of getting a 'double six'?
What is the probability of getting any 'double'?
What is the probability that exactly one 'six' is obtained?

2nd roll

6	1 and 6	2 and 6	3 and 6	4 and 6	5 and 6	6 and 6
5	1 and 5	2 and 5	3 and 5	4 and 5	5 and 5	6 and 5
4	1 and 4	2 and 4	3 and 4	4 and 4	5 and 4	6 and 4
3	1 and 3	2 and 3	3 and 3	4 and 3	5 and 3	6 and 3
2	1 and 2	2 and 2	3 and 2	4 and 2	5 and 2	6 and 2
1	1 and 1	2 and 1	3 and 1	4 and 1	5 and 1	6 and 1
	1	2	3	4	5	6

1st roll

The dice is fair so there are 36 equally likely
outcomes.

P(double 6)
There is one outcome in the event (6 and 6).
P(double 6) = $\frac{1}{36}$

P(any double)
The 6 outcomes in the event are shaded green.
P(any double) = $\frac{6}{36} = \frac{1}{6}$

P(exactly one six)
The 10 outcomes in the event are shaded grey.
P(exactly one six) = $\frac{10}{36} = \frac{5}{18}$

1 Two fair dice are rolled and the numbers obtained are added.
(a) Draw a possibility space diagram to show all of the possible outcomes.
(b) Use your diagram to work out:
　(i)　the probability of obtaining a total of 10,
　(ii)　the probability of obtaining a total greater than 10,
　(iii)　the probability of obtaining a total less than 10.
(c) Explain why the probabilities you worked out in (b) should add up to 1.

2 A fair coin is tossed and a fair dice is rolled.
Copy and complete the table to show all the possible outcomes.

Dice

	1	2	3	4	5	6
H		H2				
T						

Coin

What is the probability of obtaining:
(a)　a head and a 5,　　　　　　　(b)　a tail and an even number,
(c)　a tail and a 6,　　　　　　　(d)　a tail and an odd number,
(e)　a head and a number more than 4,　(f)　an odd number?

3 Sanjay has to travel to school in two stages.
Stage 1:　he can go by bus or train or he can get a lift.
Stage 2:　he can go by bus or he can walk.

(a)　List all the different ways that Sanjay can travel to school.

Sanjay decides the way that he travels on each stage at random.
(b)　What is the probability that he goes by bus in both stages?

Sanjay travels to school 200 times in a year.
(c)　On how many days is he likely to travel by bus on at least one of the stages?

4 To help Whitley Rovers choose a new football strip, 800 fans were asked to choose the colour they preferred.
280 fans chose a red strip, 320 chose a white strip and 200 chose a blue strip.

One fan was chosen at random.
(a)　Estimate the probability that he did not choose white.

Two fans were chosen at random.
(b)　Make a list of the 9 possible pairs of colours that the two fans might have chosen.
(c)　Jimmy looked at the list of 9 possible pairs of colours and said:
　　'The probability that the two fans both picked a red strip must be $\frac{1}{9}$'.
　　Explain why Jimmy was wrong.

5 The diagram shows an unbiased spinner.
It is divided into four equal sections numbered as shown.
The spinner is spun twice and the numbers the arrow lands on each time are added.
Calculate the probability of getting:
(a)　a total of 2,　(b)　a total of 3,　(c)　a total of 6.

6 Bag A contains 2 red balls and 1 white ball.
Bag B contains 2 white balls and 1 red ball.
A ball is drawn at random from each bag.

(a) Copy and complete the table to show all possible pairs of colours.
(b) Explain why the probability of each outcome is $\frac{1}{9}$.
(c) Calculate the probability that the two balls are the same colour.

Bag A

		R	R	W
	W	RW		
Bag B	W			
	R			

Two balls are drawn from another bag.
The probability that they are the same colour is 0.6.
(d) What is the probability that the balls are a different colour?

7 The diagram shows two sets of cards A and B.

One card is taken at random from set A. One card is taken at random from set B.
(a) List all the possible outcomes.

The two numbers are added together.
(b) (i) What is the probability of getting a total of 5?
(ii) What is the probability of getting a total that is not 5?

All the cards are put together and one of them is taken at random.
(c) What is the probability that it is labelled A or 2 (or both)?

8 Students at a college must choose to study two subjects from the list:
Maths   English   Science   Art
(a) Write down all the possible pairs of subjects that the students can choose.

David chooses both subjects at random.
(b) What is the probability that one of the subjects he chooses is Maths?

James chooses Maths and one other subject at random.
(c) What is the probability that he chooses Maths and Science?

9 A spinner has an equal probability of landing on either red, green, blue, yellow or white.
The spinner is spun twice.
(a) List all the possible outcomes.
(b) (i) What is the probability that, on both spins, the spinner lands on white?
(ii) What is the probability that, on both spins, the spinner lands on white at least once?
(iii) What is the probability that, on both spins, the spinner lands on the same colour?

10 The diagram shows two unbiased spinners.
Each spinner is divided into equal sections and numbered as shown.
Each spinner is spun and the numbers that each arrow lands on are added together.
(a) Calculate the probability of getting a total of 2.
(b) Calculate the probability of getting a total of 6.

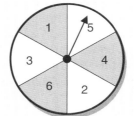 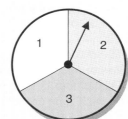

A **tree diagram** can be used to find all the possible outcomes when two or more events are combined. It can also be used to help calculate probabilities when outcomes are not equally likely.

EXAMPLE

1 **Box A** contains 1 red ball (R) and 1 blue ball (B).
Box B contains 3 red balls (R) and 2 blue balls (B).
A ball is taken at random from Box A.
A ball is then taken at random from Box B.

(a) Draw a tree diagram to show all the possible outcomes.

(b) Calculate the probability that two red balls are taken.

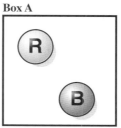
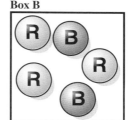

(a)
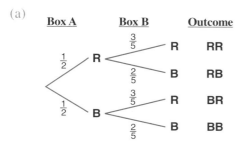

Remember:
When drawing a tree diagram probabilities must be put on the branches. Using equally likely outcomes:
In Box A
$P(R) = \frac{1}{2}$ $P(B) = \frac{1}{2}$

In Box B
$P(R) = \frac{3}{5}$ $P(B) = \frac{2}{5}$

(b) The numbers of Red and Blue balls are unequal in Box B.
This means that the outcomes RR, RB, BR and BB are not equally likely.

Method

Multiply the probabilities along the branches of the tree diagram.

$P(RR) = \frac{1}{2} \times \frac{3}{5} = \frac{1 \times 3}{2 \times 5} = \frac{3}{10}$

The probability that two red balls are taken is $\frac{3}{10}$.

Why the method works

On $\frac{3}{5}$ of the occasions that a ball is taken from Box B it will be R.
On $\frac{1}{2}$ of these occasions the ball taken from Box A will also be R.
So on $\frac{1}{2} \times \frac{3}{5}$ occasions the balls taken from Box A and Box B will be RR.

By completing the table solve the above problem using equally likely outcomes.

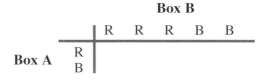

2 The probability that Amanda is late for school is 0.4.
Use a tree diagram to find the probability that on two days running:
(a) she is late twice, (b) she is late exactly once.

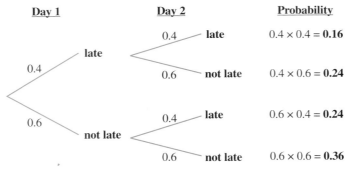

(a) The probability that Amanda is late twice.

The outcome included in this event is:
(late **and** late)
P(late twice) = 0.16

(b) The probability that Amanda is late exactly once.

The outcomes included in this event are:
(late **and** not late) **or** (not late **and** late)
These outcomes are mutually exclusive.
P(late exactly once) = 0.24 + 0.24 = 0.48

Exercise **38.7**

1 A bag contains 3 red counters and 2 blue counters.
A counter is taken at random from the bag and then replaced.
Another counter is taken at random from the bag.

(a) Copy and complete the tree diagram to show all the possible outcomes. Write the probability of each of the events on the branches of the tree diagram.

(b) (i) Calculate the probability that both counters taken are blue.
(ii) Calculate the probability that at least one counter taken is blue.

2 A manufacturer makes an electrical circuit which contains two switches.
The probability that a switch is faulty is 0.1.

(a) Copy and complete the tree diagram.
Write the probability of each of the events on the branches of the tree diagram.

(b) (i) Calculate the probability that both switches are faulty.
(ii) Calculate the probability that exactly one switch is faulty.

The circuit works if both switches are not faulty.
(c) The manufacturer makes 1000 circuits.
Estimate the number that work.

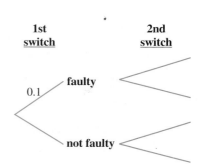

3 Five people in a group of 50 people are left handed.
There are 20 females in the group.
A person is picked at random from the group.

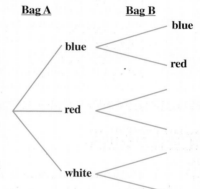

- (a) (i) What is the probability that the person is left handed?
  - (ii) What is the probability that the person is right handed?
  - (iii) What is the probability that the person is female?
  - (iv) What is the probability that the person is male?

- (b) Copy and complete the tree diagram.
  Write the probability of each of the events on the branches of the tree diagram.

- (c) (i) Calculate the probability that the person picked is a left handed female.
  - (ii) Calculate the probability that the person picked is a left handed female or is a right handed male.

4 Bag A contains 3 blue counters, 5 red counters and 2 white counters.
Bag B contains 2 blue counters and 3 red counters.
Tom takes a ball at random from Bag A.
Sam takes a ball at random from Bag B.

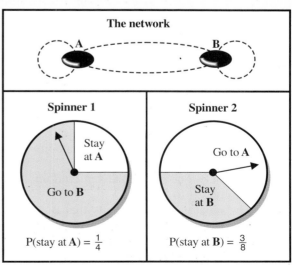

- (a) Copy and complete the tree diagram to show the possible pairs of colours that Tom and Sam can take. Write the probability of each of the events on the branches.

- (b) Calculate the probability that Tom takes a blue counter from Bag A and Sam takes a red counter from Bag B.

- (c) Calculate the probability that the counter taken by Tom is the same colour as the counter taken by Sam.

5 Seema and Dario play a game on a network with two fair spinners.
In the game, Seema and Dario each have a counter which they move between A and B on the network.
They move their counters by taking turns to spin one of the spinners.
If their counter is at A, they spin spinner 1.
If their counter is at B, they spin spinner 2.
After each spin, they move their counter depending on where the arrow on the spinner lands.
The player whose counter is at B after a given number of turns is the winner.

Dario starts at A and Seema starts at B.
Use tree diagrams to find the most likely winner:

- (a) in a game in which each player has two spins.

- (b) in a game in which each player has three spins.

The network

Spinner 1
Stay at A
Go to B
P(stay at A) = $\frac{1}{4}$

Spinner 2
Go to A
Stay at B
P(stay at B) = $\frac{3}{8}$

Independent events

When two coins are tossed, the outcome of the first toss has no affect on the outcome of the second toss.
One person being left handed does not influence another person being left handed.
These are examples of events which can happen together but which do not affect each other.
Events like this are called **independent** events.
All of the examples in Exercise 38.7 involved independent events.

When A and B are **independent** events then the probability of A and B occurring is given by:
$$P(A \text{ and } B) = P(A) \times P(B)$$

This rule can be extended to any number of independent events. For example:
$$P(A \text{ and } B \text{ and } C) = P(A) \times P(B) \times P(C)$$

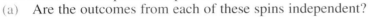

EXAMPLES

1 A fair spinner has four equal sections.
The sections are coloured blue (B), red (R), white (W) and green (G).
The arrow on the spinner is spun twice.
(a) Are the outcomes from each of these spins independent?
(b) Find the probability of the arrow landing on red and green in any order.
The arrow on the spinner is spun three times.
(c) Find the probability of the arrow landing on the same colour.

(a) Yes. The events are independent as the outcome from one spin does not affect the next spin.
$$P(B) = P(R) = P(W) = P(G) = \tfrac{1}{4}$$

Try answering part (b) using equally likely outcomes.

(b) $P((R \text{ and } G) \text{ or } (G \text{ and } R)) = P(R \text{ and } G) + P(G \text{ and } R)$
$$= P(R) \times P(G) + P(G) \times P(R)$$
$$= (\tfrac{1}{4} \times \tfrac{1}{4}) + (\tfrac{1}{4} \times \tfrac{1}{4}) = \tfrac{1}{16} + \tfrac{1}{16}$$
The probability of the arrow landing on red and green in any order is $\tfrac{1}{8}$.

(c) $P((R \text{ and } R \text{ and } R) \text{ or } (B \text{ and } B \text{ and } B) \text{ or } (G \text{ and } G \text{ and } G) \text{ or } (W \text{ and } W \text{ and } W))$
$$= P(R \text{ and } R \text{ and } R) + P(B \text{ and } B \text{ and } B) + P(G \text{ and } G \text{ and } G) + P(W \text{ and } W \text{ and } W)$$
$$= (\tfrac{1}{4} \times \tfrac{1}{4} \times \tfrac{1}{4}) + (\tfrac{1}{4} \times \tfrac{1}{4} \times \tfrac{1}{4}) + (\tfrac{1}{4} \times \tfrac{1}{4} \times \tfrac{1}{4}) + (\tfrac{1}{4} \times \tfrac{1}{4} \times \tfrac{1}{4}) = 4 \times \tfrac{1}{64}$$
The probability that the arrow lands on the same colour is $\tfrac{1}{16}$.

2 Bob has three 50p coins and two 20p coins.
Sam has four 50p coins and one 20p coin.
Bob picks one of his coins at random and gives it to Kim.
Sam picks one of his coins at random and gives it to Kim.
(a) What is the probability that Bob and Sam give Kim a total of £1?
(b) What is the probability that Bob and Sam give Kim a total of 70p?

(a) Both Bob and Sam give 50p.
$$P(50p \text{ and } 50p) = P(50p) \times P(50p)$$
$$= \tfrac{3}{5} \times \tfrac{4}{5} = \tfrac{12}{25}$$

(b) Tom gives 50p and Sam 20p, or Sam gives 20p and Tom 50p.
$$P(50p \text{ and } 20p \text{ or } 20p \text{ and } 50p)$$
$$= P(50p \text{ and } 20p) + P(20p \text{ and } 50p)$$
$$= P(50p) \times P(20p) + P(20p) \times P(50p)$$
$$= \tfrac{3}{5} \times \tfrac{1}{5} + \tfrac{2}{5} \times \tfrac{4}{5} = \tfrac{11}{25}$$

You are not asked to use a tree diagram in any of the questions in this exercise. However, you can do so if you think it will help.

1 Which of the following pairs of events are likely to be independent.
(a) A: The sun shines today.
B: The sun shines tomorrow.
(b) A: It rains on August Bank Holiday.
B: It rains on Spring Bank Holiday.
(c) Tom and Sam are brothers.
A: Tom has blue eyes.
B: Sam has blue eyes.
(d) Tom and Sam are in the same class at school.
A: Tom has blue eyes.
B: Sam has blue eyes.
(e) Mr. Rice drives to work.
A: His car breaks down.
B: Mr. Rice is late for work.
(f) A red dice and a blue dice are rolled.
A: The red dice lands on an even number.
B: The blue dice lands on an even number.

2 A fair spinner can land on either black or white.
The probability that it lands on white when it is spun is 0.3.
(a) What is the probability that it lands on black when it is spun?

The spinner is spun twice.
(b) Find the probability of getting two blacks or two whites.

3 In box A there are 3 red and 5 blue counters.
In box B there are 2 red and 3 blue counters.
In box C there are 7 red and 3 blue counters.
A counter is chosen at random from each box.
Calculate the probability that:
(a) all of the counters are red.
(b) at least one of the counters is red.

4 Each of two identical spinners can stop on red, yellow or blue.
The probability of it landing on red is 0.1.
The probability of it landing on blue is 0.3.
Both spinners are spun.
(a) What is the probability that both spinners land on blue?

Jane and Sally play a game with the spinners.
Jane spins both spinners.
If they land on the same colour she wins.
If they don't she loses.
(b) Who is more likely to win the game? Show **all** your working.

5 Samantha takes examinations in Maths and in English.
The probability that she passes Maths is 0.7.
The probability that she passes English is 0.8.
The results in each subject are independent of each other.
Calculate the probability that:
(a) Samantha passes Maths and fails English.
(b) Samantha fails both subjects.

6 The probability that it rains on a Monday is $\frac{3}{8}$.
The probability that there is a Maths test on a Monday is $\frac{1}{3}$.
These two events are independent.
(a) What does the term independent mean?
(b) Calculate the probability that there is a Maths test on a rainy Monday.
(c) In a school year there are 39 Mondays.
How many Maths tests are likely to take place in a school year on a Monday when it doesn't rain?

7 Dice A and Dice B are two normal dice.
Dice A is a fair dice.
Dice B is biased so that the probability of getting an even number is $\frac{2}{3}$.
Both of the dice are tossed.

Find the probability that:
(a) an odd number is scored on dice A and an even number on dice B.
(b) an odd number is scored on one dice and an even number on the other.

8 A bag contains red, white and blue cubes.
The cubes are numbered 1, 2, 3 and 4.
The probabilities of taking cubes from the box at random are shown in the table.

A single cube is taken from the box at random.
(a) What is the probability that:
    (i) the cube is white?
    (ii) the cube is red and numbered 4?
    (iii) the cube is white or numbered 1 (or both)?
    (iv) the cube is white or numbered 3 (or both)?

Colour of cube

	Red	White	Blue
1	0.1	0	0
2	0.1	0.1	0.1
3	0	0.2	0.2
4	0.1	0	0.1

Number of cube

A cube is taken from the box at random and then replaced.
Another cube is then taken from the box at random.
(b) Calculate the probability that the cubes are a different colour.

9 A box contains cubes which are coloured red (R), white (W) or blue (B) and numbered 1, 2 or 3.
The table shows the probabilities of obtaining each colour and each number when a cube is taken from the box at random.

A single cube is taken from the box at random.
(a) What is the probability that the cube is:
    (i) red and numbered 2,
    (ii) white or numbered 1 (or both),
    (iii) white or numbered 3 (or both)?

Colour of cube

	R	W	B
1	0.2	0	0.1
2	0.1	0.3	0
3	0	0.1	0.2

Number of cube

A cube is taken from the box at random and then replaced.
Another cube is then taken from the box at random.
(b) Calculate the probability that:
    (i) both cubes are blue and numbered 1,
    (ii) both cubes are blue or numbered 1,
    (iii) both cubes are blue or both cubes are numbered 1.

10 The tables give some information about the members of two clubs.

Club A

	Male	Female
Wears glasses	22	8
Does not wear glasses	48	22

Club B

	Male	Female
Wears glasses	8	37
Does not wear glasses	12	43

(a) A male from club A is picked at random and a male from club B is picked at random.
    What is the probability that:
    (i) both of them wear glasses?
    (ii) one of them wears glasses?

(b) A member of club A is picked at random and a member of club B is picked at random.
    What is the probability that:
    (i) both members picked are female?
    (ii) one male and one female is picked?

- You need to know the meaning of these terms:

  outcome, event   fair, unbiased, biased, taken at random

  equally likely outcomes   trial

- **Probability** describes how likely or unlikely it is that an event will occur.
  Probability is measured on a scale of 0 (**impossibility**) to 1 (**certainty**).
  Probability **must** be written as a fraction, a decimal or a percentage.

- How to determine probabilities using **equally likely outcomes**.
  The probability of an event X occurring is given by:

  $$P(X) = \frac{\text{Number of possible outcomes in an event}}{\text{Total number of possible outcomes}}$$

- How to estimate probabilities using **relative frequency.**
  The relative frequency of an event X occurring is given by:

  $$R(X) = \frac{\text{Number of times an event occurs in an experiment (or is observed)}}{\text{Total number of trials in the experiment (or observations)}}$$

  Relative frequency gives a better estimate of probability the larger the number of trials.

- How to use probabilities to **estimate** the number of times an event occurs in an **experiment** or **observation**.
  Estimate = total number of trials (or observations) × probability of event

- How to determine probabilities of **mutually exclusive** events.
  Mutually exclusive events cannot occur at the same time.

  When A and B are mutually exclusive events …   P(A or B) = P(A) + P(B).

  The events A and not A are mutually exclusive.
  A or not A is certain to occur. So …   P(not A) = 1 − P(A).

- How to find all the possible outcomes when two events are combined.
  By **listing** the outcomes systematically.
  By using a **possibility space diagram**.
  By using a **tree diagram**.

- How to find the probability of a combined event by:
  finding all the equally likely outcomes in simple situations,
  using a tree diagram.

- How to determine probabilities of two or more **independent** events.
  The outcomes of independent events do not influence each other.

  When A and B are independent events …   P(A and B) = P(A) × P(B).

The network game

The game is about moving about this network.

At A roll a dice
> If it lands on an odd number, stay at A.
> If it lands on an even number, move to B.

At B roll a dice
> If it lands on a 1 or 2, stay at B.
> If it lands on a 3, 4, 5 or 6, move to A.

Where are you most likely to end up if you …
> … start at A and throw the dice twice?
> … start at B and throw the dice twice?
> … start at A and throw the dice 5 times?
> … start at B and throw the dice 5 times?
> … start at A and throw the dice 10 times?
> … start at B and throw the dice 10 times?

Analyse the game using probability.

Investigate network games for different networks and different probabilities **a, b, c** …

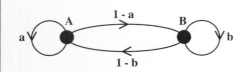

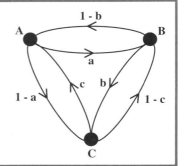

Review Exercise

1 Jane has four red beads and six blue beads.

She picks beads one at a time at random.

(a) What is the probability that the first bead she picks is red?

The first bead she picks is blue.

(b) What is the probability that the second bead she picks is red?

2 A card is chosen at random from Set 1 and another card is chosen at random from Set 2.

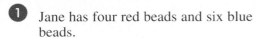

(a) List all the possible outcomes.
(b) What is the probability that a C is not one of the two cards chosen.

SEG 1997

3 One hundred students take two tests, a first aid test and a cycling test.
The results are shown in the two-way table.

Cycling

		Pass	Fail
First Aid	Pass	19	49
	Fail	26	6

(a) What is the probability that a student chosen at random passes the first aid test?
(b) What is the probability that a student chosen at random fails the cycling test?

SEG 1997

4 A fair dice is thrown 600 times.
Estimate the number of times a prime number is thrown.

5 The results from 20 spins of a numbered spinner are:

      2 1 4 3 2 1 3 4 5 2
      1 5 3 4 2 3 3 3 2 4

(a) Find the relative frequency of 2.

The results from another 20 spins are:

      1 2 2 3 2 1 2 4 5 2
      2 3 4 2 1 5 3 3 5 3

(b) Estimate the number of times a 2 will occur in 500 spins.

6 A spinner gives a score of 1, 2, 4 or 6 with the following probabilities.

Score	1	2	4	6
Probability	0.4	0.2	0.1	...

(a) Calculate the probability that the score is 6.
(b) Calculate the probability that the score is either 1 or 2.

SEG 1997

7 A game is played with two fair spinners.

 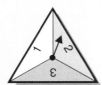

In each turn of the game both spinners are spun and the numbers are added to get a score.

(a) Copy and complete the following table to show each possible score.

	1	2	3	4
1				
2				
3				

(b) What is the probability of:
    (i) scoring 6,
    (ii) not scoring 6?

(c) To start the game a player needs to score either 2 or 5.
    What is the probability that the game starts on the first throw?

8 A fair coin is thrown 20 times.
It lands heads 12 times.
(a) What is the relative frequency of throwing a head?

The coin continues to be thrown.
The table shows the number of heads recorded for 20, 40, 60, 80 and 100 throws.

Number of throws	20	40	60	80	100
Number of heads	12	18	30	42	49

(b) Draw a graph to show the relative frequency of throwing a head for these data.

(c) Estimate the relative frequency of throwing a head for 1000 throws.

SEG 1998

9 A box contains cubes.
Each cube is coloured red or white or blue and each cube is numbered 1 or 2 or 3 or 4.
The table shows the probabilities of colour and number when a cube is taken from the box at random.

		Colour of cube		
		red	white	blue
Number on cube	1	0.1	0	0
	2	0.1	0.1	0.1
	3	0	0.2	0.2
	4	0.1	0	0.1

A cube is taken from the box at random.

(a) What is the probability that it is white?

(b) What is the probability that it is red **and** numbered 2?

(c) What is the probability that it is white **or** numbered 1 (or both)?

(d) What is the probability that it is white **or** numbered 3 (or both)?

SEG 1997

10 The table gives the probabilities of the scorer of the first goal in a mixed Hockey match.

A man over 1.8 metres tall   0.2
A woman over 1.6 metres tall 0.4
A man over 25 years old   0.5
A woman over 25 years old   0.3
A man who wears glasses   0.2
A woman who wears glasses   0.1

The first goal is scored by:
Event A
either a man who wears glasses
or a woman over 25.

Event B
either a woman over 1.6 metres
tall **or** a woman over 25.

Event C
a person who wears glasses.

Where possible, use the table to calculate the probability of each of events A, B and C.
If it is not possible explain why.

11 The diagram shows a road network.

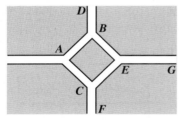

Cars enter the network at *A*.

At *A*:
the probability of a car going to *B* is 0.6.

At *B*:
the probability of a car going to *D* is 0.8.

At *C*:
the probability of a car going to *F* is 0.7.

(a)   What is the probability that a car entering the network:
    (i)   goes from *A* to *C* to *F*,
    (ii)   goes from *A* to *B* to *E*?

All cars arriving at *E* go to *G*.
(b)   1000 cars pass *A*.
    Estimate how many go to *G*.

12 David and Sita each hold a green flag in their left hand and a black flag in their right hand. David and Sita each raise one flag.
The probability that a black flag is raised by Sita is 0.4 and by David is 0.3.

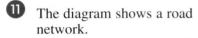

(a)   Copy and complete this tree diagram.

(b)   Calculate the probability that:
    (i)   two green flags are raised.
    (ii)   one flag of each colour is raised.

13 (a)   Suki is looking for her house keys. The probability that they are in her pocket is 0.4.
The probability that they are on her bedside table is 0.3.
What is the probability that they are either in her pocket or on her bedside table?

(b)   When Suki oversleeps she misses her first lesson of the day.
The probability that she oversleeps on any day is 0.4.
    (i)   Calculate the probability that she misses the first lesson of two successive days.
    (ii)   Calculate the probability that she misses the first lesson on Monday, but attends the first lesson on Tuesday and Wednesday.

SEG 1997

14 Boxes *P* and *Q* each contain five numbered balls.
The balls in each box are numbered as shown.

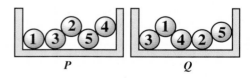

A ball is taken from each box at random.
(a)   What is the probability that both balls are numbered 2?
(b)   What is the probability that both balls have the same number?
(c)   What is the probability that the number on the ball from box *P* is greater than the number on the ball from box *Q*?

SEG 1998

Section Review - Handling Data

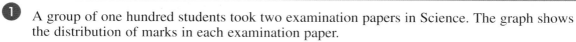

1 A group of one hundred students took two examination papers in Science. The graph shows the distribution of marks in each examination paper.

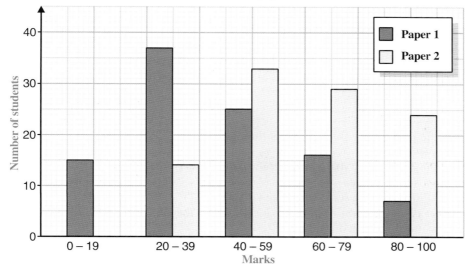

(a) Which examination paper was easier?

(b) In which examination paper was there a greater spread of marks?

(c) How many students scored 40 to 59 marks in Paper 2?

SEG 1995

2 Keith is investigating what proportion of children are left handed.
He conducts a survey in his class at school.
The results of the survey are shown.

(a) How many children were included in the survey?

(b) Keith says 'More boys than girls are left-handed'.
Give one reason why he may be wrong.

(c) Keith says 'The probability that a child is left-handed is $\frac{1}{7}$'.
Give one reason why he may be wrong.

(d) The school has 385 children.
If Keith is correct, estimate how many would be left-handed.

Right-handed	Left-handed
Boys ⊞ ⊞ ⊞ |||	Boys |||
Girls ⊞ ⊞ ||	Girls ||

SEG 1996

3 The pie chart shows information from a survey about the holiday destinations of a number of people.

(a) (i) Which holiday destination is the mode?

(ii) America is the holiday destination of 24 people. How many people go to Africa?

In another survey it was found that America is the holiday destination of 21 people out of 180 people asked.

(b) What percentage of all the people asked in these two surveys gave America as their holiday destination?

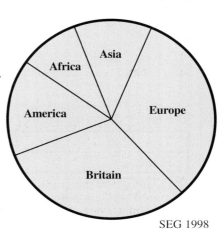

SEG 1998

4 James has two coins.
He throws both coins together.
List all the different results he could get.

SEG 1995

5 A card is taken at random from a pack of 52 playing cards.
What is the probability that it is:
(a)   a spade,   (b)   not a spade,   (c)   a four,   (d)   a red four,
(e)   the Ace of Spades,   (f)   an Ace, King, Queen or Jack?

6 In a raffle 100 tickets are sold.
Only one prize can be won.

(a)   Nicola buys one ticket.
What is the probability that she wins the prize?
(b)   Dee buys five tickets.
What is the probability that she wins the prize?
(c)   Keith buys some tickets.
The probability that he wins the prize is $\frac{3}{20}$.
(i)   What is the probability that he does not win the prize?
(ii)   How many tickets did he buy?

SEG 1994

7 One Saturday a newsagent sells the following:
National daily newspapers   510
Echo   360
Magazines and comics   210
(a)   Draw a clearly labelled pie chart to represent these sales.

The frequency polygon shows
the sales of national daily
newspapers.

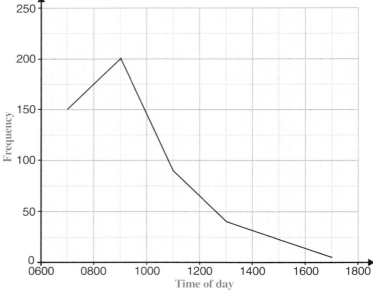

(b)   (i)   How many of these papers were sold between 1000 and 1400?
The tables shows the sales of the Echo.

Time of day	0600 -	0800 -	1000 -	1200 -	1400 -	1600 - 1800
Frequency	0	0	0	20	125	215

(ii)   Copy the graph above and on the same diagram draw a frequency polygon to show the sales of the Echo.
(iii)   Compare and comment on the sales of these two types of newspaper.

SEG 1998

8 The two-way table shows the connection between the number of cars owned and the number of adults in thirty different families.

Number of cars owned

		0	1	2	3	4
	1	4	5	0	0	0
Number of	2	1	5	3	0	0
adults	3	0	2	2	3	0
	4	0	0	1	1	1
	5	0	0	1	1	0

For example, there are four families with one adult and no cars.

(a) How many of the thirty families have one car for each adult?
(b) Find the modal number of cars owned by the thirty families.
(c) Calculate the total number of adults in the thirty families.
(d) Calculate the total number of cars owned by the thirty families.

SEG 1997

9 The relative frequency of Gemma winning a game of chess is 0.7.
In a year Gemma plays about 150 games.
Estimate the number of times that she is likely to win.

10 Marianne did a survey about height and shoe size.
Her results are shown in the table.

Name	Joe	Bill	Sue	Anne	Ted	Pat	Bob	Mary
Height (cm)	140	155	130	175	170	145	130	160
Shoe size	$4\frac{1}{2}$	$6\frac{1}{2}$	4	$8\frac{1}{2}$	8	$6\frac{1}{2}$	5	$7\frac{1}{2}$

(a) Plot these results on a scatter graph.
(b) Comment on the relationship between height and shoe size shown by this diagram.
(c) Tom wears size 6 shoes.
    Estimate his height.

SEG 1994

11 Ross keeps a record of the number of miles that he drives and the amount of petrol used, in litres.

Distance travelled (miles)	300	370	410	420	440	450
Petrol used (litres)	36	41	45	46	51	51

(a) Plot a scatter graph of these results.
(b) What relationship does the scatter graph show?
(c) (i) Draw the line of best fit on the scatter graph, and use it to estimate the amount of petrol, in litres, needed to travel 600 miles.
    (ii) Comment on the reliability of this estimate.

SEG 1996

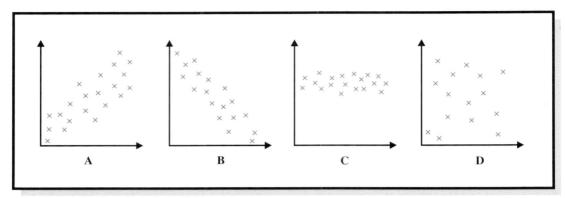

Which of these scatter graphs would best describe the following?
(a) The size of feet compared with the marks in a maths test.
(b) The age of adults compared with the heights of adults.

SEG 1995

13 John is planning to conduct a survey on the quality of food and service in the school canteen.
(a) He thinks of two questions:
       Question 1.   What is your name?
       Question 2.   How often do you use the canteen?
    (i)   Explain why each of these questions is unsuitable.
    (ii) Rewrite each of these questions so that he could include them in his questionnaire.

(b) John gives his questionnaire to all the students in his class.
     Explain why this may not be a suitable sample.

14 In an opinion poll, 2000 men in Birmingham are asked how they intend to vote in a General Election.
(a) Give two reasons why this is an unreliable way of predicting the outcome of a General Election.
(b) Give three ways in which the opinion poll could be improved.

SEG 1994

15 The number of goals scored during 12 hockey matches were recorded.

Number of goals	0	1	2	3	4	5	6	7
Number of matches	1	4	1	2	0	1	0	3

(a) One of these 12 matches is chosen at random. Find the probability that 7 goals were scored in this match.
(b) (i)   Write down the median number of goals.
     (ii) Calculate the mean number of goals per match.
     (iii) Tina is writing a newspaper article about these 12 matches. She wants to include the average number of goals scored. Give one reason for using the mean rather than the median or the mode.

SEG 1994

16 A survey asked 40 eleven year olds how many letters they received in a week. The results are shown in the table.

Number of letters	Number of children
None	25
1 - 5	13
6 - 10	1
11 - 15	1
More than 15	0

(a) Write down the midpoint of the class 1 - 5.
(b) Calculate an estimate of the mean number of letters received in a week by the 40 eleven year olds.
(c) Explain why your answer in (b) is only an estimate.
(d) What is the maximum possible range for the number of letters received in a week by the 40 eleven year olds?

A similar survey of 40 eighteen year olds was carried out. The results are summarised below.

Minimum = 0
Maximum = 20
Mean = 4

(e) Describe **two** differences between the number of letters received by the eleven year olds and the number of letters received by the eighteen year olds.

SEG 1997

17 The table shows the time, in seconds, it took each of forty students to drink a can of lemonade.

Time (seconds)	Frequency
0 and less than 8	4
8 and less than 16	9
16 and less than 24	11
24 and less than 32	6
32 and less than 40	8
40 and less than 48	2

(a) Calculate an estimate of the mean of these times.
(b) Draw a frequency polygon for this frequency distribution.

SEG 1996

18 The mass of each of 60 apples was recorded to the nearest gram.

Mass	80 -	85 -	90 -	95 -	100 -	105 -	110 - 115
Frequency	3	7	13	15	12	8	2

(a) Calculate the values of the cumulative frequencies.

Mass	< 80	< 85	< 90	< 95	< 100	< 105	< 110	< 115
Cumulative frequency								

(b) Draw the cumulative frequency curve.
(c) Use your graph to estimate the interquartile range of the mass of the apples.
(d) Use your graph to estimate the number of apples that have a mass of less than 106 g.
(e) Seventeen of the apples are rejected as they are too heavy.
What is the maximum weight of the apples that are accepted?

SEG 1996

19 The capacities, c, (in ml) of 100 milk bottles were measured.
(a) Copy and complete the table to show the cumulative frequencies.

Capacity, c, (ml)	Frequency	Cumulative frequency
$552.5 \leqslant c < 557.5$	3	
$557.5 \leqslant c < 562.5$	10	
$562.5 \leqslant c < 567.5$	21	
$567.5 \leqslant c < 572.5$	40	
$572.5 \leqslant c < 577.5$	18	
$577.5 \leqslant c < 582.5$	8	

(b) Use your table to draw a cumulative frequency curve.
The nominal capacity of a milk bottle is 568 ml.
(c) What percentage of the bottles in the sample had a capacity of less than 568 ml?
(d) Use your graph to estimate the median and interquartile range for the sample.

SEG 1996

20 Two boys, Steve and Tim are keen on archery.
The probability of each boy hitting the target is:

Boy	Steve	Tim
Probability	$\frac{1}{4}$	$\frac{1}{5}$

Each boy has one shot at the target.
(a) Draw a probability tree diagram to show all possible combinations of their hits and misses.
(b) Calculate the probability that **just** Tim hits the target.

SEG 1994

21 The diagram shows a network of roads.

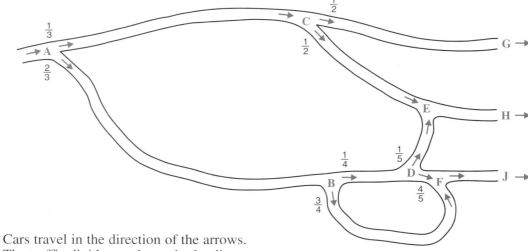

Cars travel in the direction of the arrows.
The traffic divides as shown in the diagram.
During the rush hour 300 cars enter the network at A.
(a) (i) How many cars would you expect to take the road from A to C?
(ii) How many cars would you expect to pass through G?
(b) Calculate the probability of a car passing through J.

SEG 1996

Exam Practice - Non-calculator Paper

Do not use a calculator for this exercise.

1 (a) Change $\frac{4}{5}$ to a decimal.

(b) Write these numbers in order of size. Start with the smallest.
0.805,   0.85, $\frac{4}{5}$,   0.096

SEG 1994

2 (a) Work out (i) 0.1×0.4,
(ii) $4.6 - 2.74$.

(b) Write down the value of 7^2.

(c) What is the value of $\sqrt{81}$?

3 Jeremy pays £3.72 for 3 pounds of runner beans and 2 pounds of peas. The runner beans cost 78 pence per pound.
How much per pound are the peas?

4 (a) A school party of 590 people is going to a theme park by coach. James needs to work out the cost of the coaches.
He has forgotten his calculator.
Each coach can seat 44 passengers.
Each coach costs £85 to hire.
Work out the total cost of all the coaches that are needed.
You **must** show all your working.

SEG 1997

5 A sequence begins   1,   3,   7,   15,   ...
The rule for continuing the sequence is shown.

> MULTIPLY THE LAST NUMBER
> BY 2 AND ADD 1

(a) What is the next number in the sequence?

(b) This sequence uses the same rule.
-2, -3, -5, -9, ...
What is the next number in this sequence?

SEG 1998

6 (a) What number should Stan start with to get an answer of 35?

(b) Stan starts with x. What is his answer?

I think of a number.
I double it.
Then I take away 5.

SEG 2000 S

7 This is a sketch of a company logo.

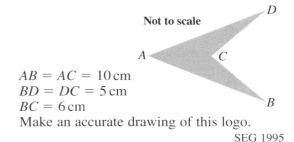

Not to scale

$AB = AC = 10\,\text{cm}$
$BD = DC = 5\,\text{cm}$
$BC = 6\,\text{cm}$
Make an accurate drawing of this logo.

SEG 1995

8 In the diagram, ABC is a triangle.
Lines AB and CD are parallel.

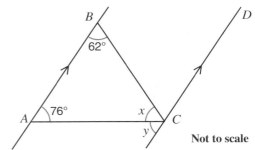

Not to scale

(a) (i)   Calculate the value of angle x.
(ii)   Give a reason for your answer.

(b) (i)   Calculate the value of angle y.
(ii)   Give a reason for your answer.

SEG 1997

9 Appleton is 8 miles due north of Berrytown.
A third town, Cooksville, is on a bearing of 125° from Appleton.
The bearing of Cooksville from Berrytown is 062°.
By using a scale of 1 cm to 1 mile, show the positions of these towns on a scale drawing.

SEG 1997

10 A plan of a college is drawn to a scale of 1 : 200.
On the plan one classroom measures 2 cm by 2.4 cm.
Work out the **actual** dimensions of the classroom in **metres**.

SEG 1996

11 Rachael receives two packets.

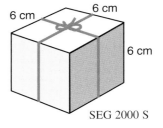

Calculate the difference between
the volumes of the two packets.
State your units.

SEG 2000 S

12 The two-way table shows the results of students taking examinations in English and French.

	A			1	1	2
	B		1		5	2
French Grade	C		1	7	2	
	D		2	3	1	
	E	3	1			
		E	D	C	B	A
			English Grade			

(a) How many of the students who achieved
grade B in English achieved a different
grade in French?

(b) How many students achieved the same grade
in both subjects?

(c) What does the table suggest about the grades
achieved by students in English and French?

SEG 1995

13 (a) (i) State the type of correlation
shown in each diagram.
(ii) State which of the diagrams
A, **B** or **C** could represent the
following situations.

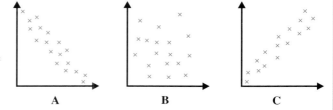

Situation
The electricity bill and size of house.
The outside temperature and the amount of gas used for central heating in the house.
The height of a person and the amount they earn in one year.

(b) A furniture store reduced the prices of their three piece suites as follows.

(i) Plot a scatter graph of these
data.
(ii) Which suite is most likely to
have been given the wrong
sale price label?
(iii) Estimate the sale price of a
suite which had a previous
selling price of £1700.

Suite	Previous selling price (£)	Sale price (£)
A	1400	900
B	1600	1000
C	1150	600
D	2100	1400
E	2000	800
F	1800	1000
G	1900	1200
H	1400	750

SEG 1995

14 At the bank James exchanged £50 for Francs.
He was given 425 Francs.
Joanna has £120.
She estimates that she will get about 900 Francs.
Use rough estimates to check whether her answer is about right.
You **must** show all your working. SEG 1996

15 (a) Apples cost 80p per kilogram.
Pears cost 15% per kilogram more than apples.
How much per kilogram are pears?
(b) Two kilograms of grapes cost £3.10.
How much will five kilograms cost?
(c) A crate full of oranges weighs 25 kg.

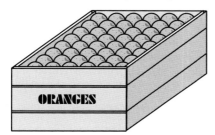

The oranges weigh 20 kg
(i) What percentage of the total weight is the weight of the oranges?
(ii) What is the ratio of the weight of the empty crate to the weight of the oranges? SEG 2000 S

16 A geography test is marked out of 80 marks.
(a) Georgina gets 60% of the marks.
How many marks does she get?
(b) Alfie gets 36 marks.
What percentage does he get?
(c) The test is taken by a class of 28 pupils.
The ratio of the number of boys to the number of girls in the class is 3 : 4.
How many boys take the test?

The teacher said, 'The class average for the test is 65.4 marks'.
(d) The 28 pupils score 1832 marks altogether. Show by using approximation, that the average is about right.
You **must** show all your working. SEG 1997

17 Solve these equations.
(a) $3x - 7 = 5$
(b) $5(x + 2) + 1 = 46$ SEG 2000 S

18 (a) Simplify $2y - y + 3y$.
(b) What is the value of $p^2 + p$ when $p = -3$?

19 The number of children per family in a recent survey of 100 families is shown.

No of children	No of families
0	14
1	19
2	32
3	14
4	10
5	7
6	4
	100

Calculate the mean number of children per family.
You **must** show all your working. SEG 2000 S

20 The first five terms of a sequence are given.
9, 7, 5, 3, 1, ...
(a) Write down the next term in the sequence.
(b) Write down the nth term in the sequence.

21 At the end of a typing course all the students are tested. The time taken to type 60 words is recorded.
The table shows the distribution of their times.

Time (w seconds)	Number of students
$0 \leqslant w < 20$	0
$20 \leqslant w < 40$	7
$40 \leqslant w < 60$	19
$60 \leqslant w < 80$	11
$80 \leqslant w < 100$	3

(a) Draw a frequency polygon for these data.
(b) Calculate an estimate of the mean of their times. SEG 1996

22

Square   Rectangle

(a) (i) How many lines of symmetry has the **square**?
(ii) How many lines of symmetry has the **rectangle**?

(b) *WXYZ* is a rectangle.

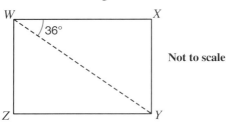

Not to scale

Angle *XWY* = 36°.
Work out the size of angle *WYZ*, giving a reason for your answer.

(c) *PQRS* is a rhombus.

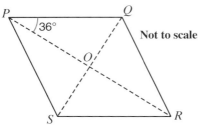

Not to scale

Angle *QPR* = 36°.
The diagonals *PR* and *QS* cross at *O*.
Work out the size of angle *PQS*, giving a reason for your answer.

SEG 1995

23

(a) Find an approximate value of the expression $19.7 \times 41.2 \div 0.0483$.

(b) All six faces of this cuboid are to be painted.
There is enough paint to cover 5 m².

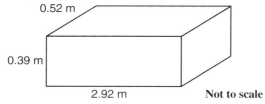

0.52 m

0.39 m

2.92 m   **Not to scale**

Use approximations to estimate whether there is enough paint to paint the cuboid.
You **must** show all your working.

SEG 2000 S

24 The diagram shows shape *A*.

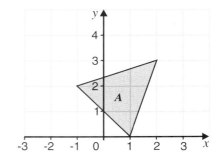

Copy the diagram.
(a) Reflect shape *A* in the line $x = 3$. Label its new position *B*.
(b) Rotate shape *A* through 90° anticlockwise about centre (1, 0). Label its new position *C*.
(c) Another triangle, *D*, has vertices $(-3, 3)$, $(-5, 5)$ and $(-2, 6)$.
Describe fully the **single** transformation which will take *A* onto *D*.

SEG 1998

25

(a) Write 12 as a product of prime factors.
(b) Write 64 as a product of prime factors.
(c) What is the lowest common multiple of 12 and 64?

26

(a) Simplify the expression $3x - 3 + 2 - x$.
(b) Solve the equation $5(x + 1) = 3x - 3$.
(c) Solve the simultaneous equations $y = 2x - 6$ and $y = 4 - 2x$ by a graphical method.

SEG 1997

27

John and Sarah are each asked to continue a sequence which begins
2,   5, ...,

(a) John writes
2,   5,   8,   11, ...
Write down the *n*th term of John's sequence.

(b) Sarah writes
2,   5,   10,   17, ...,
Write down the *n*th term of Sarah's sequence.

SEG 1998

472

28 The table shows the times taken by each of seven motorists to complete a journey.

Length of journey (km)	25	40	50	65	90	90	100
Time taken (hours)	0.5	0.8	1.2	1	1.3	1.8	1.2

(a) Use this information to draw a scatter graph.
Label the horizontal axis **Length of journey km**, from 0 to 140.
Label the vertical axis **Time (Hours)**, from 0 to 2.5.
(b) Draw a line of best fit.
(c) (i) Use your line of best fit to estimate the time taken by a motorist to complete a journey of length 130 km.
(ii) Give **one** reason why your estimate may not be very accurate.

SEG 2000 S

29 Sally is planning a survey about pets.
She tries out this question on her friends:
Pets take too much time and money. What do you think?
(a) (i) What is wrong with this question?
(ii) Write a better question to find the same information.
(b) Another question in her survey is:
How many pets do you own?
The data Sally collects are shown.

0	0	0	0	1	1	1	1	1	1	1	1
1	2	2	2	2	2	2	2	3	3	3	4
4	8	8	12	26							

She works out that
the median number of pets owned is 2;
the mean number of pets owned is 3.24.
Sally writes a report for the school magazine.
She decides that the median is a better average to use than the mean.
Give **two** reasons for this.

SEG 1997

30 The net of a triangular prism is shown.

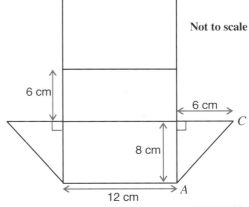

Not to scale

(a) Calculate the length of *AC*.
You **must** show all your working.
(b) Calculate the volume of the triangular prism.

SEG 2000 S

31 You are given the formula $K = Pm^2$.
(a) Use approximations to estimate the value of K when $P = 397$ and $m = 5.03$.
(b) Rearrange the formula to give m in terms of K and P.

32　(a)　Write 0.003 in standard form.
　　(b)　$P = 5 \times 10^3$
　　　　Write the value of $7P$ in standard form.
　　(c)　$Q = 3 \times 10^{-2}$
　　　　Calculate the value of PQ
　　　　Give your answer in standard form.

33　(a)　Simplify $x^2 - 2x - 3 + x - 5$.
　　(b)　Factorise completely $3a^2 - 6a$.
　　(c)　Multiply out and simplify $(2x - 1)(x - 3)$.

SEG 1998

34　(a)　Solve these inequalities.
　　　　(i)　　$2x + 1 \le 5$
　　　　(ii)　$x^2 > 25$
　　　　(iii)　$7x + 3 > 13x + 15$
　　(b)　Copy the diagram.
　　　　On your diagram label with the letter R,
　　　　the single region which satisfies all of
　　　　these inequalities.
　　　　　$y < \tfrac{1}{2}x + 1,$　　$x > 6,$　　$y > 3$

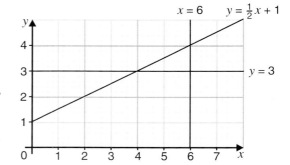

SEG 1994

35　The diagram shows a sketch of the
　　line $2y = x - 2$.

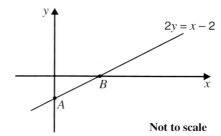

Not to scale

　　(a)　Find the coordinates of points A and B.
　　(b)　Find the gradient of the line $2y = x - 2$.
　　(c)　Explain why the simultaneous equations $2y = x - 2$ and $2y = x - 3$ have no solution.
　　(d)　Another line passes through B and through the point $(0, 2)$.
　　　　Find the equation line.

SEG 1998

36　In triangle ABC, $\sin A = \tfrac{2}{5}$.
　　Calculate the length of BC.

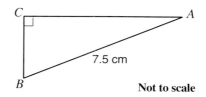

Not to scale

SEG 1996

37　(a)　Simplify
　　　　(i)　　$5p^3 \times 3p^2$,
　　　　(ii)　$8p^6 \div 4p^3$.
　　(b)　What is the value of $3^0 + 3^{-2}$?

38 (a) A ball is thrown up into the air. Which of these graphs represents its motion?

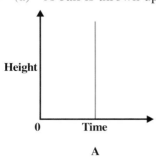
A

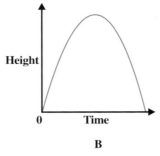
B

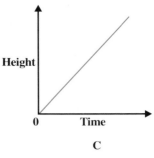
C

(b) A bath is empty. A tap is turned on.
Which of these graphs shows how the bath filled up?

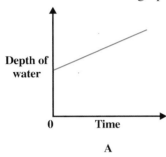
A

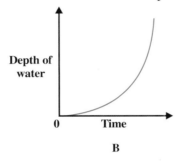
B

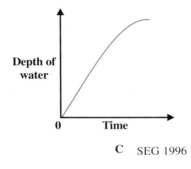
C   SEG 1996

39 A square based pyramid has a base of length x centimetres and a vertical height of h centimetres.
State, by only considering dimensions, which of the following formulae gives the total surface area of the pyramid.
Give a reason for your answer.

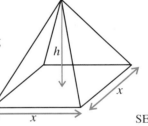

A $x + x^2 \sqrt{(4h^2 + x^2)}$ **B** $x^2 + x \sqrt{(4h^2 + x^2)}$

C $x^2 + x (4h^2 + x^2)$ **D** $x + x^2 (4h^2 + x^2)$

SEG 1997

40 Mrs Collins drives to work. On her way to work she has to cross two sets of traffic lights, marked A and B in the diagram. The probability of having to stop at the traffic lights is shown in the table.

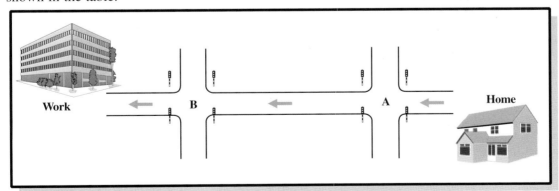

On Monday Mrs Collins drives to work.
(a) What is the probability that she will have to stop at both sets of traffic lights?
(b) What is the probability that she will have to stop at only one set of traffic lights?

Traffic lights	Probably of having to stop
A	0.3
B	0.6

SEG 2000 S

Exam Practice - Calculator Paper ●●●●●●

You may use a calculator for this exercise.

1 Laura buys 18 cartons of juice.
She pays with a £10 note.
She gets £2.98 change.
How much is each carton of juice?

2 Sue is a caretaker. She is paid at the basic rate of £4.36 per hour.
(a) When Sue works overtime, she is paid at one and a half times the basic rate.
What is her rate of pay per hour for overtime?
(b) Sue is given a pay rise of 13 pence on her basic rate per hour.
Calculate the percentage increase in her basic rate.
Give your answer to an appropriate degree of accuracy.

SEG 1998

3 A candle weighs x grams.
(a) Write an expression, in terms of x, for the weight of 20 candles.
(b) A box of 20 candles weighs 3800 grams.
The box weighs 200 grams.
What is the weight of a candle?

4 A cabbage weighs 5 pounds.
(a) Estimate its weight in kilograms.
(b) The cabbage costs 90p per kilogram. Estimate the cost of the cabbage.

SEG 1997

5 (a) Chris is 13 cm taller than Steven.
Their heights add up to 307 cm.
How tall is Steven?

Sarah is 122 cm tall.
(b) (i) Sarah's height has been given to the nearest centimetre.
What is the minimum height she could be?
(ii) Estimate Sarah's height in feet.
Give your answer to the nearest foot.

SEG 1998

6 Shara collected data on the colour of different vehicles passing her home. The table shows the results of her survey.

Type of Vehicle

		Car	Van	Lorry	Bus	Total
Colour of Vehicle	Red	15	2	3	5	25
	Blue	9	3	2	0	14
	White	9	4	1	0	14
	Green	2	2	2	1	7
	Total	35	11	8	6	60

(a) Which colour of vehicle is the mode?
(b) Draw a pie chart to show the proportion of each type of vehicle.

7 A shop sells two brands of flour.
Brand A: weight 500 g, cost 39 pence. Brand B: weight 800 g, cost 59 pence.
Which brand of flour gives more grams per penny?
You **must** show all your working.

8 Angela has three sums to work out on her calculator.

> $\frac{3}{8}$ of 224
>
> 43% of £32
>
> 2^{18}

Work out Angela's three sums.
(a) $\frac{3}{8}$ of 224   (b)   43% of £32   (c) 2^{18}

SEG 1997

9 Diana adds ice to an orange drink.
The temperature of the ice is $-5°C$.
The temperature of the orange drink is $6°$.
(a)   What is the temperature difference between the ice and the orange drink?
Approximately 5 cm³ of ice is added to the orange drink.
(b)   The volume of ice to orange drink is in the ratio 1 : 40.
What is the volume of the drink after the ice has been added?
(c)   The ice melts at the rate of 1 cm³ every 3 minutes.
What percentage of ice remains after 10 minutes?

SEG 1996

10 A sponge cake for eight people needs 120 g of sugar.
John makes a sponge cake for five people.
(a)   Calculate the weight of sugar he needs.

John cuts his cake into five equal slices.
He gives three slices to his mother.
(b)   What percentage of the cake does John have left?

SEG 2000 S

11 A cake is made from fat, flour and sugar.
The cake weighs 110 g.
The weight of the sugar is 42 g.

(a)   (i)   What percentage of the cake is sugar?
Give your answer correct to one decimal place.
(ii)   The ratio of the weight of flour to the weight of
sugar is 3 : 2.
What is the weight of the flour?

(b)   The weight of the cake has been given to the nearest 10 g.
What is the minimum weight of the cake?

SEG 1998

12 The lengths of the sides of a triangle are
$(x + 1)$ cm, $(x + 3)$ cm and $(x - 2)$ cm, as shown.

$(x + 1)$ cm

$(x - 2)$ cm

$(x + 3)$ cm

Not to scale

(a)   Write an expression, in terms of x, for
the perimeter of the triangle.
Give your answer in its simplest form.
The perimeter is 23 cm.
(b)   Write down an equation in x and use it to find the value of x.

SEG 2000 S

13 This flag is made from a coloured square and a white triangle. Work out the total area of the flag.

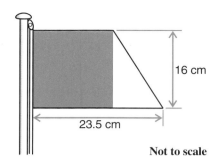

16 cm

23.5 cm

Not to scale

SEG 2000S

14 The table shows the amount of foreign currency that a tourist can buy with £1. Terry has just returned from France. He has 940 francs. His next holiday is in Italy. He changes his francs into lira. Calculate, to the nearest thousand, how many lira he will get.

TOURIST RATES
£1 will buy
France. . . . .   8.38 francs
Germany. . . . .   2.49 marks
Italy . . . . 2480.00 lira
Spain . . . . 207.80 pesetas

SEG 1998

15 A double-glazing salesman is paid a basic wage of £48 per week. He is also paid 6% commission on all his sales over £1600 in a week. In a four week period his sales are

      Week 1 £3040,   Week 2 £1100,
      Week 3 £4500,   Week 4 £9800.

Calculate his total pay for the four week period.

SEG 1997

16 Sunita has 96 beads.
(a) 37.5% of her beads are gold. How many gold beads does she have?
(b) Sunita uses $\frac{3}{4}$ of her beads to make a necklace.

    She uses her beads in the ratio 3 gold beads to 2 silver beads to 1 black bead. How many of each colour bead does she use?

SEG 1997

17 (a) On graph paper draw and label the lines $y = 2x$ and $y = 6 - x$ for values of x from -1 to 4.
(b) Solve the equation $2x = 6 - x$.

18 (a) Work out the value of 0.031^2.

(b) Work out the value of $\dfrac{1.36 \times 0.965}{1.57 + 2.29}$

SEG 2000 S

19 The following information about vitamin content is printed on the side of a breakfast cereal packet.
(a) Copy the table. Calculate and fill in the missing values.
(b) The 16.2 mg of vitamin C is 24% of the recommended daily amount of vitamin C. What is the recommended daily amount of vitamin C?
(c) The recommended daily amount of vitamin B6 is 2 mg. What percentage of the recommended daily amount is provided by the 100 g serving?

	100 g serving	30 g serving
Vitamin C	. . . . mg	16.2 mg
Vitamin B6	1.7 mg	. . . . mg

SEG 1997

20 The cost of hiring a car is £c.
This cost is given by the formula
$$c = 21.50 + k(0.27 + d),$$
where k is the number of kilometres driven,
    d is a number which depends on the type of car.
Jill hires a car and drives 90 kilometres.
For this car the value of d is 0.19.
How much will it cost her?

SEG 1995

21 (a) The first four terms in a sequence are   2,   8,   18,   32.
What is the next term in the sequence?
(b) Solve the equation $2(3x + 5) = 4x + 7$.
(c) Solve the equation $x^3 = 22$ by trial and improvement.
Start with $x = 2$.
Give your final answer correct to **one** decimal place.
You **must** show all your working.

SEG 1997

22 The diagram shows a Cumbrian tent.
A glassfibre rod forms a semi-circle ABC.
(a) What is the length of this rod?
Take π to be 3.14 or use the π key on your calculator.
(b) Calculate the area of fabric needed to cover the
semi-circular end of this tent.
Take π to be 3.14 or use the π key on your calculator.
(c) The tent is in the shape of a prism.
Calculate the volume of air inside this tent.

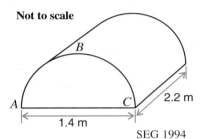

Not to scale

SEG 1994

23 An electricity bill is made up of three parts:
    (1) a fixed charge of £12.50;
    (2) a charge of 8.35 pence for each unit of electricity;
    (3) Value Added Tax (VAT) at 5% added on to the total of parts (1) and (2).

(a) Jasmin uses 1037 units of electricity.
Calculate her electricity bill.
(b) Next time Jasmin gets an electricity bill, it shows a cost of £172.49 before VAT is
added.
Calculate how many units of electricity she used.

SEG 2000 S

24 A number n, expressed in terms of its prime factors, is $2^6 \times 3^4 \times 11$.
(a) Find the value of n.
(b) Express $8n$ as a product of prime factors.
(c) Find the value of $8n$, giving your answer in standard form.

SEG 1995

25 In the diagram AB is parallel to ED.
Angle $CED = 54°$ and angle $BCD = 100°$.
(a) (i) Write down the size of angle x.
    (ii) Find the size of angle y.
(b) Triangle ABC is similar to triangle DEC.
$AC : CD$ is 3 : 2.
$AB = 5.4$ cm.
Calculate the length of DE.

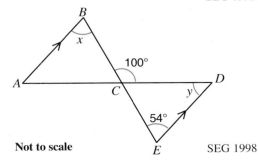

Not to scale

SEG 1998

26 The diagram shows part of a roof structure.

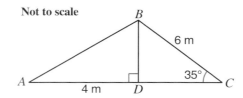

Not to scale

$AD = 4\,\text{m}$, $BC = 6\,\text{m}$ and angle $BCD = 35°$.
BD is perpendicular to AC.
(a)   Calculate the height of BD.
(b)   Calculate angle BAC.

SEG 2000 S

27 (a)   (i)   The Earth is a sphere of radius 6.35×10^6 m.
The volume of the Earth is given by the formula
$V = \frac{4\pi r^3}{3}$

where r is the radius of the Earth.
Find the volume of the Earth.
Give your answer in standard form, stating your units.
   (ii)   Ruth calculates the volume of a sphere of radius 4.1 cm.
She gets an answer of $28.9\,\text{cm}^3$.
Without using a calculator, use estimates to check whether her answer is about right.
You **must** show all your working.
(b)   Use the formula $s = ut + 0.5at^2$
to calculate the value of s when $u = 14.2$, $t = 9\frac{1}{4}$ and $a = -9.8$.

SEG 1997

28 A ball bearing has mass 0.44 pounds.
$1\,\text{kg} = 2.2$ pounds.
(a)   Calculate the mass of the ball bearing in kilograms.

(b)   Density $= \frac{\text{Mass}}{\text{Volume}}$.

When the mass is measured in kg and the volume is measured in cm^3, what are the units of the density?

SEG 1994

29 You are given the formula $a = \frac{1}{2}\,bc^2$.
(a)   Find the value of a when $b = 3.25 \times 10^7$ and $c = 0.6$.
Give your answer in standard form.
(b)   Rearrange the formula $a = \frac{1}{2}\,bc^2$ to give c in terms of a and b.

SEG 2000 S

30 Light travels at 186 284 miles per second.
(a)   Write 186 284 in standard form.

The planet Jupiter is 483.6 million miles from the Sun.
(b)   (i)   Calculate how long light takes to travel from the Sun to Jupiter.
Give your answer to the nearest minute.
   (ii)   Use approximation to check that your answer is of the right order of magnitude.
You **must** show all your working.

SEG 1998

31 The total surface area, A, of a cone is given by the equation $A = \pi rx + \pi r^2$.

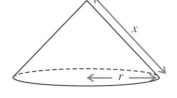

(a) (i) Express x in terms of A, π and r.
 (ii) Find x when $A = 75$ and $r = 4.1$.

(b) When $r = 5\,cm$, $A = 5\pi x + 25\pi$.
 The graph of A against x is drawn.
 (i) Write down the gradient of the line.
 (ii) Write down the value of A at the point where the line crosses the A axis.

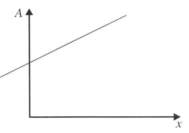

SEG 1997

32 Calculate the value of each of these expressions.
(a) $2^5 \times 3^8 + 5^0$ (b) $2.5^3 \times (2.5^4 + 2.5^{-2})$

SEG 1997

33 Lucy has carried out a survey into the hours of sleep of hospital nurses.
She asked sixty nurses how many hours of sleep they got in a typical working week.
Her results are given in the table.

(a) Construct a cumulative frequency table for the hours of sleep for the sixty nurses.
(b) Draw the cumulative frequency curve.
(c) Use your graph to find
 (i) the median,
 (ii) the interquartile range.

Hours of sleep	Frequency
Less than 20	0
20 to less than 25	4
25 to less than 30	9
30 to less than 35	25
35 to less than 40	18
40 to less than 45	4
45 or more	0

Lucy asked the sixty nurses how many hours of sleep they got in a typical week off work.
The results gave a median of 51 hours and an interquartile range of 6.5 hours.

(d) Briefly describe the sleep pattern for the week off work compared with the sleep pattern for the working week.

SEG 1997

34 (a) A sequence begins   2,   5,   8,   11,   ...
 Write an expression for the nth term of the sequence.

(b) The nth term of a different sequence is $\frac{1}{2}(n^2 - 2n)$.
 (i) Write down the first term and the second term of the sequence.
 (ii) When the nth term of the sequence is 40, the value of n can be found by solving the equation $n^2 - 2n - 80 = 0$.
 Solve this equation and hence find the value of n.
 You **must** show all your working.

SEG 1998

35 (a) When the temperature of a rod, of length x metres, is increased by $t\,°C$, the new length, y metres, is given by the formula
 $$y = x(1 + at).$$
 Calculate the value of y when $x = 2$, $t = 5$ and $a = 0.01$.

(b) The distance of the Earth from the Sun is approximately 1.496×10^8 km.
 The speed of light is approximately 2.998×10^5 km per second.
 Calculate the time that it takes light from the Sun to reach the Earth.
 Give your answer in minutes and seconds to the nearest second.

SEG 1995

GCSE Mathematics Coursework

All GCSE mathematics courses include a coursework component to test your ability to use and apply mathematics. The coursework component is worth 20% of the overall marks in examinations in mathematics. The style of coursework depends on the syllabus you are taking.

Why do I have to do coursework?

Coursework gives you the opportunity to use and apply a range of mathematical knowledge and skills. With coursework, you have the chance to be a 'real-life mathematician'.
Another important reason is that you may suffer from examination anxiety. Coursework gives you the opportunity to demonstrate the knowledge and skills which you possess.

How is coursework marked?

Coursework is marked against a set of assessment criteria which are common to all examination boards. Whilst administrative procedures may differ between boards the same coursework criteria are used by all. These criteria are divided into three strands:
1. Making and monitoring decisions to solve problems
2. Communicating mathematically
3. Developing skills of mathematical reasoning

How each strand is used to assess different aspects of your work

1. Making and monitoring decisions to solve problems
This strand is about deciding what needs to be done then doing it. You will need to select an appropriate method, obtain information and introduce your own questions to develop the task further.

> For the higher marks you will need to analyse alternative approaches, coordinate a number of variables and apply independently a range of appropriate mathematical techniques.

2. Communicating mathematically
This strand is about communicating what you are doing using words, tables, diagrams and symbols. You will need to consider how you present your mathematics, decide whether it is appropriate and amend as necessary.
For example, you might consider whether your chosen table of results allows you to find a rule or whether it might be better to draw a graph or to express your findings using symbols.

> For the higher marks you will need to use mathematical symbols accurately, concisely and efficiently in presenting a reasoned argument.

3. Developing skills of mathematical reasoning
This strand is about testing, explaining and justifying what you have done. You will need to search for patterns or rules and provide generalisations. Generalisations (or hypotheses in the case of statistics) will need to be tested, justified, explained, modified and proved.

> For the higher marks you will need to provide a sophisticated and rigorous justification, argument or proof which demonstrates a mathematical insight into the problem.

What do I have to do to get a particular grade in coursework?

Information on what you have to do to get a particular grade is provided under the heading of 'Grade Descriptors'. The following grade descriptors are provided to give a general indication of the standards of achievement you will need to show in order to achieve the given grades:

Grade F
In order to carry through tasks and solve mathematical problems, you identify and obtain necessary information; you check your results, considering whether these are sensible. You show understanding of situations, by describing them mathematically using symbols, words and diagrams. You make general statements of your own, based on evidence you have produced, and give an explanation of your reasoning.

Grade C
Starting from problems or contexts that have been presented, you introduce questions of your own which generate a fuller solution. You examine critically and justify your choice of mathematical presentation, considering alternative approaches and explaining improvements you have made. You justify your generalisations or solutions, showing some insight into the mathematical structure of the situation being investigated. You appreciate the difference between a mathematical explanation and experimental evidence.

Grade A
You give reasons for the choices you make when investigating within mathematics itself or when using mathematics to analyse tasks; these reasons explain why particular lines of enquiry are followed and others are rejected. You apply the mathematics you know in familiar and unfamiliar contexts. You use mathematical language and symbols effectively in presenting a convincing reasoned argument. Your report includes mathematical justifications and explains your solutions to problems involving a number of features or variables.

How will each strand be marked?

Each strand will be marked out of 8 according to the following criteria which have been interpreted for you to make them easier to understand.

Making and monitoring decisions to solve problems

Comment	Mark
You have tried simple approaches to solve the problem	1
You have developed and used your own strategy to solve the problem	2
You have identified and obtained the necessary information to solve the problem	3
You have broken down the given task to solve it in a methodical fashion	4
You have introduced your own relevant questions beyond that given	5
You have developed and followed through alternative approaches involving high level mathematics (beyond that required for grade C)	6
You have analysed and given reasons for your approach which involves a number of mathematical features or variables	7
You have explored independently and extensively an area of mathematics with which you were originally unfamiliar	8

Communicating mathematically

Comment	Mark
You explained your thinking and organised your work	1
You presented information in a clear and organised way	2
You showed your understanding by illustrating information using symbols, words and diagrams	3
You used appropriate forms of presentation with linking explanation and interpretation	4
You considered alternative approaches to your presentation which enabled you to make further progress with the task	5
You used mathematical symbols consistently (implying the use of algebra in a conventional way)	6
You used mathematical symbols and language accurately in presenting a reasoned argument	7
You used mathematical symbols concisely and efficiently	8

Developing skills and mathematical reasoning

Comment	Mark
You showed some understanding of the task by finding particular examples	1
You gathered further data in an attempt to find a pattern that applied to more than one case	2
You made a generalisation from your own evidence	3
You confirmed the generalisation by testing further examples	4
You provided a justification for the generalisation by showing mathematical insight into the problem	5
You examined the generalisation or solution constructively and made further progress on the task	6
You provided a sophisticated justification which coordinated a number of mathematical features or variables	7
You provided a mathematically rigorous justification, argument or proof which included the conditions for its validity	8

How will my coursework be graded?

Each of the three strands will be marked out of 8 to give a total of 24 marks.
This can then be converted into a GCSE grade by the examination board.
The table shows the link between the grade descriptors and the coursework mark.

Total	Grade
20	A
14	C
8	F

Types of coursework

There are three main types of coursework.

Investigational coursework

Investigational coursework will involve solving a problem by exploring different approaches and asking appropriate questions. You will usually be given a starting point for the investigation and this will give you some idea of the approach to explore. By asking appropriate questions you can extend the task and explore some different approaches which will lead you to ask further questions.

In answering the questions, it is useful to see if you can provide some generalisation which can be tested on further examples. You should also try to explain why your generalisation works and see if you can justify or prove it using some graphical, geometrical or algebraic proof.

When undertaking **investigational coursework** you should …

- Introduce the task so that the reader is clear what you are trying to do.
- Indicate how you intend to proceed with the investigation.
- Be systematic rather than haphazard.
- Keep things simple by changing only one variable at a time.
- Provide diagrams, tables and graphs to highlight possible relationships and generalisations.
- Consider the best way to present your findings and explain why you think that this is the best way.
- Test generalisations on further examples.

- Include information on generalisations that didn't work and say why they didn't work.
- Check your work and ensure that it is accurate.
- Use a computer where appropriate but explain how you programmed it to support your work.
- Provide information on how your task has been developed and the mathematical thinking behind this development.
- Reflect on the results at frequent stages and see if these pose further questions.
- Provide a conclusion which relates to the original task and any extension work undertaken.

Practical coursework

Practical coursework will involve solving some practical or real-life problem involving:

the use of practical equipment (ruler, protractor, compasses, etc.)
construction and measurement skills (nets, scale drawings, trigonometry, etc.)
statistical work (see next section)
estimation and calculation of probabilities
simulating real-life problems using mathematics
modelling with a computer (including databases and spreadsheets)

When undertaking **practical coursework** you should …

- Introduce the task so that the reader is clear what you are trying to do.
- Indicate how you intend to proceed with the work and what you will need.
- Provide diagrams, tables and graphs to highlight aspects of the work.
- Consider the best way to present your findings and explain why you think that this is the best way.
- Check your work and ensure that it is accurate (lengths to the nearest millimetre and angles to the nearest degree).

- Explain any measurements undertaken and detail steps to ensure their accuracy.
- Use a computer where appropriate but explain how you programmed it to support your work.
- Provide information on how your task has been developed and the mathematical thinking behind this development.
- Reflect on the results at frequent stages and see if these pose further questions.
- Provide a conclusion which relates to the original task and any extension work undertaken.

Statistical coursework

Statistical coursework is a useful vehicle for helping you to use and understand the statistics work associated with the GCSE examination. Statistical coursework can be based on 'primary' data supplied by you or else 'secondary' data which can be found in reference information such as that provided by government, business or commerce. Your statistical work should include a hypothesis which should be formulated in advance of the task being started.

Before undertaking any statistical work you should plan your work and decide what you are going to investigate. In statistical coursework, the planning stage is the most important and you need to decide:

what you want to investigate and why you want to investigate it
how you are going to collect the information for your investigation
how you intend to ensure that this data is representative and free from bias
what presumptions, if any, you are making in your investigation

The use of secondary data and comparing this with your own data is particularly recommended as an extension to your work which will allow access to the higher grades.

When undertaking **statistical coursework** you should …

- Introduce the task so that the reader is clear what you are trying to do.
- Provide a hypotheses which you intend to investigate.
- Indicate how you intend to proceed with the work, what data you will need and how you will collect it.
- Not be too ambitious and concentrate on one area of investigation at a time.
- Give reasons for the format of data collection sheets and state any assumptions you have made.
- Explain the thinking behind questions on questionnaires and include details of any improvements made.
- Provide diagrams, tables and graphs to highlight aspects of the work.

- Consider the best way to present your findings and explain why you think that this is the best way.
- Include information to explain and justify your hypothesis.
- Check your work and ensure that it is accurate (especially calculation and graph work).
- Use a computer where appropriate but explain how you programmed it to support your work.
- Provide information on how your task has been developed and the mathematical thinking behind this development.
- Reflect on the results at frequent stages and see if these pose further hypotheses..
- Provide a conclusion which relates to the original hypothesis and any extension work undertaken.

Frequently asked questions

How can I best prepare myself for undertaking coursework?
Your coursework needs to be planned and a planning sheet is recommended to help you clarify the task and provide evidence of the work undertaken on the task - you will find it helpful if you discuss your plan with your teacher and amend it if necessary.

How long will I have to complete my coursework?
No time limit is attached to the coursework although it is expected that a single task will take from one to two and a half weeks of mathematics lessons and homework time.

Is presentation important for my mathematics coursework?
Presentation is an important aspect of your coursework and it is important that you present your work neatly and clearly. Remember to include your rough work and any evidence of the thinking which has contributed to the final write up.

What is the minimum I must do to satisfy coursework requirements?
The minimum requirement is one coursework task although it is recommended that you submit two tasks as these will give much stronger evidence of your attainment under each strand.

Can I work with other students on my coursework?
Group work is acceptable although it is important that you prepare your **own** report, in your **own** words, from your **own** notes.

Can I use coursework from other subject areas?
Coursework from other subject areas is acceptable although any such coursework will need to be marked using the assessment criteria for mathematics.

Some chapters include ideas for investigational, practical and statistical tasks and give you the opportunity to improve and practice your skills of using and applying mathematics. You might like to refer to the advice given about the different types of coursework when trying any of the ideas for investigation.

Coursework tasks

SEG provides a variety of options to help students meet the requirements of the coursework component of the syllabuses. Centres can opt to use:

- suitable tasks found in the Syllabus Support Material booklet,
- their own tasks using the booklet for guidance,
- set tasks produced by SEG.

Three examples of tasks set by SEG appear below.

Trios

Three whole numbers, greater than zero, can be used to form a trio.
For example,

$(1, 2, 2)$ is a trio whose sum is $1 + 2 + 2 = 5$

and

$(2, 1, 2)$ is a different trio whose sum is also 5.

How many trios can you find with a sum of 5?

Investigate further.

SEG 1998

Spacers

Spacers are used when tiling a wall.
Three types of spacers are used for the arrangement of tiles shown.

 spacers   spacers   └ spacers

This arrangement of tiles uses 4 ╬ spacers,

8 ┬ spacers and

4 └ spacers.

Investigate for different arrangements of tiles.

SEG 1998

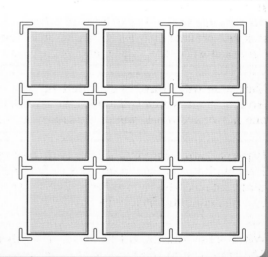

Word length

Peter is comparing two newspapers. He counts the word lengths of a passage containing 100 words from each newspaper. His findings are shown in the tally charts.

Peter says that **"The second newspaper has the longest words"**. Use the information in the tally charts to investigate this statement. What other ways might Peter use to compare the two newspapers? Choose two newspapers of your own and investigate further.

SEG 1998

Newspaper 1

Word length	Tally
1	﬈﬊ I
2	﬈﬊ ﬈﬊
3	﬈﬊ ﬈﬊ ﬈﬊ ﬈﬊ ﬈﬊ II
4	﬈﬊ ﬈﬊ ﬈﬊ ﬈﬊ ﬈﬊
5	﬈﬊ ﬈﬊ ﬈﬊
6	﬈﬊ ﬈﬊
7	﬈﬊
8	I
9	
10	I

Newspaper 2

Word length	Tally
1	III
2	﬈﬊ III
3	﬈﬊ ﬈﬊ ﬈﬊ ﬈﬊ III
4	﬈﬊ ﬈﬊ ﬈﬊ ﬈﬊ ﬈﬊
5	﬈﬊ ﬈﬊ ﬈﬊ I
6	﬈﬊ ﬈﬊ II
7	﬈﬊ I
8	III
9	II
10	II

Answers ●●●●●●●●●●●●●●●●●●●●●●●●●

Exercise 1.1   Page 1

1. (a) 396   (d) 9 002 051
    (b) 5010   (e) 762 504 019
    (c) 70 200   (f) 20 202 020

2. (a) eighty-four
    (b) twenty-three thousand five hundred and
         ninety
    (c) ninety-three million one hundred and
         forty-five thousand six hundred and
         seventy
    (d) seven hundred and sixty-four thousand
         eight hundred and nine
    (e) six thousand and forty-nine
    (f) nine million eighty thousand and four

3. (a) 30   (b) 3 000 000   (c) 600
    (d) 2000   (e) 4000   (f) 6

4. (a) 6000 + 300 + 70 + 4
    (b) 900 + 90 + 9
    (c) 2 000 000 + 3000 + 700 + 8
    (d) 900 000 + 80 000 + 7000 + 100 + 20
         + 3

5. (a) 39, 74, 168, 421
    (b) 3801, 3842, 3874, 4765, 5814

6. (a) 429, 425, 399, 103, 84
    (b) 1 070 483, 279 434, 209 951, 209 646

7. (a) 76541 (digits in descending order)
    (b) 14567 (digits in ascending order)

8. 3458   4358   5348   8345
    3485   4385   5384   8354
    3548   4538   5438   8435
    3584   4583   5483   8453
    3845   4835   5834   8534
    3854   4853   5843   8543
    6 numbers beginning with 8

Exercise 1.2   Page 1

1. (a) 788   (b) 83   (c) 174
    (d) 952   (e) 2002   (f) 12 203
    (g) 201   (h) 1541   (i) 3460
    (j) 1 000 000

2. 81 030

3. (a) 28   (b) 33

4. (a) 49   (b) 71   (c) 73   (d) 55

5. (a) 56   (b) 35   (c) 92   (d) 122

Exercise 1.3   Page 2

1. (a) 354   (b) 428   (c) 1284
    (d) 158   (e) 2224   (f) 469
    (g) 6268   (h) 3277

2. (a) 33   (b) 27

3. (a) 28   (b) 46   (c) 25   (d) 35

4. (a) 17   (b) 50   (c) 105   (d) 4

Exercise 1.4   Page 4

1. (a) 84   (b) 85   (c) 252
    (d) 549   (e) 2112   (f) 15 895
    (g) 24 072   (h) 42 084

2. (a) 1320   (b) 12 300
    (c) 47 000   (d) 38 400

3. (a) 2310   (b) 514   (c) 100

4. (a) 7590   (b) 7140   (c) 21 480
    (d) 12 300   (e) 136 020   (f) 21 510
    (g) 32 960   (h) 9940   (i) 18 960
    (j) 13 000

5. (a) × 100 then by 2, 3, 4, …
    (b) × 100 then by 2, 3, 4, …

Exercise 1.5   Page 5

1. (a) 17   (b) 157
    (c) 136   (d) 75 rem 2
    (e) 393 rem 2   (f) 206
    (g) 1098   (h) 20 140

2. (a) 456   (b) 465   (c) 64   (d) 654

3. (a) 100   (b) 702 000   (c) 10

4. (a) 253   (b) 79   (c) 537   (d) 26
    (e) 293   (f) 412   (g) 260

Exercise 1.6   Page 7

1. 1344   7. 345 015   13. 504

2. 2432   8. 6 620 544   14. 654

3. 4862   9. 463   15. 406

4. 11 130   10. 158   16. 208

5. 38 772   11. 123

6. 76 812   12. 256

1. (a) 37   (b) 3   (c) 9
    (d) 58   (e) 6   (f) 30
    (g) 0   (h) 56   (i) 56
    (j) 6   (k) 28   (l) 0

2. (a) $5 \times 6 + 7$
    (b) $5 + 6 \times 7$
    (c) $15 + 8 \times 9$
    (d) $15 \times 8 + 9$
    (e) $15 \times 8 - 9$
    (f) $15 \div 5 + 3$
    (g) $5 - 24 \div 6$
    (h) $19 \div 9 + 7 \times 0$
    (i) $4 \times 4 + 7 \times 0$ or $4 + 4 \times 7 - 2$

3. Many answers, for example:
    $6 \div 3 + 2 - 1 = 3$
    $6 \div 3 + 2 \div 1 = 4$
    $6 \div 3 + 2 + 1 = 5$
    $6 - 3 + 2 + 1 = 6$
    $6 + 3 - 2 \div 1 = 7$
    $6 + 3 - 2 + 1 = 8$
    $(6 - 3) \times (2 + 1) = 9$
    $6 + 3 + 2 - 1 = 10$

1. 148 cm

2. (a) 58p   (b) 2p   (c) 15p

3. 25

4. 75 g

5. 35 cm

6. 155 cm

7. 15 g

8. (a) 63   (b) 75

1. (a) eight hundred and seventy thousand
         three hundred and two
    (b) 3 027 409

2. (a) 987 542   (b) 245 789

3. (a) 97, 404   (b) 114, 306   (c) 92, 209

4. (a) 2059   (b) 587

5. (a) 9, 24, 384, 394, 4376, 7542
    (b) 500
    (c) 7533

6. (a) 6462   (b) 241

7. (a) 73 500   (b) 6420
    (c) 3020   (d) 462

8. £3427

9. 32

10. (a) 50   (b) 50   (c) 10   (d) 2

11. £438

1. (a) 2.99, 3.001, 3.01, 3.1, 3.15, 3.2
    (b) 3.567, 3.576, 3.657, 3.675, 3.756, 3.765
    (c) 0.1, 0.15, 0.2, 0.25, 0.3, 0.35, 0.4, 0.45,
         0.5, 0.55

2. (a) 9.87, 9.78, 8.97, 8.79, 7.98, 7.89
    (b) 15, 1.5, 0.15, 0.015, 0.0015, 0.000 15
    (c) 3.1, 3.05, 2.81, 2.701, 2.7, 2.67, 2.6,
         2.599, 1.9

3. (a) 0.4   (b) 0.009
    (c) 80   (d) 0.05

4. (a) 1.68   (b) 1.39   (c) 1.04

5. 47.5074

6. 93.07

7. (a) $7 + 0.6 + 0.002$
    (b) $30 + 7 + 0.9 + 0.02 + 0.008$
    (c) $7 + 0.5 + 0.04 + 0.001$
    (d) $20 + 0.5 + 0.003$

1. (a) 8.86   (b) 12.449   (c) 17.49

2. (a) (i) 6.23
         (ii) 24.32
         (iii) 24.68
    (b) (i) $6.23 + 3.24 = 9.47$
         (ii) $24.32 + 13.28 = 37.6$
         (iii) $24.68 + 20.36 = 45.04$

3. (a) 6.84   (b) 86.33   (c) 5.22
    (d) 5.003   (e) 3   (f) 1.24
    (g) 15.781   (h) 8.28   (i) 16.033
    (j) 6.273

4. (a) (i) £3.30   (ii) £1.70
    (b) (i) £11.24   (ii) £3.76
    (c) (i) £0.83   (ii) £9.17
    (d) (i) £16.24   (ii) £33.76

5. 4.88 m

6. (a) Team A 148.93 s
     Team B 149.08 s
     Team C 149.53 s
   (b) A, B, C

7. 0.719 s

8. (a) 95.21 s   (b) 47.72 s

Exercise 2.3   Page 15

1. (a) 250.6   (b) 2506   (c) 25 060
   (d) 9.3   (e) 93   (f) 930
   (g) 0.623   (h) 723.8   (i) 62.3
   (j) 94.51   (k) 945.1   (l) 9451

2. (a) 3.77   (b) 0.377   (c) 0.0377
   (d) 0.027   (e) 0.0027   (f) 0.000 27
   (g) 18.902   (h) 1.8902   (i) 0.189 02
   (j) 0.9   (k) 0.09   (l) 0.009

3. (a) (i)   0.64   (b) (i)   0.0064
       (ii) 6.4   (ii) 0.000 64
       (iii) 64   (iii) 0.000 064

4. (a) (i)   £20.50
       (ii) £205
       (iii) £2050
   (b) (i)   5.04 km
       (ii) 50.4 km
       (iii) 504 km
   (c) £7.95
   (d) 12p (£0.12)
   (e) 66.9p per litre

5. 12.3 × 1000 & 12.3 ÷ 0.001 (12300)
   12.3 × 100 & 12.3 ÷ 0.01 (1230)
   12.3 × 10 & 12.3 ÷ 0.1 (123)
   12.3 × 0.1 & 12.3 ÷ 10 (1.23)
   12.3 × 0.01 & 12.3 ÷ 100 (0.123)
   12.3 × 0.001 & 12.3 ÷ 1000 (0.0123)

Exercise 2.4   Page 16

1. (a) 8.75   (b) 54.53
   (c) 1.03   (d) 29.808
   (e) 0.0007   (f) 0.01
   (g) 0.0001   (h) 97.82
   (i) 57.78   (j) 0.000 177 6

2. (a) £13.93   (b) £10.08
   (c) £54.21   (d) £26.78

3. (a) (i)   35.1 fr   (b) (i) $12.30
       (ii) 5.85 fr   (ii) $1.23
       (iii) 528.45 fr   (iii) $59.86

4. (a) £4.34   (b) £5.28
   (c) £2.60   (d) £2.34

Exercise 2.5   Page 18

1. (a) 12.3   (b) 2.92   (c) 6.05
   (d) 1430   (e) 0.05   (f) 12.5
   (g) 6.54   (h) 37.5

2. (a) 37   (b) 5.6   (c) 43.75
   (d) 46.9   (e) 10.62   (f) 34.2

3. 67

4. 45

5. (a) £1.35   (b) 11p   (c) 9p
   (d) 66.8p   (e) 3-litre

Review Exercise 2   Page 19

1. (a) (i)   20.745   (b) (i)   0.87
       (ii) 14.407   (ii) 4.33
       (iii) 179.22   (iii) 1.53

2. 40 s

3. 2.37 m

4. (a) (i)   76.2   (b) (i)   0.762
       (ii) 762   (ii) 0.0762
       (iii) 7620   (iii) 0.007 62

5. (a) (i)   1746   (b) (i)   4.365
       (ii) 2619   (ii) 2.91
       (iii) 3492   (iii) 2.1825

6. (a) £247.50   (b) £7.99

7. (a) 46.62   (b) 10.152   (c) 105.9

8. (a) 7.2   (b) 1235   (c) 13 700

9. (a) Any 3 values between 0 and 1.
   (b) Any 3 values between 0 and 1.

10. 4.63

11. 240.159574 …

Exercise 3.1   Page 21

1.

980	1000	1000
61 120	61 100	61 000
9710	9700	10 000
620	600	1000
9950	9900	10 000
5760	5800	6000
7500	7500	8000
7500	7500	8000
7500	7500	7000

2. (a) 19 000, nearest 1000
(b) 260, nearest 10
(c) 140, nearest 10
(d) £50, nearest £10
(e) 130, nearest 10
(f) 24 000, nearest 1000
(g) 310 000 km², nearest 10 000 km²
(h) 190 km, nearest 25 km
(i) £50, nearest £10
(j) 700, nearest 50

3. (a) 745 − 749 (b) 750 − 754
(c) 8450 − 8499 (d) 8500 − 8549

4. 42 500

5. 135, 144

6. 2749

Exercise 3.2 Page 22

1. 4

2. 5

3. Depends on the classroom

4. 10

5. 5

6. 9

7. 24

8. 29

9. 19

10. 5

Exercise 3.3 Page 23

1. 0.96, 0.97, 3.962, 3.96, 4.0, 0.06, 567.65,
567.7, 4.99, 5.00

2. (a) 46.1, 59.7, 569.4, 17.1, 0.7
(b) 46.14, 59.70, 569.43, 17.06, 0.66
(c) 46.145, 59.697, 569.434, 17.059, 0.662

3. (a) £12.16, nearest p
(b) £3.57, nearest p
(c) £2.37, nearest p
(d) 35.7 cm, nearest mm
(e) £1.33, nearest p

Exercise 3.4 Page 25

1. 450 000, 7 980 000, 8 000 000, 1300,
0.000 57, 0.094, 0.0937, 0.093 75, 0.010,
0.030

2. (a) 83 000, 83, 1000, 0.0073, 0.0019
(b) 82 700, 82.7, 1000, 0.007 28, 0.001 90
(c) 82 660, 82.66, 1001, 0.007 281,
0.001 899

3. (a) 51 cm² (2 s.f.)
(b) 157 cm² (3 s.f.)
(c) 6100 m² (2 s.f.)
(d) 1.23 m (nearest cm)
(e) 154 000 m² (3 s.f.)

Exercise 3.5 Page 26

1. (a) 8, 7.56 (b) 27, 27.59
(c) 200, 202.02 (d) 300, 299.86

2. (a) 2, 2.2 (b) 5, 4.8
(c) 10, 9.5 (d) 40, 39.9

3. (a) 6.4, 6.41875
(b) 20, 18.709677 …
(c) 20, 20.45631 …

4. (a) Meadow View 66 m², Park View 61 m²
(b) Meadow View 65.72 m²,
Park View 60.07 m²

Review Exercise 3 Page 27

1. (a) 8480 (b) 8500 (c) 8000

2. (a) (i) 6 700 000
(ii) 100 000
(b) 109 500

3. (a) 9.2 (b) 9.18 (c) 9.177

4. (a) 1 (b) 1.5 (c) 1.49

5. 9.2

6. (a) 37.8226 m²
(b) (i) 38 m²
(ii) Carpet sold in whole m²

7. (a) 2, 1.99972 …
(b) 10, 9.85276 …
(c) 6, 5.6283 …

8. (a) 400 ÷ 20 = 20 (b) 18

9. 0.4 × 90 ÷ 6 = 6, not correct

10. 200 × 0.5 ÷ 10 = 10, not correct

Exercise 4.1 Page 29

1. (a) Colombo
(b) Moscow
(c) −22°C, −17°C, −7°C, 0°C, 3°C, 15°C,
21°C

2. (a) $-28°C$, $-13°C$, $-7°C$, $-3°C$, $19°C$, $23°C$

(b) $-11°C$, $-9°C$, $-7°C$, $0°C$, $10°C$, $12°C$

(c) $-29°C$, $-27°C$, $-15°C$, $2°C$, $18°C$, $27°C$

(d) $-20°C$, $-15°C$, $-10°C$, $-5°C$, $0°C$, $5°C$, $10°C$, $15°C$, $20°C$

3. (a) -78, -39, -16, -9, 11, 30, 31, 51, 52

(b) -5, -4, -3, -2, -1, 0, 1, 2, 3, 4, 5

(c) -103, -63, -19, -3, 1, 5, 10, 52, 99, 104

(d) -50, -40, -30, -20, -10, 0, 10, 20, 30, 40, 50

(e) -30, -15, -10, 0, 8, 16, 17, 27, 30

Exercise 4.2 — Page 30

1. (a) -3 (b) -4 (c) -7
(d) -32 (e) 0 (f) -27
(g) -61 (h) -1

2. (b) (i) -1 (ii) -4 (iii) -4

3. (a) 9 (b) 1 (c) 12 (d) -10
(e) 30 (f) 15

4. (a) $-£75$ (£75 overdrawn)   (b) £40

Exercise 4.3 — Page 31

1. (a) 2 (b) 1 (c) -9
(d) 8 (e) 4 (f) -5
(g) -7 (h) -15 (i) -3
(j) -6

2. (a) 13 (b) 6 (c) 7
(d) 7 (e) 5 (f) -12
(g) -1 (h) 11 (i) 9
(j) 0

3. (a) 5 (b) 3 (c) 3
(d) -7 (e) -6 (f) -1

4. (a) 6 (b) -8 (c) -28
(d) 0 (e) -35 (f) 19

5. (a) 7 (b) -1 (c) 36
(d) -6 (e) 38 (f) 15
(g) -15 (h) 25 (i) 15
(j) -6

6. (a) $3°C$ (b) $10°C$ (c) $5°C$
(d) $6°C$ (e) $37°C$

7. $-15°C$

Exercise 4.4 — Page 33

1. 35 **2.** -35

3. 35

4. 10

5. -10

6. 1

7. -24

8. -45

9. 64

10. -42

11. -80

12. -20

13. 60

14. -30

15. 60

Exercise 4.5 — Page 34

1. -4

2. 4

3. 5

4. -5

5. -5

6. 5

7. 6

8. -6

9. 4

10. -8

11. 8

12. 8

13. -8

14. -8

15. 8

16. 7.5

17. -7.5

18. 1.5

19. 4

20. -4

Review Exercise 4 — Page 34

1. (a) -4 (b) -7 (c) -30
(d) -32 (e) 0 (f) 33
(g) -1 (h) 0 (i) -40
(j) 10

2. (a) 13 (b) 12 (c) 1
(d) -1 (e) 1 (f) -15
(g) 15

3. (a) 24 (b) -24 (c) -24
(d) 24 (e) 40 (f) -40
(g) -40 (h) 40

4. (a) -5 (b) 2 (c) -6 (d) 4

5. $29°F$

6. $11°C$

7. (a) $13°C$ (b) $6°C$

8. £191

9. I CAN NOW USE NEGATIVE NUMBERS

10. (a) $21°C$ (b) $-0.4°F$

1. (a) 9
(b) 27

(c) (i)

0 cuts	1	3^0
1 cut	3	3^1
2 cuts	$9 = 3 \times 3$	3^2
3 cuts	$27 = 3 \times 3 \times 3$	3^3
4 cuts	$81 = 3 \times 3 \times 3 \times 3$	3^4
5 cuts	$243 = 3 \times 3 \times 3 \times 3 \times 3$	3^5

(ii) 729
(iii) 3^{10}
(iv) 3^{20}
(v) 3^n
(vi) 3, 1

2. (a) 128   (b) 27
(c) 36   (d) 4096
(e) 10 000 000 000   (f) 16 384
(g) 1   (h) 1728
(i) 11   (j) 343
(k) 243   (l) 1
(m) 27   (n) 0.04

3. (a)

Expression	Index form	Value
$10 \times 10 \times 10 \times 10 \times 10 \times 10$	10^6	1 000 000
$10 \times 10 \times 10 \times 10 \times 10$	10^5	100 000
$10 \times 10 \times 10 \times 10$	10^4	10 000
$10 \times 10 \times 10$	10^3	1000
10×10	10^2	100
10	10^1	10
1	10^0	1

(b) (i)

Expression	Index form	Value
$5 \times 5 \times 5 \times 5 \times 5 \times 5$	5^6	15 625
$5 \times 5 \times 5 \times 5 \times 5$	5^5	3125
$5 \times 5 \times 5 \times 5$	5^4	625
$5 \times 5 \times 5$	5^3	125
5×5	5^2	25
5	5^1	5
1	5^0	1

(ii)

Expression	Index form	Value
$4 \times 4 \times 4 \times 4 \times 4 \times 4$	4^6	4096
$4 \times 4 \times 4 \times 4 \times 4$	4^5	1024
$4 \times 4 \times 4 \times 4$	4^4	256
$4 \times 4 \times 4$	4^3	64
4×4	4^2	16
4	4^1	4
1	4^0	1

(c) 1

4. (a) 4^4 (b) 3^8 (c) 8^9
(d) 0.3^3 (e) 1.6^5 (f) 12^7

1. (a) 79.62624   (b) 1.728   (c) 0.49
(d) 90   (e) 60   (f) 864
(g) 1944   (h) 128   (i) 8192
(j) 0.860 518 4

2. (a) 30   (b) 66
(c) 2592   (d) 1440
(e) 1080   (f) 6.770 83
(g) 126 216   (h) 0.281 25
(i) 20 000

3. (a) 1   (d) 1
(b) 1   (e) 1
(c) 1 $a^0 = 1$

4. (a) 44.89   (b) 39.304
(c) 0.49   (d) 0.000 064

5. In general $(n + 1)^2 = n^2 + (2n + 1)$

7. (a) 3   (b) 0   (c) 1
(d) 2   (e) 6   (f) 3
(g) 4   (h) 3

8. (a) 2   (b) 4   (c) 3
(d) 2   (e) 2

1. (a) (i) 4.5
(ii) 10.4
(iii) 2.8

2. (a) 3.6   (b) 5.8   (c) 1.7

3. 7.42 m

4. 16.51 mm

Page 42

1. (a) (i) 0.16
      (ii) 0.4096
      (iii) 0.05
      (iv) 6.5536
      (v) 100 000
   (b) Any number between 0 and 1.
   (c) Any number greater than 1.

2. (a) $\frac{1}{2}$ (b) $\frac{1}{27}$ (c) $\frac{1}{125}$
   (d) $\frac{1}{16}$ (e) $\frac{1}{64}$ (f) $\frac{1}{100\,000}$

Exercise **5.5**   Page 43

1. (a) 2^7 (b) 4^9 (c) 6^3
   (d) 8^7 (e) $7^7 \times 2^8$

2. (a) $\frac{1}{2^2}$ (b) $\frac{1}{5^2}$ (c) $\frac{1}{3}$
   (d) $\frac{1}{8^5}$ (e) $9^0 = 1$

3. (a) 2^3 (b) 4^2 (c) 6
   (d) 8 (e) 3^6

4. (a) $\frac{1}{2^4}$ (b) 5^{12} (c) $\frac{1}{3^3}$
   (d) $\frac{1}{7}$ (e) $\frac{1}{11^5}$

5. (a) 8^2 (b) 7^{-5} (c) 2.5^{-1}
   (d) $4^0 = 1$ (e) 10^{-1} (f) 6^{-4}
   (g) 0.1^{-12} (h) 5^{-3}

6. (a) $4^2 \times 8^7$ (b) 4×5^{-2}
   (c) $6^5 \times 9$ (d) $3^3 \times 4^4 \times 7^{-2}$

7. (a) $\frac{5^5}{2^2}$ (b) $\frac{8^4}{3^3}$
   (c) $2^3 \times 5^5$ (d) $\frac{4^2}{7^3 \times 9^4}$

Exercise **5.6**   Page 44

1. (a) a^7 (b) x^{16} (c) b^5
   (d) t^7 (e) x^8 (f) $8b^7$
   (g) $6t^6$ (h) $8x^6$ (i) $25y^8$
   (j) $12x^9$ (k) x^6y^5 (l) y^4z^4
   (m) x^5y^7 (n) $6r^9s^4$ (o) $12p^8q^8$

2. (a) b^8 (b) x^6 (c) $2x^{12}$
   (d) $4y^6$ (e) $81a^8$ (f) x^4y^6
   (g) $27a^3b^6$ (h) $25p^6q^8$ (i) $16x^{20}y^4$
   (j) $125r^3s^6t^9$

3. (a) a (b) x^6 (c) x
   (d) $x^0 = 1$ (e) a^2 (f) $4b^3$
   (g) $2y^2$ (h) $5z^2$ (i) $3x^4$
   (j) $4t$ (k) x^4 (l) p^2q^5
   (m) $4r$ (n) $3x$ (o) qr^2t

4. (a) x^6y^6 (b) $2n$ (c) $4r$
   (d) $2pq^5$ (e) abc^3 (f) $3y$

(g) rs^3t^2 (h) a^4bc (i) $9yz^3$
(j) $5ab^5$ (k) $2x^2yz^7$ (l) $16l^3$

Review Exercise **5**   Page 46

1. (a) 10^2 (b) 10^6 (c) 10^0
   (d) 10^{-1} (e) 10^{-3} (f) 10^{-6}
   (g) 10^{-9} (h) 10^1 (i) 10^{-2}
   (j) 10^{-5}

2. (a) 32 (b) 1 (c) 625
   (d) 272 (e) 90 (f) 500
   (g) 40 (h) 50 (i) 50
   (j) 40

3. (a) $\frac{1}{4}$ (b) $\frac{1}{8}$ (c) $\frac{1}{3}$
   (d) $\frac{1}{125}$ (e) $\frac{1}{64}$ (f) $\frac{1}{32}$

4. (a) 3^8 (b) 5^{11} (c) 9^6
   (d) 4^{13} (e) $2^8 \times 3^{10}$ (f) 4^5
   (g) 7^5 (h) 8^3 (i) 6^4
   (j) 3^9 (k) 2^{-3} (l) 5^{-7}
   (m) 4^{-3} (n) 3^{13} (o) $2^{-7} \times 7^2$

5. (a) $\frac{5^4}{2}$ (b) $\frac{1}{2^2}$ (c) $\frac{5^4}{3^5}$ (d) $\frac{3^2}{2^2}$

6. (a) a^7 (b) y^8 (c) x^9
   (d) $8x^5$ (e) $16x^6$ (f) x^4y^4
   (g) a^7b^5 (h) p^8q^6 (i) $12x^5y^6$
   (j) $6x^9y^6$

7. (a) a^2 (b) p (c) $y^0 = 1$
   (d) $3x$ (e) $3x^5$ (f) $7x^5$
   (g) xy (h) x^4 (i) $5x^3y$
   (j) $4x^2yz$

8. (a) x^9 (b) a^6 (c) $9x^4$
   (d) $8p^{15}$ (e) $64t^6$ (f) $27x^9$
   (g) a^6b^2 (h) $25x^4y^2$ (i) $25p^{10}$
   (j) $8t^{15}$ (k) $16x^6$ (l) $512s^9t^6$

9. (a) x^6y^3 (b) $2t$ (c) $3x^4$
   (d) $2x^3y^6$ (e) a^3 (f) xy^3
   (g) 4 (h) $10x^2y^4$ (i) $4abc^7$

10. (a)

Power form	Expression	Value
4^3	$4 \times 4 \times 4$	64
4^2	4×4	16
4^1	4	4
4^0	1	1
4^{-1}	$\frac{1}{4}$	0.25
4^{-2}	$\frac{1}{4 \times 4}$	0.0625
4^{-3}	$\frac{1}{4 \times 4 \times 4}$	0.015 625

(b)

Power form	Expression	Value
8^3	$8 \times 8 \times 8$	512
8^2	8×8	64
8^1	8	8
8^0	1	1
8^{-1}	$\frac{1}{8}$	0.125
8^{-2}	$\frac{1}{8 \times 8}$	0.015 625
8^{-3}	$\frac{1}{8 \times 8 \times 8}$	0.001 953 125

11. (b) (i) 3.464 101 615   (ii) 3.464

12. 2.57

13. (a) 31 104   (b) 0.029 43
     (c) 0.000 065 61   (d) 8145
     (e) −16 384   (f) 786 432
     (g) 24.256 96   (h) −59.7000 …
     (i) 0.003 64   (j) 3.81944 …
     (k) 1   (l) 390 500

14. (a) 4.625   (b) 520   (c) 82.024
     (d) 4004.1625   (e) 260   (f) 665

15. (a) 0   (b) 4   (c) 3
     (d) 6   (e) 3   (f) 3
     (g) −3   (h) −2   (i) −2

Exercise 6.1   Page 48

1. (a) 12, 24, 36, 48, 60
     (b) 19, 38, 57, 76, 95
     (c) 20, 40, 60, 80, 100
     (d) 45, 90, 135, 180, 225
     (e) 85, 170, 255, 340, 425

2. (a) 1, 2, 3, 4, 6, 12
     (b) 1, 2, 3, 4, 6, 9, 12, 18, 36
     (c) 1, 2, 3, 4, 5, 6, 10, 12, 15, 20, 30, 60
     (d) 1, 2, 4, 5, 8, 10, 16, 20, 40, 80
     (e) 1, 3, 5, 9, 15, 45

3. (a) 9, 27   (b) 14, 35
     (c) 4, 5, 20   (d) 3, 9, 27
     (e) 3, 5

4. (a) 4   . (b) 8   (c) 6   (d) 5

Exercise 6.2   Page 50

1. (a) 2, 3   (b) 2, 5   (c) 2, 7
     (d) 3, 5   (e) 2, 3, 11

2. (a) $2^2 \times 3$ (b) $2^2 \times 5$ (c) $2^2 \times 7$
     (d) $3^2 \times 5$ (e) $2 \times 3 \times 11$

3. (a) 1, 2, 2×3, 2×3^2, 2×3^3, 2^2, $2^2 \times 3$,
     $2^2 \times 3^2$, $2^2 \times 3^3$, 2^3, $2^3 \times 3$, $2^3 \times 3^2$,
     $2^3 \times 3^3$, 2^4, $2^4 \times 3$, $2^4 \times 3^2$, $2^4 \times 3^3$, 2^5,
     $2^5 \times 3$, $2^5 \times 3^2$, $2^5 \times 3^3$, 3, 3^2, 3^3
     (b) 1, 5, 5×7, 5×7^2, 5×7^3, 5×7^4, 5^2,
     $5^2 \times 7$, $5^2 \times 7^2$, $5^2 \times 7^3$, $5^2 \times 7^4$, 5^3,
     $5^3 \times 7$, $5^3 \times 7^2$, $5^3 \times 7^3$, $5^3 \times 7^4$, 7, 7^2,
     7^3, 7^4

4. (a) 1000   56 250 000
        1 000 000   3 294 225
        2700   926 859 375
     (b) Square numbers:
        1 000 000
        56 250 000
        3 294 225
        Cube numbers:
        1000
        1 000 000
        926 859 375
        Square numbers − powers are multiples
        of 2.
        Cube numbers − powers are multiples
        of 3.

5. 2700, 3528, 4500

6. 56, 88, 104

7. 126, 132, 150

Exercise 6.3   Page 51

1. (a) 24   (b) 160   (c) 20
     (d) 90   (e) 90   (f) 24
     (g) 40   (h) 630

2. (a) 6   (b) 8   (c) 2
     (d) 4   (e) 11   (f) 4
     (g) 3   (h) 15

4. (a) 3   (b) $2^2 \times 3^4$
     (c) 54   (d) 324

5. (a) $2^2 \times 3^3$ (b) $2^5 \times 3^2$
     (c) 72   (d) 864

6. 9.18 am

Review Exercise 6   Page 53

1. (a) 1, 3, 5, 15
     (b) 1, 2, 3, 5, 6, 10, 15, 30
     (c) 1, 2, 5, 10, 25, 50
     (d) 1, 2, 3, 4, 6, 8, 12, 16, 24, 32, 48, 96
     (e) 1, 107
     (f) 1, 2, 3, 4, 5, 6, 8, 10, 12, 15, 20, 24, 30,
     40, 60, 120

2. (a) 21, 24, 27
  (b) 21, 28
  (c) 24
  (d) 20, 23, 24, 25
  (e) 21, 27, 28
  (f) 20, 22, 25

3. 16

4. (a) 3, 6, 9, 12,15, 18, 21, 24, 27, 30, 33, 36, 39, 42, 45, 48
  (b) 104, 112, 120, 128, 136, 144
  (c) 1, 2, 5, 10, 25, 50
  (d) 1, 2, 3, 4, 6, 8, 12, 16, 24, 32, 48
  (e) 53, 59, 61, 67, 71, 73, 79, 83, 89, 97

5. (a) (i) 3 (b) (i) 12
  (ii) 8 (ii) 90
  (iii) 12 (iii) 240

6. 60

7. (a) 1, 2, 4, 8
  1, 3, 9
  1, 11
  1, 17
  1, 11, 121
  (b) (i) 11, 17 (ii) prime numbers
  (c) (i) 9, 121 (ii) square numbers

8. (a) (i) $2 \times 3^2 \times 7$ (b) (i) 630
  (ii) $2 \times 3^2 \times 5$ (ii) 18
  (iii) $2 \times 3 \times 5 \times 7$

9. (a) 4 (b) $2^3 \times 3^2$
  (c) 24 (d) 144

10. (a) $3^3 \times 7^2$ (b) $2^2 \times 3^4 \times 7$
  (c) 441 (d) 6

11. 90 seconds

Exercise 7.1 Page 55

1. Missing entries:
  (a) 7.5×10^4
  (b) 800 000 000, 8×10^8
  (c) 35 000 000 000 000, $3.5 \times 10\,000\,000\,000\,000$
  (d) $6.23 \times 10\,000\,000\,000\,000$, 6.23×10^{13}
  (e) 5 400 000 000, $5.4 \times 1\,000\,000\,000$
  (f) 69 300 000, 6.93×10^7
  (g) $4.531 \times 100\,000\,000\,000$, 4.53×10^{11}
  (h) 697 000, $6.97 \times 100\,000$
  (i) $4.5312 \times 100\,000$, 4.5312×10^5
  (j) 109 700, 1.097×10^5

2. (a) 6 E 13, 6×10^{13}, 60 000 000 000 000
  (b) 9.6 E 12, 9.6×10^{12}, 9 600 000 000 000
  (c) 1.05 E 13, 1.05×10^{13}, 10 500 000 000 000

  (d) 1.3 E 14, 1.3×10^{14}, 130 000 000 000 000
  (e) 2.4 E 14, 2.4×10^{14}, 240 000 000 000 000
  (f) 2.5 E 12, 2.5×10^{12}, 2 500 000 000 000
  (g) 1.408 E 16, 1.408×10^{16}, 14 080 000 000 000 000
  (h) 2.288 E 14, 2.288×10^{14}, 228 800 000 000 000
  (i) 8.073 E 11, 8.073×10^{11}, 807 300 000 000
  (j) 1.1 E 15, 1.1×10^{15}, 1 100 000 000 000 000

3. (a) 3×10^{11} (b) 8×10^7
  (c) 7×10^8 (d) 2×10^9
  (e) 4.2×10^7 (f) 2.1×10^{10}
  (g) 3.7×10^9 (h) 6.3×10^2
  (i) 3.219×10^9 (j) 6.5412×10^8
  (k) 8.97213×10^5 (l) 4.267×10^{10}

4. (a) 600 000 (b) 2000
  (c) 50 000 000 (d) 900 000 000
  (e) 3 700 000 000 (f) 28
  (g) 99 000 000 000 (h) 71 000
  (i) 397 (j) 817.2
  (k) 7 431 200 (l) 1 234 000 000

Exercise 7.2 Page 56

1. (a) -1 (b) -5 (c) -9
  (d) -3 (e) -11 (f) -13

2. Missing entries:
  (b) 7.5×10^{-3}
  (c) 8.75×10^{-6}
  (d) $3.5 \times 0.000\,000\,001$, 3.5×10^{-9}
  (e) $6.23 \times 0.000\,000\,000\,001$, 6.23×10^{-12}
  (f) $5 \times 0.000\,000\,1$, 5×10^{-7}
  (g) $4.725 \times 0.000\,000\,01$, 4.725×10^{-8}
  (h) 5×0.01, 5×10^{-2}
  (i) $7.85 \times 0.000\,001$, 7.85×10^{-6}

3. (a) 0.35
  (b) 0.0005
  (c) 0.000 072
  (d) 0.0061
  (e) 0.000 000 000 117
  (f) 0.000 000 813 5
  (g) 0.064 62
  (h) 0.000 000 004 001

4. (a) 7×10^{-3} (b) 4×10^{-2}
  (c) 5×10^{-9} (d) 8×10^{-4}
  (e) 2.3×10^{-9} (f) 4.5×10^{-8}
  (g) 2.34×10^{-2} (h) 2.34×10^{-9}
  (i) 6.7×10^{-3} (j) 3×10^{-1}
  (k) 7.395×10^{-8} (l) 3.4×10^{-13}

5. (a) 0.000 005 5
   (b) 0.000 000 065
   (c) 32 000 000
   (d) 290
   (e) 0.000 000 000 031 67
   (f) 11 150
   (g) 0.000 014 12
   (h) 40

6. (a) $6 \text{ E} -12$, 6×10^{-12}, 0.000 000 000 006
   (b) $1.35 \text{ E} -10$, 1.35×10^{-10},
       0.000 000 000 135
   (c) $3 \text{ E} -11$, 3×10^{-11}, 0.000 000 000 03
   (d) $1.15 \text{ E} -10$, 1.15×10^{-10},
       0.000 000 000 115
   (e) $4.24 \text{ E} -09$, 4.24×10^{-9},
       0.000 000 004 24
   (f) $9.728 \text{ E} -11$, 9.728×10^{-11},
       0.000 000 000 097 28
   (g) $2.891 \text{ E} -13$, 2.891×10^{-13},
       0.000 000 000 000 289 1
   (h) $3 \text{ E} -10$, 3×10^{-10}, 0.000 000 000 3
   (i) $1.055 \text{ E } 11$, 1.055×10^{11},
       105 500 000 000
   (j) $9.25 \text{ E } 11$, 9.25×10^{11}, 925 000 000 000

Exercise 7.3   Page 58

1. (a) 262 500
   (b) 105 000 000 000 000
   (c) 72 250 000 000 000
   (d) 0.000 000 125
   (e) 30 000 000 000
   (f) 263 160 000 000 000 000 000

2. (a) 9.38×10^{19} (b) 1.6×10^{1}
   (c) 2.25×10^{26} (d) 1.25×10^{-37}
   (e) 2.4×10^{20} (f) 5×10^{-2}

3. (a) 2.088×10^{9} (b) $1.525\,965 \times 10^{16}\,\text{km}$

4. (a) Pluto, Jupiter, Saturn
   (b) $1.397 \times 10^{5}\,\text{km}$, 139 700 km

5. (a) $9.273 \times 10^{6}\,\text{km}^2$ (b) $4.93 \times 10^{5}\,\text{km}^2$

6. 9×10^{-28} grams

7. (a) 4.55×10^{9} years
   (b) About 6.6×10^{3} times

Exercise 7.4   Page 60

1. (a) 5.2×10^{3} (b) 8.4×10^{6}
   (c) 4×10^{4} (d) 5×10^{4}
   (e) 4.9×10^{5} (f) 4×10^{7}

2. (a) 2.8×10^{3} (b) 9×10^{5}
   (c) 3×10^{7} (d) 9.5×10^{8}
   (e) 6.4×10^{6} (f) 7.25×10^{9}

3. (a) 8×10^{7} (b) 6×10^{7}
   (c) 2.4×10^{8} (d) 2.7×10^{15}
   (e) 1.3×10^{4} (f) 3.6×10^{6}

4. (a) 3×10^{3} (b) 3×10^{3}
   (c) 5×10^{1} (d) 2×10^{11}
   (e) 4×10^{5} (f) 3×10^{-3}

5. (a) 1.5×10^{0} (b) 2.7×10^{13}
   (c) 4.5×10^{4} (d) 1.25×10^{-13}
   (e) 6.25×10^{-17} (f) 1.5×10^{4}
   (g) 2.25×10^{10} (h) 7.5×10^{-5}
   (i) 2.25×10^{2} (j) 6.75×10^{4}

6. (a) 1.5×10^{11} (b) 2.4×10^{3}
   (c) 4.2×10^{-8} (d) 6.4×10^{7}
   (e) 6.25×10^{14} (f) 2.16×10^{-13}
   (g) 5×10^{1} (h) 3×10^{9}
   (i) 6.25×10^{-6} (j) 2.5×10^{4}

7. (a) 7.05×10^{-4} 1.25×10^{-2}
       0.000 75 4.5×10^{-1}
       3.5×10^{-3}
   (b) 4.15×10^{-5} 9.31×10^{-4}
       0.000 050 612 4.05×10^{-2}
       5.6×10^{-5}

Review Exercise 7   Page 61

1. (a) 2.4×10^{3} (b) 5.26×10^{4}
   (c) 8×10^{6} (d) 2.4×10^{-9}
   (e) 1.26×10^{-5} (f) 2.34×10^{-10}

2. (a) 3400   (b) 14 600 000
   (c) 831 200   (d) 0.000 171 4
   (e) 0.000 000 092 13   (f) 73 500 000

3. (a) 6.5×10^{4} (b) 4.5×10^{5}
   (c) 3×10^{8} (d) 2.45×10^{4}
   (e) 9×10^{9} (f) 3.25×10^{9}

4. (a) 3×10^{3} (b) 2.5×10^{-11}
   (c) 2.16×10^{-25} (d) 9×10^{1}
   (e) 4×10^{13}

5. (a) 1.68×10^{20}
   (b) 1.2949×10^{6}
   (c) 1.23×10^{1} (3 s.f.)
   (d) 5.00×10^{-2} (3 s.f.)
   (e) 8×10^{6}
   (f) 1.25×10^{-7}
   (g) 8×10^{-6}
   (h) 1.25×10^{5}

6. $\$6.146 \times 10^{9}$

7. £1.285×10^{11}

8. (a) 9000 million
   (b) 2.5×10^{-7} metres
   (c) 7.5×10^{-6} metres

9. (a) 1.188×10^8 (b) $1\,140\,480\,\text{cm}$

10. (a) 8×10^{-3} seconds   (b) $75\,000\,000\,000$

Exercise 8.1   Page 63

1. (a) $\frac{4}{9}$ (b) $\frac{2}{8} = \frac{1}{4}$
    (c) $\frac{8}{16} = \frac{1}{2}$ (d) $\frac{3}{12} = \frac{1}{4}$

2. E.g. $\frac{15}{24}, \frac{30}{48}, \frac{45}{72}, \cdots, \frac{10}{16}, \frac{20}{32}, \cdots$

    simplest form $\frac{5}{8}$

3. (a) P   (b) P   (c) R
    (d) R   (e) Q   (f) S

4. (a) $\frac{1}{3}$ (b) $\frac{1}{3}$ (c) $\frac{1}{3}$
    (d) $\frac{1}{3}$ (e) $\frac{1}{2}$

5. (a) E.g. $\frac{2}{6}, \frac{3}{9}, \frac{4}{12},$ (b) E.g. $\frac{4}{18}, \frac{6}{27}, \frac{8}{36},$
    (c) E.g. $\frac{10}{16}, \frac{15}{24}, \frac{20}{32},$ (d) E.g. $\frac{8}{10}, \frac{12}{15}, \frac{16}{20},$
    (e) E.g. $\frac{6}{20}, \frac{9}{30}, \frac{12}{40},$ (f) E.g. $\frac{14}{24}, \frac{21}{36}, \frac{28}{48},$

6. (a) 2   (b) 3   (c) 6
    (d) 3   (e) 8   (f) 7

7. (a) $\frac{3}{4}$ (b) $\frac{4}{5}$ (c) $\frac{2}{3}$
    (d) $\frac{2}{9}$ (e) $\frac{2}{3}$ (f) $\frac{2}{5}$
    (g) $\frac{6}{25}$ (h) $\frac{4}{5}$

8. (a) $\frac{1}{5}$ (b) $\frac{1}{4}$ (c) $\frac{2}{3}$
    (d) $\frac{2}{5}$ (e) $\frac{4}{7}$

9. (a) $\frac{7}{10}$ (b) $\frac{1}{5}$

10. (a) 24   (b) $\frac{1}{6}$

Exercise 8.2   Page 66

1. (a) $1\frac{3}{10}$ (b) $1\frac{1}{2}$ (c) $2\frac{1}{8}$
    (d) $3\frac{3}{4}$ (e) $4\frac{3}{5}$ (f) $4\frac{6}{7}$

2. (a) $\frac{27}{10}$ (b) $\frac{8}{5}$ (c) $\frac{35}{6}$
    (d) $\frac{63}{20}$ (e) $\frac{41}{9}$ (f) $\frac{53}{7}$

3. (a) 9   (b) 12   (c) 20
    (d) 26   (e) 21   (f) 25
    (g) 68   (h) 55   (i) 119
    (j) 207

4. £92

5. £743.75

6. £132.50

7. (a) (i) 20   (ii) 25
    (b) $\frac{19}{10}, 1\frac{9}{10}$

Exercise 8.3   Page 68

1. (a) $\frac{5}{8}$ (b) $\frac{9}{20}$ (c) $\frac{9}{14}$
    (d) $\frac{5}{8}$ (e) $\frac{1}{2}$ (f) $\frac{29}{35}$
    (g) $\frac{11}{12}$ (h) $\frac{29}{30}$ (i) $1\frac{1}{12}$
    (j) $\frac{29}{36}$ (k) $1\frac{3}{8}$ (l) $1\frac{4}{15}$

2. (a) $\frac{5}{8}$ (b) $\frac{1}{8}$ (c) $\frac{1}{12}$
    (d) $\frac{8}{15}$ (e) $\frac{5}{8}$ (f) $\frac{17}{45}$
    (g) $\frac{5}{24}$ (h) $\frac{19}{48}$

3. (a) $4\frac{1}{4}$ (b) $3\frac{5}{6}$ (c) $4\frac{3}{8}$
    (d) $5\frac{17}{20}$ (e) $6\frac{13}{20}$ (f) $5\frac{9}{20}$

4. (a) $1\frac{1}{10}$ (b) $\frac{5}{12}$ (c) $\frac{5}{8}$
    (d) $3\frac{3}{10}$ (e) $1\frac{27}{40}$ (f) $\frac{47}{48}$

5. (a) $\frac{7}{20}$ (b) $\frac{17}{20}$

6. $\frac{7}{60}$

7. (a) $\frac{27}{80}$ (b) Andy

Exercise 8.4   Page 69

1. (a) $\frac{1}{8}$ (b) $\frac{1}{12}$ (c) $\frac{1}{30}$
    (d) $\frac{1}{3}$ (e) $\frac{3}{80}$ (f) $\frac{2}{35}$
    (g) $\frac{1}{2}$ (h) $\frac{1}{4}$ (i) $\frac{1}{18}$
    (j) $\frac{1}{6}$

2. (a) $1\frac{1}{8}$ (b) 2   (c) $3\frac{3}{4}$
    (d) $3\frac{17}{20}$ (e) $4\frac{7}{8}$ (f) $1\frac{13}{15}$
    (g) 14   (h) $13\frac{1}{2}$ (i) $2\frac{7}{10}$
    (j) $8\frac{3}{4}$

3. (a) $2\frac{3}{5}$ (b) $3\frac{1}{2}$ (c) $5\frac{2}{5}$
    (d) $2\frac{1}{2}$ (e) $1\frac{1}{3}$ (f) $3\frac{4}{7}$
    (g) $\frac{2}{3}$ (h) $1\frac{1}{3}$

4. (a) $\frac{4}{15}$ (b) 15

Exercise 8.5   Page 70

1. (a) $\frac{3}{5}$ (b) $\frac{1}{4}$ (c) $2\frac{2}{5}$
    (d) $1\frac{1}{3}$ (e) $\frac{2}{3}$ (f) $1\frac{1}{2}$
    (g) $\frac{2}{3}$ (h) $1\frac{1}{6}$ (i) $1\frac{1}{2}$
    (j) $1\frac{4}{5}$

2. (a) $\frac{2}{3}$ (b) $1\frac{3}{8}$ (c) $1\frac{1}{7}$

    (d) $4\frac{2}{3}$ (e) $13\frac{1}{2}$ (f) $\frac{4}{5}$

    (g) $1\frac{1}{2}$ (h) $1\frac{1}{4}$ (i) $2\frac{2}{7}$

    (j) $3\frac{6}{25}$

3. (a) $21, \frac{17}{38}$ cm   (b) $23, \frac{2}{7}$ cm

4. (a) $\frac{32}{45}$ (b) $2\frac{2}{5}$

5. $\frac{16}{21}$

Exercise 8.6   Page 71

1. £3.20

2. 70 km

3. £3.20

4. £5

5. 96 cm

6. 189

Review Exercise 8   Page 72

1. $\frac{5}{8}$

2. $6\frac{2}{3}$

3. (a) 24   (b) 10   (c) 4

4. (a) $\frac{10}{17}$ (b) $\frac{2}{7}$ (c) $\frac{7}{11}$

5. (a) $1\frac{3}{7}$ (b) $5\frac{1}{3}$ (c) $7\frac{1}{2}$

6. (a) $\frac{21}{8}$ (b) $\frac{19}{5}$ (c) $\frac{31}{4}$

7. (a) $6\frac{1}{12}$ (b) $4\frac{10}{63}$ (c) $2\frac{1}{10}$

    (d) $2\frac{19}{30}$ (e) $4\frac{1}{2}$ (f) 10

    (g) $1\frac{5}{7}$ (h) $2\frac{1}{2}$

8. £10.20

9. £80

10. (a) $\frac{1}{12}$ (b) 84

11. 208 km

12. $\frac{2}{3}$

13. (a) $2\frac{1}{12}$ m   (b) $\frac{1}{4}$ m²

14. A £274, B £299.25

15. (a) $\frac{1}{2}$ (b) $\frac{1}{12}$ (c) $\frac{1}{2} + \frac{1}{5}$

16. $\frac{1}{10}$

Exercise 9.1   Page 75

1. Percentages are: 10%, 20%, 25%, 30%, 40%, 50%, 60%, 70%, 75%, 80%, 90%

2. (a) 34%   (b) 48%   (c) 15%
    (d) 80%   (e) 27%   (f) 65%

3. (a) $\frac{9}{50}$ (b) $\frac{13}{25}$ (c) $\frac{23}{100}$
    (d) $\frac{1}{8}$ (e) $\frac{57}{200}$ (f) $\frac{29}{40}$

4. (a) 45%   (b) 32%   (c) 12.5%
    (d) 7%   (e) 112%   (f) 1.5%

5. (a) 0.8   (b) 0.15   (c) 0.47
    (d) 0.72   (e) 0.875   (f) 1.5

6. (a) $66.\dot{6}\%$ (b) $37\frac{1}{2}\%$ (c) $22.\dot{2}\%$
    (d) $37\frac{7}{9}\%$ (e) $46.\dot{6}\%$ (f) $141.\dot{6}\%$

7. $0.42, \frac{17}{40}, 43\%, \frac{13}{30}$

8. $28\%, 0.2805, \frac{57}{200}, \frac{2}{7}$

9. (a) 90%   (b) 85%
    (c) 88%   (d) 80%

10. B

11. A

Exercise 9.2   Page 77

1. (a) £16   (b) £15   (c) £66
    (d) £52.50   (e) £25   (f) £30
    (g) £27   (h) 4 m   (i) 24 kg
    (j) 280   (k) £11.25   (l) 12

2. (a) £80   (b) £13
    (c) £16.50   (d) £57.50

3. (a) £510   (b) £5.50
    (c) £33.60   (d) £40.95

4. £20

5. 270

6. (a) £42   (b) £70.50

7. £1.95

8. 40 pence per minute

9. 24 g

10. 759 g

11. £215

12. (a) 660   (b) 198

13. 8400 cm²

Exercise 9.3 — Page 78

1. (a) 32% (b) $12\frac{1}{2}$% (c) 50%
   (d) 90% (e) 30%

2. 20%

3. 30%

4. $12\frac{1}{2}$%

5. $37\frac{1}{2}$%

6. (a) $33\frac{1}{3}$% (b) $66\frac{2}{3}$% (c) $11\frac{1}{9}$%
   (d) $42\frac{1}{2}$% (e) $56\frac{1}{2}$%

7. 9.5%

8. 8%

9. 45%

Exercise 9.4 — Page 79

1. £18.45

2. £171.50

3. (a) £74.38 (b) £323.75 (c) £4.11

4. £258.50

5. (a) £244.64 (b) £4706 (c) £2372.50

6. $83\frac{1}{3}$%

7. (a) $6.27\,\text{cm}^2$ (b) 6.15%

8. (a) £14 541.75 (b) £113.10

9. (a) £10 530 (b) 17.3%

10. (a) £34.13 (b) £41.39

11. (a) 36.3% (b) 23.7% (c) 37.8%

12. $1.35 \times 10^9\,\text{km}^3$

13. 1.49×10^9 square miles

14. 2.53%

Exercise 9.5 — Page 81

1. £242

2. £330.75

3. (a) earns 78p more interest

4. (a) £11 576.25 (b) £11 910.16
   (c) £12 250.43 (d) £12 597.12

5. (a) (i) £8268.73 (ii) 63.6%
   (b) (i) £12 721.12 (ii) 63.6%
   (c) Same percentage reduction

6. 1.64×10^8

7. (a) £2420 (b) £1938.66

8. $5.63 \times 10^6\,\text{km}^2$

Exercise 9.6 — Page 82

1. 20%

2. 20%

3. 25%

4. Becky
   Sam's increase = 32%
   Becky's increase = 40%

5. (a) $12\frac{1}{2}$% (b) 12%
   Rent went up by a greater percentage.

6. 16.7%

7. 12%

8. Car A 13.8%, Car B 18.2%

9. 1995 - 1996 (9.2%)

10. 19.5%

11. 3.51%

12. 18.6%

Exercise 9.7 — Page 83

1. 600 ml

2. £600

3. £220

4. (a) 50 (b) 90

5. 67.5 mg

6. £1.60

7. £293.75

8. £1420

9. £1600

10. School A 425, School B 450

11. £400

12. £150

1. (a) 45%   (b) 30%   (c) $37\frac{1}{2}\%$

2. (a) $\frac{4}{25}$ (b) $\frac{14}{25}$ (c) $\frac{9}{40}$

3. (a) 31%   (b) 5%   (c) 2.5%

4. $\frac{2}{5}$, 0.405, 0.41, 41.05%, $\frac{83}{200}$

5. (a) £9   (b) £6.60
(c) £105   (d) £9.60

6. 180

7. (a) £48   (b) £17.50

8. (a) 16%   (b) 15%

9. £2.40

10. 90%

11. (a) £605   (b) £2315.25

12. £11 000

13. $37\frac{1}{2}\%$

14. £144.90

15. (a) £7.08   (b) £51.92

16. (a) 166.4 cm   (b) 13.7%

17. (a) 8.80 m   (b) 15%

18. £2280

19. (a) £77 000   (b) £12 320

20. £212.31

21. 68.1%

22. (a) £23.60   (b) £43.66

23. (a) 252   (b) 362

1. (a) 8 SMILERS and 2 GLUMS
(b) (i) 8 SMILERS and 4 GLUMS
    (ii) 3 SMILERS and 9 GLUMS
(c) (i) 16 SMILERS and 4 GLUMS
    (ii) 8 SMILERS and 12 GLUMS

2. (a) (i) 75   (ii) 200
(b) (i) 12   (ii) 32
(c) (i) 56   (ii) 140

3. (a) (i) 16   (ii) 80
(b) (i) 9   (ii) 45
(c) (i) 84   (ii) 112

4. (a) (i) 14 SMILERS and 6 GLUMS
    (ii) 35 SMILERS and 15 GLUMS
(b) (i) 9 SMILERS and 6 GLUMS
    (ii) 30 SMILERS and 20 GLUMS

1. (a) E.g. 12 : 2, 18 : 3, 24 : 4,
(b) E.g. 14 : 4, 21 : 6, 28 : 8,
(c) E.g. 6 : 10, 9 : 15, 12 : 20.

2. (a) 1 : 2   (b) 1 : 3   (c) 3 : 4
(d) 2 : 5   (e) 3 : 4   (f) 2 : 5
(g) 3 : 7   (h) 9 : 4   (i) 4 : 9
(j) 7 : 3

3. (a) 12   (b) 28   (c) 100   (d) 20

4. 198 cm

5. 400 g

6. 64

7. 18 years

8. 2 : 3

9. 40 : 9

10. 1 : 250

11. 1 : 1500

12. (a) 4 : 1   (b) 2 : 25   (c) 11 : 2
(d) 5 : 2   (e) 4 : 1   (f) 40 : 17
(g) 9 : 20   (h) 3 : 4   (i) 5 : 1
(j) 4 : 1   (k) 1 : 15   (l) 2 : 1

13. (a) 100 ml   (b) 4 : 1

1. (a) 14, 21   (b) 32, 24   (c) 3.5, 2

2. (a) £64.35, £17.55   (b) £37.50, £60
(c) £64.75, £46.25   (d) £34.65, £19.80

3. 50

4. (a) 5 : 2   (b) 6   (c) 55
(d) Total beads must be a multiple of 7.

5. £4900

6. 5

7. 170 000 km²

8. 200 kg

9. 40°, 60°, 80°

10. 8 cm, 12 cm, 18 cm

1. £446.40

2. £32.29

3. (a) £1.54   (b) 12 minutes

4. (a) 180 g   (b) 637.5 ml   (c) 210 g

5. (a) 12 minutes   (b) 16 miles

6. (a) 12 m^2 (b) 12 litres

7. (a) £130   (b) 32

8. $17\frac{1}{2}$ minutes

9. Large jar

10. Standard box

11. (a) 168.75 g   (b) 36   (c) 540 ml

1. (a) (i) $\frac{1}{4}$ (b) (i) $\frac{1}{5}, \frac{4}{5}$, 20%

     (ii) $\frac{3}{4}$ (ii) $\frac{3}{10}, \frac{7}{10}$, 30%

     (iii) 25%   (iii) $\frac{7}{20}, \frac{13}{20}$, 35%

     (iv) $\frac{17}{40}, \frac{23}{40}$, 42.5%

2. 9 : 11

3. 8 : 17

4. 35.7%

5. 45%

6. (a) $12\frac{1}{2}$%, $37\frac{1}{2}$%, 50%   (b) $\frac{1}{3}$ (c) $\frac{3}{5}$

1. (a) 7 m   (b) 30 cm

2. (a) 1 : 4000   (b) 48 m   (c) 0.9 cm

3. 12.5 m

4. 7 cm

5. (a) 1 : 20   (b) 5.8 m   (c) 22.5 cm

6. (a) 5 cm   (b) 100 m

1. (a) E.g. 6 : 8, 9 : 12, 12 : 16
   (b) E.g. 14 : 40, 21 : 60, 28 : 80
   (c) E.g. 4 : 18, 6 : 27, 8 : 36
   (d) E.g. 12 : 10, 18 : 15, 24 : 20

2. 18

3. 124 cm

4. 326 480

5. Red 1.5 litres, Yellow 0.9 litres

6. 12

7. (a) 18   (b) 35%

8. (a) £15   (b) 40%

9. Economy sack

10. Anne £567, Carl £453.60, Lee £340.20

11. (a) 6 cm   (b) 0.6 cm

12. (a) 25 g   (b) 750 g

13. £78.75

14. £1.45

15. 40 balloons, 80 sausage rolls, 30 jellies, 13 or 14 packets of biscuits

16. (a) $\frac{3}{4}$ (b) $12\frac{1}{2}$%   (c) 200 cm^3

17. 1 : 200 000

18. (a) 5 m   (b) 8.5 feet

19. 4.5 cm

1. (a) 1030   (b) 2230   (c) 0145
   (d) 1345   (e) 0750

2. (a) 2.15 pm   (b) 5.25 am
   (c) 11.20 pm   (d) 10.05 am
   (e) 9.40 am

3. (a) 2.28 pm   (b) 48 minutes

4. (a) 1.15 pm   (b) 2 hours 50 minutes

5. (a) 1330   (b) 1.30 pm

6. (a) 1525   (b) 3.25 pm

1. (a) 49 minutes   (b) 1 hour 35 minutes
   (c) 1.42 pm   (d) 0815

2. (a) 1215   (b) 1 hour 48 minutes
   (c) 5.42 pm

3. (a) 0900   (b) 44 minutes
   (c) 2 hours 20 minutes

4. (a) 40 minutes
(b) (i) 1520 (ii) 1610
(c) 1650

5. (a) 36 minutes (b) 1503 (c) 1713

Exercise 11.3 — Page 102

1. £313.60   **4.** £15 600

2. £272   **5.** £23 220

3. £203.40   **6.** £1100

Exercise 11.4 — Page 103

1. £881   **5.** £4357.15

2. £809   **6.** £228.92

3. £67.08   **7.** £413.69

4. £15.06   **8.** £2549.00

Exercise 11.5 — Page 104

1. (a) £300 (b) £25

2. £74.84

3. 810

4. £6.30

5. £112

6. £46.76

7. (a) 57 (b) 81 (c) £83 000
(d) £92.50 (e) £222.50 (f) £67.50

Exercise 11.6 — Page 105

1. (a) £59.50 (b) £399.50

2. (a) £15.75 (b) £105.75

3. £170.37

4. £291.40

5. (a) £8.97 (b) £188.50

6. £216.20

7. £44.13

8. £428.87

9. £69.32

Exercise 11.7 — Page 106

1. (a) 0.5 p (b) 5.25 p

2. 700 g

3. Large pot

4. Medium size

5. 1 kg

6. Arnolds £109.37, Bertram £112,
Cuthbert £113.33

7. 1.5 litre

Exercise 11.8 — Page 108

1. (a) £70 (b) £48
(c) £225 (d) £225

2. (a) £296 (b) £592

3. (a) £24.72 (b) £832

4. (a) £63.05 (b) £675.13

5. £8988.80

6. £6298.56

Exercise 11.9 — Page 108

1. (a) 1420.50 francs (b) 426 marks
(c) 74 700 drachmas (d) 422 400 lira
(e) 35 850 pesetas (f) 241.50 dollars

2. (a) £9.50 (b) £5.23 (c) £25
(d) £21.74 (e) £39.77 (f) £18.07

3. (a) $805 (b) £74.64

4. £132.16

Review Exercise 11 — Page 109

1. Tonight with Jonathan Ross

2. (a) (i) 315.18 s (ii) 5 minutes 15.18 s
(b) 4.78 s

3. 1715

4. 4 hours 10 minutes

5. (a) 0750 (b) 33 minutes

6. £32.30

7. 4

8. (a) £1827.80 (b) £30.46

9. (a) £15 515   (b) £3753.75

10. £530.92

11. (a) £16 875   (b) £3894

12. £275.40

13. (a) 464.4   (b) £208.98
      (c) £218.78

14. (a) 435   (b) £53.62

15. Shop B, by 16p

16. £15 sweatshirt

17. Small

18. Medium

19. £5.76

20. £2450.09

21. 121.20 guilders

22. (a) 71 marks   (b) £14.79

Exercise 12.1   Page 114

1. 8 miles per hour

2. 8 km/hour

3. 25 m per minute

4. 6 km/hour

5. (a) 24 000 m/hour   (b) 24 km/hour

6. (a) 57.5 km/hour   (b) 1 hour

7. (a) 56 km/hour   (b) 60 km/hour

8. 10.14 m/s, 9.37 m/s, 9.20 m/s, 8.22 m/s, 7.77 m/s, 7.05 m/s

9. (a) 8.86 m/s, 8.95 m/s, 8.96 m/s, 9.04 m/s
      (b) 8.95 m/s

Exercise 12.2   Page 116

1. 8 km

2. 3 km

3. 6 km

4. (a) $2\frac{1}{2}$ hours   (b) 50 minutes

5. (a) 8 m/s   (b) 100 km
      (c) 12 cm   (d) 1 hour
      (e) 1 s

6. B 4 hours, C 70 km/hour, D 100 km/hour

7. 10 km/hour

8. 10.30 am

9. 11.09 am

10. 4.81 m/s

11. 0.23 km/min

12. 3×10^8 m/s

13. (a) Coach B, by 30 km
      (b) Coach A, by 16 minutes
      (c) Coach B, by 17.9 km/hour

Exercise 12.3   Page 118

1. (a) 50 km/hour
      (b) 20 m/s
      (c) 0.2 km/min

2. (a) Amy walks, Ben cycles, Cathy bus, Dan car
      (b) Amy 7.5 km/hour, Cathy 20 km/hour, Dan 60 km/hour

3. (a) 80 seconds   (b) 6 m/s

4. (a) 66.6 m/min (4 km/hour)
      (b) No. Walks, runs, stops (to recover after missing bus), walks

5. (a) 0.5 km/min
      (b) 0.33 km/min
      (c) 0.4 km/min

6. (a) (i) 2
        (ii) 45 minutes
      (b) (i) 12.5 km/hour
        (ii) 7 km/hour
        (iii) 10 am and noon

7. (a) 0945
      (b) 1015 to 1042
      (c) 80 km/hour

8. (a) 0936   (b) 7 km
      (c) 90 minutes   (d) 4 km/hour

9. (b) 15 km/hour

10. (b) 30 seconds

11. (b) 2.4 km/hour

13. (b) 60 km/hour   (c) 90 km/hour

14. (b) (i) 1220
        (ii) 1102
        (iii) 14 km/hour

Exercise 12.4 — Page 123

1. 8 g/cm³
2. 9 g/cm³
3. 28.6 g/cm³
4. 7200 g
5. 9360 g
6. 2000 cm³
7. 0.0008 kg/cm³
8. 100 g
9. 118.3 people/km²
10. (a) 30 530 km²
    (b) 104.2 people/km²
    (c) 5.74×10^7

Review Exercise 12 — Page 124

1. Jane $3\frac{1}{3}$ m/s, Tom $8\frac{1}{3}$ m/s, Sam 4 m/s
2. (a) 142.9 s   (b) 252 m
3. (a) 16 km/hour   (b) 20 km/hour
4. 5 hours 48 minutes
5. (a) $63\frac{1}{3}$ miles per hour
   (b) $85\frac{1}{2}$ miles per hour
6. 1.28 seconds
8. (a) (i) *BC*
       (ii) *DE*
       (iii) At any point from *E* to *H*.
   (b) (i) 1 km/minute
       (ii) 0.28 km/minute
       (iii) 0.286 km/minute
10. (b) 20 km/hour
11. Steel 2.5 g/cm³, Concrete 1600 cm³, Foam 200 g
12. Europe 0.065 people/km²
    Asia 0.068 people/km²
    Asia
13. 11 500 g

Section Review — Page 126

1. 62p
2. 10 080 minutes

3. 24 degrees.
4. £13
5. 1.25 p.m.
6. 13.7 cm, 13.66 cm
7. (a) £113.85   (b) £4.86
8. (a) $\frac{1}{6}$ (b) 12   (c) $33\frac{1}{3}\%$
9. (a) £0.96   (b) £68
10. 26 000 to the nearest thousand.
11. 325 ml
12. (a) 5 cups   (b) 350 ml
13. (a) 23p   (b) 20%   (c) 50 g
14. 60%
15. 3499, 2450
16. (a) $x = 504$, $y = 756$
    (b) $2^5 \times 3^5 \times 7^2$
    (c) $2^3 \times 3^2 \times 7^2$
    (d) $2^2 \times 3^5 \times 7$
    (e) $2^4 \times 3^2 \times 7^2$, **all** powers are even numbers.
17. (a) 1.5×10^3 (b) 6×10^5
18. £33.60
19. (a) $2\frac{1}{2}$ hours
    (b) (i) 1800   (ii) 6 pm
20. $\frac{4}{13}$, $\frac{11}{35}$, 0.315, 0.32, 32.5%
21. (a) £0.43   (b) £2.95
22. (a) 5%   (b) 3   (c) $\frac{1}{6}$
23. (a) Claire   (b) 28
24. 4.29 (3 s.f.)
25. $20\frac{11}{35}°F$ (20.3°F)
26. (a) 32%
    (b) (i) 36   (ii) 31
27. (a) 36.2 minutes
    (b) $\frac{40}{60} \times 60 = 40$ minutes
28. 26 km/h
29. (a) 24 kg   (b) 28%
    (c) $\frac{4}{7}$ (d) $\frac{3}{20}$
30. 0.215

505

31. (a) 2.07
    (b) (i) $C = 229.08$
       (ii) $C = 20 + 0.5 (2 \times 50 + 200)$
          $= 170$
       Sarah's answer is wrong (£164.88)

32. (a) 3 906 250
    (b) (i) 0.111
       (ii) More accurate than numbers given
          in the question, 3 sig. figs.

33. (a) 0.8611326   (b) 4.94 to 3 s.f.

34. 1.53×10^{-1}

35. (a) £17.10   (b) £31

36. (a) 52 000 000   (b) 1.2×10^{-1} cm

37. 5.1×10^{6}

38. (a) 161 000   (b) 17.9%

39. (a) both even numbers
    (b) both multiples of 3
    (c) 2×3^{3}
    (d) (i) 324   (ii) 216

40. (a) (i) 2.1×10^{3}
       (ii) $2^{2} \times 3 \times 5^{2} \times 7$
    (b) 3.43×10^{20}

Exercise 13.1   Page 132

1. (a) $n + 4$ (b) $n - 3$ (c) $3n$

2. (a) $n + 6$ (b) $n - 12$ (c) $8n$

3. (a) $p - 1$ (b) $p + 5$ (c) $25p$

4. $6k$

5. $5n$ pence

6. (a) 96   (b) 480   (c) $48t$

Exercise 13.2   Page 133

1. $12e$

2. $b - 3$

3. (a) $(a + 1)$ years
    (b) $(a - 4)$ years
    (c) $(a + n)$ years

4. $(h + 12)$ cm

5. (a) $2d$ (b) $2d + 5$

6. (a) $P = y + 5$ (b) $P = y - 2$
    (c) $P = 2y$ (d) $P = 2y + 3$
    (e) $P = 3y - 1$

7. Ben $d - 2$
Charlotte $2d$
Erica $\frac{1}{2} d$
Frank $3d - 5$
Gillian $3d - 1$

Exercise 13.3   Page 134

1. (a) $3c$ (b) $5x$ (c) $7p$
    (d) $5y$ (e) $10g$ (f) $13z$
    (g) $8m$ (h) $2r$ (i) $5t$
    (j) $3j$ (k) $4c$ (l) w
    (m) 0 (n) $-5x$ (o) $-14a$

2. (a) $4x$ (b) $6a$ (c) $9y$ (d) $2u + 2v$

3. (a) $8x$
    (b) $2v$
    (c) cannot be simplified
    (d) cannot be simplified
    (e) $p + 4q$
    (f) $12d$
    (g) cannot be simplified
    (h) $4m + 3n$
    (i) $8c$
    (j) $x + y$
    (k) $6p$
    (l) 0

4. (a) $3a + 5$ (b) $2x + 3y$
    (c) $3m + 2n$ (d) cannot be simplified
    (e) $3p + 3q$ (f) $d + 3$
    (g) $-2a$ (h) 7
    (i) $c - d + 11$ (j) 0
    (k) $3v - 2w$ (l) $-2 - 5t$

5. (a) $P = 4x + 2$ (b) $P = 4a + 6b$
    (c) $P = 3x$ (d) $P = 6y + 9$

Exercise 13.4   Page 136

1. (a) $2x + 10$ (b) $3a + 18$

2. (a) $3x + 6$ (b) $4r + 28$
    (c) $2y + 10$ (d) $6t + 3$
    (e) $20z + 35$ (f) $2x + 2y$

3. (a) $2x + 8$ (b) $4b + 4$
    (c) $3p + 18$ (d) $5a + 35$
    (e) $8x + 4$ (f) $6a + 2b$
    (g) $3t - 6$ (h) $20 - 4a$
    (i) $6 - 12p$ (j) $6p + 12c$
    (k) $6m - 15n$ (l) $7a + 7b + 7c$

4. $2(q + 2) = 2q + 4$
$2(q - 1) = 2q - 2$
$2(2q + 1) = 4q + 2$
$2(2 - q) = 4 - 2q$

5. (a) $2x + 5$ (b) $3a + 11$
   (c) $6w + 31$ (d) $5z + 8$
   (e) $8t + 15$ (f) $2c - 6$
   (g) $8a + 23$ (h) $6x - 20$
   (i) $2p - 11$

6. (a) $5x + 8$ (b) $5a + 13$
   (c) $9y + 23$ (d) $9a + 5$
   (e) $26t + 30$ (f) $5z + 13$
   (g) $12q + 16$ (h) $11x - 3$
   (i) $20e - 16$ (j) $8d + 10$

Exercise 13.5   Page 137

1. (a) $3y$ (b) $5p$ (c) xy (d) a^2
   (e) $2a^2$ (f) $4a^2$ (g) h^3 (h) w^3
   (i) $2d^3$ (j) $2m^3$ (k) $6x^3$ (l) $6a^2$

2. (a) $4x^2$ (b) $10y^2$ (c) $24a^2$ (d) $15a^2$

3. (a) $3x^3$ (b) $6d^3$ (c) $60t^3$

4. (a) fg (b) $20c$ (c) $4de$
   (d) $2ab$ (e) $12xy$ (f) $8ab$
   (g) $2h^2j$ (h) $5wy$ (i) $14mp^2$
   (j) $6x^3y$ (k) $21a^3b^3$ (l) $15e^2f^4g^2$

Exercise 13.6   Page 138

1. (a) 5 (b) 15 (c) 28

2. (a) 20 (b) 56 (c) 10

3. (a) 11 (b) 21 (c) 3

4. (a) 3 (b) 5 (c) -3

5. $F = 15$

6. $V = 31$

7. $P = 22$

8. $C = 144$

9. $S = 8.8$

10. $S = 52.8$

11. (a) $S = 18$ (b) $S = 18$

12. (a) $S = 36$ (b) $S = 36$

13. (a) $S = 8$ (b) $S = 18$

14. (a) $S = 4$ (b) $S = 9$

15. 33

16. (a) $96\,\text{m}$ (b) $720\,\text{m}$ (c) $36\,\text{m}$

Exercise 13.7   Page 139

1. (a) 3 (b) 4 (c) 17
   (d) 6 (e) 6 (f) 14
   (g) 3 (h) 2 (i) 8

2. (a) $x = 8$ (b) $x = 7$ (c) $x = 5$
   (d) $x = 7$ (e) $x = 3$ (f) $x = 2$
   (g) $x = 4$ (h) $x = 9$ (i) $x = 1$

3. (a) $y = 2$ (b) $d = 5$
   (c) $a = 9$ (d) $a = 9$

4. (a) 6 (b) 3 (c) 8
   (d) 4 (e) 5

Review Exercise 13   Page 140

1. (a) $(n - 2)$ years   (b) $3n$ years
   (c) $(3n + 4)$ years   (d) $8n + 2$

2. (a) Cost $= 25n$ (b) $6n$ pence

3. (a) (i) $2x$ (ii) $2x - 3$
   (b) $5x - 3$

4. (a) $3x - 5$ (b) 1

5. (a) either   (b) odd   (c) even

6. (a) 90 (b) 15

7. (a) 5 amp   (b) 3120 watts

8. £$8(p + q)$

9. (a) $w = 5$ (b) $9y + 5z$

10. (a) $(4x + 20)°$
   (b) (i) $4x + 20 = 180$ (ii) $44°$

Exercise 14.1   Page 142

1. (a) $x = 4$ (b) $a = 8$ (c) $y = 8$
   (d) $t = 6$ (e) $h = 4.2$ (f) $d = 4\frac{1}{2}$
   (g) $z = 425$ (h) $p = 4.4$ (i) $c = 999$

2. (a) $a = 9$ (b) $c = 5$ (c) $e = 7$
   (d) $t = 60$ (e) $y = 90$ (f) $g = 5$
   (g) $d = 14$ (h) $d = 6$ (i) $h = 40$

Exercise 14.2   Page 144

1. (a) $y = 3$ (b) $m = -16$
   (c) $f = -50$ (d) $b = 7$
   (e) $x = 14$ (f) $t = -11.5$

2. (a) $c = -4$ (b) $a = 15$
   (c) $f = -16$ (d) $h = 2\frac{1}{2}$
   (e) $p = 8$ (f) $t = -0.9$

3. (a) $x = 2$ (b) $n = 3$
  (c) $a = 0$ (d) $d = 7.5$
  (e) $c = 1\frac{1}{2}$ (f) $a = -10$
  (g) $p = 1\frac{1}{2}$ (h) $w = -1$
  (i) $m = -1\frac{1}{2}$ (j) $z = 10$
  (k) $t = 20$ (l) $x = -18$

4. (a) $p = 4$ (b) $t = 3$
  (c) $h = 7$ (d) $d = 10$
  (e) $b = 6$ (f) $x = 10$
  (g) $y = 5$ (h) $z = 8$
  (i) $n = 24$

5. (a) $p = -10$ (b) $a = 2\frac{1}{2}$
  (c) $t = 7$ (d) $n = 4$
  (e) $c = -0.5$ (f) $h = -4$
  (g) $x = 3$ (h) $y = -8$
  (i) $y = 12$ (j) $m = -3$
  (k) $t = -18$ (l) $v = -9$

Exercise **14.3** Page 145

1. (a) $x = 2$ (b) $a = 1$
  (c) $p = 2$ (d) $m = 2$
  (e) $y = 3$ (f) $t = 3$
  (g) $n = 1$ (h) $c = 7$
  (i) $h = 2$ (j) $d = 4\frac{1}{2}$
  (k) $k = 1$ (l) $x = 6$
  (m) $a = -1$ (n) $x = 1$

2. (a) $c = 7$ (b) $p = 3$
  (c) $a = 3$ (d) $t = 2$
  (e) $h = 4$ (f) $u = 2$
  (g) $b = 1$ (h) $d = -2\frac{1}{2}$
  (i) $n = -1$ (j) $x = 3$

3. (a) $t = -5$ (b) $y = 2$
  (c) $s = \frac{1}{2}$ (d) $q = 3$
  (e) $a = 1.8$ (f) $c = 0.11$
  (g) $p = 5$ (h) $x = -6$

Exercise **14.4** Page 146

1. (a) $x = 3$ (b) $a = 2$
  (c) $c = 6$ (d) $p = 5$
  (e) $d = 3$ (f) $t = 3$
  (g) $a = 1$ (h) $t = -1$

2. (a) $n = 2$ (b) $z = 6$
  (c) $w = 3$ (d) $m = 4$
  (e) $h = 2$ (f) $x = -3$
  (g) $w = 3$ (h) $y = 1\frac{1}{2}$
  (i) $v = -8$ (j) $c = -1\frac{1}{2}$

Exercise **14.5** Page 147

1. (a) Multiply both sides by 12.
  (b) Multiply both sides by 8.
  (c) Multiply both sides by 7.
  (d) Multiply both sides by 15.

2. (a) $x = 6$ (b) $w = 8$
  (c) $n = 24$ (d) $a = \frac{15}{32}$
  (e) $p = \frac{16}{21}$ (f) $b = \frac{5}{6}$

3. (a) $y = 28$ (b) $a = 24$
  (c) $a = 24$ (d) $t = 8$
  (e) $h = 11$ (f) $x = -4$
  (g) $x = -3$ (h) $a = 5$
  (i) $x = \frac{7}{9}$

Exercise **14.6** Page 149

1. (a) $(7x - 4)$ cm
  (b) $7x - 4 = 59, x = 9$
  (c) 13 cm, 17 cm, 29 cm

2. (a) $18x = 540$ (b) $150°$

3. (a) $(6x + 16)$ cm
  (b) $x = 2$
  (c) 28 cm

4. (a) (i) $6x$ years
   (ii) $(x + 20)$ years
   (iii) $(6x + 20)$ years
  (b) 5 years

5. (a) (i) $x - 10$ (ii) $x - 8$
  (b) (i) $x + 2 = 3(x - 8)$
   (ii) $x = 13$
   (iii) 5

Review Exercise **14** Page 150

1. (a) $q = -2$ (b) $s = -1\frac{1}{2}$
  (c) $p = 2$ (d) $t = 1\frac{1}{2}$
  (e) $p = 6$ (f) $x = 10\frac{1}{2}$

2. $x = 20$

3. (a) $x = 2$ (b) $x = 1\frac{1}{2}$

4. (a) $(3x + 1)$ cm
  (b) (i) $3x + 1 = 22$
   (ii) 7 cm, 5 cm, 10 cm

5. (a) $8x$ cm^2
  (b) (i) $x = \frac{3}{4}$ (ii) 11 cm

6. $x = 2$
  4 cm, 3 cm; 2 cm, 6 cm

7. (a) (i) $(x + 9)$ years (ii) $(3x + 9)$ years
   (b) 9 years

8. (a) $3n$ pence
   (b) $4(n - 5)$ pence
   (c) (i) $3n + 4(n - 5) = 85$ (ii) 15

9. (a) $(5c + 1)$ kg
   (b) (i) $2c + 10 = 5c + 1$ (ii) 3 kg

10. (a) (i) $(x + 7)$ pence (ii) $(4x + 7)$ pence
   (b) 67p

Exercise **15.1** — Page 153

1. (a) (i) 15 (ii) 30 (iii) 300
   (b) $3n$

2. (a) (i) 17 (ii) 81
   (b) 7
   (c) $4n + 1$

3. (a) (i) 51   (ii) 100
   (b) (i) $x + 1$ (ii) $2x$

4. (a) 22 cm²
   (b) 42 cm²
   (c) $(4n + 2)$ cm²

5. (a) 11   (b) 18   (c) $2n + 1$

Exercise **15.2** — Page 155

1. (a) 13, 21, 24   (b) 144

2. (a) 49, 97   (b) 1537

3. (a) 16, linear   (b) 21, quadratic
   (c) 31, linear   (d) 4, linear
   (e) 50, quadratic (f) 21, linear

4. (a) $4n$ (b) $2n - 1$ (c) $4n + 3$
   (d) $5n - 3$ (e) $4n + 4$ (f) $8 - 2n$

5. (a) $n^2 - 1$ (b) $n^2 + 3$
   (c) $2n^2$ (d) $n^2 + n$

6. (a) $3n + 2$ (b) $n^2 + 4$
   (c) $6n + 2$ (d) $3n^2$
   (e) $5n - 2$ (f) $n^2 + 2$
   (g) $n^2 - n$ (h) $\frac{n}{n + 1}$

Exercise **15.3** — Page 156

1. $A = 75$ **4.** $F = 144$

2. 240 volts   **5.** 138 minutes

3. $F = 4100$ **6.** 0.3

7. £40.14

8. (a) $C = 15$ (b) $-15°C$

9. (a) $T = 1.80$ (b) $T = 2.46$

10. (a) $v = 6.3$ (b) $v = 7.4$

Exercise **15.4** — Page 157

1. (a) $x = y - 5$ (b) $x = y + 2$
   (c) $x = \frac{y}{4}$ (d) $x = 2y$
   (e) $x = \frac{y}{2} - 3$ (f) $x = \frac{y}{3} + 3$
   (g) $x = 2y + \frac{5}{2}$ (h) $x = \frac{2y}{3} - 2$

2. $K = \frac{20P}{9}$

3. $C = \frac{5F - 160}{9}$

4. $y = x + 3,\ x = y - 3$
   $y = 3x + 1,\ x = \frac{1}{3}(y - 1)$
   $y = \frac{1}{3}x,\ x = 3y$
   $y = 3x,\ x = \frac{1}{3}y$
   $y = 3x - 1,\ x = \frac{1}{3}y + \frac{1}{3}$

5. (a) $v = u - 3$ (b) $v = r + u$
   (c) $v = \frac{r}{2}$ (d) $v = \frac{u}{i}$
   (e) $v = tx$ (f) $v = u + at$
   (g) $v = \frac{p - d}{m}$ (h) $v = \sqrt{\frac{F}{m}}$

6. (a) £107   (b) 9 days

7. $a = \frac{2A}{h} - b$

8. (a) $V = IR$ (b) $m = \frac{E}{c^2}$
   (c) $x = \sqrt{\frac{y - b}{a}}$ (d) $v = \sqrt{\frac{2e}{m}}$

9. (a) $a = b - c^2$ (b) $a = \sqrt{b}$
   (c) $a = 2b + \frac{c}{4}$ (d) $a = \frac{b}{3}$
   (e) $a = \frac{4b}{15}$ (f) $a = \frac{3b}{2}$
   (g) $a = 2\sqrt{b}$ (h) $a = \sqrt{\frac{3b + 5}{2}}$

Exercise **15.5** — Page 158

1. B

2. (a)

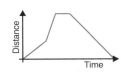

3. 1. C 2. B 3. E 4. A

4.

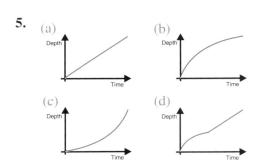

5. (a)

Depth / Time

(b)

Depth / Time

(c)

Depth / Time

(d)

Depth / Time

6. (a) **1.** D　　**2.** A　　**3.** C　　**4.** B

Review Exercise **15**　　Page 161

1. (a) 30
　　(b) 40 is not a multiple of 3.
　　(c) $3p$

2. (a) Entries are: 11, 16, 21
　　(b) 7
　　(c) (i) 501　　(ii) $5p + 1$

3. (a) (i) Entries are: 14, 17, 38, $3n + 2$　(ii) 9
　　(b) 12, 20, 132, $n^2 - n$

4. (a) $4n - 1$　　(b) $\frac{1}{3^n}$

5. (a) 6, 7　　(b) No, 6, $\frac{6 + 4}{2}$ so 5

6. (a) $1, \frac{2}{3}, \frac{3}{5}, \frac{4}{7}, \frac{5}{9}$　　(b) $\frac{n}{3n - 1}$

7. (a) (i) 20　　(ii) $2n$
　　(b) (i) 50, 72
　　　　(ii) square numbers
　　　　(iii) $2n^2$

8. £190.12

9. (a) $v = 9\frac{1}{5}$　　(b) $t = \frac{v - u}{a}$

10. (a) 75　　(b) 66　　(c) $y = 9c^2 - 25$

11.
　(a) (i)　　　　　(ii)

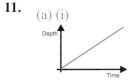

　(b)

12. $A : W, B : Z, C : X$

13. 473m²

Exercise **16.1**　　Page 166

1. (1) $y = 4$　　　(4) $y = -1$
　　(2) $x = -3$　　(5) $y = x$
　　(3) $x = 1$

2.

x	1	2	3
(a) y	3	4	5
(b) y	2	4	6
(c) y	4	2	0

3. (a)　　　(b)　　　(c)

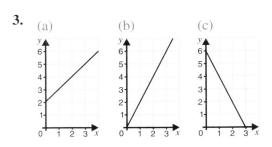

4.

x	-2	-1	0	1	2	3
(a) y	-3	-2	-1	0	1	2
(b) y	-8	-5	-2	1	4	7

5. Entries are 6, 4, 3

7. (b) Same slope, parallel
　　　　y intercept is different

8. (b) Same slope, parallel
　　　　y intercept is different

9. (b) Same y intercept, 3
　　　　Different slope

Exercise **16.2**　　Page 168

1. (a) Gradient 3, Intercept -1

2. $y = 3x, y = 3x + 2$

3. Gradients: 4, 3, 2, $-2, \frac{1}{2}, 2, 0, -\frac{1}{2}$
　　Intercepts: 3, 5, -3, 4, 3, 0, 3, 4

4. (1) C　　(2) D　　(3) B　　(4) A

5. (a) $y = 5x - 4$　　(b) $y = -\frac{1}{2}x + 6$

6. (a) $y = x - 2$　　(b) $y = -2x - 2$

7. (c) 1　　(d) $(0, -4)$　　(e) $y = x - 4$

8. (c) $y = -2x - 1$

1. $y = \frac{3x}{2} + 3$

2. (a) $y = -\frac{4}{5}x + 4$ (b) $y = \frac{2}{7}x - 2$
   (c) $y = -\frac{2}{3}x + \frac{4}{3}$ (d) $y = x + \frac{2}{3}$

3. $y = -\frac{3}{2}x +$ (any number)

4. (a) $\frac{4}{5}$
   (b) 2
   (c) $y =$ (any number)$x + 2$

5. (a) $(0, 5)$ (b) $(3, 0)$

6. (a) $(0, 4), (5, 0)$
   (b) $(0, -2), (0.5, 0)$
   (c) $(0, 5), (7.5, 0)$

1. (a)

x	1	2	3
$y = x + 2$	3	4	5
$y = 5 - x$	4	3	2

   (c) $x = 1.5$

2. (b) $x = 2.5$

3. (a) $x = 8$ (b) $x = 2$ (c) $x = 3$

4. (b) $y = 9$ (c) $x = 3$

5. (c) The number of hours for which the two firms charge the same amount.

6. (d) B   (e) A   (f) 6 days

1. S

2. (a) $y = 2x +$ (any number)
   (b) $y =$ (any number)$x + 7$
   (c) $y = \frac{2}{3}x - 3$

3. (a) Entries are: $-4, -1, 2, 5, 8$
   (c) $\left(\frac{1}{5}, 3\frac{1}{2}\right)$

4. (a) $y = 4x + 60$
   (b) £460

5. (a) Entries are: $-1, 1, 3, 5, 7$
   (b) $(-2, 1)$
   (c) $x = -4$

6. (b) $(-5, 0), (0, -5)$
   (c) $y = -x - 5$

7. (b) (i) -2
   (ii)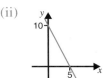

8. (a) (i) Entries are: 3, 7, 9, 11
   (b) (i) Entries are: 1, 4, 7, 10
   (c) (i) £3   (ii) £7

9. $C = 3.5n - 1$

10. (a) £32.50
    (b) (i) 0.5
        (ii) Charge for each extra minute.
    (c) $C = 0.5t + 10$
    (d) 148 minutes

1. $x = 4, y = 2$ 4. $x = 2, y = 3$
2. $x = 3, y = 5$ 5. $x = 3, y = 1$
3. $x = 2, y = 3$ 6. $x = 4, y = 3$

1. (a) Both sides have gradient -1.
   (b) Both sides have gradient 4.
   (c) Both lines are the same.
   (d) Both lines have gradient 0.4.

2. (a) $y = -2x + 6, y = -2x + 3$
   (b) $y = 2x + 3.5, y = 2x + 2$
   (c) $y = 2.5x - 4, y = 2.5x + 1.75$
   (d) $y = -3x + 1.25, y = -3x + 0.5$

3. (b) and (d) have no solution.
   (a) $x = 0.4, y = 4,$
   (c) $x = -0.125, y = 1.875$

1. $x = 1, y = 2$ 11. $x = 4, y = 1$
2. $x = 3, y = 4$ 12. $x = 4, y = 2$
3. $x = 2, y = 1$ 13. $x = 2, y = 3$
4. $x = 1, y = 7$ 14. $x = 4, y = -2$
5. $x = 3, y = 1$ 15. $x = 2, y = -1.5$
6. $x = 2, y = 3$ 16. $x = -1, y = 3$
7. $x = 5, y = 2$ 17. $x = -5, y = 6$
8. $x = 4, y = 2$ 18. $x = 2.5, y = -1$
9. $x = 5, y = 4$ 19. $x = -6, y = 2.5$
10. $x = 3, y = 2$ 20. $x = 3, y = -1.5$

Exercise 17.4 Page 182

1. $x = 2, y = 1$
2. $x = 2, y = 3$
3. $x = 3, y = 1$
4. $x = 4, y = 2$
5. $x = 2, y = 1$
6. $x = 4, y = -3$
7. $x = 4, y = 0.5$
8. $x = -3, y = 0.5$
9. $x = 4, y = 1$
10. $x = 2.2, y = 5.6$
11. $x = 1.5, y = 2$
12. $x = 1, y = 2$
13. $x = 5, y = 2$
14. $x = 1, y = -2$
15. $x = -1, y = 2$
16. $x = 2, y = 1$
17. $x = -1, y = 1$
18. $x = -2, y = 3$
19. $x = -1, y = 7$
20. $x = 4, y = -1$
21. $x = 1, y = 2$
22. $x = 2, y = -1$
23. $x = 1, y = -2$
24. $x = -2, y = 0.5$

Exercise 17.5 Page 183

1. $x = 2, y = 6$
2. $x = 9, y = 18$
3. $x = 8, y = 2$
4. $x = 3, y = 6$
5. $x = 2, y = 13$
6. $x = 0, y = 2$
7. $x = 2, y = 4$
8. $x = 7, y = 6$
9. $x = 4, y = 8$
10. $x = 10.5, y = 0.5$
11. $x = -68, y = -122$
12. $x = 8, y = 6$

Exercise 17.6 Page 184

1. $x = 108, y = 12$
2. $x = 95, y = 82$
3. 32 children, 3 adults
4. $x = 100, y = 70$
5. Coffee 50p, Tea 40p
6. $x = 160, y = 120$

Review Exercise 17 Page 185

1. (a) $x = 3, y = 7$
   (b) $x = 7.5, y = 0.5$
   (c) $x = 4.5, y = 1.25$
   (d) $x = 2, y = -6$

2. (a) $x = 2, y = 1$
   (b) $x = 3, y = 2$
   (c) $x = 1, y = 4$
   (d) $x = 3, y = 2$
   (e) $x = -1, y = 2$
   (f) $x = 4, y = -2$
   (g) $x = 3, y = -2$
   (h) $x = 2, y = -0.5$
   (i) $x = 2, y = 3$
   (j) $x = 3, y = -1$
   (k) $x = 2, y = -1$
   (l) $x = 1, y = 2$
   (m) $x = 3, y = 4$
   (n) $x = -7, y = 4$
   (o) $x = 22, y = 20$
   (p) $x = -2, y = 1$

3. (a) Same gradient, 2
   $y = 2x - 2, y = 2x - \frac{3}{2}$
   (b) Same gradient, $\frac{1}{4}$
   $y = \frac{1}{4}x + \frac{1}{4}, y = \frac{1}{4}x + \frac{3}{8}$
   (c) $a = 3, b = $ any number
   (d) Any values where $p = -3q$

4. $x = 1.2, y = 1.4$

5. $x = 7, y = 3$

6. (a) $4x + y = 72, 6x + y = 90$
   (b) $x = 9, y = 36$

Exercise 18.1 Page 187

1. (a) True (b) True (c) True
   (d) False (e) True (f) False
   (g) False (h) True

2. (a) E.g. 5, 4, 3, …
   (b) E.g. −2, −1, 0 …
   (c) E.g. 5, 4, 3, …
   (d) E.g. 7, 6, 5, …
   (e) E.g. 11, 12, 13, …
   (f) −1
   (g) 5
   (h) One of: −6, −5, −4, −3, −2

3. (a) 2, 3, 4   (b) −1, 0, 1, 2, 3
   (c) −4, −3, −2, −1   (d) −1, 0, 1, 2

4. (a) −6, −2, −1, 0, 1, 2, 4
   (b) −5, −3, −1, 1, 2, 4, 6
   (c) −8.5, −6.0, −3.5, 0.5, 1.0, 2.5, 3.5

5. (a) $x \geqslant 2$ (b) $-6 \leqslant x \leqslant -2$
   (c) $-2 < x < 1$ (d) $x < 5$ and $x \geqslant 8$

6. (a)
   (b)
   (c)

Exercise **18.2**   Page 189

1. $a < 4$
2. $b \geq 1$
3. $a > 2$
4. $b \leq 1$
5. $c > 5$
6. $d < -3$
7. $a \geq 6$
8. $b < 15$
9. $c \leq 3$
10. $d > 4$
11. $e \geq 2$
12. $f < -2$
13. $g \leq \frac{1}{2}$
14. $h < 2$
15. $j \geq 2\frac{1}{2}$
16. $k > -4$
17. $m > -6\frac{1}{2}$
18. $n \leq 2$
19. $p > 8$
20. $q > 1$
21. $r \geq -1\frac{1}{2}$
22. $t > 13$
23. $u \leq 9$
24. $v < 1\frac{1}{2}$
25. $w > 8$
26. $x \geq -6$

Exercise **18.3**   Page 190

1. $a < -2$
2. $b \geq 3$
3. $c \leq -4$
4. $d > -2\frac{1}{2}$
5. $e \geq -2$
6. $f < 1$
7. $g > -4$
8. $h \geq 2$
9. $j \leq 1$
10. $k > -\frac{1}{3}$
11. $m < -3$
12. $n > -4$
13. $p \geq \frac{5}{9}$
14. $q > -2\frac{1}{5}$

Exercise **18.4**   Page 191

1. (a) $1 < x \leq 5$
   (b) $-1 \leq x < 9$
   (c) $-7 < x \leq 4$
   (d) $1 < x \leq 3$
   (e) $-2 \leq x < 4$
   (f) $3 < x < 4\frac{1}{2}$
   (g) $-\frac{1}{3} \leq x \leq 4$
   (h) $2 < x \leq 5$
   (i) $-3 \leq x < 6$
   (j) $-2 < x < 2$
   (k) $3 \leq x < 6$
   (l) $-4\frac{1}{2} \leq x \leq -1$

2. (a) $6, 7, 8$
   (b) $-2, -1, 0, 1, 2, 3, 4$
   (c) $0, 1, 2$
   (d) $4, 5, 6, 7$
   (e) 5
   (f) $2, 3$
   (g) $-2, -1, 0$
   (h) $-1, 0, 1, 2, 3$
   (i) $-4, -3, -2, -1, 0, 1, 2, 3, 4, 5, 6$

Exercise **18.5**   Page 191

1. (a) $x \leq -3$ and $x \geq 3$
   (b) $-6 < x < 6$
   (c) $x < -1$ and $x > 1$
   (d) $-5 \geq x \geq 5$
   (e) $-2 < x < 2$
   (f) $x \leq -7$ and $x \geq 7$
   (g) $x < -1$ and $x > 1$
   (h) $-2 \leq x \leq 2$

2. (a) $-1, 0, 1$
   (b) $-4, -3, -2, -1, 0, 1, 2, 3, 4$
   (c) $\ldots, -5, -4$ and $4, 5, \ldots$
   (d) $\ldots, -8, -7$ and $7, 8, \ldots$
   (e) $-2, -1, 0, 1, 2$
   (f) $\ldots, -4, -3$ and $3, 4, \ldots$
   (g) $-6, -5, -4, -3, -2, -1, 0, 1, 2, 3, 4,$
       $5, 6$
   (h) $\ldots, -4, -3$ and $3, 4, \ldots$

Review Exercise **18**   Page 195

1. (a) $x \geq -5$ (b) $x < 3$
   (c) $x \leq 6$ (d) $x \geq -2$

2. (a)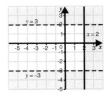
   (b)
   (c)

3. (a) $-1, 0, 1, 2, 3, 4$
   (b) $-3, -2, -1, 0, 1$ (c) $-2, -1$

4. (a) $a < -3$ and $a > 3$
   (b) $-10 \leq a \leq 10$ (c) $-4 \leq a \leq 4$

5. (a) $-4, -3, -2, -1, 0, 1, 2, 3, 4$
   (b) $\ldots, -7, -6$ and $6, 7, \ldots$
   (c) $-3, -2, -1, 0, 1, 2, 3$

6. (a)
   (b)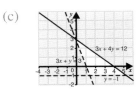
   (c)

7. $-3, -2, -1, 0, 1, 2, 3$

8. $-1 \leqslant x < 1$

9. $-1, 0, 1$

10. $a > 5$

11. (a) $-4, -3, -2, -1, 0, 1$
(b) (i) $x < \frac{1}{2}$
    (ii) $y \leqslant -5$ and $y \geqslant 5$

12. A2, B4, C1, D3

13. $(2, 5), (3, 5)$

14.

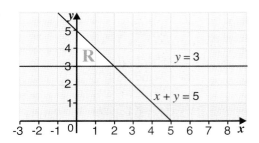

1. (a) $3a - 12$ (b) $bc - 3b$
(c) $d^2 + 2d$ (d) $3e^2 - 3e$
(e) $6f - 4f^2$ (f) $2g^2 + 3gh$
(g) $15jk - 20j^2$ (h) $6m - 8m^2$
(i) $6p^2 + 9pq - 12p$ (j) $r^2s + rs^2 + 2rs$

2. (a) $4(a + b)$ (b) $5(c - d)$
(c) $e(f + g)$ (d) $j(h + k)$
(e) $l(l - 1)$ (f) $m(1 + m)$
(g) $5(n + 2p)$

3. (a) $2(a + b)$ (b) $7(c + d)$
(c) $2(4e - f)$ (d) $7(g + 2h)$
(e) $8(3j - 2k)$ (f) $a(b - 1)$
(g) $d(c + e)$ (h) $f(g + h)$
(i) $2j(2k + 1)$ (j) $3l(2 - 3m)$
(k) $a(a - 1)$ (l) $b(1 - b)$
(m) $cd(d + 1)$ (n) $e(ef - 1)$
(o) $gh(h - g)$

1. $x^2 + 7x + 12$ **7.** $x^2 + 6x - 16$

2. $x^2 + 6x + 5$ **8.** $x^2 + 3x - 10$

3. $x^2 - 3x - 10$ **9.** $x^2 + 2x - 3$

4. $2x^2 - 3x - 2$ **10.** $x^2 - 5x + 6$

5. $3x^2 - 20x + 12$ **11.** $x^2 - 5x + 4$

6. $6x^2 + 7x + 2$ **12.** $x^2 - 5x - 14$

13. $2x^2 + x - 3$ **19.** $x^2 - 100$

14. $3x^2 + 14x - 5$ **20.** $x^2 + 6x + 9$

15. $12x^2 + 14x - 10$ **21.** $x^2 + 10x + 25$

16. $x^2 - 9$ **22.** $x^2 - 6x + 9$

17. $x^2 - 25$ **23.** $x^2 - 14x + 49$

18. $x^2 - 49$ **24.** $4x^2 - 12x + 9$

1. (a) $(x + 5)(x + 1)$ (b) $(x + 7)(x + 2)$
(c) $(x + 2)(x + 4)$ (d) $(x + 3)(x + 6)$
(e) $(x - 5)(x - 1)$ (f) $(x - 5)(x - 2)$
(g) $(x - 4)(x - 3)$ (h) $(x + 4)(x - 1)$
(i) $(x + 7)(x - 2)$ (j) $(x - 5)(x + 1)$

2. (a) $(x + 1)(x + 2)$ (b) $(x + 1)(x + 7)$
(c) $(x + 3)(x + 5)$ (d) $(x + 2)(x + 6)$
(e) $(x + 1)(x + 11)$ (f) $(x + 4)(x + 5)$
(g) $(x + 4)(x + 6)$ (h) $(x + 4)(x + 9)$

3. (a) $(x - 3)^2$ (b) $(x - 4)(x - 2)$
(c) $(x - 10)(x - 1)$ (d) $(x - 5)(x - 2)$
(e) $(x - 5)(x - 3)$ (f) $(x - 8)(x - 2)$
(g) $(x - 10)(x - 2)$ (h) $(x - 8)(x - 3)$
(i) $(x - 6)(x - 5)$ (j) $(x - 6)(x - 3)$

4. (a) $(x - 3)(x + 2)$ (b) $(x - 6)(x + 1)$
(c) $(x - 4)(x + 6)$ (d) $(x - 3)(x + 8)$
(e) $(x - 5)(x + 3)$ (f) $(x - 3)(x + 6)$
(g) $(x - 8)(x + 5)$ (h) $(x - 6)(x + 2)$

5. (a) $(x - 2)^2$ (b) $(x + 5)(x + 6)$
(c) $(x - 2)(x + 4)$ (d) $(x - 7)(x + 3)$
(e) $(x - 3)(x + 5)$ (f) $(x + 2)(x + 6)$
(g) $(x + 4)^2$ (h) $(x - 1)^2$

6. (a) $(x - 3)(x + 3)$ (b) $(x - 5)(x + 5)$
(c) $(x - 9)(x + 9)$ (d) $(10 - x)(10 + x)$
(e) $(6 - x)(6 + x)$ (f) $(x - 1)(x + 1)$

1. (a) $x = 2$ or 3 (b) $x = -4$ or -6
(c) $x = 3$ or -1 (d) $x = 5$ or -2
(e) $x = 0$ or 4 (f) $x = 0$ or -2

2. (a) $x = 1$ or 2 (b) $y = -3$ or -4
(c) $m = 4$ or -2 (d) $a = 3$ or -4
(e) $n = 9$ or -4 (f) $z = 6$ or 3
(g) $k = -3$ or -5 (h) $c = -7$ or -8
(i) $b = 4$ or -5 (j) $v = 12$ or -5
(k) $w = 4$ or -12 (l) $p = 9$ or -8

3. (a) $x = 0$ or 5 (b) $y = 0$ or -1
(c) $p = 0$ or -3 (d) $a = 0$ or 4
(e) $t = 0$ or 6 (f) $g = 0$ or 4

4. (a) $x = \pm 2$ (b) $y = \pm 12$
    (c) $a = \pm 3$ (d) $d = \pm 4$

Exercise 19.5   Page 202

1. (a) Entries are: 8, 2, 0, 2, 8
    (c) $x = 0$

2. (a) Entries are: 6, 2, 0, 0, 2, 6
    (c) $x = -1$ or 1
    (d) $\left(-\frac{1}{2}, -\frac{1}{4}\right)$

3. (a) Entries are: 5, 1, -1, -1, 1
    (c) $x = -0.6$ or 1.6

4. (b) $x = -3$ or 1

5. (a) Entries are: -6, 1, 6, 9, 10, 9, 6, 1, -6
    (c) $x = \pm 3.2$

6. (a) Entries are: -3, 7, 13, 15, 13, 7, -3
    (c) $x = \pm 2.7$

7. (a) $x = \pm 2.8$ (b) $x = \pm 2.2$
    (c) $x = 0$ (d) $x = \pm 2.4$

9. (a) Entries are: 24, 0, 8, 6, 0, -4, 0, 18
    (c) $x = -3$ or 0 or 2

10. (a) Entries are: -6, 8, 10, 6, 2, 4, 18
    (c) $x = -2.7$

Exercise 19.6   Page 204

1. $a = 11.9$

2. (a) $x = 1.7$ (b) $t = 4.1$ (c) $c = 9.7$
    (d) $p = 7.0$ (e) $y = 2.9$ (f) $d = 7.7$

3. (a) $w = 4.2$ (b) $x = 2.3$ (c) $y = 5.1$

Review Exercise 19   Page 205

1. $2a(3a - 1)$

2. (a) $a(2b - 1)$ (b) $3a(a - 2)$

3. $2x^2 + 5x - 12$

4. $6x^2 + 5xy - 4y^2$

5. (a) $3p^2 - 11p - 4$ (b) $p(3p + 5)$

6. (a) $x = 4$ (b) $x = -3$ or 4

7. (a) $(x - 5)(x + 2)$ (b) $x = 0$ or -3

8. (a) $x(x + 3) = 2(x + 1)$ (b) 1 cm

9.

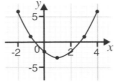

10. (a) Entries are: 1, -3, -2, 6
    (b)

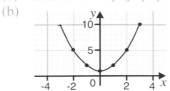

    (c) $x = -0.7$ or 2.7

11. (a) Entries are: 5, 2, 1, 2, 5, 10
    (b)

    (c) $x = \pm 2.8$

12. $x = 2.8$

13. $x = 2.59$

Section Review   Page 206

1. (a) $2a + 1$ (b) $2y^2 - y$

2. (a) $x = 2$ (b) $x = 4$ (c) $x = 12$

3. 6.5

4. 7

5. 7

6. (a) 192
    (b) $C = 5$
    (c) $x = 2$, $y = 7$, $z = 9$
    or $x = 7$, $y = 2$, $z = 9$

7. (a) 10
    (b) 8
    (c) (i) 10   (ii) 55

8. (a) 38   (b) Outside edges $= 4n + 6$

9. (a) wx
    (b) $2w + 2x = 2(w + x)$
    (c) $2(\frac{1}{2}x) + 2x = 48$, $x = 16$

10. (a) $3x$ cm
    (b) (i) $3x + 6$ (ii) $x = 2.5$ (iii) 13.5 cm

515

11. (a) $x = 4$ (b) $n = 7$

12. $x = -2.5$

13. £228.62

14. (a) (i) 31
       (ii) 9th term is 511, work backwards,
          $(1023 - 1) \div 2 = 511$,
          subtract 1, then divide by 2.
     (b) (i) $\frac{31}{32}$
       (ii) denominator = previous
          denominator $\times$ 2 numerator =
          denominator $-$ 1
     (c) $n^2 - 1$

15. (a) $1, -2, -5$
       10th term $= -17$
       n th term : $13 - 3n$
     (b) 26, 37, 50
       10th term $= 101$
       n th term : $n^2 + 1$

16. (a) $\frac{1}{2}, \frac{2}{5}, \frac{3}{10}, \frac{4}{17}, \frac{5}{26}$ (b) $\frac{n}{2n+1}$

17. (a) $3(2p - 1)$ (b) $p(p + 2)$

18. $x = 2.7$

19. (a) (i) 2, 3, 4, 5
       (ii) $-3.08 < x < 3.08$
     (b) $x = 2.8$

20. (b) $x = -1.2$

21. (a) (ii) $x = 2.4$ (b) $x = 3, y = 2$

22. (a) $x = -4$ (b) $x = 2.6, y = -0.8$

23. (b) $x = 1.7$, value of x at point where $y = 2x$
       and $x + y = 5$ intersect.
     (c)

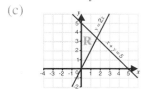

24. (a) 5 hours, £50   (b) VOLTMEND

25. (a) $x = 2, y = 0.5$
     (b) $-3, -2, -1, 0, 1, 2, 3$

26. (a) $x = 4.5$ (b) $x = 2.4, y = 1.6$
     (c) $x < 2.5$ (d)

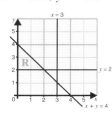

27. (b) $x < 2.5$

28. (a) $x = 2.3, y = 4.3$
     (b) (i)

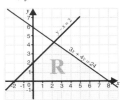

29. (a) $v = 19.4$

30. (a) $4x - 2x^2$
     (b) $7y^2(2x - 3y)$
     (c) $d = \sqrt{\frac{4A}{\pi}} = 2\sqrt{\frac{A}{\pi}}$
     (d) $x \geqslant \pm 5$

31. (a) $-4, -3, -2, -1, 0, 1$
     (b) $x < -0.8$
     (c) $x = \sqrt{\frac{3A-2}{5}}$

32. (a) $\pi r (2r + h)$
     (b) $h = \frac{A - 2\pi r^2}{\pi r}$

33. (a) $r = \sqrt[3]{\frac{3v}{4\pi}}$
     (b) $r = 2.6$

34. Area $= (x - 18)(x - 9)$
        $= x^2 - 27x + 162$

35. (a) $x^2 - 5x + 6$
     (b) $x = 1$ and $x = -8$

36. $(x + 2)(x + 1) = 6$
     $x^2 + 3x - 4 = 0$

Exercise 20.1   Page 212

1. (a) 180°   (b) 90°   (c) 270°
     (d) 90°   (e) 120°   (f) 6°
     (g) 42°   (h) 720°   (i) 540°
     (j) 810°

2. (a) 45°   (b) 315°

3. (a) 45°   (b) 360°

4. acute: A, Q
     right angle: E
     obtuse: B, C, F, H
     reflex: D, I

Exercise 20.2   Page 213

1. (a) 39°   (b) 118°   (c) 42°

2. (a) 217°   (b) 234°

1. (a) $a = 30°$
   (b) $b = 150°$
   (c) $c = 42°$
   (d) $d = 20°$
   (e) $e = 126°$
   (f) $f = 203°$
   (g) $g = 133°, h = 47°$
   (h) $i = 112°$
   (i) $j = 127°, k = 53°, l = 37°$
   (j) $m = 96°$
   (k) $n = 47°, p = 43°$

2. (a) 45°   (b) 30°   (c) 60°
   (d) 36°   (e) 40°   (f) 80°
   (g) 20°   (h) 30°

1. (a) $a = 130°, b = 130°$
   (b) $c = 60°, d = 120°$
   (c) $e = 40°, f = 40°$
   (d) $g = 65°, h = 65°$
   (e) $j = 125°, k = 125°$
   (f) $l = 65°$
   (g) $m = 84°, n = 116°$
   (h) $p = 56°, q = 116°$

2. (a) $a = 63°$
   (b) $b = 68°, c = 112°$
   (c) $d = 87°$
   (d) $e = 124°$
   (e) $f = 74°, g = 106°$
   (f) $h = 52°, i = 128°$
   (g) $j = 61°$
   (h) $k = 270°$

1. $a = \angle QPS$ $d = \angle QRS$
   $b = \angle PQS$ $e = \angle QSR$
   $c = \angle RQS$ $f = \angle PSQ$

2. (a) 93°   (b) 108°   (c) 52°
   (d) 110°   (e) 65°   (f) 295°
   (g) 283°   (h) 326°

3. (a) 132°
   (b) 126°
   (c) 141°
   (d) 85°
   (e) 65°
   (f) $\angle QSP = 105°, \angle STU = 105°$

4. (a) $\angle AOB = 153°, \angle COD = 37°$
   (b) $\angle QTU = 48°, \angle QTS = 132°$
   (c) reflex $\angle TUV = 280°$

1. (a) 45°   (b) 135°   (c) 90°
   (d) 90°   (e) 180°

2. (a) north-west   (b) north-east

3. Entries are: south-east, south-east, south,
   north-west

4. (a) (i)   Bike Hire Centre
          (ii) Bikers' Cafe
          (iii) Bikers' Rest
          (iv) High Peak
   (b) (i)   Highlands
          (ii) north-east
          (iii) Country Garden

1. (a) 065°   (b) 140°   (c) 249°
   (d) 228°   (e) 300°   (f) 090°

2. (b) (i)   230°   (iv) 080°
          (ii) 305°   (v)   125°
          (iii) 015°   (vi) 355°

3. (a) 315°   (b) 135°   (c) 285°
   (d) 105°   (e) 230°   (f) 050°

1. (a) (i)   308°   (ii) 128°
   (b) (i)   4.7 cm   (ii) 47 km

2. (a) 13.5 km   (b) 252°   (c) 072°

3. (a) 8 km   (b) 114°   (c) 296°

4. (a) 6300 km   (b) 248°

5. (a) 50 km   (b) 347°   (c) 167°

1. (a) (i) d (ii) a, c (iii) b (iv) e, f
   (b) $a = 106°, b = 90°, c = 111°,$
       $d = 53°, e = 307°, f = 254°$

2.

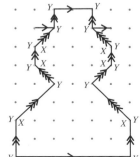

3. (a) 120°   (b) 540°   (c)

4. (a) $x = 30°$ (b) $y = 30°$ (c) $z = 80°$

5. (a) (i) 153°   (ii) 63°
    (b) $\angle BOQ$

6. (a) 53°   (b) 37°

7. (a) 080°   (b) 310°

8. (a) 236°   (b) 36 km

9. (a) 020°

10. (b) 245°
    (c) (i) 64 km   (ii) 197°

Exercise 21.1   Page 229

1. (a) yes   (b) yes   (c) no
    (d) no   (e) yes   (f) no

2. (a) yes, obtuse-angled
    (b) no
    (c) yes, acute-angled
    (d) yes, right-angled
    (e) yes, obtuse-angled

3. (a) $a = 70°$ (b) $b = 37°$
    (c) $c = 114°$ (d) $d = 43°$
    (e) $e = 63°$ (f) $f = 13°$

Exercise 21.2   Page 230

1. (a) $a = 120°$ (b) $b = 110°$
    (c) $c = 50°$ (d) $d = 80°$
    (e) $e = 88°$ (f) $f = 55°$

Exercise 21.3   Page 231

1. ΔABE, ΔBCE, ΔCDE

2. (a) $\angle ACB$ (b) $\angle ADB$ (c) $\angle DBE$

3. (b) (i) acute-angled, scalene
      (ii) right angled, scalene
      (iii) acute-angled, isosceles
      (iv) obtuse-angled, isosceles

4. $AC = BC$, $\angle CAB = \angle CBA$

5. Any point on the line $y = x$, except (1.5, 1.5)

6. (6, 2), (6, 8)

7. $a = 40°$ $f = 144°$
   $b = 120°$ $g = 85°$
   $c = 62°$ $h = 116°$
   $d = 128°$ $i = 26.5°$
   $e = 18°$ $j = 153.5°$

8. (a) $\angle BCD = 120°$
    (b) $\angle PRQ = 80°$, $\angle QRS = 160°$
    (c) $\angle MNX = 50°$

Exercise 21.4   Page 234

4. (b) 9.3 cm   (c) 39°

Exercise 21.5   Page 235

1. (a) $a = 90°$, $b = 50°$
    (b) $c = 12°$
    (c) $d = 62°$
    (d) $e = 40°$, $f = 54°$
    (e) $g = 70°$
    (f) $h = 45°$

Exercise 21.6   Page 236

1. (a) 13 cm
    (b) 13.3 cm
    (c) 19.9 cm

2. $\Delta PQR = 33$ cm, $\Delta QRS = 32$ cm,
   $\Delta RST = 35$ cm; ΔRST

3. (a) $a = 7$ cm   (b) $b = 5$ cm
    (c) $c = 8$ cm   (d) $d = 3.8$ cm
    (e) $e = 7.8$ cm   (f) $f = 1$ cm

4. (a) 9 cm²   (b) 6 cm²
    (c) 7.2 cm²   (d) 3.8 cm²
    (e) 4.16 cm²   (f) 11.52 cm²

5. (a) $h = 6$ cm
    (b) $h = 12$ cm
    (c) $h = 4$ cm

6. (a) $a = 8$ cm
    (b) $b = 4$ cm
    (c) $c = 16$ cm

7. 67.5 cm²

8. 30 cm

Review Exercise 21   Page 238

1. (a) B
    (b) Angles total 170°, so b should be 35°.

2. (a) $\angle CDA = 53°$
    (b) $\angle BAC = 50°$

3. (a) $\angle BCA = 36°$, ΔABC is isosceles
    (b) (i) $\angle CAE = 65°$, ΔAEC is right-angled
        (ii) $\angle CDY = 65°$

4. $x = 20°$, $\angle DAC = 40°$

5. (a) $\angle BAC = 50°$, ΔAEC is isosceles,
        $\angle EAC = \angle ACE$
    (b) $\angle AEC = 80°$, sum of angles in a
        triangle $= 180°$

6. (a) $x = 29°$, ΔAPB is right-angled
    (b) $y = 61°$, ΔABC is isosceles

8. (b) $103°$

9. (a) $\angle DCA = 50°$
    (b) (i) $\angle BAC$
        (ii)   alternate angles, BA is parallel to CD
    (c) $\angle ABC = 65°$

10. $14\,cm^2$

11. (a) $120\,cm^2$ (b) $72°$

12. (a) $45\,cm$ (b) $75\,cm^2$ (c) $10\,cm$

Exercise **22.1**   **Page 241**

3. (a) 2   (b)   2   (c) 0
    (d) 5   (e)   3   (f) 0

4. 1, 1, 1, 2, 0, 0, infinite

Exercise **22.2**   **Page 243**

1. (a) 2   (b) 3   (c) 4
    (d) 2   (e) 6   (f) 8

2. (a) MY   (b) NZ
    (c) NXZ   (d) JP

3. (a) 1

4. (a) 1
    (b) (ii)   3

5. (a) (i)   0   (ii) 2
    (b) (i)   1   (ii) 1
    (c) (i)   2   (ii) 2
    (d) (i)   0   (ii) 4
    (e) (i)   1   (ii) 1

Exercise **22.3**   **Page 245**

1. 9

2. (a) 4   (b) 4   (c) 2   (d) infinite

3. (a) 2   (b) 2   (c) 4

4. (a) 1   (b) 1, 4

5. (a) 4   (b) 4

Exercise **22.4**   **Page 246**

1. A, O   F, L
    C, G   H, J
    D, P

Exercise **22.5**   **Page 247**

1. No lengths given, one triangle is larger than
    the other

2. (a) Yes, ASA   (b) No
    (c) Yes, SAS   (d) Yes, SSS
    (e) No   (f) Yes, RHS
    (g) Yes, SAS   (h) No
    (i) Yes, ASA

3. (a) No   (b) No
    (c) Yes, RHS   (d) No
    (e) Yes, ASA   (f) Yes, ASA
    (g) Yes, SSS   (h) Yes, SAS
    (i) Yes, ASA

4. $DE = PQ$ (given)
    $DF = PR$ (given)
    $\angle EDF = \angle QPR$ (70°)
    Congruent, SAS

5. (a) $\angle BDC = 25°$
    (b) BD is common
        $AB = CD$ (7 cm)
        $\angle ABD = \angle BDC$ (alt. $\angle$s)
        Congruent, SAS
    (c) $\angle ADB$

Review Exercise **22**   **Page 248**

1. (a) A   (b) C

2. B

3. I

4.

5. (a)

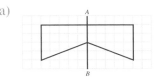

    (b)

    (c) 2

6. (a) No line symmetry,
Rotational symmetry order 4

7. X2, Y4, Z1

9.

10. (a) *CDE* (b) *CEF* (c) *CDEF*

11. *B* and *D*, SAS.

Exercise **23.1**
Page 253

1. (b) (i) isosceles trapezium
(ii) parallelogram
(iii) rhombus
(iv) kite
(v) square

2. *S* (3, 2)

3. *C* (5, 4)

4. *Y* (6, 4)

5. *A* (1, 3)

6. *L* (2, 3)

7. (a) $a = 62°$
(b) $b = 54°, c = 36°$
(c) $d = 62°$
(d) $e = 116°, f = 86°$
(e) $g = 124°$
(f) $h = 75°$
(g) $i = 38°, j = 42°$
(h) $k = 55°, l = 45°$

8. (b) 2 (c) 2

9.

A	B	C	D	E	F	G	H	I
1	0	1	4	2	2	0	0	1
1	1	1	4	2	2	1	2	1

10. (a) C (b) D (c) E
(d) A (e) B (f) G

Exercise **23.2**
Page 257

1.
A	8 cm²	E	8 cm²
B	12 cm²	F	15 cm²
C	8 cm²	G	6 cm²
D	9 cm²	H	4 cm²

2. (a) 12.25 cm² (b) 3.92 cm²
(c) 4.68 cm² (d) 12.24 cm²
(e) 4.35 cm² (f) 5.75 cm²

3. 14 m²

4. 84 cm²

5. 6 m²

6. 64 cm²

7. 4 cm

8. 8 cm

9. 4 cm

10. $h = 5.4$ cm, $l = 9$ cm

11. (a) $a = 4$ cm (b) $b = 5$ cm
(c) $c = 10$ cm (d) $d = 4$ cm
(e) $e = 3$ cm (f) $f = 11$ cm
(g) $g = 8$ cm (h) $h = 10$ cm
(i) $i = 8$ cm (j) $j = 2$ cm

Review Exercise **23**
Page 260

1. (a) 360°
(b) (i) kite
(ii) $n = 85°, s = 42°$

2. $∠BDA = 40°, ∠ABD = 90°$

3. (a) isosceles trapezium
(b)

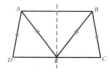

(c) $∠AED$ (alt. $∠$s)
$∠ABE$ (ΔABE is isoceles)

4. (a) (i) 70° ($∠QPR = ∠QRP = ∠SQR$)
(ii) 30°
(b) kite
(c) (i) 2 (ii) rhombus (iii) 30°

5. (a) (i) 52° (ii) alternate angles
(b) 116°

6. (a) Missing entries: 16 cm, 9 cm²
(b) 8 cm, 32 cm

7. (a)

(b) 2 (c) 23 cm² (d) 3.2 cm

8. (a) 5 m (b) kite (c) 28°

9. 15.75 cm²

10. 15.6 cm²

11. 5 cm

12. (a) $a = 12$ cm
(b) $b = 8.75$ cm
(c) $c = 7.2$ cm

13. (a) 25 cm² (b) 12.54 cm² (c) 50.16%

Exercise 24.1 — Page 264

1. (a) 900° (b) 1080° (c) 1260°

2. (a) $a = 80°$ (b) $b = 70°$
   (c) $c = 85°$ (d) $d = 120°$
   (e) $e = 130°$ (f) $f = 250°$
   (g) $g = 60°$ (h) $h = 199°$
   (i) $i = 45°$

Exercise 24.2 — Page 265

1. (a) 72° (b) 108° (c) 540°

2. (a) (i) 120° (b) (i) 60°
       (ii) 90°   (ii) 90°
       (iii) 60°   (iii) 120°
       (iv) 45°   (iv) 135°

3. 20

4. (a) 40 (b) 15 (c) 9 (d) 6

5. 8

6. (a) 5 (b) 20 (c) 40 (d) 4

7. $a = 150°$ $b = 105°$
   $c = 126°$ $d = 156°$
   $e = 66°$ $f = 96°$
   $g = 132°$ $h = 102°$

8. (a) 720° (b) 1080° (c) 1440°

9. $y = 180 - \dfrac{360}{x}$

10. (a) 234° (b) 306°

Exercise 24.3 — Page 267

4. At any vertex, sum of angles cannot equal 360°.

5. (b) hexagons and equilateral triangles, squares and equilateral triangles, dodecagons and equilateral triangles.

7. Yes, all quadrilaterals tessellate.
   (a) (i) Yes (ii) Yes

Review Exercise 24 — Page 269

1. (a) pentagon (b) (i) $w = 50°$
                    (ii) $x = 40°$
                    (iii) $y = 80°$
                    (iv) $z = 50°$

2. (a) $\angle ABC = 108°$
   (b) $\angle CAE = 72°$
   (c) $\angle AEX = 72°$

3. (a) $p = 45°$ (b) $q = 135°$

4. (a) regular hexagon
   (b) $x = 60°$
   (c) 720°

5. (a) Line of symmetry is a perpendicular bisector.
   (b) $y = 45°$ (c) $z = 125°$

6. (a) x = 22.5° (isoscelesΔ)
   (b) isosceles trapezium

7. (a) 135°
   (b) 225° clockwise or 135° anticlockwise

8. (a) hexagon : 6, 9
       heptagon : 7, 4
   (b) 35

9. $a = 120°$, $b = 225°$, $c = 240°$,

10. (a) $a = 120°$, $b = 135°$
    (b) Interior angles are each 108°. 360 is not a multiple of 108.

Exercise 25.1 — Page 274

1.

Radius (cm)	Diameter (cm)	Circumference (cm)
4	8	24
10	20	60
15	30	90
12	24	72
20	40	120
35	70	210

2. (a) 31.4 cm (b) 22.0 cm (c) 47.1 cm

3. (a) 25.1 m (b) 28.3 m (c) 101 m

4. (a) 20.6 cm (b) 26.8 m

5. 75.4 cm

6. 57.5 m

8. 18.9 cm

9. (a) 188 cm (b) 283 cm

10. 31.4 m

11. 60 cm

12. 3.8 cm

13. 30 mm

14. 13.3 cm

1.

Radius (cm)	Diameter (cm)	Area (cm²)
5	10	75
4	8	48
3	6	27
8	16	192
10	20	300

2.　(a)　1020 cm²　(b)　18.1 cm²
　　(c)　1960 cm²　(d)　55.4 km²
　　(e)　0.503 cm²　(f)　105 000 m²

3.　22 200 cm²

4.　21.5 cm²

5.　(a)　157 cm²　(b)　38.5 m²

6.　(a)　707 cm²　(b)　94. 2 cm

7.　(a)　37.7 m　(b)　17

1.　(a)　134 m²　(b)　588 cm²　(c)　450 km²

2.　(a)　360 cm²　(b)　1104 cm²　(c)　480 cm²

3.　58 cm²

4.　(a)　129 cm²　(b)　41.1 cm²　(c)　116 m²

5.　(a)　0.383 m²　(b)　3.26 m

6.　13.7 cm², 25.1 cm

7.　A　14.1 cm²　　B　25.1 cm²
　　C　39.3 cm²　　A + B = C

1.　8510 cm²

2.　(a)　980 m²　(b)　700 m²　(c)　1700 m²

3.　9.9 cm²

4.　(a)　50.3 cm²　(b)　40.6 cm

5.　(a)　151 inches　(b)　1670 square inches

6.　(a)　38.5 cm²　(b)　3.82 cm

7.　1330

8.　(a)　39.8　(b)　47.1 cm　(c)　3217 cm²

9.　(a)　113 square inches
　　(b)　(i)　300　(ii)　14 100 square inches

10.　(a)　50.9 cm　(b)　380 cm²

6.　Circle

5.　Perpendicular bisectors pass through the centre of the circle.

7. 　　**8.**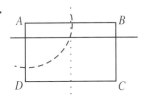

9. 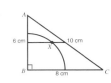　　**10.**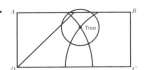

1.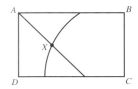

2.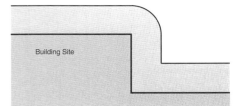

3.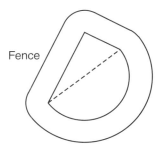

4.

　　(a)　A and B, any points on the dotted line
　　(b)　Dotted line.

5.

6. y = 3

7.

Exercise **27.2**   Page 292

2. (a) scale factor 3, centre (0, 0)
   (b) scale factor 3, centre (5, 0)
   (c) scale factor 2.5, centre (0, 5)

3. (a) scale factor 2   (b) scale factor 2

Exercise **27.3**   Page 293

3. (a) scale factor $\frac{1}{3}$, centre (5, 7)
   (b) scale factor $\frac{1}{3}$, centre (1, 7)
   (c) scale factor $\frac{2}{5}$, centre (5, 5)
   (d) scale factor $\frac{2}{5}$, centre (5, 0)
   (e) scale factor $\frac{1}{3}$, centre (0, 7)

Exercise **27.4**   Page 296

1. (a) $x = 1.5$, $y = 2.4$, $a = 70°$
   (b) $x = 5$, $y = 1.5$, $a = 53°$
   (c) $x = 30$, $y = 20.8$, $z = 10$

2. 15 cm   **4.** 5 cm

3. 3 cm   **5.** $x = 16$, $y = 48$

Exercise **27.5**   Page 298

1. (a) $x = 10$, $y = 27$
   (b) $x = 6$, $y = 10$
   (c) $x = 12$, $y = 12$
   (d) $x = 12$, $y = 5$

2. (a) $AB = 2.96$ cm, $QR = 3.25$ cm
   (b) $XZ = 14.4$ m, $BC = 6.25$ m
   (c) $EG = 1.6$ cm, $MN = 4.0$ cm
   (d) $AC = 4.0$ m, $XZ = 2.0$ m

3. $AB = 8$, $AE = 5$

4. (a) $AB = 6$
   (b) $BC = 7.5$, $AC = 6.9$
   (c) $EC = 4.6$

5. (a) $PR = 10$
   (b) $QR = 5$, $PQ = 7.5$, $QS = 4.5$

6. $GH = 6$, $FH = 3$

Exercise **27.6**   Page 300

1. (a) $AC = 2.4$ cm, $AP = 2.2$ cm
   (b) $AC = 4.5$ cm, $BP = 1$ cm
   (c) $BC = 4.2$ cm, $BP = 1.6$ cm
   (d) $AP = 2.5$ cm, $BC = 7$ cm
   (e) $AP = 4\frac{2}{3}$ cm, $BQ = 16\frac{2}{3}$ cm

2. (a) $x = 58°$ (b) $x = 56°$

3. (a) $61°$ (b) $29°$

4. (a) $QR = 7.2$ cm, $QY = 0.4$ cm
   (b) $PR = 3.6$ cm, $QY = 10.7$ cm
   (c) $YZ = 12$ cm, $PR = 9$ cm
   (d) $YZ = 3.8$ cm, $QY = 2.7$ cm

Review Exercise **27**   Page 302

3. 11.2 cm

4. (a) 3.6 cm   (b) 3.8 cm   (c) $\theta = 105°$

5. $XY = 59.5$

6. (a) $x = 4.5$ (b) $y = 10$ (c) $z = 46°$

7. 64 m

8. $AB = 10$ cm

9. (a) $DE = 4.5$ cm   (b) $AC = 12$ cm

10. No. Not *all* corresponding lengths are in the same ratio.

11. (a) $BC = 1.73$ cm
   (b) (i) $\angle A$ is common
           $\angle AEB = \angle ACD$ (given)
           Triangles AEB and ACD are similar, equal angles.
     (ii) $ED = 5.5$ cm

Exercise **28.1**   Page 306

1. (a) 4   (b) 2 faces overlap

Exercise **28.2**   Page 308

1. (a) (i)   8   (b) (i)   24 cm²
      (ii)   27   (ii)   54 cm²
      (iii)   64   (iii)   96 cm²
      (iv)   125   (iv)   150 cm²

2. (a) 27 cm³, 54 cm²
(b) 24 cm³, 52 cm²
(c) 140 cm³, 166 cm²

3. (a) 150 cm³, 190 cm²
(b) 51.84 cm³, 89.28 cm²
(c) 19 440 cm³, 4644 cm²
(d) 96.8 cm³, 131.5 cm²
(e) 916.1 cm³, 611.7 cm²

Exercise 28.3 — Page 310

1. (a) 40 cm³ (b) 140 cm³ (c) 52.8 cm³

2. (a) 6 cm², 24 cm³ (b) 8 cm², 24 cm³

3. (a) 36 cm³ (b) 56 cm³ (c) 330 cm³
(d) 113 cm³ (e) 393 cm³ (f) 120 cm³
(g) 848 cm³ (h) 48 cm³

4. P

5. 10 cm

6. 4.5 cm

7. 11.5 cm

8. 2.7 cm

Exercise 28.4 — Page 312

1. (a) 339 cm² (b) 90.9 cm²

3. (a) 1260 cm²
(b) 6280 cm²
(c) 62 800 cm³

4. (a) 14 100 cm² (b) 18 800 cm²

Review Exercise 28 — Page 314

1. (a) 207 cm²

2. (a)

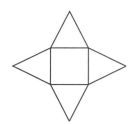

(b) (ii) 55°

3. 4.752 m³

4. (a) 31.2 cm² (b) 100 cm³

5. (a) 19.6 cm² (b) 1960 cm³

6. (a) 9 m² (b) 135 m³

7. (a) 6 (b) 9 cm

8. (a) 462 cm³ (b) 3 cm

9. 1890 cm³

10. (a) 2640 cm³ (b) 5.9 cm

11. (a) 66.4° (b) 10.1 m³

Exercise 29.1 — Page 318

1. (a) 10 cm (b) 25 cm (c) 26 cm

2. (a) 7.8 cm (b) 12.8 cm (c) 10.3 cm

3. 7.3 cm

4. (a) 7.21 cm (b) 4.47 cm

Exercise 29.2 — Page 319

1. (a) 8 cm (b) 6 cm (c) 2 cm

2. (a) 6.9 cm (b) 10.9 cm (c) 9.5 cm

3. 339 m

4. 36 cm²

5. 3.6 cm

Exercise 29.3 — Page 321

1. (a) 9.4 cm (b) 4.6 cm (c) 5.7 cm
(d) 2.9 cm (e) 2.1 cm (f) 2.0 cm

2. 17 cm

3. 10 cm

4. 8.5 cm

5. 10.6 cm

6. 15 cm

7. 6.9 cm

8. 74.3 cm

9. 13 cm

10. 24 cm

Review Exercise 29 — Page 322

1. (a) 2.95 m (b) X

2. 28.3 km

3. 728 m

4. 94.3 cm

5. 10.4 cm

6. (a) 64 cm²   (b) 6.93 cm

7. 8.60

8. 17.3 m

9. (a) 8.60 cm   (b) 10.9 cm

10. 4.24 cm

11. 361 m

12. 17.7 km

13. 155 m

Exercise 30.1   Page 326

1. (a) $h = 2.27$ m
   (b) $h = 4.02$ m
   (c) $h = 8.02$ m

2. (a) $x = 1.50$ cm
   (b) $x = 2.99$ cm
   (c) $x = 5.78$ cm

3. (a) $BC = 3.39$ m
   (b) $AC = 11.4$ m
   (c) $BC = 4.74$ cm
   (d) $\angle ABC = 55°$, $AC = 6.96$ cm

Exercise 30.2   Page 327

1. (a) $a = 62.1°$
   (b) $a = 25.0°$
   (c) $a = 50.9°$

2. (a) $x = 52.3°$
   (b) $x = 60.5°$
   (c) $x = 61.4°$

3. (a) $\angle QPR = 23.6°$
   (b) $\angle PRQ = 64.7°$
   (c) $\angle QPR = 21.8°$
   (d) $\angle QRP = 24.0°$, $\angle QPR = 66.0°$

Exercise 30.3   Page 328

1. (a) $l = 7.00$ m
   (b) $l = 7.49$ m
   (c) $l = 4.93$ m

2. (a) $x = 6.49$ cm
   (b) $x = 5.31$ cm
   (c) $x = 10.61$ cm

3. (a) $AB = 7.62$ m
   (b) $AB = 17.5$ cm
   (c) $AB = 66.9$ cm
   (d) $\angle ABC = 17.2°$, $AB = 25.7$ m

Exercise 30.4   Page 330

1.

	$\sin p$	$\cos p$	$\tan p$
(a)	$\frac{5}{13}$	$\frac{12}{13}$	$\frac{5}{12}$
(b)	$\frac{7}{25}$	$\frac{24}{25}$	$\frac{7}{24}$
(c)	$\frac{4}{5}$	$\frac{3}{5}$	$\frac{4}{3}$

2. (a) $p = 40.9°$ (b) $p = 38.0°$
   (c) $p = 38.8°$ (d) $p = 53.3°$
   (e) $p = 39.7°$ (f) $p = 35.5°$

3. (a) $a = 5.77$ cm   (b) $a = 6.47$ cm
   (c) $a = 4.18$ cm   (d) $a = 3.78$ cm
   (e) $a = 4.72$ cm   (f) $a = 4.04$ cm

4. 4.33 cm

5. 72.5°, 72.5°, 34.9°

Exercise 30.5   Page 332

1. 21.4 m

2. 40.1 m

3. (a) 135 m   (b) 53.5°

4. 222 m

5. 31.0°

Exercise 30.6   Page 333

1. (a) 152 km   (b) 199 km

2. 22.2 km

3. 145°

4. 41.9 km

5. 164°

6. 6.40 km

7. 174 km

8. 283°

Review Exercise 30   Page 334

1. 3.25 m

2. (a) 34.9°   (b) 154 cm

3. 14.0 m

4. 3.22 m

5. (a) 9.64 cm   (b) 51.3°

6. (a) 5.46 m   (b) 64.1°

7. (a) 3620 m   (b) 3.9°

8. (a) (i) $\frac{5}{12}$ (ii) $\frac{5}{13}$
  (b) 6.5 cm, 2.5 cm

9. (a) 2.5 m
  (b) (i) 5.00 m   (ii) Safe, 78.5°

10. (a) 47.7 km   (b) 197.7 km, 069°

11. 21.3 m

Exercise **31.1**   Page 338

5. (a) (3, −4)   (b) (−3, 4)
  (c) (5, 4)   (d) (−5, 4)
  (e) (4, 3)

Exercise **31.2**   Page 340

3. (a) (4, −3)   (b) (−4, 3)
  (c) (−3, −4)   (d) (6, 1)
  (e) (0, 1)   (f) (3, −2)

Exercise **31.3**   Page 341

2. (a) (5, 5)   (b) (1, 6)
  (c) (4, 1)   (d) (1, 1)

3. T (7, 2)

4. (a) $\begin{pmatrix} 2 \\ 1 \end{pmatrix}$ (b) $\begin{pmatrix} 1 \\ -2 \end{pmatrix}$

  (c) $\begin{pmatrix} -3 \\ 1 \end{pmatrix}$ (d) $\begin{pmatrix} -3 \\ -2 \end{pmatrix}$

5. (b) $\begin{pmatrix} -3 \\ -2 \end{pmatrix}$

Exercise **31.4**   Page 342

4. (a) (6, 8)   (b) (9, 12)   (c) (6, 6)
  (d) (3, 10)   (e) (5, 5)   (f) (5, 4)

Exercise **31.5**   Page 344

1. L_1 reflection in the x axis ($y = 0$)
  L_2 rotation, 90° anticlockwise, about (0, 0)

  L_3 translation $\begin{pmatrix} 3 \\ 2 \end{pmatrix}$

  L_4 reflection in $y = -x$
  L_5 reflection in $x = 7$
  L_6 rotation, 180°, about (6, 0)

2. (a) translation $\begin{pmatrix} -7 \\ -4 \end{pmatrix}$

  (b) reflection in $y = -x$
  (c) rotation, 90° anticlockwise, about (1, 0)

3. (a) reflection in $x = -1$
  (b) rotation, 90° clockwise, about (1, −2)

  (c) translation $\begin{pmatrix} 5 \\ 1 \end{pmatrix}$

4. enlargement, scale factor 2, centre (1, 2)

5. enlargement, scale factor $\frac{1}{2}$, centre (0, 0)

Exercise **31.6**   Page 346

1. (c) $\begin{pmatrix} 8 \\ 0 \end{pmatrix}$

2. (c) rotation, 90° anticlockwise, about (5, 5)

3. (d) rotation, 90° anticlockwise, about (0, 0)

4. (c) rotation, 180°, about (1, −1)

5. translation $\begin{pmatrix} -4 \\ 3 \end{pmatrix}$

6. translation $\begin{pmatrix} 6 \\ 0 \end{pmatrix}$

Review Exercise **31**   Page 348

1. (c) reflection in $y = x$

2. rotation, 90° clockwise, about B (4, 4)

4. (a) reflection in $y = x$
  (b) enlargement, scale factor 2,
    centre (−7, 1)

5. (a) C_1 (−2, 5)
  (b) C_2 (−1, 4)
  (c) C_3 (9, 7)

6. (a) reflection in y axis (x = 0)
  (b) rotation, 90° clockwise, about (0, 0)

7. (a) enlargement, scale factor $\frac{1}{2}$, centre (0, 1)

  (d) translation $\begin{pmatrix} 4 \\ 0 \end{pmatrix}$

8. (b) translation $\begin{pmatrix} -3 \\ 1 \end{pmatrix}$

9. (c) rotation, 90° clockwise, about (0, 0)

10. (d) rotation, 90° anticlockwise, about (1, 3).

Exercise **32.1**   Page 354

3. (a) 3.123 m   (b) 450 cm
  (c) 3240 km   (d) 1 000 000 g
  (e) 0.4 l

2. 1.98 l

3. 20

4. 50 ml

5. 80 g

6. 60

7. (a) 22 pounds   (b) 35 pints
    (c) 195 inches   (d) 150 mm
    (e) 20 inches

8. 22 pounds

9. 170 cm

10. 66.4 kg

11. (a) 610 m   (b) 4.8 km
    (c) 5.57 feet   (d) 2.75 pounds

12. 1500 cm²

Exercise 32.2   Page 355

2. 6.4 m, nearest 0.1 m

3. 72 kg, nearest kilogram

4. 175 ml, nearest 5 ml

5. (a) 12 m, nearest metre
       5.9 m, nearest 10 cm
       5 l, nearest litre
       500 m², nearest 50 m²
    (b) 1200 cm, nearest 100 cm
       5900 mm, nearest 100 mm
       5000 ml, nearest 1000 ml
       500 000 000 mm², nearest 50 000 000 mm²

Exercise 32.3   Page 356

1. 3.35 kg, nearest 10 g

2. (a) 156 cm³, nearest cm³
    (b) 705 ft³, nearest ft³

3. 6.6 m³, 1 d.p.

4. 33.5 m², nearest 0.1 m²

5. (a) 48 km/hour
    (b) 80 km/hour
    (c) 108 km/hour

6. (a) 37.5 miles per hour
    (b) 90 miles per hour

7. 5×10^7 kg/m³

8. (a) 12.8 km/litre
    (b) 30 miles per gallon

9. (a) 79 miles per hour
    (b) 126.4 km/hour

10. 0850

Exercise 32.4   Page 358

1. (a) continuous   (b) discrete
    (c) discrete   (d) continuous
    (e) discrete   (f) continuous

2. (a) exact
    (b) 4.5 mins $\leq t < $ 5.5 mins
    (c) exact
    (d) 62.5 kg $\leq w < $ 63.5 kg
    (e) 152.5 cm $\leq J < $ 153.5 cm

3. (a) 12.5 s $\leq t < $ 13.5 s
    (b) 82.55 s $\leq t < $ 82.65 s

4. (a) nearest 0.01 m (centimetre)
    (b) 1.525 m $\leq h < $ 1.535 m

5. (a) 61.5 kg
    (b) 2.25 m
    (c) 12.625 s

6. (a) nearest 10 m
    (b) nearest 50 m
    (c) nearest 100 m

Exercise 32.5   Page 360

1. (a) area   (b) length
    (c) length   (d) length
    (e) volume   (f) area
    (g) volume   (h) area

2. (a) perimeter   (b) area
    (c) volume   (d) none
    (e) area   (f) perimeter
    (g) perimeter   (h) none
    (i) volume   (j) volume
    (k) none   (l) area

3. (a) (i) $2\pi (x + y)$
    (b) (ii) $\pi (x^2 + y^2)$, πxy

5. $\frac{1}{2} pqs$, volume
    $2 (p + q + r + \frac{3s}{2})$, edge length
    $s (p + q + r) + pq$, surface area

6. (a) correct   (b) correct   (c) correct
    (d) wrong   (e) correct   (f) wrong

7. (a), (b), (c), (e)

Review Exercise 32   Page 361

1. (a) 0.18 m   (b) 3 mm

2. 75

3. 55

4. 200

5. 25

6. 2.763 kg

8. (a)   10 000 m
   (b) $\frac{3}{8}$ inch

9. (a)   10 pounds
   (b)   4.5 l

10. Taller Tim by about 10 cm,
   heavier Sam by about 2.6 kg

11. (a)   1.925 25 kg
   (b)   (i)   1.93 kg   (ii)   nearest 10 g

12. (a)   250 000 cm²
   (b)   270 square feet

13. 44 feet per second

14. Both same speed

15. (a)   130 m²
   (b)   1.3 litres

16. nearest 1 million square kilometres

18. (a)   continuous
   (b)   discrete

19. 135 tonnes

20. (a)   0.1 s   (b)   24.5 cm

21. Any volume from 645 ml up to, but not
   including 650 ml

22. (a)   (i)   950 m, 1050 m
      (ii)   995 m, 1005 m
      (iii)   999.5 m, 1000.5 m
      (iv)   999.95 m, 1000.05 m
   (b)   (i)   4500 gallons, 5500 gallons
      (ii)   4950 gallons, 5050 gallons
      (iii)   4995 gallons, 5005 gallons
      (iv)   4999.5 gallons, 5000.5 gallons
   (c)   (i)   19.5 s, 20.5 s
      (ii)   19.95 s, 20.05 s
      (iii)   19.995 s, 20.005 s
   (d)   (i)   750 kg, 1250 kg
      (ii)   975 kg, 1025 kg
      (iii)   997.5 kg, 1002.5 kg
      (iv)   990 kg, 1010 kg
      (v)   900 kg, 1100 kg

23. 11.2 r^2

25. In order: length, volume, area

26. (a) $ab, 4\pi rl$

27. Entries are: volume, length, area, volume

1. (b) $\angle ACB = 48°$

2. (a) $z = 180 - (65 + 55) = 60$, sum of
      angles in a triangle $= 180$
   (b)   (i) $x = 55°$ (ii)   Alt. $\angle$ to $\angle B$
   (c) $y = 35°$

3. (a) $x = 80°$ (b) $y = 100°$

4. (a)   P

5. (a)   12.25 cm²   (b)   7 cm²   (c)   40.25 cm²

6. Clara: 5 foot 2 inches $= 157.36$ cm
   Clara is taller.

7. (a)   159.9 cm to 1 dp.   (b)   63.5 kg to 1 dp.

9. (a)   12 cm³

10. (a)   188 cm   (b)   3 complete turns

11. (b)   2.88 m²   (c)   1.13 m²

12. (a) $a = 120°$ (b) $b = 135°$

13. (a) $x = 45°$ (b) $y = 67.5°$

14. (a) $a = 110°$ (b) $\angle CEA = 70°$

15. 250 000 mm²

16. (a)   720 cm³   (b)   6 boxes   (c)   9.0 cm

17. (a)   5.50 m³   (b)   8.64 m²

18. (a)   5.7 cm   (b)   103 cm²

19. 83.5 m, 82.5 m

20.

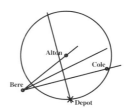

22. (a)   (i)   Enlargement, scale factor 2, centre
         (0, 0)
      (ii)   Rotation, 90° anticlockwise, about
         (3, 1)
   (b)   Translation by vector $\begin{pmatrix} 5 \\ 0 \end{pmatrix}$
   (c)   Triangle A and any other triangle.

23. (a) $(-1, 0)$ (b)   90° anticlockwise

24. (b) A_1 (1, 2), B_1 (1, 4), C_1 (2, 4)
   (c) A_2 (1, -2), B_2 (1, -4), C_2 (2, -4)
   (d)   Rotation, 90° clockwise, about (0, 0)

25. (a) (i) 26 cm (ii) 22.6°
(b) 37.5 cm

26. (a) 25.0 m (b) 50.2°

27. (a) 104.4 m
(b) Not suitable. Angle $BCE = 16.7°$

28. (a) $AB = 20$ cm (b) $\angle QPA = 65°$

29. (a) $AB = 3.6$ cm (b) $\angle QRS = 153°$

30. 299°

31. (a) $2(a + b + c) + 3d$
(b) $ad + bd + cd + ab$
(c) $\frac{1}{2} abd$

32. πab, $\pi (a + b)l$

Exercise 33.1 — Page 372

1. qualitative

2. quantitative, continuous

3. quantitative, discrete

4. qualitative

5. quantitative, discrete

6. quantitative, continuous

7. quantitative, discrete

8. qualitative

9. quantitative, discrete

10. quantitative, continuous

Exercise 33.2 — Page 374

1. (a)

Colour of car	Colour of car
Black	1
Blue	9
Green	4
Grey	2
Red	11
Silver	4
White	9
Total	40

(b) red

2. (a)

Day	Frequency
Monday	8
Tuesday	7
Wednesday	6
Thursday	7
Friday	7
Saturday	3
Sunday	5
Total	43

(b) 10 years
(c) 10
(d) 11
(e) 8

4. (a)

Height h cm	Frequency
$145 \leqslant h < 150$	2
$150 \leqslant h < 155$	2
$155 \leqslant h < 160$	7
$160 \leqslant h < 165$	9
$165 \leqslant h < 170$	6
$170 \leqslant h < 175$	8
$175 \leqslant h < 180$	2
Total	36

(b) 5 cm
(c) 7
(d) 11
(e) 32

Exercise 33.3 — Page 376

1. (a) Wendy
(b) F
(c) Tony and Mark 180 cm,
Peter and Jane 168 cm
(d) 5
(e) Mary, Jim, Wendy, Beryl
(f) 20 beats per minute

2. (a) (i)

Make	Frequency
Ford	4
Nissan	3
Vauxhall	5
Total	12

Colour	Frequency
Blue	2
Green	1
Grey	2
Red	3
White	4
Total	12

Registration letter	Frequency
L	2
M	3
N	2
P	4
R	1
Total	12

(ii)

Mileage (m)	Frequency
$0 \leqslant m < 5000$	0
$5000 \leqslant m < 10\,000$	2
$10\,000 \leqslant m < 15\,000$	0
$15\,000 \leqslant m < 20\,000$	2
$20\,000 \leqslant m < 25\,000$	1
$25\,000 \leqslant m < 30\,000$	2
$30\,000 \leqslant m < 35\,000$	4
$35\,000 \leqslant m < 40\,000$	1
Total	12

(b) (i) Vauxhall (ii) 2 (iii) 5 (iv) 4

Exercise 33.4   Page 378

1. (a) Too open
   (b) Too open
   (c) Leading

2. (a) Too personal
   (b) Too open
   (c) Too open
   (d) Too open

Exercise 33.6   Page 380

1. Disprove, Boys $\frac{3}{21} = \frac{1}{7}$, Girls $\frac{2}{14} = \frac{1}{7}$, same proportion

2. (a) 20
   (b) 27
   (c) Prove, Maths ABC = 27,
       English ABC = 32, English > Maths

3. (a) (i) 10
       (ii) No. Less 8, More 12
   (b) (i) 37
       (ii) No. Girls 37, Boys 37, same

4. Fewer females than males, no-one under 18.

Review Exercise 33   Page 381

1. (a) 2   (b) Russia

2.

Weight (g)	Frequency
$80 \leqslant g < 120$	7
$120 \leqslant g < 180$	9
$180 \leqslant g < 250$	8

3. (a) Too open   (b) Too open

4. (a) A Strength: can give information to own
       degree of accuracy
       B Weakness: classes overlap

5. Only males asked.
   No-one under 11
   Mainly adults surveyed.

6. A: People can express any opinion.
   B: Easier to collect and analyse information

7. For example:
   Question 1. Which age group are you in?
   Under 18 18 to 50 Over 50
   Question 2: Which type of sport do you
       prefer?
   Team games Racket sports Swimming

8. For example:
   How often do you visit the superstore each
       week?
   Once 2 or 3 times More than 3 times
   How far from the superstore do you live?
   Less than 2 miles 2 to 5 miles
   More than 5 miles
   How much do you spend per visit?
   Less than £5 £5 to £20 More than £20

9. For example:
   Which is your age group?
   0 - 11 12 - 18 19 - 30 31 - 60 Over 60
   How many times per week do you use a bus?
   1 or 2 3 to 5 6 to 10 More than 10

10. (a) 51
    (b) 11
    (c) Yes. 52 chose outdoor sports, 50 chose
        indoor sports

11. Yes. Over 30: $\frac{40}{80} = 0.5$, Under 30: $\frac{27}{60} = 0.45$

12. (a) 8   (b) 40   (c) 34

Exercise 34.1 — Page 385

1. (a) 70   (b) 103
2. (a) 39   (b) 84

Exercise 34.2 — Page 388

1. (a) Saturday   (b) 5 hours
   (c) 41 hours   (d) Sunday
   (e) $\frac{1}{4}$ (f) 6 hours
2. (b) £5   (c) £7   (d) 20%
3. (a) 15   (b) 1   (c) 5   (d) 20%
4. (a) 5   (f) 4
   (b) 7   (g) 5
   (c) 7   (h) Boys have higher mode
   (d) $33\frac{1}{3}$%   and larger range than
   (e) 35%   girls.
5. (a) 38   (b) Monday
   (c)

Day of birth	S	M	T	W	T	F	S
Number of boys	1	3	4	4	1	5	1

Exercise 34.3 — Page 391

1.

Colour	Blue	Green	Red	Silver	White
Angle	100°	30°	80°	60°	90°

2.

Tree	Ash	Beech	Maple	Rowan	Silver Birch
Angle	60°	80°	20°	76°	124°

3.

Takeaway	Fish & Chips	Chicken & Chips	Chinese	Pizza
Angle	110°	136°	52°	62°

4.

TV Channel	BBC1	BBC2	ITV	CH4	CH5
Angle	119°	50°	115°	47°	29°

5.

Cereal	Cornflakes	Muesli	Porridge	Bran Flakes
Angle	125°	100°	60°	75°

Exercise 34.4 — Page 392

1. (a) France   (b) 45   (c) 55   (d) 20
2. (a) 14   (b) 72
3. (a) Heathrow   (b) 540   (c) 1080

4. (a) Brown   (b) 26   (c) 25%
5. (a) 288   (b) 174°

Exercise 34.5 — Page 394

1. (a) 20°C
   (b) Temperature variations during each day are not known.
   Line only indicates trend in midday temperatures.
2. (b) (i) 154 cm   (ii) 15 years 4 months
3. (b) £118 - £119
   (c) Money withdrawn

Exercise 34.6 — Page 395

3. (b) Females have less variation in height than males.
4. (b) 1998 results are more spread, 1997 mode is higher

Review Exercise 34 — Page 397

1. (a) 1400   (b) 950
2. (a) medium
   (b) 6
   (c) 50
   (d) 12%
   (e) More ice-creams sold.
   Higher percentage of large ice-creams.
3. (b) Bed & Breakfast   (c) 50   (d) 34%
4. (b) Mirror   (c) 16%
5. (a) medical treatment   (b) 75   (c) $\frac{3}{8}$
6. (a)

Flavour	Strawberry	Vanilla	Chocolate
Angle	135°	165°	60°

7. (a) (i) 90°
   (b) Average 'Western' diet consists of more fat and protein and less carbohydrate than 'Healthy' diet.
8. (a) ITV   (b) 120
9. (b) £87 000
   (c) Prices of houses rise and fall, future prices unpredictable.
10. (a)

Time (mins)	0 -	10 -	20 -	30 -	40 -50
Frequency	9	16	8	4	3

   (c) E.g. First point scored within 20 minutes in over half of all matches.

11. (a) (i) 132 (ii) 280
    (b) (i) overslept (ii) 8

12. (a) £240 (b) £24 (c) 20%

13. (b) 34

14. (b) 25

15. (b) Type Y
    (c) (i) Type X
        (ii) Weights spread over more weight class intervals.

Exercise **35.1** Page 403

1. (a) 5, 5, 5
   (b) 110, 110, 110
   (c) 3 m, 5.5 m, 5 m
   (d) 2 kg, 3.5 kg, 3.9 kg
   (e) £3.50, £3.50, £3.50

2. 63
3. 4

4. 8

5. 129 cm

6. 31

7. (a) 3.7 kg, 4.2 kg   (b) 5.01 m, 5.06 m
   (c) £3.43, £2.70   (d) 20.1, 19.15
   (e) 125, 124.2

Exercise **35.2** Page 405

1. (a)

Shoe size	3	4	5	6	7	8	9
Frequency	1	4	3	2	1	1	1

   (b) 5
   (c) 4
   (d) 5.38 No shoe of this size, could display size 5 or 6.

2. (a)

Weekly earnings (£)	15	20	25	30	35
Frequency	5	4	6	1	3

   (b) £25
   (c) 19
   (d) £25
   (e) 440
   (f) £23.16

3. (a) 2.5, 2.73
   (b) 2, 2, 2.1
   (c) 0, 5, 4.5

4. 31p, 30p, 30.2p

Exercise **35.3** Page 408

1. (a) 30 - 40 hours, 29.4 hours, 30 - 40 hours
   (b) $1 \, cm \leqslant d < 2 \, cm$, 2.0 cm, $1 \, cm \leqslant d < 2 \, cm$
   (c) £10 000 < s < £15 000, £15 200, £10 000 $\leqslant$ s < £15 000

2. (a) 4.9 (b) 4.27 m

3. (a) 27.7 (b) 30 - 34

4. (a) $20 \leqslant t < 24$ minutes
   (b) 23 minutes

Exercise **35.4** Page 409

1. (a) Jays: mean 1.93, range 5
       Wasps: mean 2.4, range 3
       Wasps: scored more on average and had less spread.
   (b) Women: mean 1.5, range 5
       Men: mean 1.45, range 2
       Women made more visits to the cinema, though the number of visits is more spread

2. (a) Before: median 3, range 4
       After: median 3, range 5
       Would have been better to calculate the means. Before 2.2, After 3.0
   (b) Before: median 2.5, range 5
       After: median 1.5, range 5
       Fewer faults after service, same spread.

3. Mean age of customers at MacQuicks (26.8 years) is lower than mean age of customers at Pizza Pit (36.4 years).

4. (a) 42 words
   (b) 60.9 words per minute
   (c) First group has a much higher average. Second group is more spread out.

5. (b) April (c) March

6. No. Girls' average (median 7) greater than boys' (median 6).
   Correct about variation.

Exercise **35.5** Page 412

1. Mode trainers. Cannot calculate others

2. Mode 15 s, median 12 s, mean 22.15 s.
   Median most sensible, not affected by 200 as is mean, mode not much use.

3. Mode 81, median 83, mean 69.8
   Median most sensible, not affected by 5 & 6 as is mean, mode not much use.

4. Swimmer A.
Mean is lower (A 30.88s, B 31.38s), range less (A 1.7s, B 15s), median is higher (A 30.9s, B 30.0s)

5. Batsman B.
Higher median (B 31.5, A 21)

6. 8. This is the mode.

Review Exercise 35   Page 413

1. (a) 6.2 m, 4.5 m, 4.5 m, 5 m
   (b) £10.75, £8.00, £9.65, £9.38

2. (a) (i) 12 cm   (ii) 32 cm
   (b) English cucumbers are longer on average and slightly more varied in length.

3. (a) (i) 6.48%   (ii) 6.38%
   (b) Roman higher

4. (a) £200 - £300
   (b) £300 - £400
   (c) Mean, influenced by 12 people earning £600 - £1000.

5. (a) 24 cm
   (b) 24.32 cm
   (c) 1st group had higher mode (1st 25, 2nd 23), but lower range (1st 7, 2nd 13).

6. (a) (i) 2   (ii) 2.28
   (b) (i) 2.5   (ii) 2.63
   (c) The calculation for the mean involves the number of runs scored off every ball.

7. (a) Entries are: 1, 6, 3, 4   (b) 82.1 years

8. (a) 13.7
   (b) (ii) Girls have higher mean, range the same.

Exercise 36.1   Page 416

1. (a) 2
   (b) 164 cm
   (c) No
   (d) Taller girls usually have larger shoe sizes than shorter girls.

2. (a) 72
   (b) (i) English 46, French 88
       (ii) French could be her first language.

3. (a) 4 (b) 43 kg (c) Tend to be higher

Exercise 36.2   Page 418

1. (a) B   (b) C   (c) D

2. (a) negative   (b) positive
   (c) zero   (d) positive
   (e) negative

3. (b) positive correlation
   (c) Different conditions, types of road, etc.

4. (b) negative correlation
   (c) Different road surfaces, driving styles, etc.

Exercise 36.3   Page 420

1. (b) 4.8 - 4.9 kg

2. (b) (i) £96 - £98   (ii) £310 - £320

3. (b) (i) 27 - 28   (ii) 91 - 92 kg

4. (b) 46 - 48

Review Exercise 36   Page 422

1. 1 B, 2 C, 3 A

2.

3. (b) positive   (c) 49 - 51

4. (a) (i) 10 to 12 cm   (ii) 21 to 23 cm
   (b) (i), as estimated value is between known values.

5. (a) positive
   (c) 9

6. (a) (i)

      (ii)
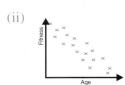

   (b) (ii) 102 - 104
      (iii) May be fit for her age or overweight for her age, etc.

7. (b) As cars get older they lose value.
   (c) High mileage car, poor condition, etc.
   (c) £5500 - £6000

8. (b) (i) 24.5 - 25.5 mpg   (ii) 13 - 14 mpg
   (c) (b) (i). (b) (ii) is beyond known values.
   (d) 1.7 litres

9. (b) (ii) Arctic Wolf
   (d) (i) 5.5 - 6 years (ii) 30 - 32 days

10. (a) (ii) positive correlation
   (c) (i) £240
   (ii) Same rating can apply to different priced holidays, holiday may be affected by special circumstances, etc.

Exercise 37.1 — Page 429

1. (a) Entries are: 0, 3, 11, 23, 33, 38, 40
   (c) (i) 14 mins
   (ii) 18.5 mins
   (iii) 9.5 mins
   (d) 9 mins

2. (a) 53
   (b) Entries are: 2, 6, 18, 25, 33, 50, 53
   (d) (i) 62 g (ii) 30 g

3. (a)

Time (t hours)	<5	<10	<15	<20	<25	<30
Cum. freq.	2	10	15	29	36	40

   (c) (i) 17 hours (ii) 11 hours

4. (a)

Annual salary (£000's)	<10	<15	<20	<25	<30	<35	<40
Cum. freq.	0	79	111	125	125	126	127

   (c) (i) £14 000 (ii) £5000

Exercise 37.2 — Page 432

1. (a) Entries are: 0, 7, 28, 65, 77, 80
   (c) (i) 6 minutes (ii) 12

2. (a) 26.5 (b) 8 (c) 15 (d) 17

3. (a) Entries are: 0, 15, 51, 105, 117, 120
   (c) (i) 39 g (ii) 25 g
   (d) 8

4. (a) 95
   (b)

Height (cm)	<80	<85	<90	<95	<100	<105
Cum. freq.	0	20	55	70	81	95

   (d) (i) 89 cm (ii) 10 cm (iii) 19
   (e) 83 cm

5. (a)

Time (t hours)	<0	<5	<10	<15	<20	<30	<40
Cum. freq.	0	7	22	40	64	76	80

   (c) 9.5 hours (d) 9

6. (a) 175 cm, 14.5 cm (b) 3 (c) 41
   (d) 172.5 cm (e) 185.5 cm

Exercise 37.3 — Page 434

1. (a) 40
   (b) 13 cm
   (c) 8 cm
   (d) Girls heights are more varied, etc.
   (e) 1

2. (b) (i) 18 litres (ii) 10 litres
   (c) Neighbour's cows have higher average yield, but the yield is more varied, etc.

3. (a) Entries are: 2, 7, 13, 20, 28, 32, 36
   (b) 19
   (c) Median lower for second meeting and the times were less varied, etc.

4. (b) 9
   (c) (i) 25 hours (ii) 5.5 hours
   (d) No. Greater spread means that some batteries will have shorter life, etc.

Review Exercise 37 — Page 436

1. (a) 3 miles
   (b) 0.5 miles
   (c) Range is affected by a few long journeys, etc.

2. (a) 98 minutes
   (b) 15.5 minutes
   (c) 40

3. (a) Entries are: 2, 5, 13, 22, 28, 35, 40
   (c) 78.5 g
   (d) 19 g
   (e) The spread of the second sample is greater (1QR 38 g compared with 19 g), etc.

4. (a) Entries are: 12, 37, 79, 114, 132, 140
   (b) 27.5 minutes
   (c) 18 minutes
   (d) The times of the second group are less varied, etc.

5. (a) Entries are: 9, 18, 32, 47, 65, 82, 97, 105
   (b) (i) 84.5 mm
   (c) (i) 91 mm (ii) 15.5 mm

6. (b) £9   (c)   17

7. (a) Entries are: 4, 11, 19, 25, 28, 32, 32
   (b) (ii)   27   (iii) 6
   (c) (i)   17
      (ii) The journeys of the first group were more spread (1QR 24), more people with fewer journeys, etc.

8. (a)   43
   (b) (i)   7   (ii)   more varied
   (c)   2

9. (a) Entries are: 30, 90, 130, 150, 160
   (c)   1.55 mins
   (d)   18

Exercise 38.1 — Page 441

1. (a) unlikely   (b) likely
   (c) certain   (d) likely
   (e) unlikely   (f) impossible
   (g) unlikely   (h) likely

Exercise 38.2 — Page 442

1. (a) $\frac{4}{11}$ (b) $\frac{4}{11}$ (c) $\frac{2}{11}$

2. (a) $\frac{1}{6}$ (b) $\frac{1}{6}$ (c) $\frac{1}{3}$

3. (a) $\frac{4}{52} = \frac{1}{13}$ (b) $\frac{13}{52} = \frac{1}{4}$ (c) $\frac{16}{52} = \frac{4}{13}$

4. (a) $\frac{1}{6}$ (b) $\frac{2}{6} = \frac{1}{3}$ (c) $\frac{2}{6} = \frac{1}{3}$

5. (a) $\frac{4}{10} = \frac{2}{5}$ (b) $\frac{6}{10} = \frac{3}{5}$ (c) $\frac{6}{10} = \frac{3}{5}$
   (d) $\frac{10}{10} = 1$ (e)   0

6. (a) $\frac{1}{500}$
   (b) Depends how many tickets are bought by girls.

7. (a) $\frac{6}{10} = \frac{3}{5}$ (b) $\frac{5}{9}$ (c) $\frac{6}{9} = \frac{2}{3}$

8. (a) $\frac{8}{12} = \frac{2}{3}$ (b) $\frac{4}{12} = \frac{1}{3}$ (c) $\frac{9}{12} = \frac{3}{4}$

9. (a) $\frac{20}{50} = \frac{2}{5}$ (b) $\frac{30}{50} = \frac{3}{5}$ (c) $\frac{8}{50} = \frac{4}{25}$
   (d) $\frac{8}{30} = \frac{4}{15}$ (e) $\frac{8}{20} = \frac{2}{5}$

10. (a) $\frac{40}{120} = \frac{1}{3}$ (b) $\frac{8}{120} = \frac{1}{15}$ (c) $\frac{55}{120} = \frac{11}{24}$
   (d) $\frac{17}{50}$ (e) $\frac{42}{50} = \frac{21}{25}$ (f) $\frac{20}{25} = \frac{4}{5}$

11. (a) (i) $\frac{14}{30} = \frac{7}{15}$ (ii) $\frac{15}{30} = \frac{1}{2}$
   (b) $\frac{1}{16}$
   (c) $\frac{3}{4}$

12. Depends on the ability of the players.

Exercise 38.3 — Page 445

1. $\frac{36}{40} = \frac{9}{10}$

2. (a) $\frac{9}{30} = \frac{3}{10}$ (b) $\frac{120}{300} = \frac{2}{5}$

3. $\frac{21}{30} = \frac{7}{10}$

4. (a) Tom $\frac{4}{12} = \frac{1}{3}$ Kim $\frac{3}{4}$
      Sam $\frac{8}{16} = \frac{1}{2}$ Pam $\frac{9}{20}$
   (b) Pam. Most games played.
   (c) Pam. $\frac{9}{20} > \frac{1}{3}$

5. $\frac{19}{50}$
   Not good, only 50 in sample.

6. (a) Only 20 trials
   (b) Daron, most trials
   (c) 1. $\frac{181}{520}$ 2. $\frac{180}{520} = \frac{9}{26}$
      3. $\frac{75}{520} = \frac{15}{104}$ 4. $\frac{84}{520} = \frac{21}{130}$

7. (a) $\frac{52}{100} = 0.52$ $\frac{102}{200} = 0.51$ $\frac{141}{300} = 0.47$
   (b)   0.47

8. (a) R (1) is about 0.25
   (b) Varies around 0.5

Exercise 38.4 — Page 447

1. (a) 50   (b) 50   (c) 50   (d) 200

2. (a) 6
   (b) E.g. 0.02 may not be exact, there may be a run of faulty switches, etc.

3. (a) 1100   (b) 900

4. Red 13, Blue 15, White 22

5. 500

Exercise 38.5 — Page 449

1. (a) yes   (b) no   (c) yes
   (d) yes   (e) no   (f) no

2. $\frac{3}{5}$

3. $\frac{7}{15}$

4. 0.04

5. $\frac{94}{100} = \frac{47}{50}$

6. 0.6

7. (a) 0.5   (b) 0.3

8. (a) (i) Probabilities add to more than 100%
      (ii) 5%
   (b) (i) 45%   (ii) 75%   (iii) 80%

535

9. (a) 0.4
(b) 0.6
(c) (i) Yes (ii) No
(d) (i) 0.6 (ii) 0.6

Exercise 38.6
Page 451

1. (a)

2nd die		1st die					
6	7	8	9	10	11	12
5	6	7	8	9	10	11
4	5	6	7	8	9	10
3	4	5	6	7	8	9
2	3	4	5	6	7	8
1	2	3	4	5	6	7
	1	2	3	4	5	6

1st die

(b) (i) $\frac{3}{36} = \frac{1}{12}$

(ii) $\frac{3}{36} = \frac{1}{12}$

(iii) $\frac{30}{36} = \frac{5}{6}$

(c) Total must be less than, equal to, or greater than 10.

2.

Dice

Coin		1	2	3	4	5	6
	H	H1	H2	H3	H4	H5	H6
	T	T1	T2	T3	T4	T5	T6

(a) $\frac{1}{12}$ (b) $\frac{3}{12} = \frac{1}{4}$ (c) $\frac{1}{12}$

(d) $\frac{3}{12} = \frac{1}{4}$ (e) $\frac{2}{12} = \frac{1}{6}$ (f) $\frac{6}{12} = \frac{1}{2}$

3. (a)

Stage 1	Stage 2
Bus	Bus
Bus	Walk
Train	Bus
Train	Walk
Lift	Bus
Lift	Walk

(b) $\frac{1}{6}$

(c) 133

4. (a) $\frac{480}{800} = \frac{3}{5}$

(b)

1st fan	2nd fan
Red	Red
Red	White
Red	Blue
White	Red
White	White
White	Blue
Blue	Red
Blue	White
Blue	Blue

(c) Events not equally likely.

5. (a) $\frac{1}{16}$ (b) $\frac{2}{16} = \frac{1}{8}$ (c) $\frac{3}{16}$

6. (a)

Bag A

		R	R	W
Bag B	W	RW	RW	WW
	W	RW	RW	WW
	R	RR	RR	WR

(c) $\frac{4}{9}$

(d) 0.4

7. (a)

A	B
1	2
1	3
2	2
2	3
3	2
3	3

(b) (i) $\frac{2}{6} = \frac{1}{3}$ (ii) $\frac{4}{6} = \frac{2}{3}$

(c) $\frac{4}{5}$

8. (a) Maths, English
Maths, Science
Maths, Art
English, Science
English, Art
Science, Art

(b) $\frac{3}{6} = \frac{1}{2}$

(c) $\frac{1}{3}$

9. (a)

2nd spin	W	RW	GW	BW	YW	WW
	Y	RY	GY	BY	YY	WY
	B	RB	GB	BB	YB	WB
	G	RG	GG	BG	YG	WG
	R	RR	GR	BR	YR	WR
		R	G	B	Y	W

1st spin

(b) (i) $\frac{1}{25}$ (ii) $\frac{9}{25}$ (iii) $\frac{5}{25} = \frac{1}{5}$

10. (a) $\frac{1}{15}$ (b) $\frac{3}{15} = \frac{1}{5}$

Exercise 38.7
Page 454

1. (a)

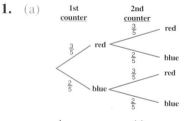

(b) (i) $\frac{4}{25}$ (ii) $\frac{16}{25}$

2. (a)
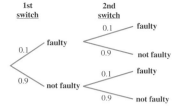

(b) (i) 0.01   (ii) 0.18
(c) 810

3. (a) (i) $\frac{5}{50} = \frac{1}{10}$ (ii) $\frac{45}{50} = \frac{9}{10}$
(iii) $\frac{20}{50} = \frac{2}{5}$ (iv) $\frac{30}{50} = \frac{3}{5}$

(b)
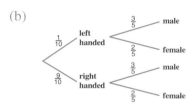

(c) (i) $\frac{2}{50} = \frac{1}{25}$ (ii) $\frac{29}{50}$

4. (a)
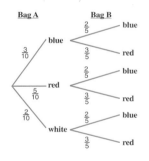

(b) $\frac{9}{50}$ (c) $\frac{21}{50}$

5. (a) Seema. P(Dario ends on B) $= \frac{30}{64}$
P(Seema ends on B) $= \frac{39}{64}$

(b) Damo. P (Dario ends on B) $= \frac{294}{512}$
P(Seema ends on B) $= \frac{267}{512}$

Exercise **38.8**   Page 457

1. (a) not   (b) independent
(c) not   (d) independent
(e) not   (f) independent

2. (a) 0.7   (b) 0.58

3. (a) $\frac{21}{200}$ (b) $\frac{71}{80}$

4. (a) 0.09   (b) Sally (0.54)

5. (a) 0.14   (b) 0.06

6. (a) The events do not influence each other.
(b) $\frac{1}{8}$ (c) 8

7. (a) $\frac{1}{3}$ (b) $\frac{1}{2}$

8. (a) (i) 0.3   (ii) 0.1
(iii) 0.4   (iv) 0.5
(b) 0.66

9. (a) (i) 0.1   (b) (i) 0.01
(ii) 0.7   (ii) 0.25
(iii) 0.6   (iii) 0.18

10. (a) (i) $\frac{22}{175}$ (b) (i) $\frac{24}{100} = \frac{6}{25}$
(ii) $\frac{81}{175}$ (ii) $\frac{31}{50}$

Review Exercise **38**   Page 460

1. (a) $\frac{4}{10} = \frac{2}{5}$
(b) $\frac{4}{9}$

2. (a) Set 1   Set 2
A   A
A   B
A   C
B   A
B   B
B   C
C   A
C   B
C   C
(b) $\frac{4}{9}$

3. (a) $\frac{68}{100} = \frac{17}{25}$ (b) $\frac{55}{100} = \frac{11}{20}$

4. 300

5. (a) $\frac{5}{20} = \frac{1}{4}$ (b) 150

6. (a) 0.3   (b) 0.6

7. (a)

		1	2	3	4
	1	2	3	4	5
	2	3	4	5	6
	3	4	5	6	7

(b) (i) $\frac{2}{12} = \frac{1}{6}$ (ii) $\frac{10}{12} = \frac{5}{6}$
(c) $\frac{4}{12} = \frac{1}{3}$

8. (a) $\frac{12}{20} = \frac{3}{5}$ (c) 0.5

9. (a) 0.3 (b) 0.1 (c) 0.4 (d) 0.5

10. A 0.5
B not possible, not mutually exclusive
C 0.3

11. (a) (i) 0.28   (ii) 0.12
(b) 240

12. (a)

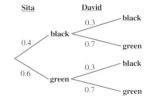

Sita   David

(b) (i) 0.42   (ii) 0.46

13. (a) 0.7
    (b) (i) 0.16   (ii) 0.144

14. (a) $\frac{1}{25}$ (b) $\frac{1}{5}$ (c) $\frac{10}{25} = \frac{2}{5}$

Section Review   Page 463

1. (a) Paper 2   (b) Paper 1   (c) 33

2. (a) 35
    (b) More boys than girls were included in the survey.
    (c) Survey is based on a small sample.
    (d) 55

3. (a) (i) Britain   (ii) 15
    (b) 13.5%

4. HH, HT, TH, TT

5. (a) $\frac{1}{4}$ (b) $\frac{3}{4}$ (c) $\frac{1}{13}$
    (d) $\frac{1}{26}$ (e) $\frac{1}{52}$ (f) $\frac{4}{13}$

6. (a) $\frac{1}{100}$ (b) $\frac{1}{20}$ (c) $\frac{17}{20}$ (d) 15

7. (a)

Sale	Newspapers	Echo	Mags
Angle	170°	120°	10°

    (b) (i) 130
       (iii) Echo only available from midday and has the greater number of sales in one hour.

8. (a) 12   (b) 1   (c) 30   (d) 45

9. 105

10. (b) There is a positive correlation between shoe size and height.
    (c) 145 cm

11. (b) Positive correlation between distance travelled and amount of fuel used.
    (c) (i) 65 litres
       (ii) Not very reliable, Graph plotted using a small number of points.

12. (a) D   (b) A

13. (a) (i) Question 1 - irrelevant to survey.
Question 2 - not likely to get the required response
       (ii) Question 1 - Which year are you in?
Question 2 - How many times, per week do you use the canteen?
         1   2   3   4   5
    (b) The opinions of one class may not be representative of the whole school.

14. (a) Only men surveyed
Local issues may affect voting.
    (b) Survey people from different parts of the country.
Survey equal numbers of men and women.
Survey more people.

15. (a) $\frac{3}{12} = \frac{1}{4}$
    (b) (i) 2.5
       (ii) 3.2
       (iii) The mean includes data from all matches.

16. (a) 3
    (b) 2.125
    (c) Actual data not used.
    (d) 15
    (e) Eighteen year olds receive a greater range (20) and a greater mean (4).

17. (a) 22.2 seconds

18. (a) Entries are : 0, 3, 10, 23, 38, 50, 58, 60
    (c) 11 g
    (d) 52
    (e) 102 g

19. (a) Entries are : 3, 13, 34, 74, 92, 100
    (c) 36%
    (d) medium = 569 ml
       IQR = 7 ml

20. (a)

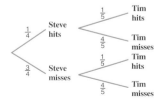

    (b) $\frac{3}{20}$

21. (a) (i) 100   (ii) 50
    (b) $\frac{19}{30}$

1. (a) 0.8
   (b) $0.096, \frac{4}{5}, 0.805, 0.85$

2. (a) (i) 0.04   (ii) 1.86
   (b) 49
   (c) 9

3. 69p

4. (a) £1190

5. (a) 31   (b) −17

6. (a) 20   (b) $2x - 5$

8. (a) (i) $x = 42°$
      (ii) sum of angles in a triangle = 180°
   (b) (i) $y = 76°$
      (ii) Alternate angles (= ∠BAC)

10. 4 m by 4.8 m

11. 48 cm³

12. (a) 4
   (b) 19
   (c) There is a positive correlation between the grades in English and French.

13. (a) (i) A negative correlation
         B zero correlation
         C positive correlation.
      (ii) C, A, B
   (b) (ii) E   (iii) £1000

15. (a) 92p
   (b) £7.75
   (c) (i) 80%   (ii) 1 : 4

16. (a) 48   (b) 45%
   (c) 12   (d) $\frac{2000}{30} \simeq 63$

17. (a) $x = 4$ (b) $x = 7$

18. (a) $4y$ (b) 6

19. 2.24

20. (a) −1   (b) $11 - 2n$

21. (b) 55 seconds

22. (a) (i) 4   (ii) 2
   (b) 36°, alternate angles
   (c) 54°, sum of angles in a triangle equals 180°, diagonals of a rhombus bisect each other at 90°.

23. (a) 1600   (b) Not enough paint.

24. (c) Translation $\begin{pmatrix} -4 \\ 3 \end{pmatrix}$

25. (a) $2^2 \times 3$ (b) 2^6 (c) 192

26. (a) $2x - 1$
   (b) $x = -4$
   (c) $x = 2.5, y = -1$

27. (a) $3n - 1$ (b) $n^2 + 1$

28. (c) (i) 2.2 hours
      (ii) Only small number of points used to draw graph.

29. (a) (i) Leading question
      (ii) What are the disadvantages of keeping pets?
   (b) (i) The mean reflects the extreme values.

30. (a) 10 cm   (b) 288 cm³

31. (a) $K = 10\,000$ (b) $m = \sqrt{\dfrac{K}{P}}$

32. (a) 3×10^{-3}
   (b) 2.1×10^{4}
   (c) 1.5×10^{2}

33. (a) $x^2 - x - 8$
   (b) $3a(a - 2)$
   (c) $2x^2 - 7x + 3$

34. (a) (i) $x \leqslant 2$
      (ii) $x < 5$ and $x > 5$
      (iii) $x < -2$
   (b)

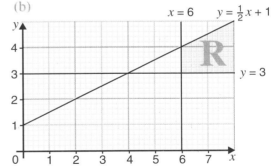

35. (a) $A\,(0, -2), B\,(2, 0)$
   (b) $\frac{1}{2}$
   (c) The lines are parallel, same gradient $\frac{1}{2}$
   (d) $x + y = 2$

36. 3 cm

37. (a) (i) $15p^5$ (ii) $2p^3$
   (b) $1\frac{1}{9}$

38. (a) B   (b) C

39. B

40. (a) 0.18   (b) 0.54

1. 39p

2. (a) £6.54   (b) 3.0% to 1 dp.

3. (a) $20x$ grams   (b) 180 grams

4. (a) 2.3 kg   (b) £2

5. (a) 147 cm
   (b) (i) 121.5 cm   (ii) 4 feet

6. (a) red
   (b)

Vehicle	Car	Van	Lorry	Bus
Angle	210°	66°	48°	36°

7. Brand B

8. (a) 84   (b) £13.76   (c) 262 144

9. (a) 11 degrees C
   (b) 205 cm³
   (c) $33\frac{1}{3}\%$

10. (a) 75 g   (b) 40%

11. (a) (i) 38.2%   (ii) 63 g
    (b) 105 g

12. (a) $(3x + 2)$ cm
    (b) $3x + 2 = 23$
        $x = 7$

13. 316 cm²

14. 278 000 lira

15. £944.40

16. (a) 36   (b) 36 gold, 24 silver, 12 black

17. (b) $x = 2$

18. (a) 0.000 961   (b) 0.34

19. (a) Vit. C 54 mg; Vit. B6 0.51 mg
    (b) 67.5 mg
    (c) 85%

20. £62.90

21. (a) 50   (b) $x = -1.5$ (c) $x = 2.8$

22. (a) 3.6 m   (b) 0.77 m²   (c) 1.69 m³

23. (a) £104.04   (b) 1916 units

24. (a) 57 024
    (b) $2^9 \times 3^4 \times 11$
    (c) 4.56192×10^5

25. (a) (i) $x = 54°$ (ii) $y = 46°$
    (b) $DE = 3.6$ cm

26. (a) 3.44 m   (b) 40.7°

27. (a) (i) 1.07×10^{21} m³
    (b) -287.90625

28. (a) 0.2 kg   (b) kg/cm³

29. (a) 5.85×10^6 (b) $c = \sqrt{\frac{2a}{b}}$

30. (a) 1.86284×10^5
    (b) (i) 43 seconds

31. (a) (i) $x = \frac{A - \pi r^2}{\pi r}$ (ii) $x = 1.72$
    (b) (i) 5π (ii) 25π

32. (a) 209 953   (b) 612.8515625

33. (a)

Hours of sleep	<20	<25	<30	<35	<40	<45
Cum. freq.	0	4	13	38	56	60

    (c) (i) 34 hours   (ii) 5 hours
    (d) Nurses get much more sleep on their week off work.
        75% of nurses get more sleep than the upper quartile number of hours during a working week.

34. (a) $3n - 1$
    (b) (i) $-\frac{1}{2}, 0$ (ii) $n = 10$

35. (a) $y = 2.1$ (b) 8 minutes 19 seconds.

)

Index